About Pearson

Pearson is the world's learning company, with presence across 70 countries worldwide. Our unique insights and world-class expertise comes from a long history of working closely with renowned teachers, authors and thought leaders, as a result of which, we have emerged as the preferred choice for millions of teachers and learners across the world.

We believe learning opens up opportunities, creates fulfilling careers and hence better lives. We hence collaborate with the best of minds to deliver you class-leading products, spread across the Higher Education and K12 spectrum.

Superior learning experience and improved outcomes are at the heart of everything we do. This product is the result of one such effort.

Your feedback plays a critical role in the evolution of our products and you can contact us - reachus@pearson.com. We look forward to it.

A First Course in Probability

Ninth Edition

Sheldon Ross
University of Southern California

Contributions by

Sudheesh Kumar Kattumannil
Indian Statistical Institute
Chennai

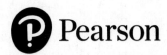 Pearson

Authorized adaptation from the United States edition, entitled *A First Course in Probability*, 9th Edition, ISBN 978-0-321-79477-2 by Ross, Sheldon, published by Pearson Education, Inc, Copyright © 2014.

Indian Subcontinent Adaptation
Copyright © 2019 Pearson India Education Services Pvt. Ltd

ISBN 978-93-530-6560-7

First Impression

This edition is manufactured in India and is authorized for sale only in India, Bangladesh, Bhutan, Pakistan, Nepal, Sri Lanka and the Maldives. Circulation of this edition outside of these territories is UNAUTHORIZED.

Published by Pearson India Education Services Pvt. Ltd, CIN: U72200TN2005PTC057128.

Head Office: 15th Floor, Tower-B, World Trade Tower, Plot No. 1, Block-C, Sector 16, Noida 201 301, Uttar Pradesh, India.
Registered Office: 4th Floor, Software Block, Elnet Software City, TS-140, Block 2 & 9, Rajiv Gandhi Salai, Taramani, Chennai 600 113, Tamil Nadu, India.
Fax: 080-30461003, Phone: 080-30461060
Website: in.pearson.com, Email: companysecretary.india@pearson.com

Printed in India by Sai Printo Pack Pvt Ltd

For Rebecca

CONTENTS

Preface ix

1 COMBINATORIAL ANALYSIS 1

1.1 Introduction 1
1.2 The Basic Principle of Counting 2
1.3 Permutations 3
1.4 Combinations 5
1.5 Multinomial Coefficients 9
1.6 The Number of Integer Solutions of Equations 12
Summary 15
Problems 15
Theoretical Exercises 17
Self-Test Problems and Exercises 19

2 AXIOMS OF PROBABILITY 21

2.1 Introduction 21
2.2 Sample Space and Events 21
2.3 Axioms of Probability 25
2.4 Some Simple Propositions 28
2.5 Sample Spaces Having Equally Likely Outcomes 32
2.6 Probability as a Continuous Set Function 42
2.7 Probability as a Measure of Belief 46
Summary 47
Problems 48
Theoretical Exercises 52
Self-Test Problems and Exercises 54

3 CONDITIONAL PROBABILITY AND INDEPENDENCE 56

3.1 Introduction 56
3.2 Conditional Probabilities 56
3.3 Bayes's Formula 62
3.4 Independent Events 75
3.5 $P(\cdot|F)$ Is a Probability 89
Summary 97
Problems 97
Theoretical Exercises 106
Self-Test Problems and Exercises 109

4 RANDOM VARIABLES 112

4.1 Random Variables 112
4.2 Discrete Random Variables 116
4.3 Expected Value 119
4.4 Expectation of a Function of a Random Variable 121
4.5 Variance 125
4.6 The Bernoulli and Binomial Random Variables 127
4.7 The Poisson Random Variable 135
4.8 Other Discrete Probability Distributions 147
4.9 Expected Value of Sums of Random Variables 155
4.10 Properties of the Cumulative Distribution Function 159
Summary 162
Problems 163
Theoretical Exercises 169
Self-Test Problems and Exercises 173

5 CONTINUOUS RANDOM VARIABLES 176

5.1 Introduction 176
5.2 Expectation and Variance of Continuous Random Variables 179
5.3 The Uniform Random Variable 184
5.4 Normal Random Variables 187
5.5 Exponential Random Variables 197
5.6 Other Continuous Distributions 203
5.7 The Distribution of a Function of a Random Variable 208
Summary 210
Problems 212
Theoretical Exercises 214
Self-Test Problems and Exercises 217

6 JOINTLY DISTRIBUTED RANDOM VARIABLES 220

6.1 Joint Distribution Functions 220

6.2 Independent Random Variables 228

6.3 Sums of Independent Random Variables 239

6.4 Conditional Distributions: Discrete Case 248

6.5 Conditional Distributions: Continuous Case 250

6.6 Order Statistics 256

6.7 Joint Probability Distribution of Functions of Random Variables 260

6.8 Exchangeable Random Variables 267

Summary 270

Problems 271

Theoretical Exercises 275

Self-Test Problems and Exercises 277

7 PROPERTIES OF EXPECTATION 280

7.1 Introduction 280

7.2 Expectation of Sums of Random Variables 281

7.3 Moments of the Number of Events that Occur 298

7.4 Covariance, Variance of Sums, and Correlations 304

7.5 Conditional Expectation 313

7.6 Conditional Expectation and Prediction 330

7.7 Moment Generating Functions 334

7.8 Additional Properties of Normal Random Variables 345

7.9 General Definition of Expectation 349

Summary 351

Problems 352

Theoretical Exercises 359

Self-Test Problems and Exercises 363

8 LIMIT THEOREMS 367

8.1 Introduction 367

8.2 Chebyshev's Inequality and the Weak Law of Large Numbers 367

8.3 The Central Limit Theorem 370

8.4 The Strong Law of Large Numbers 378

8.5 Other Inequalities 382

8.6 Bounding the Error Probability When Approximating a Sum of Independent Bernoulli Random Variables by a Poisson Random Variable 388

Summary 390

Problems 390

Theoretical Exercises 392

Self-Test Problems and Exercises 393

9 ADDITIONAL TOPICS IN PROBABILITY 395

9.1 The Poisson Process 395

9.2 Markov Chains 397

9.3 Surprise, Uncertainty, and Entropy 402

9.4 Coding Theory and Entropy 405

Summary 411

Problems and Theoretical Exercises 412

Self-Test Problems and Exercises 413

10 SIMULATION 415

10.1 Introduction 415

10.2 General Techniques for Simulating Continuous Random Variables 417

10.3 Simulating from Discrete Distributions 424

10.4 Variance Reduction Techniques 426

Summary 430

Problems 430

Self-Test Problems and Exercises 431

Answers to Selected Problems 433

Solutions to Self-Test Problems and Exercises 435

Index 461

Common Discrete Distributions 465

Common Continuous Distributions 467

PREFACE

"We see that the theory of probability is at bottom only common sense reduced to calculation; it makes us appreciate with exactitude what reasonable minds feel by a sort of instinct, often without being able to account for it.... It is remarkable that this science, which originated in the consideration of games of chance, should have become the most important object of human knowledge.... The most important questions of life are, for the most part, really only problems of probability." So said the famous French mathematician and astronomer (the "Newton of France") Pierre-Simon, Marquis de Laplace. Although many people believe that the famous marquis, who was also one of the great contributors to the development of probability, might have exaggerated somewhat, it is nevertheless true that probability theory has become a tool of fundamental importance to nearly all scientists, engineers, medical practitioners, jurists, and industrialists. In fact, the enlightened individual had learned to ask not "Is it so?" but rather "What is the probability that it is so?"

General Approach and Mathematical Level

This book is intended as an elementary introduction to the theory of probability for students in mathematics, statistics, engineering, and the sciences (including computer science, biology, the social sciences, and management science) who possess the prerequisite knowledge of elementary calculus. It attempts to present not only the mathematics of probability theory, but also, through numerous examples, the many diverse possible applications of this subject.

Content and Course Planning

Chapter 1 presents the basic principles of combinatorial analysis, which are most useful in computing probabilities.

Chapter 2 handles the axioms of probability theory and shows how they can be applied to compute various probabilities of interest.

Chapter 3 deals with the extremely important subjects of conditional probability and independence of events. By a series of examples, we illustrate how conditional probabilities come into play not only when some partial information is available, but also as a tool to enable us to compute probabilities more easily, even when no partial information is present. This extremely important technique of obtaining probabilities by "conditioning" reappears in Chapter 7, where we use it to obtain expectations.

The concept of random variables is introduced in Chapters 4, 5, and 6. Discrete random variables are dealt with in Chapter 4, continuous random variables in Chapter 5, and jointly distributed random variables in Chapter 6. The important concepts of the expected value and the variance of a random variable are introduced in Chapters 4 and 5, and these quantities are then determined for many of the common types of random variables.

Additional properties of the expected value are considered in Chapter 7. Many examples illustrating the usefulness of the result that the expected value of a sum of random variables is equal to the sum of their expected values are presented. Sections on conditional expectation, including its use in prediction, and on moment-generating functions are contained in this chapter. In addition, the final section introduces the multivariate normal distribution and presents a simple proof concerning the joint distribution of the sample mean and sample variance of a sample from a normal distribution.

Chapter 8 presents the major theoretical results of probability theory. In particular, we prove the strong law of large numbers and the central limit theorem. Our proof of the strong law is a relatively simple one that assumes that the random variables have a finite fourth moment, and our proof of the central limit theorem assumes Levy's continuity theorem. This chapter also presents such probability inequalities as Markov's inequality, Chebyshev's inequality, and Chernoff bounds. The final section of Chapter 8 gives a bound on the error involved when a probability concerning a sum of independent Bernoulli random variables is approximated by the corresponding probability of a Poisson random variable having the same expected value.

Chapter 9 presents some additional topics, such as Markov chains, the Poisson process, and an introduction to information and coding theory, and Chapter 10 considers simulation.

As in the previous edition, three sets of exercises are given at the end of each chapter. They are designated as **Problems, Theoretical Exercises**, and **Self-Test Problems and Exercises**. This last set of exercises, for which complete solutions appear in Solutions to Self-Test Problems and Exercises, is designed to help students test their comprehension and study for exams.

Changes for the Ninth Edition

The ninth edition continues the evolution and fine tuning of the text. Aside from a multitude of small changes made to increase the clarity of the text, the new edition includes many new and updated problems, exercises, and text material chosen both for inherent interest and for their use in building student intuition about probability. Illustrative of these goals are Examples 3h and 4k of Chapter 3, which deal with estimating the fraction of twin pairs that are identical and with analyzing serve and rally games.

Online Resources

Instructor's Solutions Manual (downloadable)

The Instructor's Solutions Manual contains worked-out solutions to Problems and Theoretical Exercises in *A First Course in Probability*. It can be downloaded from the Pearson Resource Center, **www.pearsoned.co.in/sheldonross**.

Acknowledgments

I would like to thank the following people who have graciously taken the time to contact me with comments for improving the text: Amir Ardestani, Polytechnic University of Teheran; Joe Blitzstein, Harvard University; Peter Nuesch, University of Lausaunne; Joseph Mitchell, SUNY, Stony Brook; Alan Chambless, actuary;

Robert Kriner; Israel David, Ben-Gurion University; T. Lim, George Mason University; Wei Chen, Rutgers; D. Monrad, University of Illinois; W. Rosenberger, George Mason University; E. Ionides, University of Michigan; J. Corvino, Lafayette College; T. Seppalainen, University of Wisconsin; Jack Goldberg; University of Michigan; Sunil Dhar, New Jersey Institute of Technology; Vladislav Kargin, Stanford University; Marlene Miller; Ahmad Parsian; and Fritz Scholz, University of Washington.

I would also like to especially thank the reviewers of the ninth edition: Richard Laugesen, University of Illinois; Stacey Hancock, Clark University; Stefan Heinz, University of Wyoming; and Brian Thelen, University of Michigan. I would like to thank the accuracy checkers, Keith Friedman (University of Texas at Austin) and Stacey Hancock (Clark University), for their careful review.

Finally, I would like to thank the following reviewers for their many helpful comments. Reviewers of the ninth edition are marked with an asterisk.

K. B. Athreya, *Iowa State University*
Richard Bass, *University of Connecticut*
Robert Bauer, *University of Illinois at Urbana-Champaign*
Phillip Beckwith, *Michigan Tech*
Arthur Benjamin, *Harvey Mudd College*
Geoffrey Berresford, *Long Island University*
Baidurya Bhattacharya, *University of Delaware*
Howard Bird, *St. Cloud State University*
Shahar Boneh, *Metropolitan State College of Denver*
Jean Cadet, *State University of New York at Stony Brook*
Steven Chiappari, *Santa Clara University*
Nicolas Christou, *University of California, Los Angeles*
James Clay, *University of Arizona at Tucson*
Francis Conlan, *University of Santa Clara*
Justin Corvino, *Lafayette College*
Jay DeVore, *California Polytechnic University, San Luis Obispo*
Scott Emerson, *University of Washington*
Thomas R. Fischer, *Texas A & M University*
Anant Godbole, *Michigan Technical University*
Zakkula Govindarajulu, *University of Kentucky*
Richard Groeneveld, *Iowa State University*
*Stacey Hancock, *Clark University*
Mike Hardy, *Massachusetts Institute of Technology*
Bernard Harris, *University of Wisconsin*
Larry Harris, *University of Kentucky*

David Heath, *Cornell University*
*Stefan Heinz, *University of Wyoming*
Stephen Herschkorn, *Rutgers University*
Julia L. Higle, *University of Arizona*
Mark Huber, *Duke University*
Edward Ionides, *University of Michigan*
Anastasia Ivanova, *University of North Carolina*
Hamid Jafarkhani, *University of California, Irvine*
Chuanshu Ji, *University of North Carolina, Chapel Hill*
Robert Keener, *University of Michigan*
*Richard Laugesen, *University of Illinois*
Fred Leysieffer, *Florida State University*
Thomas Liggett, *University of California, Los Angeles*
Helmut Mayer, *University of Georgia*
Bill McCormick, *University of Georgia*
Ian McKeague, *Florida State University*
R. Miller, *Stanford University*
Ditlev Monrad, *University of Illinois*
Robb J. Muirhead, *University of Michigan*
Joe Naus, *Rutgers University*
Nhu Nguyen, *New Mexico State University*
Ellen O'Brien, *George Mason University*
N. U. Prabhu, *Cornell University*
Kathryn Prewitt, *Arizona State University*
Jim Propp, *University of Wisconsin*
William F. Rosenberger, *George Mason University*
Myra Samuels, *Purdue University*
I. R. Savage, *Yale University*

Art Schwartz, *University of Michigan at Ann Arbor*
Therese Shelton, *Southwestern University*
Malcolm Sherman, *State University of New York at Albany*
Murad Taqqu, *Boston University*

*Brian Thelen, *University of Michigan*
Eli Upfal, *Brown University*
Ed Wheeler, *University of Tennessee*
Allen Webster, *Bradley University*

S. R.
smross@usc.edu

COMBINATORIAL ANALYSIS

Chapter

1

Contents

1.1 Introduction
1.2 The Basic Principle of Counting
1.3 Permutations
1.4 Combinations

1.5 Multinomial Coefficients
1.6 The Number of Integer Solutions of
Equations

1.1 Introduction

Here is a typical problem of interest involving probability: A communication system is to consist of n seemingly identical antennas that are to be lined up in a linear order. The resulting system will then be able to receive all incoming signals—and will be called *functional*—as long as no two consecutive antennas are defective. If it turns out that exactly m of the n antennas are defective, what is the probability that the resulting system will be functional? For instance, in the special case where $n = 4$ and $m = 2$, there are 6 possible system configurations, namely,

$$
\begin{array}{cccc}
0 & 1 & 1 & 0 \\
0 & 1 & 0 & 1 \\
1 & 0 & 1 & 0 \\
0 & 0 & 1 & 1 \\
1 & 0 & 0 & 1 \\
1 & 1 & 0 & 0
\end{array}
$$

where 1 means that the antenna is working and 0 that it is defective. Because the resulting system will be functional in the first 3 arrangements and not functional in the remaining 3, it seems reasonable to take $\frac{3}{6} = \frac{1}{2}$ as the desired probability. In the case of general n and m, we could compute the probability that the system is functional in a similar fashion. That is, we could count the number of configurations that result in the system's being functional and then divide by the total number of all possible configurations.

From the preceding discussion, we see that it would be useful to have an effective method for counting the number of ways that things can occur. In fact, many problems in probability theory can be solved simply by counting the number of different ways that a certain event can occur. The mathematical theory of counting is formally known as *combinatorial analysis*.

1

1.2   The Basic Principle of Counting

The basic principle of counting will be fundamental to all our work. Loosely put, it states that if one experiment can result in any of m possible outcomes and if another experiment can result in any of n possible outcomes, then there are mn possible outcomes of the two experiments.

The basic principle of counting

Suppose that two experiments are to be performed. Then if experiment 1 can result in any one of m possible outcomes and if, for each outcome of experiment 1, there are n possible outcomes of experiment 2, then together there are mn possible outcomes of the two experiments.

Proof of the Basic Principle: The basic principle may be proven by enumerating all the possible outcomes of the two experiments; that is,

$$(1,1), \ (1,2), \ \ldots, \ (1,n)$$
$$(2,1), \ (2,2), \ \ldots, \ (2,n)$$
$$\vdots$$
$$(m,1), \ (m,2), \ \ldots, \ (m,n)$$

where we say that the outcome is (i, j) if experiment 1 results in its ith possible outcome and experiment 2 then results in its jth possible outcome. Hence, the set of possible outcomes consists of m rows, each containing n elements. This proves the result.

Example 2a

A small community consists of 10 women, each of whom has 3 children. If one woman and one of her children are to be chosen as mother and child of the year, how many different choices are possible?

Solution By regarding the choice of the woman as the outcome of the first experiment and the subsequent choice of one of her children as the outcome of the second experiment, we see from the basic principle that there are $10 \times 3 = 30$ possible choices. ■

When there are more than two experiments to be performed, the basic principle can be generalized.

The generalized basic principle of counting

If r experiments that are to be performed are such that the first one may result in any of n_1 possible outcomes; and if, for each of these n_1 possible outcomes, there are n_2 possible outcomes of the second experiment; and if, for each of the possible outcomes of the first two experiments, there are n_3 possible outcomes of the third experiment; and if ..., then there is a total of $n_1 \cdot n_2 \cdots n_r$ possible outcomes of the r experiments.

Example 2b

A college planning committee consists of 3 freshmen, 4 sophomores, 5 juniors, and 2 seniors. A subcommittee of 4, consisting of 1 person from each class, is to be chosen. How many different subcommittees are possible?

Solution We may regard the choice of a subcommittee as the combined outcome of the four separate experiments of choosing a single representative from each of the classes. It then follows from the generalized version of the basic principle that there are $3 \times 4 \times 5 \times 2 = 120$ possible subcommittees. ∎

Example 2c How many different 7-place license plates are possible if the first 3 places are to be occupied by letters and the final 4 by numbers?

Solution By the generalized version of the basic principle, the answer is $26 \cdot 26 \cdot 26 \cdot 10 \cdot 10 \cdot 10 \cdot 10 = 175,760,000$. ∎

Example 2d How many functions defined on n points are possible if each functional value is either 0 or 1?

Solution Let the points be $1, 2, \ldots, n$. Since $f(i)$ must be either 0 or 1 for each $i = 1, 2, \ldots, n$, it follows that there are 2^n possible functions. ∎

Example 2e In Example 2c, how many license plates would be possible if repetition among letters or numbers were prohibited?

Solution In this case, there would be $26 \cdot 25 \cdot 24 \cdot 10 \cdot 9 \cdot 8 \cdot 7 = 78,624,000$ possible license plates. ∎

1.3 Permutations

How many different ordered arrangements of the letters a, b, and c are possible? By direct enumeration we see that there are 6, namely, *abc, acb, bac, bca, cab,* and *cba*. Each arrangement is known as a *permutation*. Thus, there are 6 possible permutations of a set of 3 objects. This result could also have been obtained from the basic principle, since the first object in the permutation can be any of the 3, the second object in the permutation can then be chosen from any of the remaining 2, and the third object in the permutation is then the remaining 1. Thus, there are $3 \cdot 2 \cdot 1 = 6$ possible permutations.

> Suppose now that we have n objects. Reasoning similar to that we have just used for the 3 letters then shows that there are
>
> $$n(n - 1)(n - 2) \cdots 3 \cdot 2 \cdot 1 = n!$$
>
> different permutations of the n objects.

Whereas $n!$ (read as "n factorial") is defined to equal $1 \cdot 2 \cdots n$ when n is a positive integer, it is convenient to define 0! to equal 1.

Example 3a How many different batting orders are possible for a baseball team consisting of 9 players?

Solution There are $9! = 362,880$ possible batting orders. ∎

Example 3b A class in probability theory consists of 6 men and 4 women. An examination is given, and the students are ranked according to their performance. Assume that no two students obtain the same score.

(a) How many different rankings are possible?

(b) If the men are ranked just among themselves and the women just among themselves, how many different rankings are possible?

Solution (a) Because each ranking corresponds to a particular ordered arrangement of the 10 people, the answer to this part is $10! = 3,628,800$.

(b) Since there are $6!$ possible rankings of the men among themselves and $4!$ possible rankings of the women among themselves, it follows from the basic principle that there are $(6!)(4!) = (720)(24) = 17,280$ possible rankings in this case. ∎

Example 3c

Ms. Jones has 10 books that she is going to put on her bookshelf. Of these, 4 are mathematics books, 3 are chemistry books, 2 are history books, and 1 is a language book. Ms. Jones wants to arrange her books so that all the books dealing with the same subject are together on the shelf. How many different arrangements are possible?

Solution There are $4! \, 3! \, 2! \, 1!$ arrangements such that the mathematics books are first in line, then the chemistry books, then the history books, and then the language book. Similarly, for each possible ordering of the subjects, there are $4! \, 3! \, 2! \, 1!$ possible arrangements. Hence, as there are $4!$ possible orderings of the subjects, the desired answer is $4! \, 4! \, 3! \, 2! \, 1! = 6912$. ∎

We shall now determine the number of permutations of a set of n objects when certain of the objects are indistinguishable from one another. To set this situation straight in our minds, consider the following example.

Example 3d

How many different letter arrangements can be formed from the letters *PEPPER*?

Solution We first note that there are $6!$ permutations of the letters $P_1E_1P_2P_3E_2R$ when the $3P$'s and the $2E$'s are distinguished from one another. However, consider any one of these permutations—for instance, $P_1P_2E_1P_3E_2R$. If we now permute the P's among themselves and the E's among themselves, then the resultant arrangement would still be of the form *PPEPER*. That is, all $3! \, 2!$ permutations

$$
\begin{array}{ll}
P_1P_2E_1P_3E_2R & P_1P_2E_2P_3E_1R \\
P_1P_3E_1P_2E_2R & P_1P_3E_2P_2E_1R \\
P_2P_1E_1P_3E_2R & P_2P_1E_2P_3E_1R \\
P_2P_3E_1P_1E_2R & P_2P_3E_2P_1E_1R \\
P_3P_1E_1P_2E_2R & P_3P_1E_2P_2E_1R \\
P_3P_2E_1P_1E_2R & P_3P_2E_2P_1E_1R
\end{array}
$$

are of the form *PPEPER*. Hence, there are $6!/(3! \, 2!) = 60$ possible letter arrangements of the letters *PEPPER*. ∎

In general, the same reasoning as that used in Example 3d shows that there are

$$
\frac{n!}{n_1! \, n_2! \, \cdots \, n_r!}
$$

different permutations of n objects, of which n_1 are alike, n_2 are alike, ..., n_r are alike.

Example 3e

A chess tournament has 10 competitors, of which 4 are Russian, 3 are from the United States, 2 are from Great Britain, and 1 is from Brazil. If the tournament result lists just the nationalities of the players in the order in which they placed, how many outcomes are possible?

Solution There are

$$\frac{10!}{4!\ 3!\ 2!\ 1!} = 12,600$$

possible outcomes. ∎

Example 3f

How many different signals, each consisting of 9 flags hung in a line, can be made from a set of 4 white flags, 3 red flags, and 2 blue flags if all flags of the same color are identical?

Solution There are

$$\frac{9!}{4!\ 3!\ 2!} = 1260$$

different signals. ∎

1.4 Combinations

We are often interested in determining the number of different groups of r objects that could be formed from a total of n objects. For instance, how many different groups of 3 could be selected from the 5 items A, B, C, D, and E? To answer this question, reason as follows: Since there are 5 ways to select the initial item, 4 ways to then select the next item, and 3 ways to select the final item, there are thus $5 \cdot 4 \cdot 3$ ways of selecting the group of 3 when the order in which the items are selected is relevant. However, since every group of 3—say, the group consisting of items A, B, and C—will be counted 6 times (that is, all of the permutations ABC, ACB, BAC, BCA, CAB, and CBA will be counted when the order of selection is relevant), it follows that the total number of groups that can be formed is

$$\frac{5 \cdot 4 \cdot 3}{3 \cdot 2 \cdot 1} = 10$$

In general, as $n(n-1)\cdots(n-r+1)$ represents the number of different ways that a group of r items could be selected from n items when the order of selection is relevant, and as each group of r items will be counted $r!$ times in this count, it follows that the number of different groups of r items that could be formed from a set of n items is

$$\frac{n(n-1)\cdots(n-r+1)}{r!} = \frac{n!}{(n-r)!\ r!}$$

Notation and terminology

We define $\binom{n}{r}$, for $r \le n$, by

$$\binom{n}{r} = \frac{n!}{(n-r)!\ r!}$$

and say that $\binom{n}{r}$ (read as "n choose r") represents the number of possible combinations of n objects taken r at a time.[†]

[†] By convention, 0! is defined to be 1. Thus, $\binom{n}{0} = \binom{n}{n} = 1$. We also take $\binom{n}{i}$ to be equal to 0 when either $i < 0$ or $i > n$.

Thus, $\binom{n}{r}$ represents the number of different groups of size r that could be selected from a set of n objects when the order of selection is not considered relevant.

Equivalently, $\binom{n}{r}$ is the number of subsets of size r that can be chosen from a set of size n. Using that $0! = 1$, note that $\binom{n}{n} = \binom{n}{0} = \dfrac{n!}{0!n!} = 1$, which is consistent with the preceding interpretation because in a set of size n there is exactly 1 subset of size n (namely, the entire set), and exactly one subset of size 0 (namely the empty set). A useful convention is to define $\binom{n}{r}$ equal to 0 when either $r > n$ or $r < 0$.

Example 4a

A committee of 3 is to be formed from a group of 20 people. How many different committees are possible?

Solution There are $\binom{20}{3} = \dfrac{20 \cdot 19 \cdot 18}{3 \cdot 2 \cdot 1} = 1140$ possible committees. ■

Example 4b

From a group of 5 women and 7 men, how many different committees consisting of 2 women and 3 men can be formed? What if 2 of the men are feuding and refuse to serve on the committee together?

Solution As there are $\binom{5}{2}$ possible groups of 2 women, and $\binom{7}{3}$ possible groups of 3 men, it follows from the basic principle that there are $\binom{5}{2}\binom{7}{3} = \left(\dfrac{5 \cdot 4}{2 \cdot 1}\right)\dfrac{7 \cdot 6 \cdot 5}{3 \cdot 2 \cdot 1} = 350$ possible committees consisting of 2 women and 3 men.

Now suppose that 2 of the men refuse to serve together. Because a total of $\binom{2}{2}\binom{5}{1} = 5$ out of the $\binom{7}{3} = 35$ possible groups of 3 men contain both of the feuding men, it follows that there are $35 - 5 = 30$ groups that do not contain both of the feuding men. Because there are still $\binom{5}{2} = 10$ ways to choose the 2 women, there are $30 \cdot 10 = 300$ possible committees in this case. ■

Example 4c

Consider a set of n antennas of which m are defective and $n - m$ are functional and assume that all of the defectives and all of the functionals are considered indistinguishable. How many linear orderings are there in which no two defectives are consecutive?

Solution Imagine that the $n - m$ functional antennas are lined up among themselves. Now, if no two defectives are to be consecutive, then the spaces between the functional antennas must each contain at most one defective antenna. That is, in the $n - m + 1$ possible positions—represented in Figure 1.1 by carets—between the $n - m$ functional antennas, we must select m of these in which to put the defective antennas. Hence, there are $\binom{n - m + 1}{m}$ possible orderings in which there is at least one functional antenna between any two defective ones. ■

$$\wedge\, 1 \,\wedge\, 1 \,\wedge\, 1 \ldots \wedge\, 1 \,\wedge\, 1 \,\wedge$$

1 = functional

∧ = place for at most one defective

Figure 1.1 No consecutive defectives.

A useful combinatorial identity is

$$\binom{n}{r} = \binom{n-1}{r-1} + \binom{n-1}{r} \qquad 1 \le r \le n \tag{4.1}$$

Equation (4.1) may be proved analytically or by the following combinatorial argument: Consider a group of n objects, and fix attention on some particular one of these objects—call it object 1. Now, there are $\binom{n-1}{r-1}$ groups of size r that contain object 1 (since each such group is formed by selecting $r-1$ from the remaining $n-1$ objects). Also, there are $\binom{n-1}{r}$ groups of size r that do not contain object 1. As there is a total of $\binom{n}{r}$ groups of size r, Equation (4.1) follows.

The values $\binom{n}{r}$ are often referred to as *binomial coefficients* because of their prominence in the binomial theorem.

The binomial theorem

$$(x + y)^n = \sum_{k=0}^{n} \binom{n}{k} x^k y^{n-k} \tag{4.2}$$

We shall present two proofs of the binomial theorem. The first is a proof by mathematical induction, and the second is a proof based on combinatorial considerations.

Proof of the Binomial Theorem by Induction: When $n = 1$, Equation (4.2) reduces to

$$x + y = \binom{1}{0} x^0 y^1 + \binom{1}{1} x^1 y^0 = y + x$$

Assume Equation (4.2) for $n-1$. Now,

$$(x + y)^n = (x + y)(x + y)^{n-1}$$

$$= (x + y) \sum_{k=0}^{n-1} \binom{n-1}{k} x^k y^{n-1-k}$$

$$= \sum_{k=0}^{n-1} \binom{n-1}{k} x^{k+1} y^{n-1-k} + \sum_{k=0}^{n-1} \binom{n-1}{k} x^k y^{n-k}$$

Letting $i = k + 1$ in the first sum and $i = k$ in the second sum, we find that

$$(x + y)^n = \sum_{i=1}^{n} \binom{n-1}{i-1} x^i y^{n-i} + \sum_{i=0}^{n-1} \binom{n-1}{i} x^i y^{n-i}$$

$$= x^n + \sum_{i=1}^{n-1} \left[\binom{n-1}{i-1} + \binom{n-1}{i} \right] x^i y^{n-i} + y^n$$

$$= x^n + \sum_{i=1}^{n-1} \binom{n}{i} x^i y^{n-i} + y^n$$

$$= \sum_{i=0}^{n} \binom{n}{i} x^i y^{n-i}$$

where the next-to-last equality follows by Equation (4.1). By induction, the theorem is now proved.

Combinatorial Proof of the Binomial Theorem: Consider the product

$$(x_1 + y_1)(x_2 + y_2) \cdots (x_n + y_n)$$

Its expansion consists of the sum of 2^n terms, each term being the product of n factors. Furthermore, each of the 2^n terms in the sum will contain as a factor either x_i or y_i for each $i = 1, 2, \ldots, n$. For example,

$$(x_1 + y_1)(x_2 + y_2) = x_1 x_2 + x_1 y_2 + y_1 x_2 + y_1 y_2$$

Now, how many of the 2^n terms in the sum will have k of the x_i's and $(n - k)$ of the y_i's as factors? As each term consisting of k of the x_i's and $(n - k)$ of the y_i's corresponds to a choice of a group of k from the n values $x_1, x_2, \ldots, x_n$, there are $\binom{n}{k}$ such terms. Thus, letting $x_i = x, y_i = y, i = 1, \ldots, n$, we see that

$$(x + y)^n = \sum_{k=0}^{n} \binom{n}{k} x^k y^{n-k}$$

Example 4d   Expand $(x + y)^3$.

Solution

$$(x + y)^3 = \binom{3}{0} x^0 y^3 + \binom{3}{1} x^1 y^2 + \binom{3}{2} x^2 y^1 + \binom{3}{3} x^3 y^0$$

$$= y^3 + 3xy^2 + 3x^2 y + x^3$$

∎

Example 4e   How many subsets are there of a set consisting of n elements?

Solution Since there are $\binom{n}{k}$ subsets of size k, the desired answer is

$$\sum_{k=0}^{n} \binom{n}{k} = (1 + 1)^n = 2^n$$

This result could also have been obtained by assigning either the number 0 or the number 1 to each element in the set. To each assignment of numbers, there corresponds, in a one-to-one fashion, a subset, namely, that subset consisting of all elements that were assigned the value 1. As there are 2^n possible assignments, the result follows.

Note that we have included the set consisting of 0 elements (that is, the null set) as a subset of the original set. Hence, the number of subsets that contain at least 1 element is $2^n - 1$. ∎

1.5 Multinomial Coefficients

In this section, we consider the following problem: A set of n distinct items is to be divided into r distinct groups of respective sizes $n_1, n_2, \ldots, n_r$, where $\sum_{i=1}^r n_i = n$. How many different divisions are possible? To answer this question, we note that there are $\binom{n}{n_1}$ possible choices for the first group; for each choice of the first group, there are $\binom{n-n_1}{n_2}$ possible choices for the second group; for each choice of the first two groups, there are $\binom{n - n_1 - n_2}{n_3}$ possible choices for the third group; and so on. It then follows from the generalized version of the basic counting principle that there are

$$\binom{n}{n_1}\binom{n-n_1}{n_2}\cdots\binom{n - n_1 - n_2 - \cdots - n_{r-1}}{n_r}$$

$$= \frac{n!}{(n-n_1)!\,n_1!}\frac{(n-n_1)!}{(n-n_1-n_2)!\,n_2!}\cdots\frac{(n-n_1-n_2-\cdots-n_{r-1})!}{0!\,n_r!}$$

$$= \frac{n!}{n_1!\,n_2!\cdots n_r!}$$

possible divisions.

Another way to see this result is to consider the n values $1, 1, \ldots, 1, 2, \ldots, 2, \ldots, r, \ldots, r$, where i appears n_i times, for $i = 1, \ldots, r$. Every permutation of these values corresponds to a division of the n items into the r groups in the following manner: Let the permutation $i_1, i_2, \ldots, i_n$ correspond to assigning item 1 to group i_1, item 2 to group i_2, and so on. For instance, if $n = 8$ and if $n_1 = 4$, $n_2 = 3$, and $n_3 = 1$, then the permutation $1, 1, 2, 3, 2, 1, 2, 1$ corresponds to assigning items $1, 2, 6, 8$ to the first group, items $3, 5, 7$ to the second group, and item 4 to the third group. Because every permutation yields a division of the items and every possible division results from some permutation, it follows that the number of divisions of n items into r distinct groups of sizes $n_1, n_2, \ldots, n_r$ is the same as the number of permutations of n items of which n_1 are alike, and n_2 are alike, $\ldots$, and n_r are alike, which was shown in Section 1.3 to equal $\dfrac{n!}{n_1!\,n_2!\cdots n_r!}$.

Notation

If $n_1 + n_2 + \cdots + n_r = n$, we define $\binom{n}{n_1, n_2, \ldots, n_r}$ by

$$\binom{n}{n_1, n_2, \ldots, n_r} = \frac{n!}{n_1! \, n_2! \cdots n_r!}$$

Thus, $\binom{n}{n_1, n_2, \ldots, n_r}$ represents the number of possible divisions of n distinct objects into r distinct groups of respective sizes $n_1, n_2, \ldots, n_r$.

Example 5a

A police department in a small city consists of 10 officers. If the department policy is to have 5 of the officers patrolling the streets, 2 of the officers working full time at the station, and 3 of the officers on reserve at the station, how many different divisions of the 10 officers into the 3 groups are possible?

Solution There are $\dfrac{10!}{5! \, 2! \, 3!} = 2520$ possible divisions. ∎

Example 5b

Ten children are to be divided into an A team and a B team of 5 each. The A team will play in one league and the B team in another. How many different divisions are possible?

Solution There are $\dfrac{10!}{5! \, 5!} = 252$ possible divisions. ∎

Example 5c

In order to play a game of basketball, 10 children at a playground divide themselves into two teams of 5 each. How many different divisions are possible?

Solution Note that this example is different from Example 5b because now the order of the two teams is irrelevant. That is, there is no A or B team, but just a division consisting of 2 groups of 5 each. Hence, the desired answer is

$$\frac{10!/(5! \, 5!)}{2!} = 126$$
∎

The proof of the following theorem, which generalizes the binomial theorem, is left as an exercise.

The multinomial theorem

$$(x_1 + x_2 + \cdots + x_r)^n =$$

$$\sum_{\substack{(n_1, \ldots, n_r): \\ n_1 + \cdots + n_r = n}} \binom{n}{n_1, n_2, \ldots, n_r} x_1^{n_1} x_2^{n_2} \cdots x_r^{n_r}$$

That is, the sum is over all nonnegative integer-valued vectors $(n_1, n_2, \ldots, n_r)$ such that $n_1 + n_2 + \cdots + n_r = n$.

The numbers $\binom{n}{n_1, n_2, \ldots, n_r}$ are known as *multinomial coefficients*.

Example 5d	In the first round of a knockout tournament involving $n = 2^m$ players, the n players are divided into $n/2$ pairs, with each of these pairs then playing a game. The losers of the games are eliminated while the winners go on to the next round, where the process is repeated until only a single player remains. Suppose we have a knockout tournament of 8 players.

(a) How many possible outcomes are there for the initial round? (For instance, one outcome is that 1 beats 2, 3 beats 4, 5 beats 6, and 7 beats 8.)

(b) How many outcomes of the tournament are possible, where an outcome gives complete information for all rounds?

Solution One way to determine the number of possible outcomes for the initial round is to first determine the number of possible pairings for that round. To do so, note that the number of ways to divide the 8 players into a *first* pair, a *second* pair, a *third* pair, and a *fourth* pair is $\binom{8}{2,2,2,2} = \dfrac{8!}{2^4}$. Thus, the number of possible pairings when there is no ordering of the 4 pairs is $\dfrac{8!}{2^4\,4!}$. For each such pairing, there are 2 possible choices from each pair as to the winner of that game, showing that there are $\dfrac{8!2^4}{2^4\,4!} = \dfrac{8!}{4!}$ possible results of round 1. [Another way to see this is to note that there are $\binom{8}{4}$ possible choices of the 4 winners and, for each such choice, there are 4! ways to pair the 4 winners with the 4 losers, showing that there are $4!\binom{8}{4} = \dfrac{8!}{4!}$ possible results for the first round.]

Similarly, for each result of round 1, there are $\dfrac{4!}{2!}$ possible outcomes of round 2, and for each of the outcomes of the first two rounds, there are $\dfrac{2!}{1!}$ possible outcomes of round 3. Consequently, by the generalized basic principle of counting, there are $\dfrac{8!}{4!}\dfrac{4!}{2!}\dfrac{2!}{1!} = 8!$ possible outcomes of the tournament. Indeed, the same argument can be used to show that a knockout tournament of $n = 2^m$ players has $n!$ possible outcomes.

Knowing the preceding result, it is not difficult to come up with a more direct argument by showing that there is a one-to-one correspondence between the set of possible tournament results and the set of permutations of $1, \ldots, n$. To obtain such a correspondence, rank the players as follows for any tournament result: Give the tournament winner rank 1, and give the final-round loser rank 2. For the two players who lost in the next-to-last round, give rank 3 to the one who lost to the player ranked 1 and give rank 4 to the one who lost to the player ranked 2. For the four players who lost in the second-to-last round, give rank 5 to the one who lost to player ranked 1, rank 6 to the one who lost to the player ranked 2, rank 7 to the one who lost to the player ranked 3, and rank 8 to the one who lost to the player ranked 4. Continuing on in this manner gives a rank to each player. (A more succinct description is to give the winner of the tournament rank 1 and let the rank of a player who lost in a round having 2^k matches be 2^k plus the rank of the player who beat him, for $k = 0, \ldots, m - 1$.) In this manner, the result of the tournament can be represented by a permutation $i_1, i_2, \ldots, i_n$, where i_j is the player who was given rank j. Because different tournament results give rise to different permutations, and because there is a tournament result for each permutation, it follows that there are the same number of possible tournament results as there are permutations of $1, \ldots, n$. ∎

Example 5e

$$(x_1 + x_2 + x_3)^2 = \begin{pmatrix} 2 \\ 2,0,0 \end{pmatrix} x_1^2 x_2^0 x_3^0 + \begin{pmatrix} 2 \\ 0,2,0 \end{pmatrix} x_1^0 x_2^2 x_3^0$$

$$+ \begin{pmatrix} 2 \\ 0,0,2 \end{pmatrix} x_1^0 x_2^0 x_3^2 + \begin{pmatrix} 2 \\ 1,1,0 \end{pmatrix} x_1^1 x_2^1 x_3^0$$

$$+ \begin{pmatrix} 2 \\ 1,0,1 \end{pmatrix} x_1^1 x_2^0 x_3^1 + \begin{pmatrix} 2 \\ 0,1,1 \end{pmatrix} x_1^0 x_2^1 x_3^1$$

$$= x_1^2 + x_2^2 + x_3^2 + 2x_1 x_2 + 2x_1 x_3 + 2x_2 x_3 \qquad \blacksquare$$

*1.6 The Number of Integer Solutions of Equations

An individual has gone fishing at Lake Ticonderoga, which contains four types of fish: lake trout, catfish, bass, and bluefish. If we take the result of the fishing trip to be the numbers of each type of fish caught, let us determine the number of possible outcomes when a total of 10 fish are caught. To do so, note that we can denote the outcome of the fishing trip by the vector (x_1, x_2, x_3, x_4) where x_1 is the number of trout that are caught, x_2 is the number of catfish, x_3 is the number of bass, and x_4 is the number of bluefish. Thus, the number of possible outcomes when a total of 10 fish are caught is the number of nonnegative vectors (x_1, x_2, x_3, x_4) that sum to 10.

More generally, if we supposed there were r types of fish and that a total of n were caught then the number of possible outcomes would be the number of nonnegative integer-valued vectors $x_1, \ldots, x_r$ such that

$$x_1 + x_2 + \ldots + x_r = n \qquad (6.1)$$

To compute this number, let us start by considering the number of positive integer-valued vectors $x_1, \ldots, x_r$ that satisfy the preceding. To determine this number, suppose that we have n consecutive values zero lined up in a row:

$$0 \; 0 \; 0 \; \ldots \; 0 \; 0$$

Note that any selection of $r - 1$ of the $n - 1$ spaces between adjacent zeroes (see Figure 1.2) corresponds to a positive solution of (6.1) by letting x_1 be the number of zeroes before the first chosen space, x_2 be the number of zeroes between the first and second chosen space, ..., and x_n being the number of zeroes following the last chosen space.

$$0 \wedge 0 \wedge 0 \wedge \ldots \wedge 0 \wedge 0$$

n objects 0

Choose $r - 1$ of the spaces $\wedge$.

Figure 1.2 Number of positive solutions.

For instance, if we have $n = 8$ and $r = 3$, then (with the choices represented by dots) the choice

$$0.0000.000$$

corresponds to the solution $x_1 = 1, x_2 = 4, x_3 = 3$. As positive solutions of (6.1) correspond, in a one-to-one fashion, to choices of $r - 1$ of the adjacent spaces, it follows that the number of differerent positive solutions is equal to the number of different selections of $r - 1$ of the $n - 1$ adjacent spaces. Consequently, we have the following proposition.

Proposition 6.1

There are $\binom{n - 1}{r - 1}$ distinct positive integer-valued vectors $(x_1, x_2, \ldots, x_r)$ satisfying the equation

$$x_1 + x_2 + \cdots + x_r = n \quad x_i > 0, \quad i = 1, \ldots, r$$

To obtain the number of nonnegative (as opposed to positive) solutions, note that the number of nonnegative solutions of $x_1 + x_2 + \cdots + x_r = n$ is the same as the number of positive solutions of $y_1 + \cdots + y_r = n + r$ (seen by letting $y_i = x_i + 1, i = 1, \ldots, r$). Hence, from Proposition 6.1, we obtain the following proposition.

Proposition 6.2

There are $\binom{n + r - 1}{r - 1}$ distinct nonnegative integer-valued vectors $(x_1, x_2, \ldots, x_r)$ satisfying the equation

$$x_1 + x_2 + \cdots + x_r = n$$

Thus, using Proposition 6.2, we see that there are $\binom{13}{3} = 286$ possible outcomes when a total of 10 Lake Ticonderoga fish are caught.

Example 6a

How many distinct nonnegative integer-valued solutions of $x_1 + x_2 = 3$ are possible?

Solution There are $\binom{3 + 2 - 1}{2 - 1} = 4$ such solutions: $(0, 3), (1, 2), (2, 1), (3, 0)$. ∎

Example 6b

An investor has \$20,000 to invest among 4 possible investments. Each investment must be in units of \$1000. If the total \$20,000 is to be invested, how many different investment strategies are possible? What if not all the money needs to be invested?

Solution If we let $x_i, i = 1, 2, 3, 4$, denote the number of thousands invested in investment i, then, when all is to be invested, x_1, x_2, x_3, x_4 are integers satisfying the equation

$$x_1 + x_2 + x_3 + x_4 = 20 \quad x_i \geq 0$$

Hence, by Proposition 6.2, there are $\binom{23}{3} = 1771$ possible investment strategies. If not all of the money needs to be invested, then if we let x_5 denote the amount kept in reserve, a strategy is a nonnegative integer-valued vector $(x_1, x_2, x_3, x_4, x_5)$ satisfying the equation

$$x_1 + x_2 + x_3 + x_4 + x_5 = 20$$

Hence, by Proposition 6.2, there are now $\binom{24}{4} = 10{,}626$ possible strategies. ∎

Example 6c

How many terms are there in the multinomial expansion of $(x_1 + x_2 + \cdots + x_r)^n$?

Solution

$$(x_1 + x_2 + \cdots + x_r)^n = \sum \binom{n}{n_1, \ldots, n_r} x_1^{n_1} \cdots x_r^{n_r}$$

where the sum is over all nonnegative integer-valued $(n_1, \ldots, n_r)$ such that $n_1 + \cdots + n_r = n$. Hence, by Proposition 6.2, there are $\binom{n + r - 1}{r - 1}$ such terms. ∎

Example 6d

Let us consider again Example 4c, in which we have a set of n items, of which m are (indistinguishable and) defective and the remaining $n - m$ are (also indistinguishable and) functional. Our objective is to determine the number of linear orderings in which no two defectives are next to each other. To determine this number, let us imagine that the defective items are lined up among themselves and the functional ones are now to be put in position. Let us denote x_1 as the number of functional items to the left of the first defective, x_2 as the number of functional items between the first two defectives, and so on. That is, schematically, we have

$$x_1 \ 0 \ x_2 \ 0 \cdots x_m \ 0 \ x_{m+1}$$

Now, there will be at least one functional item between any pair of defectives as long as $x_i > 0, i = 2, \ldots, m$. Hence, the number of outcomes satisfying the condition is the number of vectors $x_1, \ldots, x_{m+1}$ that satisfy the equation

$$x_1 + \cdots + x_{m+1} = n - m \quad x_1 \geq 0, \ x_{m+1} \geq 0, \ x_i > 0, \ i = 2, \ldots, m$$

But, on letting $y_1 = x_1 + 1, y_i = x_i, i = 2, \ldots, m, y_{m+1} = x_{m+1} + 1$, we see that this number is equal to the number of positive vectors $(y_1, \ldots, y_{m+1})$ that satisfy the equation

$$y_1 + y_2 + \cdots + y_{m+1} = n - m + 2$$

Hence, by Proposition 6.1, there are $\binom{n - m + 1}{m}$ such outcomes, in agreement with the results of Example 4c.

Suppose now that we are interested in the number of outcomes in which each pair of defective items is separated by at least 2 functional items. By the same reasoning as that applied previously, this would equal the number of vectors satisfying the equation

$$x_1 + \cdots + x_{m+1} = n - m \quad x_1 \geq 0, \ x_{m+1} \geq 0, \ x_i \geq 2, \ i = 2, \ldots, m$$

Upon letting $y_1 = x_1 + 1, y_i = x_i - 1, i = 2, \ldots, m, y_{m+1} = x_{m+1} + 1$, we see that this is the same as the number of positive solutions of the equation

$$y_1 + \cdots + y_{m+1} = n - 2m + 3$$

Hence, from Proposition 6.1, there are $\binom{n - 2m + 2}{m}$ such outcomes. ∎

Summary

The basic principle of counting states that if an experiment consisting of two phases is such that there are n possible outcomes of phase 1 and, for each of these n outcomes, there are m possible outcomes of phase 2, then there are nm possible outcomes of the experiment.

There are $n! = n(n - 1)\cdots 3 \cdot 2 \cdot 1$ possible linear orderings of n items. The quantity $0!$ is defined to equal 1.

Let

$$\binom{n}{i} = \frac{n!}{(n - i)! \, i!}$$

when $0 \leq i \leq n$, and let it equal 0 otherwise. This quantity represents the number of different subgroups of size i that can be chosen from a set of size n. It is often called a *binomial coefficient* because of its prominence in the binomial theorem, which states that

$$(x + y)^n = \sum_{i=0}^{n} \binom{n}{i} x^i y^{n-i}$$

For nonnegative integers $n_1, \ldots, n_r$ summing to n,

$$\binom{n}{n_1, n_2, \ldots, n_r} = \frac{n!}{n_1! n_2! \cdots n_r!}$$

is the number of divisions of n items into r distinct nonoverlapping subgroups of sizes $n_1, n_2 \ldots, n_r$. These quantities are called *multinomial coefficients*.

Problems

1. You have six balls numbered 1 to 6 placed in a box. How many different ways are there to choose 4 balls from the lot, if

(a) the ball chosen is returned to the box before the next draw?

(b) the ball once chosen is not returned?

2. How many outcome sequences are possible when a die is rolled four times, where we say, for instance, that the outcome is 3, 4, 3, 1 if the first roll landed on 3, the second on 4, the third on 3, and the fourth on 1?

3. Twenty workers are to be assigned to 20 different jobs, one to each job. How many different assignments are possible?

4. John, Jim, Jay, and Jack have formed a band consisting of 4 instruments. If each of the boys can play all 4 instruments, how many different arrangements are possible? What if John and Jim can play all 4 instruments, but Jay and Jack can each play only piano and drums?

5. A password contains 6 digits 1, 2, 3, 0, 0, 5. If it takes 10 seconds to try out a password. How many minutes will it take to try all the possible combinations?

6. A well-known nursery rhyme starts as follows:
   "As I was going to St. Ives

   I met a man with 7 wives.

   Each wife had 7 sacks.

   Each sack had 7 cats.

   Each cat had 7 kittens..."

   How many kittens did the traveler meet?

7. (a) In how many ways can 3 boys and 3 girls sit in a row?

(b) In how many ways can 3 boys and 3 girls sit in a row if the boys and the girls are each to sit together?

(c) In how many ways if only the boys must sit together?

(d) In how many ways if no two people of the same sex are allowed to sit together?

8. How many different letter arrangement can be made from the letters,

(a) Spain

(b) India

(c) Antarctica

9. A child has 12 blocks, of which 6 are black, 4 are red, 1 is white, and 1 is blue. If the child puts the blocks in a line, how many arrangements are possible?

10. In how many ways can 8 people be seated in a row if

(a) there are no restrictions on the seating arrangement?

(b) persons A and B must sit next to each other?

(c) there are 4 men and 4 women and no 2 men or 2 women can sit next to each other?

(d) there are 5 men and they must sit next to one another?

(e) there are 4 married couples and each couple must sit together?

11. In how many ways can 3 novels, 2 mathematics books, and 1 chemistry book be arranged on a bookshelf if

(a) the books can be arranged in any order?

(b) the mathematics books must be together and the novels must be together?

(c) the novels must be together, but the other books can be arranged in any order?

12. Five separate awards (best scholarship, best leadership qualities, and so on) are to be presented to selected students from a class of 30. How many different outcomes are possible if

(a) a student can receive any number of awards?

(b) each student can receive at most 1 award?

13. Consider a group of 20 people. If everyone shakes hands with everyone else, how many handshakes take place?

14. Consider a 4×4 matrix, whose each element are either 0 or 1. How many such different matrices can be constructed?

15. A dance class consists of 22 students, of which 10 are women and 12 are men. If 5 men and 5 women are to be chosen and then paired off, how many results are possible?

16. A football team coach has to form a playing eleven consisting of 1 goal keeper, 4 defenders, 4 mid-fielders and 2 strikers from an available squad consisting of 2 goal keepers, 7 defenders, 8 mid fielders and 6 strikers. How many possible team choices are available for the coach?

17. Seven different gifts are to be distributed among 10 children. How many distinct results are possible if no child is to receive more than one gift?

18. A workshop at an institute is conducted for 15 persons. In a class of 30 students, 6 students has already paid the registration fee and have enroled in advance. 5 students do not wish to participate in the workshop at all. How many possible ways can the seats for the workshop be filled?

19. From a group of 8 women and 6 men, a committee consisting of 3 men and 3 women is to be formed. How many different committees are possible if

(a) 2 of the men refuse to serve together?

(b) 2 of the women refuse to serve together?

(c) 1 man and 1 woman refuse to serve together?

20. A person has 8 friends, of whom 5 will be invited to a party.

(a) How many choices are there if 2 of the friends are feuding and will not attend together?

(b) How many choices if 2 of the friends will only attend together?

21. Consider the grid of points shown at the top of the next column. Suppose that, starting at the point labeled *A*, you can go one step up or one step to the right at each move. This procedure is continued until the point labeled *B* is reached. How many different paths from *A* to *B* are possible?

Hint: Note that to reach *B* from *A*, you must take 4 steps to the right and 3 steps upward.

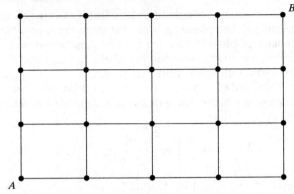

22. In Problem 21, how many different paths are there from *A* to *B* that go through the point circled in the following lattice?

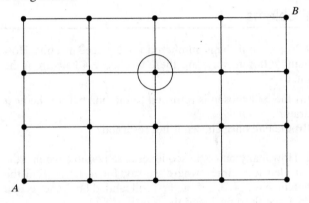

23. A psychology laboratory conducting dream research contains 3 rooms, with 2 beds in each room. If 3 sets of identical twins are to be assigned to these 6 beds so that each set of twins sleeps in different beds in the same room, how many assignments are possible?

24. Expand $(4x^4 + y)^4$.

25. How many triangles can be formed from 8 points when
(a) no three of them are collinear?
(b) four of them are in a straight line?

26. Expand $(x_1 + 2x_2 + 3x_3)^4$.

27. Seven guests arriving at a hotel has to be accommodated in 2 double occupancy bedrooms and 3 single occupancy bedroom. How many different ways can this be arranged?

28. If 8 new teachers are to be divided among 4 schools, how many divisions are possible? What if each school must receive 2 teachers?

29. In how many ways can one obtain a total sum of 13 when casting three fair dice?

30. Two couples and their four kids are to be seated in a movie theater. What is the different seating arrangement possible if they are seated randomly. If they are seated such that each of the couples sit together, then how many possible seating arrangements can be made.

*31. If 8 identical blackboards are to be divided among 4 schools, how many divisions are possible? How many if each school must receive at least 1 blackboard?

*32. An elevator starts at the basement with 8 people (not including the elevator operator) and discharges them all by the time it reaches the top floor, number 6. In how many ways could the operator have perceived the people leaving the elevator if all people look alike to him? What if the 8 people consisted of 5 men and 3 women and the operator could tell a man from a woman?

*33. We have $20,000 that must be invested among 4 possible opportunities. Each investment must be integral in

units of $1000, and there are minimal investments that need to be made if one is to invest in these opportunities. The minimal investments are $2000, $2000, $3000, and $4000. How many different investment strategies are available if

(a) an investment must be made in each opportunity?

(b) investments must be made in at least 3 of the 4 opportunities?

*34. Suppose that 10 fish are caught at a lake that contains 5 distinct types of fish.

(a) How many different outcomes are possible, where an outcome specifies the numbers of caught fish of each of the 5 types?

(b) How many outcomes are possible when 3 of the 10 fish caught are trout?

(c) How many when at least 2 of the 10 are trout?

Theoretical Exercises

1. Prove the generalized version of the basic counting principle.

2. Consider a a function defined from *set A* to *set B* with m and n elements respectively.
(a) How many such distinct functions are possible from A to B?
(b) How many distinct one to one functions are possible if $m \geq n$?

3. How many possible subsets are possible for a set containing n elements?

4. There are $\binom{n}{r}$ different linear arrangements of n balls of which r are black and $n - r$ are white. Give a combinatorial explanation of this fact.

5. Determine the number of vectors $(x_1, \ldots, x_n)$, such that each x_i is either 0 or 1 and

$$\sum_{i=1}^{n} x_i \geq k$$

6. How many vectors $x_1, \ldots, x_k$ are there for which each x_i is a positive integer such that $1 \leq x_i \leq n$ and $x_1 < x_2 < \cdots < x_k$?

7. Give an analytic proof of Equation (4.1).

8. Prove the Chu-Vandermonde Identity given by

$$\binom{x+a}{n} = \sum_{k=0}^{n} \binom{x}{k}\binom{a}{n-k}$$

9. Use the Identity in Theoretical Exercise 8 to prove that

$$\binom{m+n}{k} = \sum_{l=0}^{\max(k,n)} \binom{m}{k-l}\binom{n}{l}$$

10. From a group of n people, suppose that we want to choose a committee of $k, k \leq n$, one of whom is to be designated as chairperson.

(a) By focusing first on the choice of the committee and then on the choice of the chair, argue that there are $\binom{n}{k} k$ possible choices.

(b) By focusing first on the choice of the nonchair committee members and then on the choice of the chair, argue that there are $\binom{n}{k-1}(n-k+1)$ possible choices.

(c) By focusing first on the choice of the chair and then on the choice of the other committee members, argue that there are $n\binom{n-1}{k-1}$ possible choices.

(d) Conclude from parts (a), (b), and (c) that

$$k\binom{n}{k} = (n-k+1)\binom{n}{k-1} = n\binom{n-1}{k-1}$$

(e) Use the factorial definition of $\binom{m}{r}$ to verify the identity in part (d).

11. The following identity is known as Fermat's combinatorial identity:

$$\binom{n}{k} = \sum_{i=k}^{n} \binom{i-1}{k-1} \quad n \geq k$$

Give a combinatorial argument (no computations are needed) to establish this identity.

Hint: Consider the set of numbers 1 through n. How many subsets of size k have i as their highest numbered member?

12. Consider the following combinatorial identity:

$$\sum_{k=1}^{n} k \binom{n}{k} = n \cdot 2^{n-1}$$

(a) Present a combinatorial argument for this identity by considering a set of n people and determining, in two ways, the number of possible selections of a committee of any size and a chairperson for the committee.

Hint:

  (i) How many possible selections are there of a committee of size k and its chairperson?

  (ii) How many possible selections are there of a chairperson and the other committee members?

(b) Verify the following identity for $n = 1, 2, 3, 4, 5$:

$$\sum_{k=1}^{n} \binom{n}{k} k^2 = 2^{n-2} n(n+1)$$

For a combinatorial proof of the preceding, consider a set of n people and argue that both sides of the identity represent the number of different selections of a committee, its chairperson, and its secretary (possibly the same as the chairperson).

Hint:

  (i) How many different selections result in the committee containing exactly k people?

  (ii) How many different selections are there in which the chairperson and the secretary are the same? (ANSWER: $n2^{n-1}$.)

  (iii) How many different selections result in the chairperson and the secretary being different?

(c) Now argue that

$$\sum_{k=1}^{n} \binom{n}{k} k^3 = 2^{n-3} n^2 (n+3)$$

13. By considering the coefficients of x^n on both sides of the identity $(1+x)^n (1-x)^n = (1-x^2)^n$, prove that

$$\sum_{k=0}^{n} (-1)^k \binom{n}{k}^2 \text{ is equal to}$$

(a) 0 if n is odd

(b) $\dfrac{(-1)^{n/2} n!}{(n/2)!^2}$ if n is even.

14. From a set of n people, a committee of size j is to be chosen, and from this committee, a subcommittee of size $i, i \leq j$, is also to be chosen.

(a) Derive a combinatorial identity by computing, in two ways, the number of possible choices of the committee and subcommittee—first by supposing that the committee is chosen first and then the subcommittee is chosen, and second by supposing that the subcommittee is chosen first and then the remaining members of the committee are chosen.

(b) Use part (a) to prove the following combinatorial identity:

$$\sum_{j=i}^{n} \binom{n}{j} \binom{j}{i} = \binom{n}{i} 2^{n-i} \quad i \leq n$$

(c) Use part (a) and Theoretical Exercise 13 to show that

$$\sum_{j=i}^{n} \binom{n}{j} \binom{j}{i} (-1)^{n-j} = 0 \quad i < n$$

15. Let $H_k(n)$ be the number of vectors $x_1, \ldots, x_k$ for which each x_i is a positive integer satisfying $1 \leq x_i \leq n$ and $x_1 \leq x_2 \leq \cdots \leq x_k$.

(a) Without any computations, argue that

$$H_1(n) = n$$

$$H_k(n) = \sum_{j=1}^{n} H_{k-1}(j) \quad k > 1$$

Hint: How many vectors are there in which $x_k = j$?

(b) Use the preceding recursion to compute $H_3(5)$.

Hint: First compute $H_2(n)$ for $n = 1, 2, 3, 4, 5$.

16. Consider a tournament of n contestants in which the outcome is an ordering of these contestants, with ties allowed. That is, the outcome partitions the players into groups, with the first group consisting of the players who tied for first place, the next group being those who tied for the next-best position, and so on. Let $N(n)$ denote the number of different possible outcomes. For instance, $N(2) = 3$, since, in a tournament with 2 contestants, player 1 could be uniquely first, player 2 could be uniquely first, or they could tie for first.

(a) List all the possible outcomes when $n = 3$.

(b) With $N(0)$ defined to equal 1, argue, without any computations, that

$$N(n) = \sum_{i=1}^{n} \binom{n}{i} N(n-i)$$

Hint: How many outcomes are there in which i players tie for last place?

(c) Show that the formula of part (b) is equivalent to the following:

$$N(n) = \sum_{i=0}^{n-1} \binom{n}{i} N(i)$$

(d) Use the recursion to find $N(3)$ and $N(4)$.

17. Prove $\sum_{k=1}^{n} kx^k \binom{x}{k} = nx(1+x)^{n-1}$

18. Prove that $(n-2k)\binom{n}{k} = n\left[\binom{n-1}{k} - \binom{n-1}{k-1}\right]$.

19. Prove that if p is prime and $0 < k < p$, then $\binom{p}{k}$ is divisible by p.

*20. In how many ways can n identical balls be distributed into r urns so that the ith urn contains at least m_i balls, for each $i = 1, \ldots, r$? Assume that $n \geq \sum_{i=1}^{r} m_i$.

*21. Argue that there are exactly $\binom{r}{k}\binom{n-1}{n-r+k}$ solutions of

$$x_1 + x_2 + \cdots + x_r = n$$

for which exactly k of the x_i are equal to 0.

*22. Consider a function $f(x_1, \ldots, x_n)$ of n variables. How many different partial derivatives of order r does f possess?

*23. Determine the number of vectors $(x_1, \ldots, x_n)$ such that each x_i is a nonnegative integer and

$$\sum_{i=1}^{n} x_i \leq k$$

Self-Test Problems and Exercises

1. How many different linear arrangements are there of the letters A, B, C, D, E, F for which

(a) A and B are next to each other?

(b) A is before B?

(c) A is before B and B is before C?

(d) A is before B and C is before D?

(e) A and B are next to each other and C and D are also next to each other?

(f) E is not last in line?

2. A shopkeeper wants to arrange 5 shirts and four trousers in a row such that no trousers are placed next to each other how many possible ways are there to do it?

3. 10 students numbered 1 to 10 are seated in a circle. How many distinct seating arrangements are possible if

(a) there are no restrictions?

(b) If students numbered 1 and 2 always sit together, then how many arrangements are possible?

(c) If odd numbered students do not sit next to each other?

4. A restaurant offers 3 kinds of milk shakes, 2 types of breads and 5 types of sandwiches for breakfast. If a customer is given a coupon which entails him to have any 3 items of the lot, how many possible combinations of breakfast can he have? If he is sure that he would take maximum of 1 milk shake, what is the number of choice he has?

5. There are 4 roads connecting city A and city B. How many ways can a round trip be made from city A to city B? If it is desired to take a different route on the return journey, how many ways can it be planned?

6. How many different 7-place license plates are possible when 3 of the entries are letters and 4 are digits? Assume that repetition of letters and numbers is allowed and that there is no restriction on where the letters or numbers can be placed.

7. Give a combinatorial explanation of the identity

$$\binom{n}{r} = \binom{n}{n-r}$$

8. Consider n-digit numbers where each digit is one of the 10 integers $0, 1, \ldots, 9$. How many such numbers are there for which

(a) no two consecutive digits are equal?

(b) 0 appears as a digit a total of i times, $i = 0, \ldots, n$?

9. Consider three classes, each consisting of n students. From this group of $3n$ students, a group of 3 students is to be chosen.

(a) How many choices are possible?

(b) How many choices are there in which all 3 students are in the same class?

(c) How many choices are there in which 2 of the 3 students are in the same class and the other student is in a different class?

(d) How many choices are there in which all 3 students are in different classes?

(e) Using the results of parts (a) through (d), write a combinatorial identity.

10. How many 9-digit phone numbers can be created if the first digit cannot be 0 or 1, the second must be a 9, and the third must be a 6 or 4?

11. From 10 married couples, we want to select a group of 6 people that is not allowed to contain a married couple.

(a) How many choices are there?

(b) How many choices are there if the group must also consist of 3 men and 3 women?

12. A study is to be conducted among tourists staying at a resort. If there are 6 domestic tourists, 7 tourists from other states and 8 tourists from other countries, in how many ways can a sample of 7 people can be selected by ensuring that there are at least 2 from each group?

*13. An art collection on auction consisted of 4 Dalis, 5 van Goghs, and 6 Picassos. At the auction were 5 art collectors. If a reporter noted only the number of Dalis, van Goghs, and Picassos acquired by each collector, how many different results could have been recorded if all of the works were sold?

*14. Determine the number of vectors $(x_1, \ldots, x_n)$ such that each x_i is a positive integer and

$$\sum_{i=1}^{n} x_i \leq k$$

where $k \geq n$.

15. A total of n students are enrolled in a review course for the actuarial examination in probability. The posted results of the examination will list the names of those who passed, in decreasing order of their scores. For instance, the posted result will be "Brown, Cho" if Brown and Cho are the only ones to pass, with Brown receiving the higher score. Assuming that all scores are distinct (no ties), how many posted results are possible?

16. How many subsets of size 4 of the set $S = \{1, 2, \ldots, 20\}$ contain at least one of the elements $1, 2, 3, 4, 5$?

17. Give an analytic verification of

$$\binom{n}{2} = \binom{k}{2} + k(n-k) + \binom{n-k}{2}, \quad 1 \leq k \leq n$$

Now, give a combinatorial argument for this identity.

18. In a certain community, there are 3 families consisting of a single parent and 1 child, 3 families consisting of a single parent and 2 children, 5 families consisting of 2 parents and a single child, 7 families consisting of 2 parents and 2 children, and 6 families consisting of 2 parents and 3 children. If a parent and child from the same family are to be chosen, how many possible choices are there?

19. If there are no restrictions on where the digits and letters are placed, how many 8-place license plates consisting of 5 letters and 3 digits are possible if no repetitions of letters or digits are allowed? What if the 3 digits must be consecutive?

20. Verify that the equality

$$\sum_{x_1 + \ldots + x_r = n, \, x_i \geq 0} \frac{n!}{x_1! x_2! \cdots x_r!} = r^n$$

when $n = 3, r = 2$, and then show that it always valid. (The sum is over all vectors of r nonnegative integer values whose sum is n.)

Hint: How many different n letter sequences can be formed from the first r letters of the alphabet? How many of them use letter i of the alphabet a total of x_i times for each $i = 1, \ldots, r$?

AXIOMS OF PROBABILITY

Chapter

2

Contents

2.1 Introduction
2.2 Sample Space and Events
2.3 Axioms of Probability
2.4 Some Simple Propositions

2.5 Sample Spaces Having Equally Likely Outcomes
2.6 Probability as a Continuous Set Function
2.7 Probability as a Measure of Belief

2.1 Introduction

In this chapter, we introduce the concept of the probability of an event and then show how probabilities can be computed in certain situations. As a preliminary, however, we need to discuss the concept of the sample space and the events of an experiment.

2.2 Sample Space and Events

Consider an experiment whose outcome is not predictable with certainty. However, although the outcome of the experiment will not be known in advance, let us suppose that the set of all possible outcomes is known. This set of all possible outcomes of an experiment is known as the *sample space* of the experiment and is denoted by S. Following are some examples:

1. If the outcome of an experiment consists of the determination of the sex of a newborn child, then

$$S = \{g, b\}$$

where the outcome g means that the child is a girl and b that it is a boy.

2. If the outcome of an experiment is the order of finish in a race among the 7 horses having post positions 1, 2, 3, 4, 5, 6, and 7, then

$$S = \{\text{all } 7! \text{ permutations of } (1, 2, 3, 4, 5, 6, 7)\}$$

The outcome (2, 3, 1, 6, 5, 4, 7) means, for instance, that the number 2 horse comes in first, then the number 3 horse, then the number 1 horse, and so on.

3. If the experiment consists of flipping two coins, then the sample space consists of the following four points:

$$S = \{(H, H), (H, T), (T, H), (T, T)\}$$

The outcome will be (H, H) if both coins are heads, (H, T) if the first coin is heads and the second tails, (T, H) if the first is tails and the second heads, and (T, T) if both coins are tails.

4. If the experiment consists of tossing two dice, then the sample space consists of the 36 points

$$S = \{(i, j): i, j = 1, 2, 3, 4, 5, 6\}$$

where the outcome (i, j) is said to occur if i appears on the leftmost die and j on the other die.

5. If the experiment consists of measuring (in hours) the lifetime of a transistor, then the sample space consists of all nonnegative real numbers; that is,

$$S = \{x: 0 \leq x < \infty\}$$

Any subset E of the sample space is known as an *event*. In other words, an event is a set consisting of possible outcomes of the experiment. If the outcome of the experiment is contained in E, then we say that E has occurred. Following are some examples of events.

In the preceding Example 1, if $E = \{g\}$, then E is the event that the child is a girl. Similarly, if $F = \{b\}$, then F is the event that the child is a boy.

In Example 2, if

$$E = \{\text{all outcomes in } S \text{ starting with a 3}\}$$

then E is the event that horse 3 wins the race.

In Example 3, if $E = \{(H, H), (H, T)\}$, then E is the event that a head appears on the first coin.

In Example 4, if $E = \{(1, 6), (2, 5), (3, 4), (4, 3), (5, 2), (6, 1)\}$, then E is the event that the sum of the dice equals 7.

In Example 5, if $E = \{x: 0 \leq x \leq 5\}$, then E is the event that the transistor does not last longer than 5 hours.

For any two events E and F of a sample space S, we define the new event $E \cup F$ to consist of all outcomes that are either in E or in F or in both E and F. That is, the event $E \cup F$ will occur if *either* E or F occurs. For instance, in Example 1, if $E = \{g\}$ is the event that the child is a girl and $F = \{b\}$ is the event that the child is a boy, then

$$E \cup F = \{g, b\}$$

is the whole sample space S. In Example 3, if $E = \{(H, H), (H, T)\}$ is the event that the first coin lands heads, and $F = \{(T, H), (H, H)\}$ is the event that the second coin lands heads, then

$$E \cup F = \{(H, H), (H, T), (T, H)\}$$

is the event that at least one of the coins lands heads and thus will occur provided that both coins do not land tails.

The event $E \cup F$ is called the *union* of the event E and the event F.

Similarly, for any two events E and F, we may also define the new event EF, called the *intersection* of E and F, to consist of all outcomes that are both in E and in F. That is, the event EF (sometimes written $E \cap F$) will occur only if both E and F occur. For instance, in Example 3, if $E = \{(H, H), (H, T), (T, H)\}$ is the event that at least 1 head occurs and $F = \{(H, T), (T, H), (T, T)\}$ is the event that at least 1 tail occurs, then

$$EF = \{(H, T), (T, H)\}$$

is the event that exactly 1 head and 1 tail occur. In Example 4, if $E = \{(1,6),(2,5),(3,4),(4,3),(5,2),(6,1)\}$ is the event that the sum of the dice is 7 and $F = \{(1,5),(2,4),(3,3),(4,2),(5,1)\}$ is the event that the sum is 6, then the event EF does not contain any outcomes and hence could not occur. To give such an event a name, we shall refer to it as the null event and denote it by $\emptyset$. (That is, $\emptyset$ refers to the event consisting of no outcomes.) If $EF = \emptyset$, then E and F are said to be *mutually exclusive*.

We define unions and intersections of more than two events in a similar manner. If $E_1, E_2, \ldots$ are events, then the union of these events, denoted by $\bigcup_{n=1}^{\infty} E_n$, is defined to be that event that consists of all outcomes that are in E_n for at least one value of $n = 1, 2, \ldots$. Similarly, the intersection of the events E_n, denoted by $\bigcap_{n=1}^{\infty} E_n$, is defined to be the event consisting of those outcomes that are in all of the events $E_n, n = 1, 2, \ldots$.

Finally, for any event E, we define the new event E^c, referred to as the *complement* of E, to consist of all outcomes in the sample space S that are not in E. That is, E^c will occur if and only if E does not occur. In Example 4, if event $E = \{(1,6),(2,5),(3,4),(4,3),(5,2),(6,1)\}$, then E^c will occur when the sum of the dice does not equal 7. Note that because the experiment must result in some outcome, it follows that $S^c = \emptyset$.

For any two events E and F, if all of the outcomes in E are also in F, then we say that E is *contained* in F, or E is a *subset* of F, and write $E \subset F$ (or equivalently, $F \supset E$, which we sometimes say as F is a *superset* of E). Thus, if $E \subset F$, then the occurrence of E implies the occurrence of F. If $E \subset F$ and $F \subset E$, we say that E and F are equal and write $E = F$.

A graphical representation that is useful for illustrating logical relations among events is the Venn diagram. The sample space S is represented as consisting of all the outcomes in a large rectangle, and the events $E, F, G, \ldots$ are represented as consisting of all the outcomes in given circles within the rectangle. Events of interest can then be indicated by shading appropriate regions of the diagram. For instance, in the three Venn diagrams shown in Figure 2.1, the shaded areas represent,

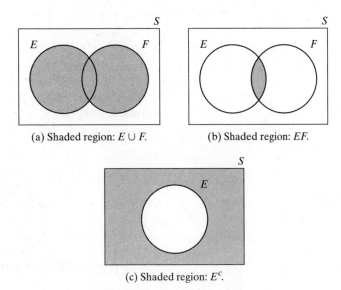

(a) Shaded region: $E \cup F$. (b) Shaded region: EF.

(c) Shaded region: E^c.

Figure 2.1 Venn diagrams.

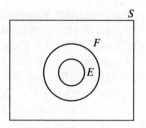

Figure 2.2 $E \subset F$.

respectively, the events $E \cup F$, EF, and E^c. The Venn diagram in Figure 2.2 indicates that $E \subset F$.

The operations of forming unions, intersections, and complements of events obey certain rules similar to the rules of algebra. We list a few of these rules:

Commutative laws $E \cup F = F \cup E$ $EF = FE$

Associative laws $(E \cup F) \cup G = E \cup (F \cup G)$ $(EF)G = E(FG)$

Distributive laws $(E \cup F)G = EG \cup FG$ $EF \cup G = (E \cup G)(F \cup G)$

These relations are verified by showing that any outcome that is contained in the event on the left side of the equality sign is also contained in the event on the right side, and vice versa. One way of showing this is by means of Venn diagrams. For instance, the distributive law may be verified by the sequence of diagrams in Figure 2.3.

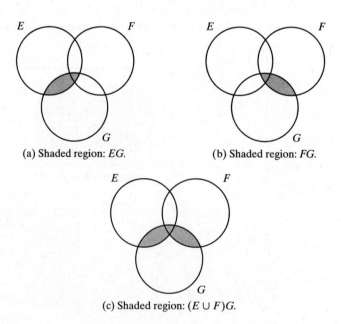

(a) Shaded region: EG.   (b) Shaded region: FG.

(c) Shaded region: $(E \cup F)G$.

Figure 2.3 $(E \cup F)G = EG \cup FG$.

The following useful relationships among the three basic operations of forming unions, intersections, and complements are known as *DeMorgan's laws*:

$$\left(\bigcup_{i=1}^{n} E_i\right)^c = \bigcap_{i=1}^{n} E_i^c$$

$$\left(\bigcap_{i=1}^{n} E_i\right)^c = \bigcup_{i=1}^{n} E_i^c$$

For instance, for two events E and F, DeMorgan's laws state that

$$(E \cup F)^c = E^c F^c \quad \text{and} \quad (EF)^c = E^c \cup F^c$$

which can be easily proven by using Venn diagrams (see Theoretical Exercise 7).

To prove DeMorgan's laws for general n, suppose first that x is an outcome of $\left(\bigcup_{i=1}^{n} E_i\right)^c$. Then x is not contained in $\bigcup_{i=1}^{n} E_i$, which means that x is not contained in any of the events $E_i, i = 1, 2, \ldots, n$, implying that x is contained in E_i^c for all $i = 1, 2, \ldots, n$ and thus is contained in $\bigcap_{i=1}^{n} E_i^c$. To go the other way, suppose that x is an outcome of $\bigcap_{i=1}^{n} E_i^c$. Then x is contained in E_i^c for all $i = 1, 2, \ldots, n$, which means that x is not contained in E_i for any $i = 1, 2, \ldots, n$, implying that x is not contained in $\bigcup_{i}^{n} E_i$, in turn implying that x is contained in $\left(\bigcup_{1}^{n} E_i\right)^c$. This proves the first of DeMorgan's laws.

To prove the second of DeMorgan's laws, we use the first law to obtain

$$\left(\bigcup_{i=1}^{n} E_i^c\right)^c = \bigcap_{i=1}^{n} (E_i^c)^c$$

which, since $(E^c)^c = E$, is equivalent to

$$\left(\bigcup_{1}^{n} E_i^c\right)^c = \bigcap_{1}^{n} E_i$$

Taking complements of both sides of the preceding equation yields the result we seek, namely,

$$\bigcup_{1}^{n} E_i^c = \left(\bigcap_{1}^{n} E_i\right)^c$$

2.3 Axioms of Probability

One way of defining the probability of an event is in terms of its *relative frequency*. Such a definition usually goes as follows: We suppose that an experiment, whose sample space is S, is repeatedly performed under exactly the same conditions. For each event E of the sample space S, we define $n(E)$ to be the number of times in the first n repetitions of the experiment that the event E occurs. Then $P(E)$, the probability of the event E, is defined as

$$P(E) = \lim_{n \to \infty} \frac{n(E)}{n}$$

That is, $P(E)$ is defined as the (limiting) proportion of time that E occurs. It is thus the limiting relative frequency of E.

Although the preceding definition is certainly intuitively pleasing and should always be kept in mind by the reader, it possesses a serious drawback: How do we know that $n(E)/n$ will converge to some constant limiting value that will be the same for each possible sequence of repetitions of the experiment? For example, suppose that the experiment to be repeatedly performed consists of flipping a coin. How do we know that the proportion of heads obtained in the first n flips will converge to some value as n gets large? Also, even if it does converge to some value, how do we know that, if the experiment is repeatedly performed a second time, we shall obtain the same limiting proportion of heads?

Proponents of the relative frequency definition of probability usually answer this objection by stating that the convergence of $n(E)/n$ to a constant limiting value is an assumption, or an *axiom*, of the system. However, to assume that $n(E)/n$ will necessarily converge to some constant value seems to be an extraordinarily complicated assumption. For, although we might indeed hope that such a constant limiting frequency exists, it does not at all seem to be a priori evident that this need be the case. In fact, would it not be more reasonable to assume a set of simpler and more self-evident axioms about probability and then attempt to prove that such a constant limiting frequency does in some sense exist? The latter approach is the modern axiomatic approach to probability theory that we shall adopt in this text. In particular, we shall assume that, for each event E in the sample space S, there exists a value $P(E)$, referred to as the probability of E. We shall then assume that all these probabilities satisfy a certain set of axioms, which, we hope the reader will agree, is in accordance with our intuitive notion of probability.

Consider an experiment whose sample space is S. For each event E of the sample space S, we assume that a number $P(E)$ is defined and satisfies the following three axioms:

The three axioms of probability

Axiom 1

$$0 \le P(E) \le 1$$

Axiom 2

$$P(S) = 1$$

Axiom 3
For any sequence of mutually exclusive events $E_1, E_2, \ldots$ (that is, events for which $E_i E_j = \emptyset$ when $i \neq j$),

$$P\left(\bigcup_{i=1}^{\infty} E_i\right) = \sum_{i=1}^{\infty} P(E_i)$$

We refer to $P(E)$ as the *probability* of the event E.

Thus, Axiom 1 states that the probability that the outcome of the experiment is an outcome in E is some number between 0 and 1. Axiom 2 states that, with probability 1, the outcome will be a point in the sample space S. Axiom 3 states that, for any sequence of mutually exclusive events, the probability of at least one of these events occurring is just the sum of their respective probabilities.

If we consider a sequence of events $E_1, E_2, \ldots$, where $E_1 = S$ and $E_i = \emptyset$ for $i > 1$, then, because the events are mutually exclusive and because $S = \bigcup_{i=1}^{\infty} E_i$, we have, from Axiom 3,

$$P(S) = \sum_{i=1}^{\infty} P(E_i) = P(S) + \sum_{i=2}^{\infty} P(\emptyset)$$

implying that

$$P(\emptyset) = 0$$

That is, the null event has probability 0 of occurring.

Note that it follows that, for any finite sequence of mutually exclusive events $E_1, E_2, \ldots, E_n$,

$$P\left(\bigcup_{1}^{n} E_i\right) = \sum_{i=1}^{n} P(E_i) \tag{3.1}$$

This equation follows from Axiom 3 by defining E_i as the null event for all values of i greater than n. Axiom 3 is equivalent to Equation (3.1) when the sample space is finite. (Why?) However, the added generality of Axiom 3 is necessary when the sample space consists of an infinite number of points.

Example 3a

If our experiment consists of tossing a coin and if we assume that a head is as likely to appear as a tail, then we would have

$$P(\{H\}) = P(\{T\}) = \frac{1}{2}$$

On the other hand, if the coin were biased and we believed that a head were twice as likely to appear as a tail, then we would have

$$P(\{H\}) = \frac{2}{3} \quad P(\{T\}) = \frac{1}{3} \qquad \blacksquare$$

Example 3b

If a die is rolled and we suppose that all six sides are equally likely to appear, then we would have $P(\{1\}) = P(\{2\}) = P(\{3\}) = P(\{4\}) = P(\{5\}) = P(\{6\}) = \frac{1}{6}$. From Axiom 3, it would thus follow that the probability of rolling an even number would equal

$$P(\{2, 4, 6\}) = P(\{2\}) + P(\{4\}) + P(\{6\}) = \frac{1}{2} \qquad \blacksquare$$

The assumption of the existence of a set function P, defined on the events of a sample space S and satisfying Axioms 1, 2, and 3, constitutes the modern mathematical approach to probability theory. It is hoped that the reader will agree that the axioms are natural and in accordance with our intuitive concept of probability as related to chance and randomness. Furthermore, using these axioms, we shall be able to prove that if an experiment is repeated over and over again, then, with probability

1, the proportion of time during which any specific event E occurs will equal $P(E)$. This result, known as the strong law of large numbers, is presented in Chapter 8. In addition, we present another possible interpretation of probability—as being a measure of belief—in Section 2.7.

Technical Remark.   We have supposed that $P(E)$ is defined for all the events E of the sample space. Actually, when the sample space is an uncountably infinite set, $P(E)$ is defined only for a class of events called *measurable*. However, this restriction need not concern us, as all events of any practical interest are measurable.

2.4   Some Simple Propositions

In this section, we prove some simple propositions regarding probabilities. We first note that since E and E^c are always mutually exclusive and since $E \cup E^c = S$, we have, by Axioms 2 and 3,

$$1 = P(S) = P(E \cup E^c) = P(E) + P(E^c)$$

Or, equivalently, we have Proposition 4.1.

Proposition 4.1

$$P(E^c) = 1 - P(E)$$

In words, Proposition 4.1 states that the probability that an event does not occur is 1 minus the probability that it does occur. For instance, if the probability of obtaining a head on the toss of a coin is $\frac{3}{8}$, then the probability of obtaining a tail must be $\frac{5}{8}$.

Our second proposition states that if the event E is contained in the event F, then the probability of E is no greater than the probability of F.

Proposition 4.2   If $E \subset F$, then $P(E) \leq P(F)$.

Proof Since $E \subset F$, it follows that we can express F as

$$F = E \cup E^c F$$

Hence, because E and $E^c F$ are mutually exclusive, we obtain, from Axiom 3,

$$P(F) = P(E) + P(E^c F)$$

which proves the result, since $P(E^c F) \geq 0$. □

Proposition 4.2 tells us, for instance, that the probability of rolling a 1 with a die is less than or equal to the probability of rolling an odd value with the die.

The next proposition gives the relationship between the probability of the union of two events, expressed in terms of the individual probabilities, and the probability of the intersection of the events.

Proposition 4.3

$$P(E \cup F) = P(E) + P(F) - P(EF)$$

Proof To derive a formula for $P(E \cup F)$, we first note that $E \cup F$ can be written as the union of the two disjoint events E and $E^c F$. Thus, from Axiom 3, we obtain

$$P(E \cup F) = P(E \cup E^c F)$$
$$= P(E) + P(E^c F)$$

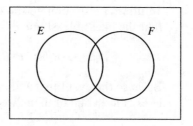

Figure 2.4 Venn diagram.

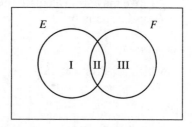

Figure 2.5 Venn diagram in sections.

Furthermore, since $F = EF \cup E^cF$, we again obtain from Axiom 3

$$P(F) = P(EF) + P(E^cF)$$

or, equivalently,

$$P(E^cF) = P(F) - P(EF)$$

thereby completing the proof. □

Proposition 4.3 could also have been proved by making use of the Venn diagram in Figure 2.4.

Let us divide $E \cup F$ into three mutually exclusive sections, as shown in Figure 2.5. In words, section I represents all the points in E that are not in F (that is, EF^c), section II represents all points both in E and in F (that is, EF), and section III represents all points in F that are not in E (that is, E^cF).

From Figure 2.5, we see that

$$E \cup F = \text{I} \cup \text{II} \cup \text{III}$$
$$E = \text{I} \cup \text{II}$$
$$F = \text{II} \cup \text{III}$$

As I, II, and III are mutually exclusive, it follows from Axiom 3 that

$$P(E \cup F) = P(\text{I}) + P(\text{II}) + P(\text{III})$$
$$P(E) = P(\text{I}) + P(\text{II})$$
$$P(F) = P(\text{II}) + P(\text{III})$$

which shows that

$$P(E \cup F) = P(E) + P(F) - P(\text{II})$$

and Proposition 4.3 is proved, since II $= EF$.

Example 4a

J is taking two books along on her holiday vacation. With probability .5, she will like the first book; with probability .4, she will like the second book; and with probability .3, she will like both books. What is the probability that she likes neither book?

Solution Let B_i denote the event that J likes book $i, i = 1, 2$. Then the probability that she likes at least one of the books is

$$P(B_1 \cup B_2) = P(B_1) + P(B_2) - P(B_1 B_2) = .5 + .4 - .3 = .6$$

Because the event that J likes neither book is the complement of the event that she likes at least one of them, we obtain the result

$$P(B_1^c B_2^c) = P\left((B_1 \cup B_2)^c\right) = 1 - P(B_1 \cup B_2) = .4 \qquad \blacksquare$$

We may also calculate the probability that any one of the three events E, F, and G occurs, namely,

$$P(E \cup F \cup G) = P[(E \cup F) \cup G]$$

which, by Proposition 4.3, equals

$$P(E \cup F) + P(G) - P[(E \cup F)G]$$

Now, it follows from the distributive law that the events $(E \cup F)G$ and $EG \cup FG$ are equivalent; hence, from the preceding equations, we obtain

$$
\begin{aligned}
P(E &\cup F \cup G) \\
&= P(E) + P(F) - P(EF) + P(G) - P(EG \cup FG) \\
&= P(E) + P(F) - P(EF) + P(G) - P(EG) - P(FG) + P(EGFG) \\
&= P(E) + P(F) + P(G) - P(EF) - P(EG) - P(FG) + P(EFG)
\end{aligned}
$$

In fact, the following proposition, known as the *inclusion–exclusion identity*, can be proved by mathematical induction:

Proposition 4.4

$$
\begin{aligned}
P(E_1 \cup E_2 \cup \cdots \cup E_n) = \sum_{i=1}^{n} P(E_i) &- \sum_{i_1 < i_2} P(E_{i_1} E_{i_2}) + \cdots \\
&+ (-1)^{r+1} \sum_{i_1 < i_2 < \cdots < i_r} P(E_{i_1} E_{i_2} \cdots E_{i_r}) \\
&+ \cdots + (-1)^{n+1} P(E_1 E_2 \cdots E_n)
\end{aligned}
$$

The summation $\sum_{i_1 < i_2 < \cdots < i_r} P(E_{i_1} E_{i_2} \cdots E_{i_r})$ is taken over all of the $\binom{n}{r}$ possible subsets of size r of the set $\{1, 2, \ldots, n\}$.

In words, Proposition 4.4 states that the probability of the union of n events equals the sum of the probabilities of these events taken one at a time, minus the sum of the probabilities of these events taken two at a time, plus the sum of the probabilities of these events taken three at a time, and so on.

Remarks 1. For a noninductive argument for Proposition 4.4, note first that if an outcome of the sample space is not a member of any of the sets E_i, then its probability does not contribute anything to either side of the equality. Now, suppose that an outcome is in exactly m of the events E_i, where $m > 0$. Then, since it is in $\bigcup_i E_i$, its probability is counted once in $P\left(\bigcup_i E_i\right)$; also, as this outcome is contained in $\binom{m}{k}$

subsets of the type $E_{i_1} E_{i_2} \cdots E_{i_k}$, its probability is counted

$$\binom{m}{1} - \binom{m}{2} + \binom{m}{3} - \cdots \pm \binom{m}{m}$$

times on the right of the equality sign in Proposition 4.4. Thus, for $m > 0$, we must show that

$$1 = \binom{m}{1} - \binom{m}{2} + \binom{m}{3} - \cdots \pm \binom{m}{m}$$

However, since $1 = \binom{m}{0}$, the preceding equation is equivalent to

$$\sum_{i=0}^{m} \binom{m}{i} (-1)^i = 0$$

and the latter equation follows from the binomial theorem, since

$$0 = (-1 + 1)^m = \sum_{i=0}^{m} \binom{m}{i} (-1)^i (1)^{m-i}$$

2. The following is a succinct way of writing the inclusion–exclusion identity:

$$P(\cup_{i=1}^{n} E_i) = \sum_{r=1}^{n} (-1)^{r+1} \sum_{i_1 < \cdots < i_r} P(E_{i_1} \cdots E_{i_r})$$

3. In the inclusion–exclusion identity, going out one term results in an upper bound on the probability of the union, going out two terms results in a lower bound on the probability, going out three terms results in an upper bound on the probability, going out four terms results in a lower bound, and so on. That is, for events $E_1, \ldots, E_n$, we have

$$P(\cup_{i=1}^{n} E_i) \leq \sum_{i=1}^{n} P(E_i) \tag{4.1}$$

$$P(\cup_{i=1}^{n} E_i) \geq \sum_{i=1}^{n} P(E_i) - \sum_{j<i} P(E_i E_j) \tag{4.2}$$

$$P(\cup_{i=1}^{n} E_i) \leq \sum_{i=1}^{n} P(E_i) - \sum_{j<i} P(E_i E_j) + \sum_{k<j<i} P(E_i E_j E_k) \tag{4.3}$$

and so on. To prove the validity of these bounds, note the identity

$$\cup_{i=1}^{n} E_i = E_1 \cup E_1^c E_2 \cup E_1^c E_2^c E_3 \cup \cdots \cup E_1^c \cdots E_{n-1}^c E_n$$

That is, at least one of the events E_i occurs if E_1 occurs, or if E_1 does not occur but E_2 does, or if E_1 and E_2 do not occur but E_3 does, and so on. Because the right-hand side is the union of disjoint events, we obtain

$$P(\cup_{i=1}^{n} E_i) = P(E_1) + P(E_1^c E_2) + P(E_1^c E_2^c E_3) + \cdots + P(E_1^c \cdots E_{n-1}^c E_n)$$

$$= P(E_1) + \sum_{i=2}^{n} P(E_1^c \cdots E_{i-1}^c E_i) \tag{4.4}$$

Now, let $B_i = E_1^c \cdots E_{i-1}^c = (\cup_{j<i} E_j)^c$ be the event that none of the first $i-1$ events occurs. Applying the identity

$$P(E_i) = P(B_i E_i) + P(B_i^c E_i)$$

shows that

$$P(E_i) = P(E_1^c \cdots E_{i-1}^c E_i) + P(E_i \cup_{j<i} E_j)$$

or, equivalently,

$$P(E_1^c \cdots E_{i-1}^c E_i) = P(E_i) - P(\cup_{j<i} E_i E_j)$$

Substituting this equation into (4.4) yields

$$P(\cup_{i=1}^n E_i) = \sum_i P(E_i) - \sum_i P(\cup_{j<i} E_i E_j) \qquad (4.5)$$

Because probabilities are always nonnegative, Inequality (4.1) follows directly from Equation (4.5). Now, fixing i and applying Inequality (4.1) to $P(\cup_{j<i} E_i E_j)$ yields

$$P(\cup_{j<i} E_i E_j) \le \sum_{j<i} P(E_i E_j)$$

which, by Equation (4.5), gives Inequality (4.2). Similarly, fixing i and applying Inequality (4.2) to $P(\cup_{j<i} E_i E_j)$ yields

$$P(\cup_{j<i} E_i E_j) \ge \sum_{j<i} P(E_i E_j) - \sum_{k<j<i} P(E_i E_j E_i E_k)$$

$$= \sum_{j<i} P(E_i E_j) - \sum_{k<j<i} P(E_i E_j E_k)$$

which, by Equation (4.5), gives Inequality (4.3). The next inclusion–exclusion inequality is now obtained by fixing i and applying Inequality (4.3) to $P(\cup_{j<i} E_i E_j)$, and so on.

2.5 Sample Spaces Having Equally Likely Outcomes

In many experiments, it is natural to assume that all outcomes in the sample space are equally likely to occur. That is, consider an experiment whose sample space S is a finite set, say, $S = \{1, 2, \ldots, N\}$. Then, it is often natural to assume that

$$P(\{1\}) = P(\{2\}) = \cdots = P(\{N\})$$

which implies, from Axioms 2 and 3 (why?), that

$$P(\{i\}) = \frac{1}{N} \quad i = 1, 2, \ldots, N$$

From this equation, it follows from Axiom 3 that, for any event E,

$$P(E) = \frac{\text{number of outcomes in } E}{\text{number of outcomes in } S}$$

In words, if we assume that all outcomes of an experiment are equally likely to occur, then the probability of any event E equals the proportion of outcomes in the sample space that are contained in E.

Example 5a

If two dice are rolled, what is the probability that the sum of the upturned faces will equal 7?

Solution We shall solve this problem under the assumption that all of the 36 possible outcomes are equally likely. Since there are 6 possible outcomes—namely, (1, 6), (2, 5), (3, 4), (4, 3), (5, 2), and (6, 1)—that result in the sum of the dice being equal to 7, the desired probability is $\frac{6}{36} = \frac{1}{6}$. ∎

Example 5b

If 3 balls are "randomly drawn" from a bowl containing 6 white and 5 black balls, what is the probability that one of the balls is white and the other two black?

Solution If we regard the balls as being distinguishable and the order in which they are selected as being relevant, then the sample space consists of $11 \cdot 10 \cdot 9 = 990$ outcomes. Furthermore, there are $6 \cdot 5 \cdot 4 = 120$ outcomes in which the first ball selected is white and the other two are black; $5 \cdot 6 \cdot 4 = 120$ outcomes in which the first is black, the second is white, and the third is black; and $5 \cdot 4 \cdot 6 = 120$ in which the first two are black and the third is white. Hence, assuming that "randomly drawn" means that each outcome in the sample space is equally likely to occur, we see that the desired probability is

$$\frac{120 + 120 + 120}{990} = \frac{4}{11}$$

This problem could also have been solved by regarding the outcome of the experiment as the unordered set of drawn balls. From this point of view, there are $\binom{11}{3} = 165$ outcomes in the sample space. Now, each set of 3 balls corresponds to 3! outcomes when the order of selection is noted. As a result, if all outcomes are assumed equally likely when the order of selection is noted, then it follows that they remain equally likely when the outcome is taken to be the unordered set of selected balls. Hence, using the latter representation of the experiment, we see that the desired probability is

$$\frac{\binom{6}{1}\binom{5}{2}}{\binom{11}{3}} = \frac{4}{11}$$

which, of course, agrees with the answer obtained previously. ∎

When the experiment consists of a random selection of k items from a set of n items, we have the flexibility of either letting the outcome of the experiment be the ordered selection of the k items or letting it be the unordered set of items selected. In the former case, we would assume that each new selection is equally likely to be any of the so far unselected items of the set, and in the latter case, we would assume that all $\binom{n}{k}$ possible subsets of k items are equally likely to be the set selected. For instance, suppose 5 people are to be randomly selected from a group of 20 individuals consisting of 10 married couples, and we want to determine $P(N)$, the probability that the 5 chosen are all unrelated. (That is, no two are married to each other.) If we regard the sample space as the set of 5 people chosen, then there are $\binom{20}{5}$ equally likely outcomes. An outcome that does not contain a married couple can be thought of as being the result of a six-stage experiment: In the first stage, 5 of the 10 couples to have a member in the group are chosen; in the next 5 stages, 1 of the 2 members of each of these couples is selected. Thus, there are $\binom{10}{5}2^5$ possible outcomes in which the 5 members selected are unrelated, yielding the desired probability of

$$P(N) = \frac{\binom{10}{5}2^5}{\binom{20}{5}}$$

In contrast, we could let the outcome of the experiment be the *ordered* selection of the 5 individuals. In this setting, there are $20 \cdot 19 \cdot 18 \cdot 17 \cdot 16$ equally likely outcomes, of which $20 \cdot 18 \cdot 16 \cdot 14 \cdot 12$ outcomes result in a group of 5 unrelated individuals, yielding the result

$$P(N) = \frac{20 \cdot 18 \cdot 16 \cdot 14 \cdot 12}{20 \cdot 19 \cdot 18 \cdot 17 \cdot 16}$$

We leave it for the reader to verify that the two answers are identical.

Example 5c

A committee of 5 is to be selected from a group of 6 men and 9 women. If the selection is made randomly, what is the probability that the committee consists of 3 men and 2 women?

Solution Because each of the $\binom{15}{5}$ possible committees is equally likely to be selected, the desired probability is

$$\frac{\binom{6}{3}\binom{9}{2}}{\binom{15}{5}} = \frac{240}{1001}$$ ∎

Example 5d

An urn contains n balls, one of which is special. If k of these balls are withdrawn one at a time, with each selection being equally likely to be any of the balls that remain at the time, what is the probability that the special ball is chosen?

Solution Since all of the balls are treated in an identical manner, it follows that the set of k balls selected is equally likely to be any of the $\binom{n}{k}$ sets of k balls. Therefore,

$$P\{\text{special ball is selected}\} = \frac{\binom{1}{1}\binom{n-1}{k-1}}{\binom{n}{k}} = \frac{k}{n}$$

We could also have obtained this result by letting A_i denote the event that the special ball is the ith ball to be chosen, $i = 1,\ldots,k$. Then, since each one of the n balls is equally likely to be the ith ball chosen, it follows that $P(A_i) = 1/n$. Hence, because these events are clearly mutually exclusive, we have

$$P\{\text{special ball is selected}\} = P\left(\bigcup_{i=1}^{k} A_i\right) = \sum_{i=1}^{k} P(A_i) = \frac{k}{n}$$

We could also have argued that $P(A_i) = 1/n$, by noting that there are $n(n-1)\cdots(n-k+1) = n!/(n-k)!$ equally likely outcomes of the experiment, of which

$(n - 1)(n - 2) \cdots (n - i + 1)(1)(n - i) \cdots (n - k + 1) = (n - 1)!/(n - k)!$ result in the special ball being the ith one chosen. From this reasoning, it follows that

$$P(A_i) = \frac{(n - 1)!}{n!} = \frac{1}{n} \qquad \blacksquare$$

Example 5e

Suppose that $n + m$ balls, of which n are red and m are blue, are arranged in a linear order in such a way that all $(n + m)!$ possible orderings are equally likely. If we record the result of this experiment by listing only the colors of the successive balls, show that all the possible results remain equally likely.

Solution Consider any one of the $(n + m)!$ possible orderings, and note that any permutation of the red balls among themselves and of the blue balls among themselves does not change the sequence of colors. As a result, every ordering of colorings corresponds to $n!\, m!$ different orderings of the $n + m$ balls, so every ordering of the colors has probability $\frac{n!m!}{(n+m)!}$ of occurring.

For example, suppose that there are 2 red balls, numbered r_1, r_2, and 2 blue balls, numbered b_1, b_2. Then, of the 4! possible orderings, there will be 2! 2! orderings that result in any specified color combination. For instance, the following orderings result in the successive balls alternating in color, with a red ball first:

$$r_1, b_1, r_2, b_2 \quad r_1, b_2, r_2, b_1 \quad r_2, b_1, r_1, b_2 \quad r_2, b_2, r_1, b_1$$

Therefore, each of the possible orderings of the colors has probability $\frac{4}{24} = \frac{1}{6}$ of occurring. $\qquad \blacksquare$

Example 5f

A poker hand consists of 5 cards. If the cards have distinct consecutive values and are not all of the same suit, we say that the hand is a straight. For instance, a hand consisting of the five of spades, six of spades, seven of spades, eight of spades, and nine of hearts is a straight. What is the probability that one is dealt a straight?

Solution We start by assuming that all $\binom{52}{5}$ possible poker hands are equally likely. To determine the number of outcomes that are straights, let us first determine the number of possible outcomes for which the poker hand consists of an ace, two, three, four, and five (the suits being irrelevant). Since the ace can be any 1 of the 4 possible aces, and similarly for the two, three, four, and five, it follows that there are 4^5 outcomes leading to exactly one ace, two, three, four, and five. Hence, since in 4 of these outcomes all the cards will be of the same suit (such a hand is called a straight flush), it follows that there are $4^5 - 4$ hands that make up a straight of the form ace, two, three, four, and five. Similarly, there are $4^5 - 4$ hands that make up a straight of the form ten, jack, queen, king, and ace. Thus, there are $10(4^5 - 4)$ hands that are straights, and it follows that the desired probability is

$$\frac{10(4^5 - 4)}{\binom{52}{5}} \approx .0039 \qquad \blacksquare$$

Example 5g

A 5-card poker hand is said to be a full house if it consists of 3 cards of the same denomination and 2 other cards of the same denomination (of course, different from the first denomination). Thus, a full house is three of a kind plus a pair. What is the probability that one is dealt a full house?

Solution Again, we assume that all $\binom{52}{5}$ possible hands are equally likely. To determine the number of possible full houses, we first note that there are $\binom{4}{2}\binom{4}{3}$ different combinations of, say, 2 tens and 3 jacks. Because there are 13 different choices for the kind of pair and, after a pair has been chosen, there are 12 other choices for the denomination of the remaining 3 cards, it follows that the probability of a full house is

$$\frac{13 \cdot 12 \cdot \binom{4}{2}\binom{4}{3}}{\binom{52}{5}} \approx .0014 \qquad \blacksquare$$

Example 5h

In the game of bridge, the entire deck of 52 cards is dealt out to 4 players. What is the probability that

(a) one of the players receives all 13 spades;

(b) each player receives 1 ace?

Solution (a) Letting E_i be the event that hand i has all 13 spades, then

$$P(E_i) = \frac{1}{\binom{52}{13}}, \quad i = 1, 2, 3, 4$$

Because the events E_i, $i = 1, 2, 3, 4$, are mutually exclusive, the probability that one of the hands is dealt all 13 spades is

$$P(\cup_{i=1}^{4} E_i) = \sum_{i=1}^{4} P(E_i) = 4/\binom{52}{13} \approx 6.3 \times 10^{-12}$$

(b) To determine the number of outcomes in which each of the distinct players receives exactly 1 ace, put aside the aces and note that there are $\binom{48}{12, 12, 12, 12}$ possible divisions of the other 48 cards when each player is to receive 12. Because there are 4! ways of dividing the 4 aces so that each player receives 1, we see that the number of possible outcomes in which each player receives exactly 1 ace is $4! \binom{48}{12, 12, 12, 12}$. As there are $\binom{52}{13, 13, 13, 13}$ possible hands, the desired probability is thus

$$\frac{4! \binom{48}{12, 12, 12, 12}}{\binom{52}{13, 13, 13, 13}} \approx .1055 \qquad \blacksquare$$

Some results in probability are quite surprising when initially encountered. Our next two examples illustrate this phenomenon.

Example 5i

If n people are present in a room, what is the probability that no two of them celebrate their birthday on the same day of the year? How large need n be so that this probability is less than $\frac{1}{2}$?

Solution As each person can celebrate his or her birthday on any one of 365 days, there are a total of $(365)^n$ possible outcomes. (We are ignoring the possibility of someone having been born on February 29.) Assuming that each outcome is equally likely, we see that the desired probability is $(365)(364)(363)\ldots(365 - n + 1)/(365)^n$. It is a rather surprising fact that when $n \geq 23$, this probability is less than $\frac{1}{2}$. That is, if there are 23 or more people in a room, then the probability that at least two of them have the same birthday exceeds $\frac{1}{2}$. Many people are initially surprised by this result, since 23 seems so small in relation to 365, the number of days of the year. However, every pair of individuals has probability $\dfrac{365}{(365)^2} = \dfrac{1}{365}$ of having the same birthday, and in a group of 23 people, there are $\dbinom{23}{2} = 253$ different pairs of individuals. Looked at this way, the result no longer seems so surprising.

When there are 50 people in the room, the probability that at least two share the same birthday is approximately .970, and with 100 persons in the room, the odds are better than 3,000,000:1. (That is, the probability is greater than $\dfrac{3 \times 10^6}{3 \times 10^6 + 1}$ that at least two people have the same birthday.) ∎

Example 5j

A deck of 52 playing cards is shuffled, and the cards are turned up one at a time until the first ace appears. Is the next card—that is, the card following the first ace—more likely to be the ace of spades or the two of clubs?

Solution To determine the probability that the card following the first ace is the ace of spades, we need to calculate how many of the $(52)!$ possible orderings of the cards have the ace of spades immediately following the first ace. To begin, note that each ordering of the 52 cards can be obtained by first ordering the 51 cards different from the ace of spades and then inserting the ace of spades into that ordering. Furthermore, for each of the $(51)!$ orderings of the other cards, there is only one place where the ace of spades can be placed so that it follows the first ace. For instance, if the ordering of the other 51 cards is

$$4c,\ 6h,\ Jd,\ 5s,\ Ac,\ 7d,\ldots,Kh$$

then the only insertion of the ace of spades into this ordering that results in its following the first ace is

$$4c,\ 6h,\ Jd,\ 5s,\ Ac,\ As,\ 7d,\ldots,Kh$$

Therefore, there are $(51)!$ orderings that result in the ace of spades following the first ace, so

$$P\{\text{the ace of spades follows the first ace}\} = \frac{(51)!}{(52)!} = \frac{1}{52}$$

In fact, by exactly the same argument, it follows that the probability that the two of clubs (or any other specified card) follows the first ace is also $\frac{1}{52}$. In other words, each of the 52 cards of the deck is equally likely to be the one that follows the first ace!

Many people find this result rather surprising. Indeed, a common reaction is to suppose initially that it is more likely that the two of clubs (rather than the ace of spades) follows the first ace, since that first ace might itself be the ace of spades. This reaction is often followed by the realization that the two of clubs might itself appear before the first ace, thus negating its chance of immediately following the first ace. However, as there is one chance in four that the ace of spades will be the first ace (because all 4 aces are equally likely to be first) and only one chance in five that the two of clubs will appear before the first ace (because each of the set of 5 cards consisting of the two of clubs and the 4 aces is equally likely to be the first of this set to appear), it again appears that the two of clubs is more likely. However, this is not the case, and our more complete analysis shows that they are equally likely. ∎

Example 5k

A football team consists of 20 offensive and 20 defensive players. The players are to be paired in groups of 2 for the purpose of determining roommates. If the pairing is done at random, what is the probability that there are no offensive–defensive roommate pairs? What is the probability that there are $2i$ offensive–defensive roommate pairs, $i = 1, 2, \ldots, 10$?

Solution There are

$$\binom{40}{2, 2, \ldots, 2} = \frac{(40)!}{(2!)^{20}}$$

ways of dividing the 40 players into 20 *ordered* pairs of two each. (That is, there are $(40)!/2^{20}$ ways of dividing the players into a *first* pair, a *second* pair, and so on.) Hence, there are $(40)!/2^{20}(20)!$ ways of dividing the players into (unordered) pairs of 2 each. Furthermore, since a division will result in no offensive–defensive pairs if the offensive (and defensive) players are paired among themselves, it follows that there are $[(20)!/2^{10}(10)!]^2$ such divisions. Hence, the probability of no offensive–defensive roommate pairs, call it P_0, is given by

$$P_0 = \frac{\left(\dfrac{(20)!}{2^{10}(10)!} \right)^2}{\dfrac{(40)!}{2^{20}(20)!}} = \frac{[(20)!]^3}{[(10)!]^2(40)!}$$

To determine P_{2i}, the probability that there are $2i$ offensive–defensive pairs, we first note that there are $\binom{20}{2i}^2$ ways of selecting the $2i$ offensive players and the $2i$ defensive players who are to be in the offensive–defensive pairs. These $4i$ players can then be paired up into $(2i)!$ possible offensive–defensive pairs. (This is so because the first offensive player can be paired with any of the $2i$ defensive players, the second offensive player with any of the remaining $2i - 1$ defensive players, and so on.) As the remaining $20 - 2i$ offensive (and defensive) players must be paired among themselves, it follows that there are

$$\binom{20}{2i}^2 (2i)! \left[\frac{(20 - 2i)!}{2^{10-i}(10 - i)!} \right]^2$$

divisions that lead to $2i$ offensive–defensive pairs. Hence,

$$P_{2i} = \frac{\binom{20}{2i}^2 (2i)! \left[\dfrac{(20 - 2i)!}{2^{10-i}(10 - i)!} \right]^2}{\dfrac{(40)!}{2^{20}(20)!}} \qquad i = 0, 1, \ldots, 10$$

The $P_{2i}, i = 0, 1, \ldots, 10$, can now be computed, or they can be approximated by making use of a result of Stirling, which shows that $n!$ can be approximated by $n^{n+1/2}e^{-n}\sqrt{2\pi}$. For instance, we obtain

$$P_0 \approx 1.3403 \times 10^{-6}$$
$$P_{10} \approx .345861$$
$$P_{20} \approx 7.6068 \times 10^{-6} \qquad \blacksquare$$

Our next three examples illustrate the usefulness of the inclusion–exclusion identity (Proposition 4.4). In Example 5l, the introduction of probability enables us to obtain a quick solution to a counting problem.

Example 5l

A total of 36 members of a club play tennis, 28 play squash, and 18 play badminton. Furthermore, 22 of the members play both tennis and squash, 12 play both tennis and badminton, 9 play both squash and badminton, and 4 play all three sports. How many members of this club play at least one of three sports?

Solution Let N denote the number of members of the club, and introduce probability by assuming that a member of the club is randomly selected. If, for any subset C of members of the club, we let $P(C)$ denote the probability that the selected member is contained in C, then

$$P(C) = \frac{\text{number of members in } C}{N}$$

Now, with T being the set of members that plays tennis, S being the set that plays squash, and B being the set that plays badminton, we have, from Proposition 4.4,

$$\begin{aligned}
P(T \cup S \cup B) \\
&= P(T) + P(S) + P(B) - P(TS) - P(TB) - P(SB) + P(TSB) \\
&= \frac{36 + 28 + 18 - 22 - 12 - 9 + 4}{N} \\
&= \frac{43}{N}
\end{aligned}$$

Hence, we can conclude that 43 members play at least one of the sports. $\qquad \blacksquare$

The next example in this section not only possesses the virtue of giving rise to a somewhat surprising answer, but is also of theoretical interest.

Example 5m

The matching problem

Suppose that each of N men at a party throws his hat into the center of the room. The hats are first mixed up, and then each man randomly selects a hat. What is the probability that none of the men selects his own hat?

Solution We first calculate the complementary probability of at least one man selecting his own hat. Let us denote by $E_i, i = 1, 2, \ldots, N$ the event that the ith man selects his own hat. Now, by Proposition 4.4, $P\left(\bigcup_{i=1}^{N} E_i\right)$, the probability that at least one of the men selects his own hat is given by

$$\begin{aligned}
P\left(\bigcup_{i=1}^{N} E_i\right) = \sum_{i=1}^{N} P(E_i) &- \sum_{i_1 < i_2} P(E_{i_1} E_{i_2}) + \cdots \\
&+ (-1)^{n+1} \sum_{i_1 < i_2 \cdots < i_n} P(E_{i_1} E_{i_2} \cdots E_{i_n}) \\
&+ \cdots + (-1)^{N+1} P(E_1 E_2 \cdots E_N)
\end{aligned}$$

If we regard the outcome of this experiment as a vector of N numbers, where the ith element is the number of the hat drawn by the ith man, then there are $N!$ possible outcomes. [The outcome $(1, 2, 3, \ldots, N)$ means, for example, that each man selects his own hat.] Furthermore, $E_{i_1} E_{i_2} \ldots E_{i_n}$, the event that each of the n men $i_1, i_2, \ldots, i_n$ selects his own hat, can occur in any of $(N - n)(N - n - 1) \cdots 3 \cdot 2 \cdot 1 = (N - n)!$ possible ways; for, of the remaining $N - n$ men, the first can select any of $N - n$ hats, the second can then select any of $N - n - 1$ hats, and so on. Hence, assuming that all $N!$ possible outcomes are equally likely, we see that

$$P(E_{i_1} E_{i_2} \cdots E_{i_n}) = \frac{(N - n)!}{N!}$$

Also, as there are $\binom{N}{n}$ terms in $\sum_{i_1 < i_2 \cdots < i_n} P(E_{i_1} E_{i_2} \cdots E_{i_n})$, it follows that

$$\sum_{i_1 < i_2 \cdots < i_n} P(E_{i_1} E_{i_2} \cdots E_{i_n}) = \frac{N!(N - n)!}{(N - n)!n!N!} = \frac{1}{n!}$$

Thus,

$$P\left(\bigcup_{i=1}^{N} E_i\right) = 1 - \frac{1}{2!} + \frac{1}{3!} - \cdots + (-1)^{N+1} \frac{1}{N!}$$

Hence, the probability that none of the men selects his own hat is

$$1 - 1 + \frac{1}{2!} - \frac{1}{3!} + \cdots + \frac{(-1)^N}{N!} = \sum_{i=0}^{N} (-1)^i / i!$$

Upon letting $x = -1$ in the identity $e^x = \sum_{i=0}^{\infty} x^i / i!$ the preceding probability when N large is seen to be approximately equal to $e^{-1} \approx .3679$. In other words, for N large, the probability that none of the men selects his own hat is approximately .37. (How many readers would have incorrectly thought that this probability would go to 1 as $N \to \infty$?) ∎

For another illustration of the usefulness of Proposition 4.4, consider the following example.

Example 5n

Compute the probability that if 10 married couples are seated at random at a round table, then no wife sits next to her husband.

Solution If we let $E_i, i = 1, 2, \ldots, 10$ denote the event that the ith couple sit next to each other, it follows that the desired probability is $1 - P\left(\bigcup_{i=1}^{10} E_i\right)$. Now, from Proposition 4.4,

$$P\left(\bigcup_{1}^{10} E_i\right) = \sum_{1}^{10} P(E_i) - \cdots + (-1)^{n+1} \sum_{i_1 < i_2 < \cdots < i_n} P(E_{i_1} E_{i_2} \cdots E_{i_n})$$
$$+ \cdots - P(E_1 E_2 \cdots E_{10})$$

To compute $P(E_{i_1} E_{i_2} \cdots E_{i_n})$, we first note that there are 19! ways of arranging 20 people around a round table. (Why?) The number of arrangements that result in a specified set of n men sitting next to their wives can most easily be obtained by first thinking of each of the n married couples as being single entities. If this were the case, then we would need to arrange $20 - n$ entities around a round table, and there are clearly $(20 - n - 1)!$ such arrangements. Finally, since each of the n married couples can be arranged next to each other in one of two possible ways, it follows that there are $2^n(20 - n - 1)!$ arrangements that result in a specified set of n men each sitting next to their wives. Therefore,

$$P(E_{i_1} E_{i_2} \cdots E_{i_n}) = \frac{2^n(19 - n)!}{(19)!}$$

Thus, from Proposition 4.4, we obtain that the probability that at least one married couple sits together, namely,

$$\binom{10}{1} 2^1 \frac{(18)!}{(19)!} - \binom{10}{2} 2^2 \frac{(17)!}{(19)!} + \binom{10}{3} 2^3 \frac{(16)!}{(19)!} - \cdots - \binom{10}{10} 2^{10} \frac{9!}{(19)!} \approx .6605$$

and the desired probability is approximately .3395. ■

*Example 5o

Runs

Consider an athletic team that had just finished its season with a final record of n wins and m losses. By examining the sequence of wins and losses, we are hoping to determine whether the team had stretches of games in which it was more likely to win than at other times. One way to gain some insight into this question is to count the number of runs of wins and then see how likely that result would be when all $(n + m)!/(n!\, m!)$ orderings of the n wins and m losses are assumed equally likely. By a run of wins, we mean a consecutive sequence of wins. For instance, if $n = 10, m = 6$, and the sequence of outcomes was $WWLLWWWLWLLLWWWW$, then there would be 4 runs of wins—the first run being of size 2, the second of size 3, the third of size 1, and the fourth of size 4.

Suppose now that a team has n wins and m losses. Assuming that all $(n + m)!/(n!\, m!) = \binom{n + m}{n}$ orderings are equally likely, let us determine the probability that there will be exactly r runs of wins. To do so, consider first any vector of positive integers $x_1, x_2, \ldots, x_r$ with $x_1 + \cdots + x_r = n$, and let us see how many outcomes result in r runs of wins in which the ith run is of size $x_i, i = 1, \ldots, r$. For any such outcome, if we let y_1 denote the number of losses before the first run of wins, y_2 the number of losses between the first 2 runs of wins, $\ldots, y_{r+1}$ the number of losses after the last run of wins, then the y_i satisfy

$$y_1 + y_2 + \cdots + y_{r+1} = m \qquad y_1 \geq 0, y_{r+1} \geq 0, y_i > 0, i = 2, \ldots, r$$

and the outcome can be represented schematically as

$$\underbrace{LL \ldots L}_{y_1} \underbrace{WW \ldots W}_{x_1} \underbrace{L \ldots L}_{y_2} \underbrace{WW \ldots W}_{x_2} \cdots \underbrace{WW}_{x_r} \underbrace{L \ldots L}_{y_{r+1}}$$

Hence, the number of outcomes that result in r runs of wins—the ith of size $x_i, i = 1, \ldots r$—is equal to the number of integers $y_1, \ldots, y_{r+1}$ that satisfy the foregoing, or, equivalently, to the number of positive integers

$$\bar{y}_1 = y_1 + 1 \quad \bar{y}_i = y_i, i = 2, \ldots, r, \ \bar{y}_{r+1} = y_{r+1} + 1$$

that satisfy

$$\bar{y}_1 + \bar{y}_2 + \cdots + \bar{y}_{r+1} = m + 2$$

By Proposition 6.1 in Chapter 1, there are $\binom{m+1}{r}$ such outcomes. Hence, the total number of outcomes that result in r runs of wins is $\binom{m+1}{r}$, multiplied by the number of positive integral solutions of $x_1 + \cdots + x_r = n$. Thus, again from Proposition 6.1, there are $\binom{m+1}{r}\binom{n-1}{r-1}$ outcomes resulting in r runs of wins. As there are $\binom{n+m}{n}$ equally likely outcomes, it follows that

$$P(\{r \text{ runs of wins}\}) = \frac{\binom{m+1}{r}\binom{n-1}{r-1}}{\binom{m+n}{n}} \quad r \geq 1$$

For example, if $n = 8$ and $m = 6$, then the probability of 7 runs is $\binom{7}{7}\binom{7}{6}/\binom{14}{8} = 1/429$ if all $\binom{14}{8}$ outcomes are equally likely. Hence, if the outcome was $WLWLWLWLWWLWLW$, then we might suspect that the team's probability of winning was changing over time. (In particular, the probability that the team wins seems to be quite high when it lost its last game and quite low when it won its last game.) On the other extreme, if the outcome were $WWWWWWWWLLLLLL$, then there would have been only 1 run, and as $P(\{1 \text{ run}\}) = \binom{7}{1}\binom{7}{0}/\binom{14}{8} = 1/429$, it would thus again seem unlikely that the team's probability of winning remained unchanged over its 14 games. ∎

*2.6 Probability as a Continuous Set Function

A sequence of events $\{E_n, n \geq 1\}$ is said to be an increasing sequence if

$$E_1 \subset E_2 \subset \cdots \subset E_n \subset E_{n+1} \subset \cdots$$

whereas it is said to be a decreasing sequence if

$$E_1 \supset E_2 \supset \cdots \supset E_n \supset E_{n+1} \supset \cdots$$

If $\{E_n, n \geq 1\}$ is an increasing sequence of events, then we define a new event, denoted by $\lim_{n \to \infty} E_n$, by

$$\lim_{n \to \infty} E_n = \bigcup_{i=1}^{\infty} E_i$$

Similarly, if $\{E_n, n \geq 1\}$ is a decreasing sequence of events, we define $\lim_{n \to \infty} E_n$, by

$$\lim_{n \to \infty} E_n = \bigcap_{i=1}^{\infty} E_i$$

We now prove the following Proposition 6.1:

Proposition 6.1 If $\{E_n, n \geq 1\}$ is either an increasing or a decreasing sequence of events, then

$$\lim_{n \to \infty} P(E_n) = P(\lim_{n \to \infty} E_n)$$

Proof Suppose, first, that $\{E_n, n \geq 1\}$ is an increasing sequence, and define the events $F_n, n \geq 1$, by

$$F_1 = E_1$$

$$F_n = E_n \left(\bigcup_1^{n-1} E_i \right)^c = E_n E_{n-1}^c \quad n > 1$$

where we have used the fact that $\bigcup_1^{n-1} E_i = E_{n-1}$, since the events are increasing. In words, F_n consists of those outcomes in E_n that are not in any of the earlier $E_i, i < n$. It is easy to verify that the F_n are mutually exclusive events such that

$$\bigcup_{i=1}^{\infty} F_i = \bigcup_{i=1}^{\infty} E_i \quad \text{and} \quad \bigcup_{i=1}^{n} F_i = \bigcup_{i=1}^{n} E_i \quad \text{for all } n \geq 1$$

Thus,

$$P\left(\bigcup_1^{\infty} E_i \right) = P\left(\bigcup_1^{\infty} F_i \right)$$

$$= \sum_1^{\infty} P(F_i) \quad \text{(by Axiom 3)}$$

$$= \lim_{n \to \infty} \sum_1^{n} P(F_i)$$

$$= \lim_{n \to \infty} P\left(\bigcup_1^{n} F_i \right)$$

$$= \lim_{n \to \infty} P\left(\bigcup_1^{n} E_i \right)$$

$$= \lim_{n \to \infty} P(E_n)$$

which proves the result when $\{E_n, n \geq 1\}$ is increasing.

If $\{E_n, n \geq 1\}$ is a decreasing sequence, then $\{E_n^c, n \geq 1\}$ is an increasing sequence; hence, from the preceding equations,

$$P\left(\bigcup_1^{\infty} E_i^c \right) = \lim_{n \to \infty} P(E_n^c)$$

However, because $\bigcup_1^{\infty} E_i^c = \left(\bigcap_1^{\infty} E_i \right)^c$, it follows that

$$P\left(\left(\bigcap_1^{\infty} E_i \right)^c \right) = \lim_{n \to \infty} P(E_n^c)$$

or, equivalently,

$$1 - P\left(\bigcap_1^\infty E_i\right) = \lim_{n\to\infty}[1 - P(E_n)] = 1 - \lim_{n\to\infty} P(E_n)$$

or

$$P\left(\bigcap_1^\infty E_i\right) = \lim_{n\to\infty} P(E_n)$$

which proves the result. $\square$

Example 6a

Probability and a "paradox"

Suppose that we possess an infinitely large urn and an infinite collection of balls labeled ball number 1, number 2, number 3, and so on. Consider an experiment performed as follows: At 1 minute to 12 P.M., balls numbered 1 through 10 are placed in the urn and ball number 10 is withdrawn. (Assume that the withdrawal takes no time.) At $\frac{1}{2}$ minute to 12 P.M., balls numbered 11 through 20 are placed in the urn and ball number 20 is withdrawn. At $\frac{1}{4}$ minute to 12 P.M., balls numbered 21 through 30 are placed in the urn and ball number 30 is withdrawn. At $\frac{1}{8}$ minute to 12 P.M., and so on. The question of interest is, How many balls are in the urn at 12 P.M.?

The answer to this question is clearly that there is an infinite number of balls in the urn at 12 P.M., since any ball whose number is not of the form $10n$, $n \geq 1$, will have been placed in the urn and will not have been withdrawn before 12 P.M. Hence, the problem is solved when the experiment is performed as described.

However, let us now change the experiment and suppose that at 1 minute to 12 P.M., balls numbered 1 through 10 are placed in the urn and ball number 1 is withdrawn; at $\frac{1}{2}$ minute to 12 P.M., balls numbered 11 through 20 are placed in the urn and ball number 2 is withdrawn; at $\frac{1}{4}$ minute to 12 P.M., balls numbered 21 through 30 are placed in the urn and ball number 3 is withdrawn; at $\frac{1}{8}$ minute to 12 P.M., balls numbered 31 through 40 are placed in the urn and ball number 4 is withdrawn, and so on. For this new experiment, how many balls are in the urn at 12 P.M.?

Surprisingly enough, the answer now is that the urn is *empty* at 12 P.M. For, consider any ball—say, ball number n. At some time prior to 12 P.M. [in particular, at $\left(\frac{1}{2}\right)^{n-1}$ minutes to 12 P.M.], this ball would have been withdrawn from the urn. Hence, for each n, ball number n is not in the urn at 12 P.M.; therefore, the urn must be empty at that time.

Because for all n, the number of balls in the urn after the nth interchange is the same in both variations of the experiment, most people are surprised that the two scenarios produce such different results in the limit. It is important to recognize that the reason the results are different is not because there is an actual *paradox*, or mathematical contradiction, but rather because of the logic of the situation, and also that the surprise results because one's initial intuition when dealing with infinity is not always correct. (This latter statement is not surprising, for when the theory of the infinite was first developed by the mathematician Georg Cantor in the second half of the nineteenth century, many of the other leading mathematicians of the day called it nonsensical and ridiculed Cantor for making such claims as that the set of all integers and the set of all even integers have the same number of elements.)

We see from the preceding discussion that the manner in which the balls are withdrawn makes a difference. For, in the first case, only balls numbered $10n, n \geq 1$, are ever withdrawn, whereas in the second case all of the balls are eventually with-drawn. Let us now suppose that whenever a ball is to be withdrawn, that ball is randomly selected from among those present. That is, suppose that at 1 minute to 12 P.M. balls numbered 1 through 10 are placed in the urn and a ball is randomly selected and withdrawn, and so on. In this case, how many balls are in the urn at 12 P.M.?

Solution We shall show that, with probability 1, the urn is empty at 12 P.M. Let us first consider ball number 1. Define E_n to be the event that ball number 1 is still in the urn after the first n withdrawals have been made. Clearly,

$$P(E_n) = \frac{9 \cdot 18 \cdot 27 \cdots (9n)}{10 \cdot 19 \cdot 28 \cdots (9n + 1)}$$

[To understand this equation, just note that if ball number 1 is still to be in the urn after the first n withdrawals, the first ball withdrawn can be any one of 9, the second any one of 18 (there are 19 balls in the urn at the time of the second with-drawal, one of which must be ball number 1), and so on. The denominator is similarly obtained.]

Now, the event that ball number 1 is in the urn at 12 P.M. is just the event $\bigcap_{n=1}^{\infty} E_n$. Because the events $E_n, n \geq 1$, are decreasing events, it follows from Proposition 6.1 that

$$P\{\text{ball number 1 is in the urn at 12 P.M.}\}$$

$$= P\left(\bigcap_{n=1}^{\infty} E_n\right)$$

$$= \lim_{n \to \infty} P(E_n)$$

$$= \prod_{n=1}^{\infty} \left(\frac{9n}{9n + 1}\right)$$

We now show that

$$\prod_{n=1}^{\infty} \frac{9n}{9n + 1} = 0$$

Since

$$\prod_{n=1}^{\infty} \left(\frac{9n}{9n + 1}\right) = \left[\prod_{n=1}^{\infty} \left(\frac{9n + 1}{9n}\right)\right]^{-1}$$

this is equivalent to showing that

$$\prod_{n=1}^{\infty} \left(1 + \frac{1}{9n}\right) = \infty$$

Now, for all $m \geq 1$,

$$\prod_{n=1}^{\infty} \left(1 + \frac{1}{9n}\right) \geq \prod_{n=1}^{m} \left(1 + \frac{1}{9n}\right)$$

$$= \left(1 + \frac{1}{9}\right) \left(1 + \frac{1}{18}\right) \left(1 + \frac{1}{27}\right) \cdots \left(1 + \frac{1}{9m}\right)$$

$$> \frac{1}{9} + \frac{1}{18} + \frac{1}{27} + \cdots + \frac{1}{9m}$$

$$= \frac{1}{9} \sum_{i=1}^{m} \frac{1}{i}$$

Hence, letting $m \to \infty$ and using the fact that $\sum_{i=1}^{\infty} 1/i = \infty$ yields

$$\prod_{n=1}^{\infty} \left(1 + \frac{1}{9n}\right) = \infty$$

Thus, letting F_i denote the event that ball number i is in the urn at 12 P.M., we have shown that $P(F_1) = 0$. Similarly, we can show that $P(F_i) = 0$ for all i.

(For instance, the same reasoning shows that $P(F_i) = \prod_{n=2}^{\infty} [9n/(9n + 1)]$ for $i = 11, 12, \ldots, 20$.) Therefore, the probability that the urn is not empty at 12 P.M., $P\left(\bigcup_{1}^{\infty} F_i\right)$, satisfies

$$P\left(\bigcup_{1}^{\infty} F_i\right) \leq \sum_{1}^{\infty} P(F_i) = 0$$

by Boole's inequality. (See Self-Test Exercise 14.)

Thus, with probability 1, the urn will be empty at 12 P.M. ∎

2.7 Probability as a Measure of Belief

Thus far we have interpreted the probability of an event of a given experiment as being a measure of how frequently the event will occur when the experiment is continually repeated. However, there are also other uses of the term *probability*. For instance, we have all heard such statements as "It is 90 percent probable that Shakespeare actually wrote *Hamlet*" or "The probability that Oswald acted alone in assassinating Kennedy is .8." How are we to interpret these statements?

The most simple and natural interpretation is that the probabilities referred to are measures of the individual's degree of belief in the statements that he or she is making. In other words, the individual making the foregoing statements is quite certain that Oswald acted alone and is even more certain that Shakespeare wrote *Hamlet*. This interpretation of probability as being a measure of the degree of one's belief is often referred to as the *personal* or *subjective* view of probability.

It seems logical to suppose that a "measure of the degree of one's belief" should satisfy all of the axioms of probability. For example, if we are 70 percent certain that Shakespeare wrote *Julius Caesar* and 10 percent certain that it was actually Marlowe, then it is logical to suppose that we are 80 percent certain that it was either

Shakespeare or Marlowe. Hence, whether we interpret probability as a measure of belief or as a long-run frequency of occurrence, its mathematical properties remain unchanged.

Example 7a

Suppose that in a 7-horse race, you believe that each of the first 2 horses has a 20 percent chance of winning, horses 3 and 4 each have a 15 percent chance, and the remaining 3 horses have a 10 percent chance each. Would it be better for you to wager at even money that the winner will be one of the first three horses or to wager, again at even money, that the winner will be one of the horses 1, 5, 6, and 7?

Solution On the basis of your personal probabilities concerning the outcome of the race, your probability of winning the first bet is $.2 + .2 + .15 = .55$, whereas it is $.2 + .1 + .1 + .1 = .5$ for the second bet. Hence, the first wager is more attractive. ∎

Note that in supposing that a person's subjective probabilities are always consistent with the axioms of probability, we are dealing with an idealized rather than an actual person. For instance, if we were to ask someone what he thought the chances were of

(a) rain today,
(b) rain tomorrow,
(c) rain both today and tomorrow,
(d) rain either today or tomorrow,

it is quite possible that, after some deliberation, he might give 30 percent, 40 percent, 20 percent, and 60 percent as answers. Unfortunately, such answers (or such subjective probabilities) are not consistent with the axioms of probability. (Why not?) We would of course hope that after this was pointed out to the respondent, he would change his answers. (One possibility we could accept is 30 percent, 40 percent, 10 percent, and 60 percent.)

Summary

Let S denote the set of all possible outcomes of an experiment. S is called the *sample space* of the experiment. An *event* is a subset of S. If $A_i, i = 1, \ldots, n$, are events, then $\bigcup_{i=1}^{n} A_i$, called the *union* of these events, consists of all outcomes that are in at least one of the events $A_i, i = 1, \ldots, n$. Similarly, $\bigcap_{i=1}^{n} A_i$, sometimes written as $A_1 \cdots A_n$, is called the *intersection* of the events A_i and consists of all outcomes that are in all of the events $A_i, i = 1, \ldots, n$.

For any event A, we define A^c to consist of all outcomes in the sample space that are not in A. We call A^c the *complement* of the event A. The event S^c, which is empty of outcomes, is designated by $\emptyset$ and is called the *null* set. If $AB = \emptyset$, then we say that A and B are *mutually exclusive*.

For each event A of the sample space S, we suppose that a number $P(A)$, called the probability of A, is defined and is such that

(i) $0 \le P(A) \le 1$
(ii) $P(S) = 1$
(iii) For mutually exclusive events $A_i, i \ge 1$,

$$P\left(\bigcup_{i=1}^{\infty} A_i\right) = \sum_{i=1}^{\infty} P(A_i)$$

$P(A)$ represents the *probability* that the outcome of the experiment is in A.

It can be shown that

$$P(A^c) = 1 - P(A)$$

A useful result is that

$$P(A \cup B) = P(A) + P(B) - P(AB)$$

which can be generalized to give

$$P\left(\bigcup_{i=1}^{n} A_i\right) = \sum_{i=1}^{n} P(A_i) - \sum\sum_{i<j} P(A_i A_j)$$
$$+ \sum\sum\sum_{i<j<k} P(A_i A_j A_k)$$
$$+ \cdots + (-1)^{n+1} P(A_1 \cdots A_n)$$

This result is known as the *inclusion–exclusion identity*.

If S is finite and each one point set is assumed to have equal probability, then

$$P(A) = \frac{|A|}{|S|}$$

where $|E|$ denotes the number of outcomes in the event E. $P(A)$ can be interpreted either as a long-run relative frequency or as a measure of one's degree of belief.

Problems

1. An aquarium had 6 fishes—3 mollies, 2 guppies and 1 platy. Sam caught 2 fishes first and then put them back before catching another fish from the aquarium. Describe the sample space. If sam didn't replace the fishes caught first, what will be the sample space?

2. In an experiment, die is rolled continually until a 6 appears, at which point the experiment stops. What is the sample space of this experiment? Let E_n denote the event that n rolls are necessary to complete the experiment. What points of the sample space are contained in E_n? What is $\left(\bigcup_{1}^{\infty} E_n\right)^c$?

3. A pair of dice consisting of a six-sided die and a four-sided die is rolled and the sum is determined. Let A be the event that a sum of 7 is rolled and let B be the event that a sum of 6 or a sum of 7 is rolled and C be the event that dies have the same value. Describe the sample space and the events AB, BC, ABC, $A \cup B \cup C$ and $AB^c C^c$.

4. Consider two events A and B such that $P(A) = 1/2$ $P(B) = 1/4$. Determine the value of $P(AB^c)$ for each of the following cases:
(a) A and B are disjoint.
(b) $B \subset A$
(c) $P(AB) = 1/10$

5. A system is composed of 5 components, each of which is either working or failed. Consider an experiment that consists of observing the status of each component, and let the outcome of the experiment be given by the vector $(x_1, x_2, x_3, x_4, x_5)$, where x_i is equal to 1 if component i is working and is equal to 0 if component i is failed.

(a) How many outcomes are in the sample space of this experiment?
(b) Suppose that the system will work if components 1 and 2 are both working, or if components 3 and 4 are both working, or if components 1, 3, and 5 are all working. Let W be the event that the system will work. Specify all the outcomes in W.
(c) Let A be the event that components 4 and 5 are both failed. How many outcomes are contained in the event A?
(d) Write out all the outcomes in the event AW.

6. A hospital administrator codes incoming patients suffering gunshot wounds according to whether they have insurance (coding 1 if they do and 0 if they do not) and according to their condition, which is rated as good (g), fair (f), or serious (s). Consider an experiment that consists of the coding of such a patient.

(a) Give the sample space of this experiment.
(b) Let A be the event that the patient is in serious condition. Specify the outcomes in A.
(c) Let B be the event that the patient is uninsured. Specify the outcomes in B.
(d) Give all the outcomes in the event $B^c \cup A$.

7. A pizza can be of two types based on its contents - either veg or non-veg - and based on its type of crust- it can be classified into - thin crust, bread crust or cheese crust. If there are 10 pizzas at a particular pizzateria, obtain the number of elements in the sample space of an experiment consisting of determining the type of these pizzas. How many outcomes are present in the event that at least one of the pizzas is non-veg?

8. Let A and B two events such that $P(A) = P(B) = 1/3$ and $P(A^c B^c) = 3/5$. Hence, obtain $P(A^c \cup B^c)$.

9. A retail establishment accepts either the American Express or the VISA credit card. A total of 24 percent of its customers carry an American Express card, 61 percent carry a VISA card, and 11 percent carry both cards. What percentage of its customers carry a credit card that the establishment will accept?

10. Sixty percent of the students at a certain school wear neither a ring nor a necklace. Twenty percent wear a ring and 30 percent wear a necklace. If one of the students is chosen randomly, what is the probability that this student is wearing

(a) a ring or a necklace?
(b) a ring and a necklace?

11. A total of 28 percent of American males smoke cigarettes, 7 percent smoke cigars, and 5 percent smoke both cigars and cigarettes.

(a) What percentage of males smokes neither cigars nor cigarettes?

(b) What percentage smokes cigars but not cigarettes?

12. An elementary school is offering 3 language classes: one in Spanish, one in French, and one in German. The classes are open to any of the 100 students in the school. There are 28 students in the Spanish class, 26 in the French class, and 16 in the German class. There are 12 students who are in both Spanish and French, 4 who are in both Spanish and German, and 6 who are in both French and German. In addition, there are 2 students taking all 3 classes.

(a) If a student is chosen randomly, what is the probability that he or she is not in any of the language classes?

(b) If a student is chosen randomly, what is the probability that he or she is taking exactly one language class?

(c) If 2 students are chosen randomly, what is the probability that at least 1 is taking a language class?

13. A certain town with a population of 100,000 has 3 newspapers: I, II, and III. The proportions of townspeople who read these papers are as follows:

I: 10 percent   I and II: 8 percent   I and II and
                                        III: 1 percent
II: 30 percent   I and III: 2 percent
III: 5 percent   II and III: 4 percent

(The list tells us, for instance, that 8000 people read newspapers I and II.)

(a) Find the number of people who read only one newspaper.

(b) How many people read at least two newspapers?

(c) If I and III are morning papers and II is an evening paper, how many people read at least one morning paper plus an evening paper?

(d) How many people do not read any newspapers?

(e) How many people read only one morning paper and one evening paper?

14. The following data were given in a study of a group of 1000 subscribers to a certain magazine: In reference to job, marital status, and education, there were 312 professionals, 470 married persons, 525 college graduates, 42 professional college graduates, 147 married college graduates, 86 married professionals, and 25 married professional college graduates. Show that the numbers reported in the study must be incorrect.

Hint: Let M, W, and G denote, respectively, the set of professionals, married persons, and college graduates. Assume that one of the 1000 persons is chosen at random, and use Proposition 4.4 to show that if the given numbers are correct, then $P(M \cup W \cup G) > 1$.

15. If it is assumed that all $\binom{52}{5}$ poker hands are equally likely, what is the probability of being dealt

(a) a flush? (A hand is said to be a flush if all 5 cards are of the same suit.)

(b) one pair? (This occurs when the cards have denominations a, a, b, c, d, where $a, b, c,$ and d are all distinct.)

(c) two pairs? (This occurs when the cards have denominations a, a, b, b, c, where $a, b,$ and c are all distinct.)

(d) three of a kind? (This occurs when the cards have denominations a, a, a, b, c, where $a, b,$ and c are all distinct.)

(e) four of a kind? (This occurs when the cards have denominations a, a, a, a, b.)

16. Poker dice is played by simultaneously rolling 5 dice. Show that

(a) $P\{\text{no two alike}\} = .0926$;

(b) $P\{\text{one pair}\} = .4630$;

(c) $P\{\text{two pair}\} = .2315$;

(d) $P\{\text{three alike}\} = .1543$;

(e) $P\{\text{full house}\} = .0386$;

(f) $P\{\text{four alike}\} = .0193$;

(g) $P\{\text{five alike}\} = .0008$.

17. If 8 rooks (castles) are randomly placed on a chessboard, compute the probability that none of the rooks can capture any of the others. That is, compute the probability that no row or file contains more than one rook.

18. A deck consists of 52 playing cards which is well shuffled. Draw 6 cards. Find the probability that among the cards there will be a representative of all suits?

19. There are 10 pair of socks kept in a cupboard. If a person randomly chooses 10 socks, what is the probability that there will be no matching pairs

20. Suppose that you are playing blackjack against a dealer. In a freshly shuffled deck, what is the probability that neither you nor the dealer is dealt a blackjack?

21. A small community organization consists of 20 families, of which 4 have one child, 8 have two children, 5 have three children, 2 have four children, and 1 has five children.

(a) If one of these families is chosen at random, what is the probability it has i children, $i = 1, 2, 3, 4, 5$?

(b) If one of the children is randomly chosen, what is the probability that child comes from a family having i children, $i = 1, 2, 3, 4, 5$?

22. Consider the following technique for shuffling a deck of n cards: For any initial ordering of the cards, go through the deck one card at a time and at each card, flip a fair coin. If the coin comes up heads, then leave the card where it is; if the coin comes up tails, then move that card to the end of the deck. After the coin has been flipped n times, say that one round has been completed. For instance, if $n = 4$ and the initial ordering is $1, 2, 3, 4$, then if the successive flips result in the outcome h, t, t, h, then the ordering at the end of the round is $1, 4, 2, 3$. Assuming that all possible outcomes of the sequence of n coin flips are equally likely, what is the probability that the ordering after one round is the same as the initial ordering?

23. 10 balls that are marked $1, 2, 3 ... 10$ are kept randomly in a box. Four balls are picked from the box and are given to four persons A, B, C and D. What is the probability that B gets the ball with the largest value (among A, B, C, D) and A gets the ball with the smallest value (among A, B, C, D)?

24. A box contains 100 balls, numbered from 1 to 100. If three balls are selected at random and with replacement from the box, what is the probability that the sum of the three numbers on the balls selected from the box will be odd? If the balls were taken without replacement, will the probabilities change?

25. A pair of dice is rolled until a sum of either 5 or 7 appears. Find the probability that a 5 occurs first.
Hint: Let E_n denote the event that a 5 occurs on the nth roll and no 5 or 7 occurs on the first $n - 1$ rolls. Compute $P(E_n)$ and argue that $\sum\limits_{n=1}^{\infty} P(E_n)$ is the desired probability.

26. The game of craps is played as follows: A player rolls two dice. If the sum of the dice is either a 2, 3, or 12, the player loses; if the sum is either a 7 or an 11, the player wins. If the outcome is anything else, the player continues to roll the dice until she rolls either the initial outcome or a 7. If the 7 comes first, the player loses, whereas if the initial outcome reoccurs before the 7 appears, the player wins. Compute the probability of a player winning at craps.
Hint: Let E_i denote the event that the initial outcome is i and the player wins. The desired probability is $\sum\limits_{i=2}^{12} P(E_i)$. To compute $P(E_i)$, define the events $E_{i,n}$ to be the event that the initial sum is i and the player wins on the nth roll. Argue that $P(E_i) = \sum\limits_{n=1}^{\infty} P(E_{i,n})$.

27. There are three secretaries who work for four departments. If each of the four departments has one report to be typed out, and the reports are randomly assigned to a secretary, what is the probability that all three secretaries are assigned at least one report?

28. An urn contains 5 red, 6 blue, and 8 green balls. If a set of 3 balls is randomly selected, what is the probability that each of the balls will be (a) of the same color? (b) of different colors? Repeat under the assumption that whenever a ball is selected, its color is noted and it is then replaced in the urn before the next selection. This is known as *sampling with replacement*.

29. An urn contains n white and m black balls, where n and m are positive numbers.

(a) If two balls are randomly withdrawn, what is the probability that they are the same color?

(b) If a ball is randomly withdrawn and then replaced before the second one is drawn, what is the probability that the withdrawn balls are the same color?

(c) Show that the probability in part (b) is always larger than the one in part (a).

30. The chess clubs of two schools consist of, respectively, 8 and 9 players. Four members from each club are randomly chosen to participate in a contest between the two schools. The chosen players from one team are then randomly paired with those from the other team, and each pairing plays a game of chess. Suppose that Rebecca and her sister Elise are on the chess clubs at different schools. What is the probability that

(a) Rebecca and Elise will be paired?

(b) Rebecca and Elise will be chosen to represent their schools but will not play each other?

(c) either Rebecca or Elise will be chosen to represent her school?

31. A 3-person basketball team consists of a guard, a forward, and a center.

(a) If a person is chosen at random from each of three different such teams, what is the probability of selecting a complete team?

(b) What is the probability that all 3 players selected play the same position?

32. A group of individuals containing b boys and g girls is lined up in random order; that is, each of the $(b + g)!$ permutations is assumed to be equally likely. What is the probability that the person in the ith position, $1 \le i \le b + g$, is a girl?

33. A forest contains 20 elk, of which 5 are captured, tagged, and then released. A certain time later, 4 of the 20 elk are captured. What is the probability that 2 of these 4 have been tagged? What assumptions are you making?

34. The second Earl of Yarborough is reported to have bet at odds of 1000 to 1 that a bridge hand of 13 cards would contain at least one card that is ten or higher. (By *ten or higher* we mean that a card is either a ten, a jack, a queen, a king, or an ace.) Nowadays, we call a hand that has no cards higher than 9 *a Yarborough*. What is the probability that a randomly selected bridge hand is a Yarborough?

35. A robber broke into a cell phone shop and managed to steal 4 phones from the counter. If there were 7 Apple phones, 6 Nokia phones and 3 Samsung phones, find the probability that

(a) all stolen phones were of the same company.

(b) all the samsung phones were not stolen.

(c) phones of all brands were stolen.

(d) either 3 nokia phones or 3 Apple phones were stolen.

36. Two cards are drawn at random from a pack of 52 cards. What is the probability that either both are black or both are Kings?

37. An instructor gives her class a set of 10 problems with the information that the final exam will consist of a random selection of 5 of them. If a student has figured out how to do 7 of the problems, what is the probability that he or she will answer correctly

(a) all 5 problems?

(b) at least 4 of the problems?

38. There are n socks, 3 of which are red, in a drawer. What is the value of n if, when 2 of the socks are chosen randomly, the probability that they are both red is $\frac{1}{2}$?

39. Three ants are sitting at the three corners of an equilateral triangle. Each ant starts to move randomly along an edge of the triangle. What is the probability that none of them collide with each other?

40. There are 3 computers were available in an internet cafe. If on a particular day 3 customers arrived (at non-overlapping times), what is the probability that k computers ($k = 1, 2, 3$) were used on that particular day?

41. If a die is rolled 4 times, what is the probability that 6 comes up at least once?

42. Two dice are thrown n times in succession. Compute the probability that double 6 appears at least once. How large need n be to make this probability at least $\frac{1}{2}$?

43. (a) If N people, including A and B, are randomly arranged in a line, what is the probability that A and B are next to each other?

(b) What would the probability be if the people were randomly arranged in a circle?

44. Five people, designated as A, B, C, D, E, are arranged in linear order. Assuming that each possible order is equally likely, what is the probability that

(a) there is exactly one person between A and B?

(b) there are exactly two people between A and B?

(c) there are three people between A and B?

45. A woman has n keys, of which one will open her door.

(a) If she tries the keys at random, discarding those that do not work, what is the probability that she will open the door on her kth try?

(b) What if she does not discard previously tried keys?

46. How many people have to be in a room in order that the probability that at least two of them celebrate their birthday in the same month is at least $\frac{1}{2}$? Assume that all possible monthly outcomes are equally likely.

47. If there are 24 students in a classroom obtain, find the probability that at least three students share the same birthday.

48. Given 20 people, what is the probability that among the 12 months in the year, there are 4 months containing exactly 2 birthdays and 4 containing exactly 3 birthdays?

49. A group of 6 men and 6 women is randomly divided into 2 groups of size 6 each. What is the probability that both groups will have the same number of men?

50. A car is parked by Tom among N cars in a row, not at either end. On his return, he finds that exactly r of them are still occupied. What is the probability that both his neighboring spots are vacant?

51. Suppose that n balls are randomly distributed into N compartments. Find the probability that m balls will fall into the first compartment. Assume that all N^n arrangements are equally likely.

52. A pair of dice is rolled until either you obtain the same two numbers on the dice or the difference of the two numbers on the dice is 1. Find the probability that you roll two dice with equal numbers before you roll two dice whose numbers differ by 1.

53. If 4 married couples are arranged in a row, find the probability that no husband sits next to his wife.

54. Three numbers are chosen at random from $\{1, 2, ..., 10\}$. Find the probability that they are in A.P?

55. A and B play a game of tossing an unbiased coin. A starts by tossing the coin once and then B toss the coin twice. This continues till either of them obtain a head. Find the probability that A is the one to obtain head first?

56. Two players play the following game: Player A chooses one of the three spinners pictured in Figure 2.6, and then player B chooses one of the remaining two spinners. Both players then spin their spinner, and the one that lands on the higher number is declared the winner. Assuming that each spinner is equally likely to land in any of its 3 regions, would you rather be player A or player B? Explain your answer!

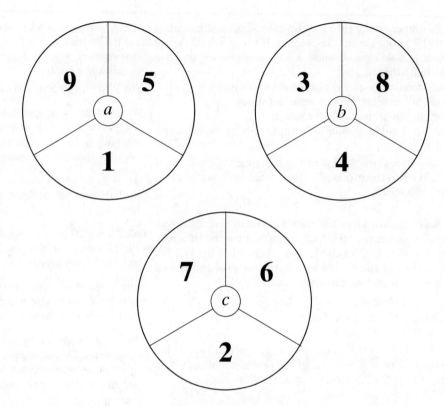

Figure 2.6 Spinners.

Theoretical Exercises

Prove the following relations:

1. $EF \subset E \subset E \cup F$.

2. If $E \subset F$, then $F^c \subset E^c$.

3. $F = FE \cup FE^c$ and $E \cup F = E \cup E^c F$.

4. $\left(\bigcup_1^\infty E_i\right) F = \bigcup_1^\infty E_i F$ and

$\left(\bigcap_1^\infty E_i\right) \cup F = \bigcap_1^\infty (E_i \cup F)$.

5. For any sequence of events $E_1, E_2, \ldots$, define a new sequence $F_1, F_2, \ldots$ of disjoint events (that is, events such that $F_i F_j = \emptyset$ whenever $i \neq j$) such that for all $n \geq 1$,

$$\bigcup_1^n F_i = \bigcup_1^n E_i$$

6. Let E, F, and G be three events. Find expressions for the events so that, of E, F, and G,

(a) only E occurs;

(b) both E and G, but not F, occur;

(c) at least one of the events occurs;

(d) at least two of the events occur;

(e) all three events occur;

(f) none of the events occurs;

(g) at most one of the events occurs;

(h) at most two of the events occur;

(i) exactly two of the events occur;

(j) at most three of the events occur.

7. Use Venn diagrams

(a) to simplify the expressions $(E \cup F)(E \cup F^c)$;

(b) to prove DeMorgan's laws for events E and F. [That is, prove $(E \cup F)^c = E^c F^c$, and $(EF)^c = E^c \cup F^c$.]

8. Let S be a given set. If, for some $k > 0$, $S_1, S_2, \ldots, S_k$ are mutually exclusive nonempty subsets of S such that

$\bigcup\limits_{i=1}^{k} S_i = S$, then we call the set $\{S_1, S_2, \ldots, S_k\}$ a *partition* of S. Let T_n denote the number of different partitions of $\{1, 2, \ldots, n\}$. Thus, $T_1 = 1$ (the only partition being $S_1 = \{1\}$) and $T_2 = 2$ (the two partitions being $\{\{1, 2, \}\}, \{\{1\}, \{2\}\}$).

(a) Show, by computing all partitions, that $T_3 = 5$, $T_4 = 15$.

(b) Show that

$$T_{n+1} = 1 + \sum_{k=1}^{n} \binom{n}{k} T_k$$

and use this equation to compute T_{10}.

Hint: One way of choosing a partition of $n + 1$ items is to call one of the items *special*. Then we obtain different partitions by first choosing $k, k = 0, 1, \ldots, n$, then a subset of size $n - k$ of the nonspecial items, and then any of the T_k partitions of the remaining k nonspecial items. By adding the special item to the subset of size $n - k$, we obtain a partition of all $n + 1$ items.

9. If n balls are kept into n boxes at random, find the probability that exactly one box remain empty?

10. Prove that $P(E \cup F \cup G) = P(E) + P(F) + P(G) - P(E^c FG) - P(EF^c G) - P(EFG^c) - 2P(EFG)$.

11. If $P(E) = .9$ and $P(F) = .8$, show that $P(EF) \geq .7$. In general, prove *Bonferroni's inequality*, namely,

$$P(EF) \geq P(E) + P(F) - 1$$

12. Check wether the following relation is true or false

$$P(A \cup B \cup C) = P(AC^c) + P(C) + P(BA^c C^c)$$

13. Prove that $P(EF^c) = P(E) - P(EF)$.

14. Let there be N persons each with identical biased coins that land heads with probability p. In each trial all persons flip their coins simultaneously and each person whose coin lands on heads is eliminated.

(a) What is the probability that every person is eliminated after t trials?

(b) What is the probability that all the people are eliminated together as a group in exactly trial number t?

15. In a sample made up of N electronic equipments in which there are M defective ones. n items are chosen at random from this sample. What is the probability that among them there are m defective ones $(m \leq M)$?

17. n sticks are broken into two parts, a long one and a short one. After that, the $2n$ parts obtained are collected into n pairs; from each pair a new "stick" is made. Find the probability that:

(a) the $2n$ parts are reassembled to form the original n sticks

(b) each long part is joined to a short part.

16. Use induction to generalize *Bonferroni's inequality* to n events. That is, show that

$$P(E_1 E_2 \cdots E_n) \geq P(E_1) + \cdots + P(E_n) - (n - 1)$$

18. Two friends A and B play a game of flipping a coin with $P(head) = p$ alternatively and whoever gets a head first wins the game. If A starts the game, show that $P(A\,wins) > 1/2$ for all values of p, $0 < p < 1$.

19. n persons have been assigned seats in a train compartment containing a total of $n + m$ seats. The first person who enters the compartment, however, lost his seat assignment and chooses a seat at random. Subsequently, people enter the train one at a time and sit in their assigned seat unless it is already occupied. If it is, they choose a seat at random from the remaining empty seats. What is the probability that person n, the last person to enter the train, finds their seat already occupied?

20. Consider an experiment whose sample space consists of a countably infinite number of points. Show that not all points can be equally likely. Can all points have a positive probability of occurring?

*21. Consider Example 5o, which is concerned with the number of runs of wins obtained when n wins and m losses are randomly permuted. Now consider the total number of runs—that is, win runs plus loss runs—and show that

$$P\{2k \text{ runs}\} = 2\frac{\binom{m-1}{k-1}\binom{n-1}{k-1}}{\binom{m+n}{n}}$$

$$P\{2k + 1 \text{ runs}\}$$

$$= \frac{\binom{m-1}{k-1}\binom{n-1}{k} + \binom{m-1}{k}\binom{n-1}{k-1}}{\binom{m+n}{n}}$$

Self-Test Problems and Exercises

1. A cafeteria offers a three-course meal consisting of an entree, a starch, and a dessert. The possible choices are given in the following table:

Course	Choices
Entree	Chicken or roast beef
Starch	Pasta or rice or potatoes
Dessert	Ice cream or Jello or apple pie or a peach

A person is to choose one course from each category.

(a) How many outcomes are in the sample space?

(b) Let A be the event that ice cream is chosen. How many outcomes are in A?

(c) Let B be the event that chicken is chosen. How many outcomes are in B?

(d) List all the outcomes in the event AB.

(e) Let C be the event that rice is chosen. How many outcomes are in C?

(f) List all the outcomes in the event ABC.

2. A customer at an ice-cream shop will order a vanilla scoop with probability 0.30, strawberry scoop with probability 0.28 and pista scoop with probability 0.35. He will order both vanilla and strawberry with probability 0.19, both strawberry and pista with probability 0.22, both vannila and pista with probability 0.18. He will order all three flavours of ice-creams with probability 0.15. What is the probability that he buys

(a) none of these flavours?
(b) two among these flavours?

3. A deck of cards is dealt out. What is the probability that the 14th card dealt is an ace? What is the probability that the first ace occurs on the 14th card?

4. Let A denote the event that the midtown temperature in Los Angeles is 70°F, and let B denote the event that the midtown temperature in New York is 70°F. Also, let C denote the event that the maximum of the midtown temperatures in New York and in Los Angeles is 70°F. If $P(A) = .3, P(B) = .4$, and $P(C) = .2$, find the probability that the minimum of the two midtown temperatures is 70°F.

5. From an ordinary deck of 52 cards, five cards are randomly drawn. What is the probability that

(a) the fifth drawn card is the first King to be drawn?
(b) all four Kings in the deck are drawn?

6. Urn A contains 3 red and 3 black balls, whereas urn B contains 4 red and 6 black balls. If a ball is randomly selected from each urn, what is the probability that the balls will be the same color?

7. In a state lottery, a player must choose 8 of the numbers from 1 to 40. The lottery commission then performs an experiment that selects 8 of these 40 numbers. Assuming that the choice of the lottery commission is equally likely to be any of the $\binom{40}{8}$ combinations, what is the probability that a player has

(a) all 8 of the numbers selected by the lottery commission?

(b) 7 of the numbers selected by the lottery commission?

(c) at least 6 of the numbers selected by the lottery commission?

8. From a group of 3 first-year students, 4 sophomores, 4 juniors, and 3 seniors, a committee of size 4 is randomly selected. Find the probability that the committee will consist of

(a) 1 from each class;
(b) 2 sophomores and 2 juniors;
(c) only sophomores or juniors.

9. For a finite set A, let $N(A)$ denote the number of elements in A.

(a) Show that

$$N(A \cup B) = N(A) + N(B) - N(AB)$$

(b) More generally, show that

$$N\left(\bigcup_{i=1}^{n} A_i\right) = \sum_{i} N(A_i) - \sum_{i<j}\sum N(A_i A_j)$$
$$+ \cdots + (-1)^{n+1} N(A_1 \cdots A_n)$$

10. Consider an experiment that consists of 6 horses, numbered 1 through 6, running a race, and suppose that the sample space consists of the 6! possible orders in which the horses finish. Let A be the event that the number-1 horse is among the top three finishers, and let B be the event that the number-2 horse comes in second. How many outcomes are in the event $A \cup B$?

11. Two cards are drawn successively from a deck of 52 cards. Find the probability that the second card is higher in rank than the first card.
Hint: Show that $1 = P(higher) + P(lower) + P(same)$ and use the fact that $P(higher) = P(lower)$.

12. A basketball team consists of 6 frontcourt and 4 backcourt players. If players are divided into roommates at random, what is the probability that there will be exactly two roommate pairs made up of a backcourt and a frontcourt player?

13. If the letters of the word CRUDE are arranged randomly in a row, what is the probability that none of the letters in the chosen word is in the same position in which it appears in CRUDE?

14. Prove *Boole's inequality*:

$$P\left(\bigcup_{i=1}^{\infty} A_i\right) \leq \sum_{i=1}^{\infty} P(A_i)$$

15. Show that if $P(A_i) = 1$ for all $i \geq 1$, then $P\left(\bigcap_{i=1}^{\infty} A_i\right) = 1$.

16. Let $T_k(n)$ denote the number of partitions of the set $\{1, \ldots, n\}$ into k nonempty subsets, where $1 \leq k \leq n$. (See Theoretical Exercise 8 for the definition of a partition.) Argue that

$$T_k(n) = kT_k(n-1) + T_{k-1}(n-1)$$

Hint: In how many partitions is $\{1\}$ a subset, and in how many is 1 an element of a subset that contains other elements?

17. An urn contains 3 red, 7 blue and 6 green balls. 3 balls are randomly selected from the urn, find the probability of getting exactly one red ball if the balls are drawn with replacement. What is the probability of the same event when balls are drawn without replacement?

18. Four red, 8 blue, and 5 green balls are randomly arranged in a line.

(a) What is the probability that the first 5 balls are blue?

(b) What is the probability that none of the first 5 balls is blue?

(c) What is the probability that the final 3 balls are of different colors?

(d) What is the probability that all the red balls are together?

19. Ten cards are randomly chosen from a deck of 52 cards that consists of 13 cards of each of 4 different suits. Each of the selected cards is put in one of 4 piles, depending on the suit of the card.

(a) What is the probability that the largest pile has 4 cards, the next largest has 3, the next largest has 2, and the smallest has 1 card?

(b) What is the probability that two of the piles have 3 cards, one has 4 cards, and one has no cards?

20. A deck consist of 13 spades and 13 hearts. Cards are drawn one by one at random from the deck without replacement. What is the probability that all the spades are drawn before the hearts. What is the probability of the same event if cards are drawn from an ordinary well shuffled deck of 52 cards (Consisting of all suits)?

CONDITIONAL PROBABILITY AND INDEPENDENCE

Chapter

3

Contents

3.1 Introduction
3.2 Conditional Probabilities
3.3 Bayes's Formula

3.4 Independent Events
3.5 $P(\cdot|F)$ Is a Probability

3.1 Introduction

In this chapter, we introduce one of the most important concepts in probability theory, that of conditional probability. The importance of this concept is twofold. In the first place, we are often interested in calculating probabilities when some partial information concerning the result of an experiment is available; in such a situation, the desired probabilities are conditional. Second, even when no partial information is available, conditional probabilities can often be used to compute the desired probabilities more easily.

3.2 Conditional Probabilities

Suppose that we toss 2 dice, and suppose that each of the 36 possible outcomes is equally likely to occur and hence has probability $\frac{1}{36}$. Suppose further that we observe that the first die is a 3. Then, given this information, what is the probability that the sum of the 2 dice equals 8? To calculate this probability, we reason as follows: Given that the initial die is a 3, there can be at most 6 possible outcomes of our experiment, namely, (3, 1), (3, 2), (3, 3), (3, 4), (3, 5), and (3, 6). Since each of these outcomes originally had the same probability of occurring, the outcomes should still have equal probabilities. That is, given that the first die is a 3, the (conditional) probability of each of the outcomes (3, 1), (3, 2), (3, 3), (3, 4), (3, 5), and (3, 6) is $\frac{1}{6}$, whereas the (conditional) probability of the other 30 points in the sample space is 0. Hence, the desired probability will be $\frac{1}{6}$.

If we let E and F denote, respectively, the event that the sum of the dice is 8 and the event that the first die is a 3, then the probability just obtained is called the *conditional probability that E occurs given that F has occurred* and is denoted by

$$P(E|F)$$

A general formula for $P(E|F)$ that is valid for all events E and F is derived in the same manner: If the event F occurs, then, in order for E to occur, it is necessary that the actual occurrence be a point both in E and in F; that is, it must be in EF. Now, since we know that F has occurred, it follows that F becomes our new, or reduced, sample space; hence, the probability that the event EF occurs will equal the probability of EF relative to the probability of F. That is, we have the following definition.

Definition

If $P(F) > 0$, then

$$P(E|F) = \frac{P(EF)}{P(F)} \qquad (2.1)$$

Example 2a

Joe is 80 percent certain that his missing key is in one of the two pockets of his hanging jacket, being 40 percent certain it is in the left-hand pocket and 40 percent certain it is in the right-hand pocket. If a search of the left-hand pocket does not find the key, what is the conditional probability that it is in the other pocket?

Solution If we let L be the event that the key is in the left-hand pocket of the jacket, and R be the event that it is in the right-hand pocket, then the desired probability $P(R|L^c)$ can be obtained as follows:

$$P(R|L^c) = \frac{P(RL^c)}{P(L^c)}$$
$$= \frac{P(R)}{1 - P(L)}$$
$$= 2/3 \qquad \blacksquare$$

If each outcome of a finite sample space S is equally likely, then, conditional on the event that the outcome lies in a subset $F \subset S$, all outcomes in F become equally likely. In such cases, it is often convenient to compute conditional probabilities of the form $P(E|F)$ by using F as the sample space. Indeed, working with this reduced sample space often results in an easier and better understood solution. Our next two examples illustrate this point.

Example 2b

A coin is flipped twice. Assuming that all four points in the sample space $S = \{(h, h), (h, t), (t, h), (t, t)\}$ are equally likely, what is the conditional probability that both flips land on heads, given that (a) the first flip lands on heads? (b) at least one flip lands on heads?

Solution Let $B = \{(h, h)\}$ be the event that both flips land on heads; let $F = \{(h, h), (h, t)\}$ be the event that the first flip lands on heads; and let $A = \{(h, h), (h, t), (t, h)\}$ be the event that at least one flip lands on heads. The probability for (a) can be obtained from

$$P(B|F) = \frac{P(BF)}{P(F)}$$
$$= \frac{P(\{(h, h)\})}{P(\{(h, h), (h, t)\})}$$
$$= \frac{1/4}{2/4} = 1/2$$

For (b), we have

$$P(B|A) = \frac{P(BA)}{P(A)}$$

$$= \frac{P(\{(h,h)\})}{P(\{(h,h),(h,t),(t,h)\})}$$

$$= \frac{1/4}{3/4} = 1/3$$

Thus, the conditional probability that both flips land on heads given that the first one does is 1/2, whereas the conditional probability that both flips land on heads given that at least one does is only 1/3. Many students initially find this latter result surprising. They reason that given that at least one flip lands on heads, there are two possible results: Either they both land on heads or only one does. Their mistake, however, is in assuming that these two possibilities are equally likely. Initially there are 4 equally likely outcomes. Because the information that at least one flip lands on heads is equivalent to the information that the outcome is not (t,t), we are left with the 3 equally likely outcomes $(h,h),(h,t),(t,h)$, only one of which results in both flips landing on heads. ∎

Example 2c

In the card game bridge, the 52 cards are dealt out equally to 4 players—called East, West, North, and South. If North and South have a total of 8 spades among them, what is the probability that East has 3 of the remaining 5 spades?

Solution Probably the easiest way to compute the desired probability is to work with the reduced sample space. That is, given that North–South have a total of 8 spades among their 26 cards, there remains a total of 26 cards, exactly 5 of them being spades, to be distributed among the East–West hands. Since each distribution is equally likely, it follows that the conditional probability that East will have exactly 3 spades among his or her 13 cards is

$$\frac{\binom{5}{3}\binom{21}{10}}{\binom{26}{13}} \approx .339$$

∎

Multiplying both sides of Equation (2.1) by $P(F)$, we obtain

$$P(EF) = P(F)P(E|F) \tag{2.2}$$

In words, Equation (2.2) states that the probability that both E and F occur is equal to the probability that F occurs multiplied by the conditional probability of E given that F occurred. Equation (2.2) is often quite useful in computing the probability of the intersection of events.

Example 2d

Celine is undecided as to whether to take a French course or a chemistry course. She estimates that her probability of receiving an A grade would be $\frac{1}{2}$ in a French course and $\frac{2}{3}$ in a chemistry course. If Celine decides to base her decision on the flip of a fair coin, what is the probability that she gets an A in chemistry?

Solution Let C be the event that Celine takes chemistry and A denote the event that she receives an A in whatever course she takes, then the desired probability is $P(CA)$, which is calculated by using Equation (2.2) as follows:

$$P(CA) = P(C)P(A|C)$$
$$= \left(\frac{1}{2}\right)\left(\frac{2}{3}\right) = \frac{1}{3}$$ ∎

Example 2e

Suppose that an urn contains 8 red balls and 4 white balls. We draw 2 balls from the urn without replacement. (a) If we assume that at each draw, each ball in the urn is equally likely to be chosen, what is the probability that both balls drawn are red? (b) Now suppose that the balls have different weights, with each red ball having weight r and each white ball having weight w. Suppose that the probability that a given ball in the urn is the next one selected is its weight divided by the sum of the weights of all balls currently in the urn. Now what is the probability that both balls are red?

Solution Let R_1 and R_2 denote, respectively, the events that the first and second balls drawn are red. Now, given that the first ball selected is red, there are 7 remaining red balls and 4 white balls, so $P(R_2|R_1) = \frac{7}{11}$. As $P(R_1)$ is clearly $\frac{8}{12}$, the desired probability is

$$P(R_1 R_2) = P(R_1)P(R_2|R_1)$$
$$= \left(\frac{2}{3}\right)\left(\frac{7}{11}\right) = \frac{14}{33}$$

Of course, this probability could have been computed by $P(R_1 R_2) = \binom{8}{2}/\binom{12}{2}$.

For part (b), we again let R_i be the event that the ith ball chosen is red and use

$$P(R_1 R_2) = P(R_1)P(R_2|R_1)$$

Now, number the red balls, and let B_i, $i = 1, \ldots, 8$ be the event that the first ball drawn is red ball number i. Then

$$P(R_1) = P(\cup_{i=1}^{8} B_i) = \sum_{i=1}^{8} P(B_i) = 8\frac{r}{8r + 4w}$$

Moreover, given that the first ball is red, the urn then contains 7 red and 4 white balls. Thus, by an argument similar to the preceding one,

$$P(R_2|R_1) = \frac{7r}{7r + 4w}$$

Hence, the probability that both balls are red is

$$P(R_1 R_2) = \frac{8r}{8r + 4w}\frac{7r}{7r + 4w}$$ ∎

A generalization of Equation (2.2), which provides an expression for the probability of the intersection of an arbitrary number of events, is sometimes referred to as the *multiplication rule*.

The multiplication rule

$$P(E_1 E_2 E_3 \cdots E_n) = P(E_1)P(E_2|E_1)P(E_3|E_1 E_2) \cdots P(E_n|E_1 \cdots E_{n-1})$$

To prove the multiplication rule, just apply the definition of conditional probability to its right-hand side, giving

$$P(E_1)\frac{P(E_1E_2)}{P(E_1)}\frac{P(E_1E_2E_3)}{P(E_1E_2)}\cdots\frac{P(E_1E_2\cdots E_n)}{P(E_1E_2\cdots E_{n-1})}=P(E_1E_2\cdots E_n)$$

Example 2f

In the match problem stated in Example 5m of Chapter 2, it was shown that P_N, the probability that there are no matches when N people randomly select from among their own N hats, is given by

$$P_N=\sum_{i=0}^{N}(-1)^i/i!$$

What is the probability that exactly k of the N people have matches?

Solution Let us fix our attention on a particular set of k people and determine the probability that these k individuals have matches and no one else does. Letting E denote the event that everyone in this set has a match, and letting G be the event that none of the other $N - k$ people have a match, we have

$$P(EG) = P(E)P(G|E)$$

Now, let F_i, $i = 1, \ldots, k$, be the event that the ith member of the set has a match. Then

$$
\begin{aligned}
P(E) &= P(F_1F_2\cdots F_k)\\
&= P(F_1)P(F_2|F_1)P(F_3|F_1F_2)\cdots P(F_k|F_1\cdots F_{k-1})\\
&= \frac{1}{N}\frac{1}{N-1}\frac{1}{N-2}\cdots\frac{1}{N-k+1}\\
&= \frac{(N-k)!}{N!}
\end{aligned}
$$

Given that everyone in the set of k has a match, the other $N - k$ people will be randomly choosing among their own $N - k$ hats, so the probability that none of them has a match is equal to the probability of no matches in a problem having $N - k$ people choosing among their own $N - k$ hats. Therefore,

$$P(G|E) = P_{N-k} = \sum_{i=0}^{N-k}(-1)^i/i!$$

showing that the probability that a specified set of k people have matches and no one else does is

$$P(EG) = \frac{(N-k)!}{N!}\,P_{N-k}$$

Because there will be exactly k matches if the preceding is true for any of the $\binom{N}{k}$ sets of k individuals, the desired probability is

$$P(\text{exactly } k \text{ matches}) = P_{N-k}/k!$$
$$\approx e^{-1}/k! \qquad \text{when } N \text{ is large} \qquad \blacksquare$$

We will now employ the multiplication rule to obtain a second approach to solving Example 5h(b) of Chapter 2.

Example 2g

An ordinary deck of 52 playing cards is randomly divided into 4 piles of 13 cards each. Compute the probability that each pile has exactly 1 ace.

Solution Define events $E_i, i = 1, 2, 3, 4$, as follows:

$E_1 = \{$the ace of spades is in any one of the piles$\}$

$E_2 = \{$the ace of spades and the ace of hearts are in different piles$\}$

$E_3 = \{$the aces of spades, hearts, and diamonds are all in different piles$\}$

$E_4 = \{$all 4 aces are in different piles$\}$

The desired probability is $P(E_1 E_2 E_3 E_4)$, and by the multiplication rule,

$$P(E_1 E_2 E_3 E_4) = P(E_1)P(E_2|E_1)P(E_3|E_1 E_2)P(E_4|E_1 E_2 E_3)$$

Now,

$$P(E_1) = 1$$

since E_1 is the sample space S. To determine $P(E_2|E_1)$, consider the pile that contains the ace of spades. Because its remaining 12 cards are equally likely to be any 12 of the remaining 51 cards, the probability that the ace of hearts is among them is 12/51, giving that

$$P(E_2|E_1) = 1 - \frac{12}{51} = \frac{39}{51}$$

Also, given that the ace of spades and ace of hearts are in different piles, it follows that the set of the remaining 24 cards of these two piles is equally likely to be any set of 24 of the remaining 50 cards. As the probability that the ace of diamonds is one of these 24 is 24/50, we see that

$$P(E_3|E_1 E_2) = 1 - \frac{24}{50} = \frac{26}{50}$$

Because the same logic as used in the preceding yields that

$$P(E_4|E_1 E_2 E_3) = 1 - \frac{36}{49} = \frac{13}{49}$$

the probability that each pile has exactly 1 ace is

$$P(E_1 E_2 E_3 E_4) = \frac{39 \cdot 26 \cdot 13}{51 \cdot 50 \cdot 49} \approx .105$$

That is, there is approximately a 10.5 percent chance that each pile will contain an ace. (Problem 13 gives another way of using the multiplication rule to solve this problem.) ∎

Remarks Our definition of $P(E|F)$ is consistent with the interpretation of probability as being a long-run relative frequency. To see this, suppose that n repetitions of the experiment are to be performed, where n is large. We claim that if we consider only those experiments in which F occurs, then $P(E|F)$ will equal the long-run proportion of them in which E also occurs. To verify this statement, note that since $P(F)$ is the long-run proportion of experiments in which F occurs, it follows that in the n repetitions of the experiment, F will occur approximately $nP(F)$ times. Similarly, in approximately $nP(EF)$ of these experiments, both E and F will occur. Hence, out of the approximately $nP(F)$ experiments in which F occurs, the proportion of them in which E also occurs is approximately equal to

$$\frac{nP(EF)}{nP(F)} = \frac{P(EF)}{P(F)}$$

Because this approximation becomes exact as n becomes larger and larger, we have the appropriate definition of $P(E|F)$.

3.3   Bayes's Formula

Let E and F be events. We may express E as

$$E = EF \cup EF^c$$

for, in order for an outcome to be in E, it must either be in both E and F or be in E but not in F. (See Figure 3.1.) As EF and EF^c are clearly mutually exclusive, we have, by Axiom 3,

$$
\begin{aligned}
P(E) &= P(EF) + P(EF^c) \\
&= P(E|F)P(F) + P(E|F^c)P(F^c) \\
&= P(E|F)P(F) + P(E|F^c)[1 - P(F)]
\end{aligned}
\tag{3.1}
$$

Equation (3.1) states that the probability of the event E is a weighted average of the conditional probability of E given that F has occurred and the conditional probability of E given that F has not occurred—each conditional probability being given as much weight as the event on which it is conditioned has of occurring. This is an extremely useful formula, because its use often enables us to determine the probability of an event by first "conditioning" upon whether or not some second event has occurred. That is, there are many instances in which it is difficult to compute the probability of an event directly, but it is straightforward to compute it once we know whether or not some second event has occurred. We illustrate this idea with some examples.

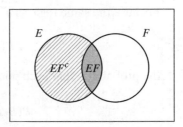

Figure 3.1 $E = EF \cup EF^c$. EF = Shaded Area; EF^c = Striped Area.

Example 3a

(Part 1)

An insurance company believes that people can be divided into two classes: those who are accident prone and those who are not. The company's statistics show that an accident-prone person will have an accident at some time within a fixed 1-year period with probability .4, whereas this probability decreases to .2 for a person who is not accident prone. If we assume that 30 percent of the population is accident prone, what is the probability that a new policyholder will have an accident within a year of purchasing a policy?

Solution We shall obtain the desired probability by first conditioning upon whether or not the policyholder is accident prone. Let A_1 denote the event that the policyholder will have an accident within a year of purchasing the policy, and let A denote the event that the policyholder is accident prone. Hence, the desired probability is given by

$$P(A_1) = P(A_1|A)P(A) + P(A_1|A^c)P(A^c)$$
$$= (.4)(.3) + (.2)(.7) = .26 \qquad \blacksquare$$

Example 3a

(Part 2)

Suppose that a new policyholder has an accident within a year of purchasing a policy. What is the probability that he or she is accident prone?

Solution The desired probability is

$$P(A|A_1) = \frac{P(AA_1)}{P(A_1)}$$
$$= \frac{P(A)P(A_1|A)}{P(A_1)}$$
$$= \frac{(.3)(.4)}{.26} = \frac{6}{13} \qquad \blacksquare$$

Example 3b

Consider the following game played with an ordinary deck of 52 playing cards: The cards are shuffled and then turned over one at a time. At any time, the player can guess that the next card to be turned over will be the ace of spades; if it is, then the player wins. In addition, the player is said to win if the ace of spades has not yet appeared when only one card remains and no guess has yet been made. What is a good strategy? What is a bad strategy?

Solution Every strategy has probability 1/52 of winning! To show this, we will use induction to prove the stronger result that for an n card deck, one of whose cards is the ace of spades, the probability of winning is $1/n$, no matter what strategy is employed. Since this is clearly true for $n = 1$, assume it to be true for an $n - 1$ card deck, and now consider an n card deck. Fix any strategy, and let p denote the probability that the strategy guesses that the first card is the ace of spades. Given that it does, the player's probability of winning is $1/n$. If, however, the strategy does not guess that the first card is the ace of spades, then the probability that the player wins is the probability that the first card is not the ace of spades, namely, $(n - 1)/n$, multiplied by the conditional probability of winning given that the first card is not the ace of spades. But this latter conditional probability is equal to the probability of winning when using an $n - 1$ card deck containing a single ace of spades; it is thus, by the induction hypothesis, $1/(n - 1)$. Hence, given that the strategy does not guess the first card, the probability of winning is

$$\frac{n - 1}{n} \frac{1}{n - 1} = \frac{1}{n}$$

Thus, letting G be the event that the first card is guessed, we obtain

$$P\{\text{win}\} = P\{\text{win}|G\}P(G) + P\{\text{win}|G^c\}(1 - P(G)) = \frac{1}{n}p + \frac{1}{n}(1 - p)$$
$$= \frac{1}{n} \qquad \blacksquare$$

Example 3c

In answering a question on a multiple-choice test, a student either knows the answer or guesses. Let p be the probability that the student knows the answer and $1 - p$ be the probability that the student guesses. Assume that a student who guesses at the answer will be correct with probability $1/m$, where m is the number of multiple-choice alternatives. What is the conditional probability that a student knew the answer to a question given that he or she answered it correctly?

Solution Let C and K denote, respectively, the events that the student answers the question correctly and the event that he or she actually knows the answer. Now,

$$
\begin{aligned}
P(K|C) &= \frac{P(KC)}{P(C)} \\
&= \frac{P(C|K)P(K)}{P(C|K)P(K) + P(C|K^c)P(K^c)} \\
&= \frac{p}{p + (1/m)(1 - p)} \\
&= \frac{mp}{1 + (m - 1)p}
\end{aligned}
$$

For example, if $m = 5, p = \frac{1}{2}$, then the probability that the student knew the answer to a question he or she answered correctly is $\frac{5}{6}$. ∎

Example 3d

A laboratory blood test is 95 percent effective in detecting a certain disease when it is, in fact, present. However, the test also yields a "false positive" result for 1 percent of the healthy persons tested. (That is, if a healthy person is tested, then, with probability .01, the test result will imply that he or she has the disease.) If .5 percent of the population actually has the disease, what is the probability that a person has the disease given that the test result is positive?

Solution Let D be the event that the person tested has the disease and E the event that the test result is positive. Then the desired probability is

$$
\begin{aligned}
P(D|E) &= \frac{P(DE)}{P(E)} \\
&= \frac{P(E|D)P(D)}{P(E|D)P(D) + P(E|D^c)P(D^c)} \\
&= \frac{(.95)(.005)}{(.95)(.005) + (.01)(.995)} \\
&= \frac{95}{294} \approx .323
\end{aligned}
$$

Thus, only 32 percent of those persons whose test results are positive actually have the disease. Many students are often surprised at this result (they expect the percentage to be much higher, since the blood test seems to be a good one), so it is probably worthwhile to present a second argument that, although less rigorous than the preceding one, is probably more revealing. We now do so.

Since .5 percent of the population actually has the disease, it follows that, on the average, 1 person out of every 200 tested will have it. The test will correctly confirm that this person has the disease with probability .95. Thus, on the average, out of every 200 persons tested, the test will correctly confirm that .95 person has the disease. On the other hand, out of the (on the average) 199 healthy people, the test will incorrectly state that (199)(.01) of these people have the disease. Hence, for every .95 diseased person that the test correctly states is ill, there are (on the average) (199)(.01) healthy persons who the test incorrectly states are ill. Thus, the proportion of time that the test result is correct when it states that a person is ill is

$$\frac{.95}{.95 + (199)(.01)} = \frac{95}{294} \approx .323 \qquad \blacksquare$$

Equation (3.1) is also useful when one has to reassess one's personal probabilities in the light of additional information. For instance, consider the examples that follow.

Example 3e

Consider a medical practitioner pondering the following dilemma: "If I'm at least 80 percent certain that my patient has this disease, then I always recommend surgery, whereas if I'm not quite as certain, then I recommend additional tests that are expensive and sometimes painful. Now, initially I was only 60 percent certain that Jones had the disease, so I ordered the series A test, which always gives a positive result when the patient has the disease and almost never does when he is healthy. The test result was positive, and I was all set to recommend surgery when Jones informed me, for the first time, that he was diabetic. This information complicates matters because, although it doesn't change my original 60 percent estimate of his chances of having the disease in question, it does affect the interpretation of the results of the A test. This is so because the A test, while never yielding a positive result when the patient is healthy, does unfortunately yield a positive result 30 percent of the time in the case of *diabetic* patients who are not suffering from the disease. Now what do I do? More tests or immediate surgery?"

Solution In order to decide whether or not to recommend surgery, the doctor should first compute her updated probability that Jones has the disease given that the A test result was positive. Let D denote the event that Jones has the disease and E the event that the A test result is positive. The desired conditional probability is then

$$\begin{aligned} P(D|E) &= \frac{P(DE)}{P(E)} \\ &= \frac{P(D)P(E|D)}{P(E|D)P(D) + P(E|D^c)P(D^c)} \\ &= \frac{(.6)1}{1(.6) + (.3)(.4)} \\ &= .833 \end{aligned}$$

Note that we have computed the probability of a positive test result by conditioning on whether or not Jones has the disease and then using the fact that because Jones is a diabetic, his conditional probability of a positive result given that he does not have the disease, $P(E|D^c)$, equals .3. Hence, as the doctor should now be more than 80 percent certain that Jones has the disease, she should recommend surgery. $\qquad \blacksquare$

Example 3f

At a certain stage of a criminal investigation, the inspector in charge is 60 percent convinced of the guilt of a certain suspect. Suppose, however, that a *new* piece of evidence which shows that the criminal has a certain characteristic (such as left-handedness, baldness, or brown hair) is uncovered. If 20 percent of the population possesses this characteristic, how certain of the guilt of the suspect should the inspector now be if it turns out that the suspect has the characteristic?

Solution Letting G denote the event that the suspect is guilty and C the event that he possesses the characteristic of the criminal, we have

$$P(G|C) = \frac{P(GC)}{P(C)}$$
$$= \frac{P(C|G)P(G)}{P(C|G)P(G) + P(C|G^c)P(G^c)}$$
$$= \frac{1(.6)}{1(.6) + (.2)(.4)}$$
$$\approx .882$$

where we have supposed that the probability of the suspect having the characteristic if he is, in fact, innocent is equal to .2, the proportion of the population possessing the characteristic. ∎

Example 3g

In the world bridge championships held in Buenos Aires in May 1965, the famous British bridge partnership of Terrence Reese and Boris Schapiro was accused of cheating by using a system of finger signals that could indicate the number of hearts held by the players. Reese and Schapiro denied the accusation, and eventually a hearing was held by the British bridge league. The hearing was in the form of a legal proceeding with prosecution and defense teams, both having the power to call and cross-examine witnesses. During the course of the proceeding, the prosecutor examined specific hands played by Reese and Schapiro and claimed that their playing these hands was consistent with the hypothesis that they were guilty of having illicit knowledge of the heart suit. At this point, the defense attorney pointed out that their play of these hands was also perfectly consistent with their standard line of play. However, the prosecution then argued that as long as their play was consistent with the hypothesis of guilt, it must be counted as evidence toward that hypothesis. What do you think of the reasoning of the prosecution?

Solution The problem is basically one of determining how the introduction of new evidence (in this example, the playing of the hands) affects the probability of a particular hypothesis. If we let H denote a particular hypothesis (such as the hypothesis that Reese and Schapiro are guilty) and E the new evidence, then

$$P(H|E) = \frac{P(HE)}{P(E)}$$
$$= \frac{P(E|H)P(H)}{P(E|H)P(H) + P(E|H^c)[1 - P(H)]} \qquad (3.2)$$

where $P(H)$ is our evaluation of the likelihood of the hypothesis before the introduction of the new evidence. The new evidence will be in support of the hypothesis whenever it makes the hypothesis more likely—that is, whenever $P(H|E) \geq P(H)$. From Equation (3.2), this will be the case whenever

$$P(E|H) \geq P(E|H)P(H) + P(E|H^c)[1 - P(H)]$$

or, equivalently, whenever

$$P(E|H) \geq P(E|H^c)$$

In other words, any new evidence can be considered to be in support of a particular hypothesis only if its occurrence is more likely when the hypothesis is true than when it is false. In fact, the new probability of the hypothesis depends on its initial probability and the ratio of these conditional probabilities, since, from Equation (3.2),

$$P(H|E) = \frac{P(H)}{P(H) + [1 - P(H)]\dfrac{P(E|H^c)}{P(E|H)}}$$

Hence, in the problem under consideration, the play of the cards can be considered to support the hypothesis of guilt only if such play would have been more likely if the partnership were cheating than if it were not. As the prosecutor never made this claim, his assertion that the evidence is in support of the guilt hypothesis is invalid. ∎

Example 3h

Twins can be either identical or fraternal. Identical, also called monozygotic, twins form when a single fertilized egg splits into two genetically identical parts. Consequently, identical twins always have the same set of genes. Fraternal, also called dizygotic, twins develop when two eggs are fertilized and implant in the uterus. The genetic connection of fraternal twins is no more or less the same as siblings born at separate times. A Los Angeles County, California, scientist wishing to know the current fraction of twin pairs born in the county that are identical twins has assigned a county statistician to study this issue. The statistician initially requested each hospital in the county to record all twin births, indicating whether or not the resulting twins were identical. The hospitals, however, told her that to determine whether newborn twins were identical was not a simple task, as it involved the permission of the twins' parents to perform complicated and expensive DNA studies that the hospitals could not afford. After some deliberation, the statistician just asked the hospitals for data listing all twin births along with an indication as to whether the twins were of the same sex. When such data indicated that approximately 64 percent of twin births were same-sexed, the statistician declared that approximately 28 percent of all twins were identical. How did she come to this conclusion?

Solution The statistician reasoned that identical twins are always of the same sex, whereas fraternal twins, having the same relationship to each other as any pair of siblings, will have probability $1/2$ of being of the same sex. Letting I be the event that a pair of twins is identical, and SS be the event that a pair of twins is of the same sex, she computed the probability $P(SS)$ by conditioning on whether the twin pair was identical. This gave

$$P(SS) = P(SS|I)P(I) + P(SS|I^c)P(I^c)$$

or

$$P(SS) = 1 \times P(I) + \frac{1}{2} \times [1 - P(I)] = \frac{1}{2} + \frac{1}{2}P(I)$$

which, using that $P(SS) \approx .64$ yielded the result

$$P(I) \approx .28$$ ∎

The change in the probability of a hypothesis when new evidence is introduced can be expressed compactly in terms of the change in the *odds* of that hypothesis, where the concept of odds is defined as follows.

Definition

The odds of an event A are defined by

$$\frac{P(A)}{P(A^c)} = \frac{P(A)}{1 - P(A)}$$

That is, the odds of an event A tell how much more likely it is that the event A occurs than it is that it does not occur. For instance, if $P(A) = \frac{2}{3}$, then $P(A) = 2P(A^c)$, so the odds are 2. If the odds are equal to α, then it is common to say that the odds are "α to 1" in favor of the hypothesis.

Consider now a hypothesis H that is true with probability $P(H)$, and suppose that new evidence E is introduced. Then, the conditional probabilities, given the evidence E, that H is true and that H is not true are respectively given by

$$P(H|E) = \frac{P(E|H)P(H)}{P(E)} \qquad P(H^c|E) = \frac{P(E|H^c)P(H^c)}{P(E)}$$

Therefore, the new odds after the evidence E has been introduced are

$$\frac{P(H|E)}{P(H^c|E)} = \frac{P(H)}{P(H^c)} \frac{P(E|H)}{P(E|H^c)} \tag{3.3}$$

That is, the new value of the odds of H is the old value multiplied by the ratio of the conditional probability of the new evidence given that H is true to the conditional probability given that H is not true. Thus, Equation (3.3) verifies the result of Example 3f, since the odds, and thus the probability of H, increase whenever the new evidence is more likely when H is true than when it is false. Similarly, the odds decrease whenever the new evidence is more likely when H is false than when it is true.

Example 3i

An urn contains two type A coins and one type B coin. When a type A coin is flipped, it comes up heads with probability 1/4, whereas when a type B coin is flipped, it comes up heads with probability 3/4. A coin is randomly chosen from the urn and flipped. Given that the flip landed on heads, what is the probability that it was a type A coin?

Solution Let A be the event that a type A coin was flipped, and let $B = A^c$ be the event that a type B coin was flipped. We want $P(A|\text{heads})$, where heads is the event that the flip landed on heads. From Equation (3.3), we see that

$$\frac{P(A|\text{heads})}{P(A^c|\text{heads})} = \frac{P(A)}{P(B)} \frac{P(\text{heads}|A)}{P(\text{heads}|B)}$$

$$= \frac{2/3}{1/3} \frac{1/4}{3/4}$$

$$= 2/3$$

Hence, the odds are 2/3 : 1, or, equivalently, the probability is 2/5 that a type A coin was flipped.   ∎

Equation (3.1) may be generalized as follows: Suppose that $F_1, F_2, \ldots, F_n$ are mutually exclusive events such that

$$\bigcup_{i=1}^{n} F_i = S$$

In other words, exactly one of the events $F_1, F_2, \ldots, F_n$ must occur. By writing

$$E = \bigcup_{i=1}^{n} EF_i$$

and using the fact that the events $EF_i, i = 1, \ldots, n$ are mutually exclusive, we obtain

$$P(E) = \sum_{i=1}^{n} P(EF_i)$$
$$= \sum_{i=1}^{n} P(E|F_i)P(F_i) \qquad (3.4)$$

Thus, Equation (3.4), often referred to as the *law of total probability*, shows how, for given events $F_1, F_2, \ldots, F_n$, of which one and only one must occur, we can compute $P(E)$ by first conditioning on which one of the F_i occurs. That is, Equation (3.4) states that $P(E)$ is equal to a weighted average of $P(E|F_i)$, each term being weighted by the probability of the event on which it is conditioned.

Example 3j

In Example 5j of Chapter 2, we considered the probability that, for a randomly shuffled deck, the card following the first ace is some specified card, and we gave a combinatorial argument to show that this probability is $\frac{1}{52}$. Here is a probabilistic argument based on conditioning: Let E be the event that the card following the first ace is some specified card, say, card x. To compute $P(E)$, we ignore card x and condition on the relative ordering of the other 51 cards in the deck. Letting $\mathbf{O}$ be the ordering gives

$$P(E) = \sum_{\mathbf{O}} P(E|\mathbf{O})P(\mathbf{O})$$

Now, given $\mathbf{O}$, there are 52 possible orderings of the cards, corresponding to having card x being the ith card in the deck, $i = 1, \ldots, 52$. But because all $52!$ possible orderings were initially equally likely, it follows that, conditional on $\mathbf{O}$, each of the 52 remaining possible orderings is equally likely. Because card x will follow the first ace for only one of these orderings, we have $P(E|\mathbf{O}) = 1/52$, implying that $P(E) = 1/52$. ∎

Again, let $F_1, \ldots, F_n$ be a set of mutually exclusive and exhaustive events (meaning that exactly one of these events must occur).

Suppose now that E has occurred and we are interested in determining which one of the F_j also occurred. Then, by Equation (3.4), we have the following proposition.

Proposition 3.1

$$P(F_j|E) = \frac{P(EF_j)}{P(E)}$$
$$= \frac{P(E|F_j)P(F_j)}{\sum_{i=1}^{n} P(E|F_i)P(F_i)} \qquad (3.5)$$

Equation (3.5) is known as *Bayes's formula*, after the English philosopher Thomas Bayes. If we think of the events F_j as being possible "hypotheses" about some subject matter, then Bayes's formula may be interpreted as showing us how opinions about these hypotheses held before the experiment was carried out [that is, the $P(F_j)$] should be modified by the evidence produced by the experiment.

Example 3k

A plane is missing, and it is presumed that it was equally likely to have gone down in any of 3 possible regions. Let $1 - \beta_i$, $i = 1, 2, 3$, denote the probability that the plane will be found upon a search of the ith region when the plane is, in fact, in that region. (The constants β_i are called *overlook probabilities*, because they represent the probability of overlooking the plane; they are generally attributable to the geographical and environmental conditions of the regions.) What is the conditional probability that the plane is in the ith region given that a search of region 1 is unsuccessful?

Solution Let R_i, $i = 1, 2, 3$, be the event that the plane is in region i, and let E be the event that a search of region 1 is unsuccessful. From Bayes's formula, we obtain

$$P(R_1|E) = \frac{P(ER_1)}{P(E)}$$

$$= \frac{P(E|R_1)P(R_1)}{\sum_{i=1}^{3} P(E|R_i)P(R_i)}$$

$$= \frac{(\beta_1)\frac{1}{3}}{(\beta_1)\frac{1}{3} + (1)\frac{1}{3} + (1)\frac{1}{3}}$$

$$= \frac{\beta_1}{\beta_1 + 2}$$

For $j = 2, 3$,

$$P(R_j|E) = \frac{P(E|R_j)P(R_j)}{P(E)}$$

$$= \frac{(1)\frac{1}{3}}{(\beta_1)\frac{1}{3} + \frac{1}{3} + \frac{1}{3}}$$

$$= \frac{1}{\beta_1 + 2} \qquad j = 2, 3$$

Note that the updated (that is, the conditional) probability that the plane is in region j, given the information that a search of region 1 did not find it, is greater than the initial probability that it was in region j when $j \neq 1$ and is less than the initial probability when $j = 1$. This statement is certainly intuitive, since not finding the plane in region 1 would seem to decrease its chance of being in that region and increase its chance of being elsewhere. Further, the conditional probability that the plane is in region 1 given an unsuccessful search of that region is an increasing function of the overlook probability β_1. This statement is also intuitive, since the larger β_1 is, the more it is reasonable to attribute the unsuccessful search to "bad luck" as opposed to the plane's not being there. Similarly, $P(R_j|E), j \neq 1$, is a decreasing function of β_1. ■

The next example has often been used by unscrupulous probability students to win money from their less enlightened friends.

Example 3l

Suppose that we have 3 cards that are identical in form, except that both sides of the first card are colored red, both sides of the second card are colored black, and one side of the third card is colored red and the other side black. The 3 cards are mixed up in a hat, and 1 card is randomly selected and put down on the ground. If the upper side of the chosen card is colored red, what is the probability that the other side is colored black?

Solution Let RR, BB, and RB denote, respectively, the events that the chosen card is all red, all black, or the red–black card. Also, let R be the event that the upturned side of the chosen card is red. Then, the desired probability is obtained by

$$P(RB|R) = \frac{P(RB \cap R)}{P(R)}$$

$$= \frac{P(R|RB)P(RB)}{P(R|RR)P(RR) + P(R|RB)P(RB) + P(R|BB)P(BB)}$$

$$= \frac{\left(\frac{1}{2}\right)\left(\frac{1}{3}\right)}{(1)\left(\frac{1}{3}\right) + \left(\frac{1}{2}\right)\left(\frac{1}{3}\right) + 0\left(\frac{1}{3}\right)} = \frac{1}{3}$$

Hence, the answer is $\frac{1}{3}$. Some students guess $\frac{1}{2}$ as the answer by incorrectly reasoning that given that a red side appears, there are two equally likely possibilities: that the card is the all-red card or the red–black card. Their mistake, however, is in assuming that these two possibilities are equally likely. For, if we think of each card as consisting of two distinct sides, then we see that there are 6 equally likely outcomes of the experiment—namely, $R_1, R_2, B_1, B_2, R_3, B_3$—where the outcome is R_1 if the first side of the all-red card is turned face up, R_2 if the second side of the all-red card is turned face up, R_3 if the red side of the red–black card is turned face up, and so on. Since the other side of the upturned red side will be black only if the outcome is R_3, we see that the desired probability is the conditional probability of R_3 given that either R_1 or R_2 or R_3 occurred, which obviously equals $\frac{1}{3}$. ∎

Example 3m

A new couple, known to have two children, has just moved into town. Suppose that the mother is encountered walking with one of her children. If this child is a girl, what is the probability that both children are girls?

Solution Let us start by defining the following events:

G_1: the first (that is, the oldest) child is a girl.

G_2: the second child is a girl.

G: the child seen with the mother is a girl.

Also, let B_1, B_2, and B denote similar events, except that "girl" is replaced by "boy." Now, the desired probability is $P(G_1 G_2|G)$, which can be expressed as follows:

$$P(G_1 G_2|G) = \frac{P(G_1 G_2 G)}{P(G)}$$

$$= \frac{P(G_1 G_2)}{P(G)}$$

Also,

$$P(G) = P(G|G_1G_2)P(G_1G_2) + P(G|G_1B_2)P(G_1B_2)$$

$$+ P(G|B_1G_2)P(B_1G_2) + P(G|B_1B_2)P(B_1B_2)$$

$$= P(G_1G_2) + P(G|G_1B_2)P(G_1B_2) + P(G|B_1G_2)P(B_1G_2)$$

where the final equation used the results $P(G|G_1G_2) = 1$ and $P(G|B_1B_2) = 0$. If we now make the usual assumption that all 4 gender possibilities are equally likely, then we see that

$$P(G_1G_2|G) = \frac{\frac{1}{4}}{\frac{1}{4} + P(G|G_1B_2)/4 + P(G|B_1G_2)/4}$$

$$= \frac{1}{1 + P(G|G_1B_2) + P(G|B_1G_2)}$$

Thus, the answer depends on whatever assumptions we want to make about the conditional probabilities that the child seen with the mother is a girl given the event G_1B_2 and that the child seen with the mother is a girl given the event G_2B_1. For instance, if we want to assume, on the one hand, that, independently of the genders of the children, the child walking with the mother is the elder child with some probability p, then it would follow that

$$P(G|G_1B_2) = p = 1 - P(G|B_1G_2)$$

implying under this scenario that

$$P(G_1G_2|G) = \frac{1}{2}$$

If, on the other hand, we were to assume that if the children are of different genders, then the mother would choose to walk with the girl with probability q, independently of the birth order of the children, then we would have

$$P(G|G_1B_2) = P(G|B_1G_2) = q$$

implying that

$$P(G_1G_2|G) = \frac{1}{1 + 2q}$$

For instance, if we took $q = 1$, meaning that the mother would always choose to walk with a daughter, then the conditional probability that she has two daughters would be $\frac{1}{3}$, which is in accord with Example 2b because seeing the mother with a daughter is now equivalent to the event that she has at least one daughter.

Hence, as stated, the problem is incapable of solution. Indeed, even when the usual assumption about equally likely gender probabilities is made, we still need to make additional assumptions before a solution can be given. This is because the sample space of the experiment consists of vectors of the form s_1, s_2, i, where s_1 is the gender of the older child, s_2 is the gender of the younger child, and i identifies the birth order of the child seen with the mother. As a result, to specify the probabilities of the events of the sample space, it is not enough to make assumptions only about the genders of the children; it is also necessary to assume something about the conditional probabilities as to which child is with the mother given the genders of the children. ∎

Example 3n

A bin contains 3 types of disposable flashlights. The probability that a type 1 flashlight will give more than 100 hours of use is .7, with the corresponding probabilities for type 2 and type 3 flashlights being .4 and .3, respectively. Suppose that 20 percent of the flashlights in the bin are type 1, 30 percent are type 2, and 50 percent are type 3.

(a) What is the probability that a randomly chosen flashlight will give more than 100 hours of use?

(b) Given that a flashlight lasted more than 100 hours, what is the conditional probability that it was a type j flashlight, $j = 1, 2, 3$?

Solution (a) Let A denote the event that the flashlight chosen will give more than 100 hours of use, and let F_j be the event that a type j flashlight is chosen, $j = 1, 2, 3$. To compute $P(A)$, we condition on the type of the flashlight, to obtain

$$P(A) = P(A|F_1)P(F_1) + P(A|F_2)P(F_2) + P(A|F_3)P(F_3)$$
$$= (.7)(.2) + (.4)(.3) + (.3)(.5) = .41$$

There is a 41 percent chance that the flashlight will last for more than 100 hours.

(b) The probability is obtained by using Bayes's formula:

$$P(F_j|A) = \frac{P(AF_j)}{P(A)}$$
$$= \frac{P(A|F_j)P(F_j)}{.41}$$

Thus,

$$P(F_1|A) = (.7)(.2)/.41 = 14/41$$
$$P(F_2|A) = (.4)(.3)/.41 = 12/41$$
$$P(F_3|A) = (.3)(.5)/.41 = 15/41$$

For instance, whereas the initial probability that a type 1 flashlight is chosen is only .2, the information that the flashlight has lasted more than 100 hours raises the probability of this event to $14/41 \approx .341$. ∎

Example 3o

A crime has been committed by a solitary individual, who left some DNA at the scene of the crime. Forensic scientists who studied the recovered DNA noted that only five strands could be identified and that each innocent person, independently, would have a probability of 10^{-5} of having his or her DNA match on all five strands. The district attorney supposes that the perpetrator of the crime could be any of the 1 million residents of the town. Ten thousand of these residents have been released from prison within the past 10 years; consequently, a sample of their DNA is on file. Before any checking of the DNA file, the district attorney thinks that each of the 10,000 ex-criminals has probability α of being guilty of the new crime, whereas each of the remaining 990,000 residents has probability β, where $\alpha = c\beta$. (That is, the district attorney supposes that each recently released convict is c times as likely to be the crime's perpetrator as is each town member who is not a recently released convict.) When the DNA that is analyzed is compared against the database of the 10,000 ex-convicts, it turns out that A. J. Jones is the only one whose DNA matches the profile. Assuming that the district attorney's estimate of the relationship between α and β is accurate, what is the probability that A. J. is guilty?

Solution To begin, note that because probabilities must sum to 1, we have

$$1 = 10{,}000\alpha + 990{,}000\beta = (10{,}000c + 990{,}000)\beta$$

Thus,

$$\beta = \frac{1}{10{,}000c + 990{,}000}, \qquad \alpha = \frac{c}{10{,}000c + 990{,}000}$$

Now, let G be the event that A. J. is guilty, and let M denote the event that A. J. is the only one of the 10,000 on file to have a match. Then,

$$P(G|M) = \frac{P(GM)}{P(M)}$$

$$= \frac{P(G)P(M|G)}{P(M|G)P(G) + P(M|G^c)P(G^c)}$$

On the one hand, if A. J. is guilty, then he will be the only one to have a DNA match if none of the others on file have a match. Therefore,

$$P(M|G) = (1 - 10^{-5})^{9999}$$

On the other hand, if A. J. is innocent, then in order for him to be the only match, his DNA must match (which will occur with probability 10^{-5}), all others in the database must be innocent, and none of these others can have a match. Now, given that A. J. is innocent, the conditional probability that all the others in the database are also innocent is

$$P(\text{all others innocent}|AJ\text{ innocent}) = \frac{P(\text{all in database innocent})}{P(AJ\text{ innocent})}$$

$$= \frac{1 - 10{,}000\alpha}{1 - \alpha}$$

Also, the conditional probability, given their innocence, that none of the others in the database will have a match is $(1 - 10^{-5})^{9999}$. Therefore,

$$P(M|G^c) = 10^{-5}\left(\frac{1 - 10{,}000\alpha}{1 - \alpha}\right)(1 - 10^{-5})^{9999}$$

Because $P(G) = \alpha$, the preceding formula gives

$$P(G|M) = \frac{\alpha}{\alpha + 10^{-5}(1 - 10{,}000\alpha)} = \frac{1}{.9 + \frac{10^{-5}}{\alpha}}$$

Thus, if the district attorney's initial thoughts were that an arbitrary ex-convict was 100 times more likely to have committed the crime than was a nonconvict (that is, $c = 100$), then $\alpha = \frac{1}{19{,}900}$ and

$$P(G|M) = \frac{1}{1.099} \approx 0.9099$$

If the district attorney initially thought that the appropriate ratio was $c = 10$, then $\alpha = \dfrac{1}{109{,}000}$ and

$$P(G|M) = \frac{1}{1.99} \approx 0.5025$$

If the district attorney initially thought that the criminal was equally likely to be any of the members of the town ($c = 1$), then $\alpha = 10^{-6}$ and

$$P(G|M) = \frac{1}{10.9} \approx 0.0917$$

Thus, the probability ranges from approximately 9 percent when the district attorney's initial assumption is that all the members of the population have the same chance of being the perpetrator to approximately 91 percent when she assumes that each ex-convict is 100 times more likely to be the criminal than is a specified townsperson who is not an ex-convict. ∎

3.4 Independent Events

The previous examples in this chapter show that $P(E|F)$, the conditional probability of E given F, is not generally equal to $P(E)$, the unconditional probability of E. In other words, knowing that F has occurred generally changes the chances of E's occurrence. In the special cases where $P(E|F)$ does in fact equal $P(E)$, we say that E is independent of F. That is, E is independent of F if knowledge that F has occurred does not change the probability that E occurs.

Since $P(E|F) = P(EF)/P(F)$, it follows that E is independent of F if

$$P(EF) = P(E)P(F) \tag{4.1}$$

The fact that Equation (4.1) is symmetric in E and F shows that whenever E is independent of F, F is also independent of E. We thus have the following definition.

Definition

Two events E and F are said to be *independent* if Equation (4.1) holds. Two events E and F that are not independent are said to be *dependent*.

Example 4a

A card is selected at random from an ordinary deck of 52 playing cards. If E is the event that the selected card is an ace and F is the event that it is a spade, then E and F are independent. This follows because $P(EF) = \frac{1}{52}$, whereas $P(E) = \frac{4}{52}$ and $P(F) = \frac{13}{52}$. ∎

Example 4b

Two coins are flipped, and all 4 outcomes are assumed to be equally likely. If E is the event that the first coin lands on heads and F the event that the second lands on tails, then E and F are independent, since $P(EF) = P(\{(H, T)\}) = \frac{1}{4}$, whereas $P(E) = P(\{(H, H), (H, T)\}) = \frac{1}{2}$ and $P(F) = P(\{(H, T), (T, T)\}) = \frac{1}{2}$. ∎

Example 4c

Suppose that we toss 2 fair dice. Let E_1 denote the event that the sum of the dice is 6 and F denote the event that the first die equals 4. Then

$$P(E_1 F) = P(\{(4, 2)\}) = \frac{1}{36}$$

whereas

$$P(E_1)P(F) = \left(\frac{5}{36}\right)\left(\frac{1}{6}\right) = \frac{5}{216}$$

Hence, E_1 and F are not independent. Intuitively, the reason for this is clear because if we are interested in the possibility of throwing a 6 (with 2 dice), we shall be quite happy if the first die lands on 4 (or, indeed, on any of the numbers 1, 2, 3, 4, and 5), for then we shall still have a possibility of getting a total of 6. If, however, the first die landed on 6, we would be unhappy because we would no longer have a chance of getting a total of 6. In other words, our chance of getting a total of 6 depends on the outcome of the first die; thus, E_1 and F cannot be independent.

Now, suppose that we let E_2 be the event that the sum of the dice equals 7. Is E_2 independent of F? The answer is yes, since

$$P(E_2F) = P(\{(4,3)\}) = \frac{1}{36}$$

whereas

$$P(E_2)P(F) = \left(\frac{1}{6}\right)\left(\frac{1}{6}\right) = \frac{1}{36}$$

We leave it for the reader to present the intuitive argument why the event that the sum of the dice equals 7 is independent of the outcome on the first die. ∎

Example 4d

If we let E denote the event that the next president is a Republican and F the event that there will be a major earthquake within the next year, then most people would probably be willing to assume that E and F are independent. However, there would probably be some controversy over whether it is reasonable to assume that E is independent of G, where G is the event that there will be a recession within two years after the election. ∎

We now show that if E is independent of F, then E is also independent of F^c.

Proposition 4.1

If E and F are independent, then so are E and F^c.

Proof Assume that E and F are independent. Since $E = EF \cup EF^c$ and EF and EF^c are obviously mutually exclusive, we have

$$P(E) = P(EF) + P(EF^c)$$
$$= P(E)P(F) + P(EF^c)$$

or, equivalently,

$$P(EF^c) = P(E)[1 - P(F)]$$
$$= P(E)P(F^c)$$

and the result is proved. □

Thus, if E is independent of F, then the probability of E's occurrence is unchanged by information as to whether or not F has occurred.

Suppose now that E is independent of F and is also independent of G. Is E then necessarily independent of FG? The answer, somewhat surprisingly, is no, as the following example demonstrates.

Example 4e

Two fair dice are thrown. Let E denote the event that the sum of the dice is 7. Let F denote the event that the first die equals 4 and G denote the event that the second die equals 3. From Example 4c, we know that E is independent of F, and the same reasoning as applied there shows that E is also independent of G; but clearly, E is not independent of FG [since $P(E|FG) = 1$]. ∎

It would appear to follow from Example 4e that an appropriate definition of the independence of three events E, F, and G would have to go further than merely assuming that all of the $\binom{3}{2}$ pairs of events are independent. We are thus led to the following definition.

Definition

Three events E, F, and G are said to be independent if

$$P(EFG) = P(E)P(F)P(G)$$
$$P(EF) = P(E)P(F)$$
$$P(EG) = P(E)P(G)$$
$$P(FG) = P(F)P(G)$$

Note that if E, F, and G are independent, then E will be independent of any event formed from F and G. For instance, E is independent of $F \cup G$, since

$$P[E(F \cup G)] = P(EF \cup EG)$$
$$= P(EF) + P(EG) - P(EFG)$$
$$= P(E)P(F) + P(E)P(G) - P(E)P(FG)$$
$$= P(E)[P(F) + P(G) - P(FG)]$$
$$= P(E)P(F \cup G)$$

Of course, we may also extend the definition of independence to more than three events. The events $E_1, E_2, \ldots, E_n$ are said to be independent if for every subset $E_{1'}, E_{2'}, \ldots, E_{r'}, r \leq n$ of these events,

$$P(E_{1'}E_{2'} \cdots E_{r'}) = P(E_{1'})P(E_{2'}) \cdots P(E_{r'})$$

Finally, we define an infinite set of events to be independent if every finite subset of those events is independent.

Sometimes, a probability experiment under consideration consists of performing a sequence of subexperiments. For instance, if the experiment consists of continually tossing a coin, we may think of each toss as being a subexperiment. In many cases, it is reasonable to assume that the outcomes of any group of the subexperiments have no effect on the probabilities of the outcomes of the other subexperiments. If such is the case, we say that the subexperiments are independent. More formally, we say that the subexperiments are independent if $E_1, E_2, \ldots, E_n, \ldots$ is necessarily an independent sequence of events whenever E_i is an event whose occurrence is completely determined by the outcome of the ith subexperiment.

If each subexperiment has the same set of possible outcomes, then the subexperiments are often called *trials*.

Example 4f

An infinite sequence of independent trials is to be performed. Each trial results in a success with probability p and a failure with probability $1 - p$. What is the probability that

(a) at least 1 success occurs in the first n trials;

(b) exactly k successes occur in the first n trials;

(c) all trials result in successes?

Solution In order to determine the probability of at least 1 success in the first n trials, it is easiest to compute first the probability of the complementary event: that of no successes in the first n trials. If we let E_i denote the event of a failure on the ith trial, then the probability of no successes is, by independence,

$$P(E_1 E_2 \cdots E_n) = P(E_1)P(E_2) \cdots P(E_n) = (1 - p)^n$$

Hence, the answer to part (a) is $1 - (1 - p)^n$.

To compute the answer to part (b), consider any particular sequence of the first n outcomes containing k successes and $n - k$ failures. Each one of these sequences will, by the assumed independence of trials, occur with probability $p^k(1 - p)^{n-k}$. Since there are $\binom{n}{k}$ such sequences [there are $n!/k!(n - k)!$ permutations of k successes and $n - k$ failures], the desired probability in part (b) is

$$P\{\text{exactly } k \text{ successes}\} = \binom{n}{k} p^k (1 - p)^{n-k}$$

To answer part (c), we note that, by part (a), the probability of the first n trials all resulting in success is given by

$$P(E_1^c E_2^c \cdots E_n^c) = p^n$$

Thus, using the continuity property of probabilities (Section 2.6), we see that the desired probability is given by

$$P\left(\bigcap_{i=1}^{\infty} E_i^c\right) = P\left(\lim_{n \to \infty} \bigcap_{i=1}^{n} E_i^c\right)$$

$$= \lim_{n \to \infty} P\left(\bigcap_{i=1}^{n} E_i^c\right)$$

$$= \lim_{n} p^n = \begin{cases} 0 & \text{if } p < 1 \\ 1 & \text{if } p = 1 \end{cases} \qquad \blacksquare$$

Example 4g

A system composed of n separate components is said to be a parallel system if it functions when at least one of the components functions. (See Figure 3.2.) For such a system, if component i, which is independent of the other components, functions with probability $p_i, i = 1, \ldots, n$, what is the probability that the system functions?

Solution Let A_i denote the event that component i functions. Then,

$$P\{\text{system functions}\} = 1 - P\{\text{system does not function}\}$$

$$= 1 - P\{\text{all components do not function}\}$$

$$= 1 - P\left(\bigcap_{i} A_i^c\right)$$

$$= 1 - \prod_{i=1}^{n}(1 - p_i) \quad \text{by independence} \qquad \blacksquare$$

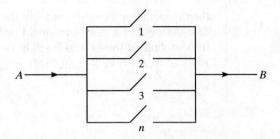

Figure 3.2 Parallel System: Functions if Current Flows from A to B.

Example 4h

Independent trials consisting of rolling a pair of fair dice are performed. What is the probability that an outcome of 5 appears before an outcome of 7 when the outcome of a roll is the sum of the dice?

Solution If we let E_n denote the event that no 5 or 7 appears on the first $n - 1$ trials and a 5 appears on the nth trial, then the desired probability is

$$P\left(\bigcup_{n=1}^{\infty} E_n\right) = \sum_{n=1}^{\infty} P(E_n)$$

Now, since $P\{5 \text{ on any trial}\} = \frac{4}{36}$ and $P\{7 \text{ on any trial}\} = \frac{6}{36}$, we obtain, by the independence of trials,

$$P(E_n) = \left(1 - \frac{10}{36}\right)^{n-1} \frac{4}{36}$$

Thus,

$$P\left(\bigcup_{n=1}^{\infty} E_n\right) = \frac{1}{9} \sum_{n=1}^{\infty} \left(\frac{13}{18}\right)^{n-1}$$

$$= \frac{1}{9} \frac{1}{1 - \frac{13}{18}}$$

$$= \frac{2}{5}$$

This result could also have been obtained by the use of conditional probabilities. If we let E be the event that a 5 occurs before a 7, then we can obtain the desired probability, $P(E)$, by conditioning on the outcome of the first trial, as follows: Let F be the event that the first trial results in a 5, let G be the event that it results in a 7, and let H be the event that the first trial results in neither a 5 nor a 7. Then, conditioning on which one of these events occurs gives

$$P(E) = P(E|F)P(F) + P(E|G)P(G) + P(E|H)P(H)$$

However,

$$P(E|F) = 1$$
$$P(E|G) = 0$$
$$P(E|H) = P(E)$$

The first two equalities are obvious. The third follows because if the first outcome results in neither a 5 nor a 7, then at that point the situation is exactly as it was when the problem first started—namely, the experimenter will continually roll a pair of fair dice until either a 5 or 7 appears. Furthermore, the trials are independent; therefore, the outcome of the first trial will have no effect on subsequent rolls of the dice. Since $P(F) = \frac{4}{36}, P(G) = \frac{6}{36}$, and $P(H) = \frac{26}{36}$, it follows that

$$P(E) = \frac{1}{9} + P(E)\frac{13}{18}$$

or

$$P(E) = \frac{2}{5}$$

The reader should note that the answer is quite intuitive. That is, because a 5 occurs on any roll with probability $\frac{4}{36}$ and a 7 with probability $\frac{6}{36}$, it seems intuitive that the odds that a 5 appears before a 7 should be 6 to 4 against. The probability should then be $\frac{4}{10}$, as indeed it is.

The same argument shows that if E and F are mutually exclusive events of an experiment, then, when independent trials of the experiment are performed, the event E will occur before the event F with probability

$$\frac{P(E)}{P(E) + P(F)}$$ ∎

Example 4i

Suppose there are n types of coupons and that each new coupon collected is, independent of previous selections, a type i coupon with probability p_i, $\sum_{i=1}^{n} p_i = 1$. Suppose k coupons are to be collected. If A_i is the event that there is at least one type i coupon among those collected, then, for $i \neq j$, find

(a) $P(A_i)$

(b) $P(A_i \cup A_j)$

(c) $P(A_i | A_j)$

Solution

$$P(A_i) = 1 - P(A_i^c)$$
$$= 1 - P\{\text{no coupon is type } i\}$$
$$= 1 - (1 - p_i)^k$$

where the preceding used that each coupon is, independently, not of type i with probability $1 - p_i$. Similarly,

$$P(A_i \cup A_j) = 1 - P\left(\left(A_i \cup A_j\right)^c\right)$$
$$= 1 - P\{\text{no coupon is either type } i \text{ or type } j\}$$
$$= 1 - (1 - p_i - p_j)^k$$

where the preceding used that each coupon is, independently, neither of type i nor type j with probability $1 - p_i - p_j$.

To determine $P(A_i | A_j)$, we will use the identity

$$P(A_i \cup A_j) = P(A_i) + P(A_j) - P(A_i A_j)$$

which, in conjunction with parts (a) and (b), yields

$$P(A_i A_j) = 1 - (1 - p_i)^k + 1 - (1 - p_j)^k - [1 - (1 - p_i - p_j)^k]$$
$$= 1 - (1 - p_i)^k - (1 - p_j)^k + (1 - p_i - p_j)^k$$

Consequently,

$$P(A_i|A_j) = \frac{P(A_iA_j)}{P(A_j)} = \frac{1 - (1 - p_i)^k - (1 - p_j)^k + (1 - p_i - p_j)^k}{1 - (1 - p_j)^k} \quad \blacksquare$$

The next example presents a problem that occupies an honored place in the history of probability theory. This is the famous *problem of the points*. In general terms, the problem is this: Two players put up stakes and play some game, with the stakes to go to the winner of the game. An interruption requires them to stop before either has won and when each has some sort of a "partial score." How should the stakes be divided?

This problem was posed to the French mathematician Blaise Pascal in 1654 by the Chevalier de Méré, who was a professional gambler at that time. In attacking the problem, Pascal introduced the important idea that the proportion of the prize deserved by the competitors should depend on their respective probabilities of winning if the game were to be continued at that point. Pascal worked out some special cases and, more importantly, initiated a correspondence with the famous Frenchman Pierre de Fermat, who had a reputation as a great mathematician. The resulting exchange of letters not only led to a complete solution to the problem of the points, but also laid the framework for the solution to many other problems connected with games of chance. This celebrated correspondence, considered by some as the birth date of probability theory, was also important in stimulating interest in probability among the mathematicians in Europe, for Pascal and Fermat were both recognized as being among the foremost mathematicians of the time. For instance, within a short time of their correspondence, the young Dutch mathematician Christiaan Huygens came to Paris to discuss these problems and solutions, and interest and activity in this new field grew rapidly.

Example 4j

The problem of the points

Independent trials resulting in a success with probability p and a failure with probability $1 - p$ are performed. What is the probability that n successes occur before m failures? If we think of A and B as playing a game such that A gains 1 point when a success occurs and B gains 1 point when a failure occurs, then the desired probability is the probability that A would win if the game were to be continued in a position where A needed n and B needed m more points to win.

Solution We shall present two solutions. The first comes from Pascal and the second from Fermat.

Let us denote by $P_{n,m}$ the probability that n successes occur before m failures. By conditioning on the outcome of the first trial, we obtain

$$P_{n,m} = pP_{n-1,m} + (1 - p)P_{n,m-1} \quad n \geq 1, m \geq 1$$

(Why? Reason it out.) Using the obvious boundary conditions $P_{n,0} = 0, P_{0,m} = 1$, we can solve these equations for $P_{n,m}$. Rather than go through the tedious details, let us instead consider Fermat's solution.

Fermat argued that in order for n successes to occur before m failures, it is necessary and sufficient that there be at least n successes in the first $m + n - 1$ trials. (Even if the game were to end before a total of $m + n - 1$ trials were completed, we could still imagine that the necessary additional trials were performed.) This is true, for if there are at least n successes in the first $m + n - 1$ trials, there could be at most $m - 1$ failures in those $m + n - 1$ trials; thus, n successes would occur before m failures. If, however, there were fewer than n successes in the first $m + n - 1$

trials, there would have to be at least m failures in that same number of trials; thus, n successes would not occur before m failures.

Hence, since, as shown in Example 4f, the probability of exactly k successes in $m + n - 1$ trials is $\binom{m + n - 1}{k} p^k (1 - p)^{m+n-1-k}$, it follows that the desired probability of n successes before m failures is

$$P_{n,m} = \sum_{k=n}^{m+n-1} \binom{m + n - 1}{k} p^k (1 - p)^{m+n-1-k} \qquad \blacksquare$$

The following example gives another instance where determining the probability that a player wins a match is made easier by assuming that the play continues even after the match winner has been determined.

Example 4k

Service protocol in a serve and rally game

Consider a serve and rally match (such as volleyball, badminton, or squash) between two players, A and B. The match consists of a sequence of rallies, with each rally beginning with a serve by one of the players and continuing until one of the players has won the rally. The winner of the rally receives a point, and the match ends when one of the players has won a total of n points, with that player being declared the winner of the match. Suppose whenever a rally begins with A as the server, that A wins that rally with probability p_A and that B wins it with probability $q_A = 1 - p_A$, and that a rally that begins with B as the server is won by A with probability p_B and by B with probability $q_B = 1 - p_B$. Player A is to be the initial server. There are two possible server protocols that are under consideration: "winner serves," which means that the winner of a rally is the server for the next rally, or "alternating serve," which means that the server alternates from rally to rally, so that no two consecutive rallies have the same server. Thus, for instance, if $n = 3$, then the successive servers under the "winner serves" protocol would be A, B, A, A if A wins the first point, then B the next, then A wins the next two. On the other hand, the sequence of servers under the "alternating serve" protocol will always be $A, B, A, B, A, \ldots$ until the match winner is decided. If you were player A, which protocol would you prefer?

Solution Surprisingly, it turns out that it makes no difference, in that the probability that A is the match winner is the same under either protocol. To show that this is the case, it is advantageous to suppose that the players continue to play until a total of $2n - 1$ rallies have been completed. The first player to win n rallies would then be the one who has won at least n of the $2n - 1$ rallies. To begin, note that if the alternating serve protocol is being used, then player A will serve exactly n times and player B will serve exactly $n - 1$ times in the $2n - 1$ rallies.

Now consider the winner serve protocol, again assuming that the players continue to play until $2n - 1$ rallies have been completed. Because it makes no difference who serves the "extra rallies" after the match winner has been decided, suppose that at the point at which the match has been decided (because one of the players has won n points), the remainder (if there are any) of the $2n - 1$ rallies are all served by the player who lost the match. Note that this modified service protocol does not change the fact that the winner of the match will still be the player who wins at least n of the $2n - 1$ rallies. We claim that under this modified service protocol, A will always serve n times and B will always serve $n - 1$ times. Two cases show this.

Case 1: A wins the match.
Because A serves first, it follows that A's second serve will immediately follow A's first point; A's third serve will immediately follow A's second point; and, in particular,

A's nth serve will immediately follow A's $(n - 1)$ point. But this will be the last serve of A before the match result is decided. This is so because either A will win the point on that serve and so have n points, or A will lose the point and so the serve will switch to, and remain with, B until A wins point number n. Thus, provided that A wins the match, it follows that A would have served a total of n times at the moment the match is decided. Because, by the modified service protocol, A will never again serve, it follows in this case that A serves exactly n times.

Case 2: B wins the match.
Because A serves first, B's first serve will come immediately after B's first point; B's second serve will come immediately after B's second point; and, in particular, B's $(n - 1)$ serve will come immediately after B's $(n - 1)$ point. But that will be the last serve of B before the match is decided because either B will win the point on that serve and so have n points, or B will lose the point and so the serve will switch to, and remain with, A until B wins point number n. Thus, provided that B wins the match, we see that B would have served a total of $n - 1$ times at the moment the match is decided. Because, by the modified service protocol, B will never again serve, it follows in this case that B serves exactly $n - 1$ times, and, as there are a total of $2n - 1$ rallies, that A serves exactly n times.

Thus, we see that under either protocol, A will always serve n times and B will serve $n - 1$ times and the winner of the match will be the one who wins at least n points. But since A wins each rally that he serves with probability p_A and wins each rally that B serves with probability p_B it follows that the probability that A is the match winner is, under either protocol, equal to the probability that there are at least n successes in $2n - 1$ independent trials, when n of these trials result in a success with probability p_A and the other $n - 1$ trials result in a success with probability p_B. Consequently, the win probabilities for both protocols are the same. ∎

Our next two examples deal with gambling problems, with the first having a surprisingly elegant analysis.*

Example 4l

Suppose that initially there are r players, with player i having n_i units, $n_i > 0$, $i = 1, \ldots, r$. At each stage, two of the players are chosen to play a game, with the winner of the game receiving 1 unit from the loser. Any player whose fortune drops to 0 is eliminated, and this continues until a single player has all $n \equiv \sum_{i=1}^{r} n_i$ units, with that player designated as the victor. Assuming that the results of successive games are independent and that each game is equally likely to be won by either of its two players, find P_i, the probability that player i is the victor.

Solution To begin, suppose that there are n players, with each player initially having 1 unit. Consider player i. Each stage she plays will be equally likely to result in her either winning or losing 1 unit, with the results from each stage being independent. In addition, she will continue to play stages until her fortune becomes either 0 or n. Because this is the same for all n players, it follows that each player has the same chance of being the victor, implying that each player has probability $1/n$ of being the victor. Now, suppose these n players are divided into r teams, with team i containing n_i players, $i = 1, \ldots, r$. Then, the probability that the victor is a member of team i is n_i/n. But because

(a) team i initially has a total fortune of n_i units, $i = 1, \ldots, r$, and

(b) each game played by members of different teams is equally likely to be won by either player and results in the fortune of members of the winning team increasing by 1 and the fortune of the members of the losing team decreasing by *1*,

---

*The remainder of this section should be considered optional.

it is easy to see that the probability that the victor is from team i is exactly the probability we desire. Thus, $P_i = n_i/n$. Interestingly, our argument shows that this result does *not* depend on how the players in each stage are chosen. ∎

In the *gambler's ruin problem*, there are only 2 gamblers, but they are not assumed to be of equal skill.

Example 4m

The gambler's ruin problem

Two gamblers, A and B, bet on the outcomes of successive flips of a coin. On each flip, if the coin comes up heads, A collects 1 unit from B, whereas if it comes up tails, A pays 1 unit to B. They continue to do this until one of them runs out of money. If it is assumed that the successive flips of the coin are independent and each flip results in a head with probability p, what is the probability that A ends up with all the money if he starts with i units and B starts with $N - i$ units?

Solution Let E denote the event that A ends up with all the money when he starts with i and B starts with $N - i$, and to make clear the dependence on the initial fortune of A, let $P_i = P(E)$. We shall obtain an expression for $P(E)$ by conditioning on the outcome of the first flip as follows: Let H denote the event that the first flip lands on heads; then

$$P_i = P(E) = P(E|H)P(H) + P(E|H^c)P(H^c)$$
$$= pP(E|H) + (1 - p)P(E|H^c)$$

Now, given that the first flip lands on heads, the situation after the first bet is that A has $i + 1$ units and B has $N - (i + 1)$. Since the successive flips are assumed to be independent with a common probability p of heads, it follows that from that point on, A's probability of winning all the money is exactly the same as if the game were just starting with A having an initial fortune of $i + 1$ and B having an initial fortune of $N - (i + 1)$. Therefore,

$$P(E|H) = P_{i+1}$$

and similarly,

$$P(E|H^c) = P_{i-1}$$

Hence, letting $q = 1 - p$, we obtain

$$P_i = pP_{i+1} + qP_{i-1} \qquad i = 1, 2, \ldots, N - 1 \tag{4.2}$$

By making use of the obvious boundary conditions $P_0 = 0$ and $P_N = 1$, we shall now solve Equation (4.2). Since $p + q = 1$, these equations are equivalent to

$$pP_i + qP_i = pP_{i+1} + qP_{i-1}$$

or

$$P_{i+1} - P_i = \frac{q}{p}(P_i - P_{i-1}) \qquad i = 1, 2, \ldots, N - 1 \tag{4.3}$$

Hence, since $P_0 = 0$, we obtain, from Equation (4.3),

$$P_2 - P_1 = \frac{q}{p}(P_1 - P_0) = \frac{q}{p}P_1$$

$$P_3 - P_2 = \frac{q}{p}(P_2 - P_1) = \left(\frac{q}{p}\right)^2 P_1$$

$$\vdots$$

$$P_i - P_{i-1} = \frac{q}{p}(P_{i-1} - P_{i-2}) = \left(\frac{q}{p}\right)^{i-1} P_1 \qquad (4.4)$$

$$\vdots$$

$$P_N - P_{N-1} = \frac{q}{p}(P_{N-1} - P_{N-2}) = \left(\frac{q}{p}\right)^{N-1} P_1$$

Adding the first $i - 1$ equations of (4.4) yields

$$P_i - P_1 = P_1\left[\left(\frac{q}{p}\right) + \left(\frac{q}{p}\right)^2 + \cdots + \left(\frac{q}{p}\right)^{i-1}\right]$$

or

$$P_i = \begin{cases} \dfrac{1 - (q/p)^i}{1 - (q/p)}P_1 & \text{if } \dfrac{q}{p} \neq 1 \\[2ex] iP_1 & \text{if } \dfrac{q}{p} = 1 \end{cases}$$

Using the fact that $P_N = 1$, we obtain

$$P_1 = \begin{cases} \dfrac{1 - (q/p)}{1 - (q/p)^N} & \text{if } p \neq \frac{1}{2} \\[2ex] \dfrac{1}{N} & \text{if } p = \frac{1}{2} \end{cases}$$

Hence,

$$P_i = \begin{cases} \dfrac{1 - (q/p)^i}{1 - (q/p)^N} & \text{if } p \neq \frac{1}{2} \\[2ex] \dfrac{i}{N} & \text{if } p = \frac{1}{2} \end{cases} \qquad (4.5)$$

Let Q_i denote the probability that B winds up with all the money when A starts with i and B starts with $N - i$. Then, by symmetry to the situation described, and on replacing p by q and i by $N - i$, it follows that

$$Q_i = \begin{cases} \dfrac{1 - (p/q)^{N-i}}{1 - (p/q)^N} & \text{if } q \neq \frac{1}{2} \\[2ex] \dfrac{N - i}{N} & \text{if } q = \frac{1}{2} \end{cases}$$

Moreover, since $q = \frac{1}{2}$ is equivalent to $p = \frac{1}{2}$, we have, when $q \neq \frac{1}{2}$,

$$P_i + Q_i = \frac{1 - (q/p)^i}{1 - (q/p)^N} + \frac{1 - (p/q)^{N-i}}{1 - (p/q)^N}$$

$$= \frac{p^N - p^N(q/p)^i}{p^N - q^N} + \frac{q^N - q^N(p/q)^{N-i}}{q^N - p^N}$$

$$= \frac{p^N - p^{N-i}q^i - q^N + q^i p^{N-i}}{p^N - q^N}$$

$$= 1$$

This result also holds when $p = q = \frac{1}{2}$, so

$$P_i + Q_i = 1$$

In words, this equation states that with probability 1, either A or B will wind up with all of the money; in other words, the probability that the game continues indefinitely with A's fortune always being between 1 and $N - 1$ is zero. (The reader must be careful because, a priori, there are three possible outcomes of this gambling game, not two: Either A wins, or B wins, or the game goes on forever with nobody winning. We have just shown that this last event has probability 0.)

As a numerical illustration of the preceding result, if A were to start with 5 units and B with 10, then the probability of A's winning would be $\frac{1}{3}$ if p were $\frac{1}{2}$, whereas it would jump to

$$\frac{1 - \left(\frac{2}{3}\right)^5}{1 - \left(\frac{2}{3}\right)^{15}} \approx .87$$

if p were .6.

A special case of the gambler's ruin problem, which is also known as the problem of *duration of play*, was proposed to Huygens by Fermat in 1657. The version Huygens proposed, which he himself solved, was that A and B have 12 coins each. They play for these coins in a game with 3 dice as follows: Whenever 11 is thrown (by either—it makes no difference who rolls the dice), A gives a coin to B. Whenever 14 is thrown, B gives a coin to A. The person who first wins all the coins wins the game. Since $P\{\text{roll } 11\} = \frac{27}{216}$ and $P\{\text{roll } 14\} = \frac{15}{216}$, we see from Example 4h that, for A, this is just the gambler's ruin problem with $p = \frac{15}{42}, i = 12$, and $N = 24$. The general form of the gambler's ruin problem was solved by the mathematician James Bernoulli and published 8 years after his death in 1713.

For an application of the gambler's ruin problem to drug testing, suppose that two new drugs have been developed for treating a certain disease. Drug i has a cure rate $P_i, i = 1, 2$, in the sense that each patient treated with drug i will be cured with probability P_i. These cure rates are, however, not known, and we are interested in finding a method for deciding whether $P_1 > P_2$ or $P_2 > P_1$. To decide on one of these alternatives, consider the following test: Pairs of patients are to be treated sequentially, with one member of the pair receiving drug 1 and the other drug 2. The results for each pair are determined, and the testing stops when the cumulative number of cures from one of the drugs exceeds the cumulative number of cures from the other by some fixed, predetermined number. More formally, let

$$X_j = \begin{cases} 1 & \text{if the patient in the } j\text{th pair that receives drug 1 is cured} \\ 0 & \text{otherwise} \end{cases}$$

$$Y_j = \begin{cases} 1 & \text{if the patient in the } j\text{th pair that receives drug 2 is cured} \\ 0 & \text{otherwise} \end{cases}$$

For a predetermined positive integer M, the test stops after pair N, where N is the first value of n such that either

$$X_1 + \cdots + X_n - (Y_1 + \cdots + Y_n) = M$$

or

$$X_1 + \cdots + X_n - (Y_1 + \cdots + Y_n) = -M$$

In the former case, we assert that $P_1 > P_2$ and in the latter that $P_2 > P_1$.

In order to help ascertain whether the foregoing is a good test, one thing we would like to know is the probability that it leads to an incorrect decision. That is, for given P_1 and P_2, where $P_1 > P_2$, what is the probability that the test will incorrectly assert that $P_2 > P_1$? To determine this probability, note that after each pair is checked, the cumulative difference of cures using drug 1 versus drug 2 will go up by 1 with probability $P_1(1 - P_2)$—since this is the probability that drug 1 leads to a cure and drug 2 does not—or go down by 1 with probability $(1 - P_1)P_2$, or remain the same with probability $P_1P_2 + (1 - P_1)(1 - P_2)$. Hence, if we consider only those pairs in which the cumulative difference changes, then the difference will go up by 1 with probability

$$P = P\{\text{up 1}|\text{up 1 or down 1}\}$$
$$= \frac{P_1(1 - P_2)}{P_1(1 - P_2) + (1 - P_1)P_2}$$

and down by 1 with probability

$$1 - P = \frac{P_2(1 - P_1)}{P_1(1 - P_2) + (1 - P_1)P_2}$$

Thus, the probability that the test will assert that $P_2 > P_1$ is equal to the probability that a gambler who wins each (one-unit) bet with probability P will go down M before going up M. But Equation (4.5), with $i = M, N = 2M$, shows that this probability is given by

$$P\{\text{test asserts that } P_2 > P_1\}$$
$$= 1 - \frac{1 - \left(\frac{1 - P}{P}\right)^M}{1 - \left(\frac{1 - P}{P}\right)^{2M}}$$
$$= 1 - \frac{1}{1 + \left(\frac{1 - P}{P}\right)^M}$$
$$= \frac{1}{1 + \gamma^M}$$

where

$$\gamma = \frac{P}{1 - P} = \frac{P_1(1 - P_2)}{P_2(1 - P_1)}$$

For instance, if $P_1 = .6$ and $P_2 = .4$, then the probability of an incorrect decision is .017 when $M = 5$ and reduces to .0003 when $M = 10$. ∎

Suppose that we are presented with a set of elements and we want to determine whether at least one member of the set has a certain property. We can attack this question probabilistically by randomly choosing an element of the set in such a way that each element has a positive probability of being selected. Then the original question can be answered by a consideration of the probability that the randomly selected element does not have the property of interest. If this probability is equal to 1, then none of the elements of the set has the property; if it is less than 1, then at least one element of the set has the property.

The final example of this section illustrates this technique.

Example 4n

The complete graph having n vertices is defined to be a set of n points (called vertices) in the plane and the $\binom{n}{2}$ lines (called edges) connecting each pair of vertices. The complete graph having 3 vertices is shown in Figure 3.3. Suppose now that each edge in a complete graph having n vertices is to be colored either red or blue. For a fixed integer k, a question of interest is, Is there a way of coloring the edges so that no set of k vertices has all of its $\binom{k}{2}$ connecting edges the same color? It can be shown by a probabilistic argument that if n is not too large, then the answer is yes.

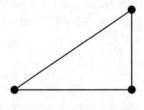

Figure 3.3

The argument runs as follows: Suppose that each edge is, independently, equally likely to be colored either red or blue. That is, each edge is red with probability $\frac{1}{2}$. Number the $\binom{n}{k}$ sets of k vertices and define the events $E_i, i = 1, \ldots, \binom{n}{k}$ as follows:

$$E_i = \{\text{all of the connecting edges of the } i\text{th set}$$
$$\text{of } k \text{ vertices are the same color}\}$$

Now, since each of the $\binom{k}{2}$ connecting edges of a set of k vertices is equally likely to be either red or blue, it follows that the probability that they are all the same color is

$$P(E_i) = 2\left(\frac{1}{2}\right)^{k(k-1)/2}$$

Therefore, because

$$P\left(\bigcup_i E_i\right) \le \sum_i P(E_i) \quad \text{(Boole's inequality)}$$

we find that $P\left(\bigcup_i E_i\right)$, the probability that there is a set of k vertices all of whose connecting edges are similarly colored, satisfies

$$P\left(\bigcup_i E_i\right) \le \binom{n}{k}\left(\frac{1}{2}\right)^{k(k-1)/2-1}$$

Hence, if

$$\binom{n}{k}\left(\frac{1}{2}\right)^{k(k-1)/2-1} < 1$$

or, equivalently, if

$$\binom{n}{k} < 2^{k(k-1)/2-1}$$

then the probability that at least one of the $\binom{n}{k}$ sets of k vertices has all of its connecting edges the same color is less than 1. Consequently, under the preceding condition on n and k, it follows that there is a positive probability that no set of k vertices has all of its connecting edges the same color. But this conclusion implies that there is at least one way of coloring the edges for which no set of k vertices has all of its connecting edges the same color. ∎

Remarks (a) Whereas the preceding argument established a condition on n and k that guarantees the existence of a coloring scheme satisfying the desired property, it gives no information about how to obtain such a scheme (although one possibility would be simply to choose the colors at random, check to see if the resulting coloring satisfies the property, and repeat the procedure until it does).

(b) The method of introducing probability into a problem whose statement is purely deterministic has been called the *probabilistic method*.[†] Other examples of this method are given in Theoretical Exercise 24 and Examples 2t and 2u of Chapter 7.

3.5 $P(\cdot|F)$ Is a Probability

Conditional probabilities satisfy all of the properties of ordinary probabilities, as is proved by Proposition 5.1, which shows that $P(E|F)$ satisfies the three axioms of a probability.

Proposition 5.1

(a) $0 \le P(E|F) \le 1$.

(b) $P(S|F) = 1$.

(c) If $E_i, i = 1, 2, \ldots,$ *are mutually exclusive events, then*

$$P\left(\bigcup_{i=1}^{\infty} E_i | F\right) = \sum_{i=1}^{\infty} P(E_i|F)$$

Proof To prove part (a), we must show that $0 \le P(EF)/P(F) \le 1$. The left-side inequality is obvious, whereas the right side follows because $EF \subset F$, which implies that $P(EF) \le P(F)$. Part (b) follows because

$$P(S|F) = \frac{P(SF)}{P(F)} = \frac{P(F)}{P(F)} = 1$$

[†] See N. Alon, J. Spencer, and P. Erdos, *The Probabilistic Method* (New York: John Wiley & Sons, Inc., 1992).

Part (c) follows from

$$P\left(\bigcup_{i=1}^{\infty} E_i | F\right) = \frac{P\left(\left(\bigcup_{i=1}^{\infty} E_i\right) F\right)}{P(F)}$$

$$= \frac{P\left(\bigcup_{1}^{\infty} E_i F\right)}{P(F)} \quad \text{since} \quad \left(\bigcup_{1}^{\infty} E_i\right) F = \bigcup_{1}^{\infty} E_i F$$

$$= \frac{\sum_{1}^{\infty} P(E_i F)}{P(F)}$$

$$= \sum_{1}^{\infty} P(E_i | F)$$

where the next-to-last equality follows because $E_i E_j = \emptyset$ implies that $E_i F E_j F = \emptyset$. □

If we define $Q(E) = P(E|F)$, then, from Proposition 5.1, $Q(E)$ may be regarded as a probability function on the events of S. Hence, all of the propositions previously proved for probabilities apply to $Q(E)$. For instance, we have

$$Q(E_1 \cup E_2) = Q(E_1) + Q(E_2) - Q(E_1 E_2)$$

or, equivalently,

$$P(E_1 \cup E_2 | F) = P(E_1|F) + P(E_2|F) - P(E_1 E_2|F)$$

Also, if we define the conditional probability $Q(E_1|E_2)$ by $Q(E_1|E_2) = Q(E_1 E_2)/Q(E_2)$, then, from Equation (3.1), we have

$$Q(E_1) = Q(E_1|E_2)Q(E_2) + Q(E_1|E_2^c)Q(E_2^c) \tag{5.1}$$

Since

$$Q(E_1|E_2) = \frac{Q(E_1 E_2)}{Q(E_2)}$$

$$= \frac{P(E_1 E_2|F)}{P(E_2|F)}$$

$$= \frac{\dfrac{P(E_1 E_2 F)}{P(F)}}{\dfrac{P(E_2 F)}{P(F)}}$$

$$= P(E_1|E_2 F)$$

Equation (5.1) is equivalent to

$$P(E_1|F) = P(E_1|E_2 F)P(E_2|F) + P(E_1|E_2^c F)P(E_2^c|F)$$

Example 5a

Consider Example 3a, which is concerned with an insurance company that believes that people can be divided into two distinct classes: those who are accident prone and those who are not. During any given year, an accident-prone person will have an accident with probability .4, whereas the corresponding figure for a person who is not prone to accidents is .2. What is the conditional probability that a new policyholder will have an accident in his or her second year of policy ownership, given that the policyholder has had an accident in the first year?

Solution If we let A be the event that the policyholder is accident prone and we let $A_i, i = 1, 2$, be the event that he or she has had an accident in the ith year, then the desired probability $P(A_2|A_1)$ may be obtained by conditioning on whether or not the policyholder is accident prone, as follows:

$$P(A_2|A_1) = P(A_2|AA_1)P(A|A_1) + P(A_2|A^cA_1)P(A^c|A_1)$$

Now,

$$P(A|A_1) = \frac{P(A_1A)}{P(A_1)} = \frac{P(A_1|A)P(A)}{P(A_1)}$$

However, $P(A)$ is assumed to equal $\frac{3}{10}$, and it was shown in Example 3a that $P(A_1) = .26$. Hence,

$$P(A|A_1) = \frac{(.4)(.3)}{.26} = \frac{6}{13}$$

Thus,

$$P(A^c|A_1) = 1 - P(A|A_1) = \frac{7}{13}$$

Since $P(A_2|AA_1) = .4$ and $P(A_2|A^cA_1) = .2$, it follows that

$$P(A_2|A_1) = (.4)\frac{6}{13} + (.2)\frac{7}{13} \approx .29$$ ∎

Example 5b

A female chimp has given birth. It is not certain, however, which of two male chimps is the father. Before any genetic analysis has been performed, it is believed that the probability that male number 1 is the father is p and the probability that male number 2 is the father is $1 - p$. DNA obtained from the mother, male number 1, and male number 2 indicates that on one specific location of the genome, the mother has the gene pair (A, A), male number 1 has the gene pair (a, a), and male number 2 has the gene pair (A, a). If a DNA test shows that the baby chimp has the gene pair (A, a), what is the probability that male number 1 is the father?

Solution Let all probabilities be conditional on the event that the mother has the gene pair (A, A), male number 1 has the gene pair (a, a), and male number 2 has the gene pair (A, a). Now, let M_i be the event that male number i, $i = 1, 2$, is the father, and let $B_{A,a}$ be the event that the baby chimp has the gene pair (A, a). Then, $P(M_1|B_{A,a})$ is obtained as follows:

$$P(M_1|B_{A,a}) = \frac{P(M_1B_{A,a})}{P(B_{A,a})}$$

$$= \frac{P(B_{A,a}|M_1)P(M_1)}{P(B_{A,a}|M_1)P(M_1) + P(B_{A,a}|M_2)P(M_2)}$$

$$= \frac{1 \cdot p}{1 \cdot p + (1/2)(1 - p)}$$

$$= \frac{2p}{1 + p}$$

Because $\frac{2p}{1+p} > p$ when $p < 1$, the information that the baby's gene pair is (A, a) increases the probability that male number 1 is the father. This result is intuitive because it is more likely that the baby would have gene pair (A, a) if M_1 is true than if M_2 is true (the respective conditional probabilities being 1 and $1/2$). ∎

The next example deals with a problem in the theory of runs.

Example 5c

Independent trials, each resulting in a success with probability p or a failure with probability $q = 1 - p$, are performed. We are interested in computing the probability that a run of n consecutive successes occurs before a run of m consecutive failures.

Solution Let E be the event that a run of n consecutive successes occurs before a run of m consecutive failures. To obtain $P(E)$, we start by conditioning on the outcome of the first trial. That is, letting H denote the event that the first trial results in a success, we obtain

$$P(E) = pP(E|H) + qP(E|H^c) \tag{5.2}$$

Now, given that the first trial was successful, one way we can get a run of n successes before a run of m failures would be to have the next $n - 1$ trials all result in successes. So, let us condition on whether or not that occurs. That is, letting F be the event that trials 2 through n all are successes, we obtain

$$P(E|H) = P(E|FH)P(F|H) + P(E|F^cH)P(F^c|H) \tag{5.3}$$

On the one hand, clearly, $P(E|FH) = 1$; on the other hand, if the event F^cH occurs, then the first trial would result in a success, but there would be a failure some time during the next $n - 1$ trials. However, when this failure occurs, it would wipe out all of the previous successes, and the situation would be exactly as if we started out with a failure. Hence,

$$P(E|F^cH) = P(E|H^c)$$

Because the independence of trials implies that F and H are independent, and because $P(F) = p^{n-1}$, it follows from Equation (5.3) that

$$P(E|H) = p^{n-1} + (1 - p^{n-1})P(E|H^c) \tag{5.4}$$

We now obtain an expression for $P(E|H^c)$ in a similar manner. That is, we let G denote the event that trials 2 through m are all *failures*. Then,

$$P(E|H^c) = P(E|GH^c)P(G|H^c) + P(E|G^cH^c)P(G^c|H^c) \tag{5.5}$$

Now, GH^c is the event that the first m trials all result in failures, so $P(E|GH^c) = 0$. Also, if G^cH^c occurs, then the first trial is a failure, but there is at least one success in the next $m - 1$ trials. Hence, since this success wipes out all previous failures, we see that

$$P(E|G^cH^c) = P(E|H)$$

Thus, because $P(G^c|H^c) = P(G^c) = 1 - q^{m-1}$, we obtain, from (5.5),

$$P(E|H^c) = (1 - q^{m-1})P(E|H) \tag{5.6}$$

Solving Equations (5.4) and (5.6) yields

$$P(E|H) = \frac{p^{n-1}}{p^{n-1} + q^{m-1} - p^{n-1}q^{m-1}}$$

and

$$P(E|H^c) = \frac{(1 - q^{m-1})p^{n-1}}{p^{n-1} + q^{m-1} - p^{n-1}q^{m-1}}$$

Thus,

$$P(E) = pP(E|H) + qP(E|H^c)$$

$$= \frac{p^n + qp^{n-1}(1 - q^{m-1})}{p^{n-1} + q^{m-1} - p^{n-1}q^{m-1}}$$

$$= \frac{p^{n-1}(1 - q^m)}{p^{n-1} + q^{m-1} - p^{n-1}q^{m-1}} \tag{5.7}$$

It is interesting to note that by the symmetry of the problem, the probability of obtaining a run of m failures before a run of n successes would be given by Equation (5.7) with p and q interchanged and n and m interchanged. Hence, this probability would equal

$$P\{\text{run of } m \text{ failures before a run of } n \text{ successes}\}$$

$$= \frac{q^{m-1}(1 - p^n)}{q^{m-1} + p^{n-1} - q^{m-1}p^{n-1}} \tag{5.8}$$

Since Equations (5.7) and (5.8) sum to 1, it follows that, with probability 1, either a run of n successes or a run of m failures will eventually occur.

As an example of Equation (5.7), we note that, in tossing a fair coin, the probability that a run of 2 heads will precede a run of 3 tails is $\frac{7}{10}$. For 2 consecutive heads before 4 consecutive tails, the probability rises to $\frac{5}{6}$. ∎

In our next example, we return to a matching problem and obtain a solution by using conditional probabilities.

Example 5d

At a party, n men take off their hats. The hats are then mixed up, and each man randomly selects one. We say that a match occurs if a man selects his own hat. What is the probability of

(a) no matches?

(b) exactly k matches? ∎

Solution (a) Let E denote the event that no matches occur, and to make explicit the dependence on n, write $P_n = P(E)$. We start by conditioning on whether or not the first man selects his own hat—call these events M and M^c, respectively. Then,

$$P_n = P(E) = P(E|M)P(M) + P(E|M^c)P(M^c)$$

Clearly, $P(E|M) = 0$, so

$$P_n = P(E|M^c)\frac{n - 1}{n} \tag{5.9}$$

Now, $P(E|M^c)$ is the probability of no matches when $n - 1$ men select from a set of $n - 1$ hats that does not contain the hat of one of these men. This can happen in either of two mutually exclusive ways: Either there are no matches and the extra man does not select the extra hat (this being the hat of the man who chose first) or there are no matches and the extra man does select the extra hat. The probability of the first of these events is just P_{n-1}, which is seen by regarding the extra hat as "belonging" to the extra man. Because the second event has probability $[1/(n - 1)]P_{n-2}$, we have

$$P(E|M^c) = P_{n-1} + \frac{1}{n - 1}P_{n-2}$$

Thus, from Equation (5.9),

$$P_n = \frac{n-1}{n}P_{n-1} + \frac{1}{n}P_{n-2}$$

or, equivalently,

$$P_n - P_{n-1} = -\frac{1}{n}(P_{n-1} - P_{n-2}) \tag{5.10}$$

However, since P_n is the probability of no matches when n men select among their own hats, we have

$$P_1 = 0 \qquad P_2 = \frac{1}{2}$$

So, from Equation (5.10),

$$P_3 - P_2 = -\frac{(P_2 - P_1)}{3} = -\frac{1}{3!} \quad \text{or} \quad P_3 = \frac{1}{2!} - \frac{1}{3!}$$

$$P_4 - P_3 = -\frac{(P_3 - P_2)}{4} = \frac{1}{4!} \quad \text{or} \quad P_4 = \frac{1}{2!} - \frac{1}{3!} + \frac{1}{4!}$$

and, in general,

$$P_n = \frac{1}{2!} - \frac{1}{3!} + \frac{1}{4!} - \cdots + \frac{(-1)^n}{n!}$$

(b) To obtain the probability of exactly k matches, we consider any fixed group of k men. The probability that they, and only they, select their own hats is

$$\frac{1}{n}\frac{1}{n-1} \cdots \frac{1}{n-(k-1)}P_{n-k} = \frac{(n-k)!}{n!}P_{n-k}$$

where P_{n-k} is the conditional probability that the other $n-k$ men, selecting among their own hats, have no matches. Since there are $\binom{n}{k}$ choices of a set of k men, the desired probability of exactly k matches is

$$\frac{P_{n-k}}{k!} = \frac{\frac{1}{2!} - \frac{1}{3!} + \cdots + \frac{(-1)^{n-k}}{(n-k)!}}{k!} \qquad \blacksquare$$

An important concept in probability theory is that of the conditional independence of events. We say that the events E_1 and E_2 are *conditionally independent* given F if given that F occurs, the conditional probability that E_1 occurs is unchanged by information as to whether or not E_2 occurs. More formally, E_1 and E_2 are said to be conditionally independent given F if

$$P(E_1|E_2F) = P(E_1|F) \tag{5.11}$$

or, equivalently,

$$P(E_1E_2|F) = P(E_1|F)P(E_2|F) \tag{5.12}$$

The notion of conditional independence can easily be extended to more than two events, and this extension is left as an exercise.

The reader should note that the concept of conditional independence was implicitly employed in Example 5a, where it was assumed that the events that a policyholder had an accident in his or her ith year, $i = 1, 2, \ldots$, were conditionally independent given whether or not the person was accident prone. The following example, sometimes referred to as *Laplace's rule of succession*, further illustrates the concept of conditional independence.

Example 5e

Laplace's rule of succession

There are $k + 1$ coins in a box. When flipped, the ith coin will turn up heads with probability i/k, $i = 0, 1, \ldots, k$. A coin is randomly selected from the box and is then repeatedly flipped. If the first n flips all result in heads, what is the conditional probability that the $(n + 1)$ flip will do likewise?

Solution Let C_i denote the event that the ith coin, $i = 0, 1, \ldots, k$, is initially selected; let F_n denote the event that the first n flips all result in heads; and let H be the event that the $(n + 1)$ flip is a head. The desired probability, $P(H|F_n)$, is now obtained as follows:

$$P(H|F_n) = \sum_{i=0}^{k} P(H|F_n C_i) P(C_i|F_n)$$

Now, given that the ith coin is selected, it is reasonable to assume that the outcomes will be conditionally independent, with each one resulting in a head with probability i/k. Hence,

$$P(H|F_n C_i) = P(H|C_i) = \frac{i}{k}$$

Also,

$$P(C_i|F_n) = \frac{P(C_i F_n)}{P(F_n)} = \frac{P(F_n|C_i)P(C_i)}{\sum_{j=0}^{k} P(F_n|C_j)P(C_j)} = \frac{(i/k)^n[1/(k+1)]}{\sum_{j=0}^{k} (j/k)^n[1/(k+1)]}$$

Thus,

$$P(H|F_n) = \frac{\sum_{i=0}^{k}(i/k)^{n+1}}{\sum_{j=0}^{k}(j/k)^n}$$

But if k is large, we can use the integral approximations

$$\frac{1}{k}\sum_{i=0}^{k}\left(\frac{i}{k}\right)^{n+1} \approx \int_0^1 x^{n+1}dx = \frac{1}{n+2}$$

$$\frac{1}{k}\sum_{j=0}^{k}\left(\frac{j}{k}\right)^{n} \approx \int_0^1 x^{n}dx = \frac{1}{n+1}$$

So, for k large,

$$P(H|F_n) \approx \frac{n+1}{n+2} \qquad \blacksquare$$

Example 5f

Updating information sequentially

Suppose there are n mutually exclusive and exhaustive possible hypotheses, with initial (sometimes referred to as *prior*) probabilities $P(H_i)$, $\sum_{i=1}^{n} P(H_i) = 1$. Now, if information that the event E has occurred is received, then the conditional probability that H_i is the true hypothesis (sometimes referred to as the *updated* or *posterior* probability of H_i) is

$$P(H_i|E) = \frac{P(E|H_i)P(H_i)}{\sum_j P(E|H_j)P(H_j)} \tag{5.13}$$

Suppose now that we learn first that E_1 has occurred and then that E_2 has occurred. Then, given only the first piece of information, the conditional probability that H_i is the true hypothesis is

$$P(H_i|E_1) = \frac{P(E_1|H_i)P(H_i)}{P(E_1)} = \frac{P(E_1|H_i)P(H_i)}{\sum_j P(E_1|H_j)P(H_j)}$$

whereas given both pieces of information, the conditional probability that H_i is the true hypothesis is $P(H_i|E_1E_2)$, which can be computed by

$$P(H_i|E_1E_2) = \frac{P(E_1E_2|H_i)P(H_i)}{\sum_j P(E_1E_2|H_j)P(H_j)}$$

One might wonder, however, when one can compute $P(H_i|E_1E_2)$ by using the right side of Equation (5.13) with $E = E_2$ and with $P(H_j)$ replaced by $P(H_j|E_1)$, $j = 1,\ldots,n$. That is, when is it legitimate to regard $P(H_j|E_1)$, $j \geq 1$, as the prior probabilities and then use (5.13) to compute the posterior probabilities?

Solution The answer is that the preceding is legitimate, provided that for each $j = 1,\ldots,n$, the events E_1 and E_2 are conditionally independent, given H_j. For if this is the case, then

$$P(E_1E_2|H_j) = P(E_2|H_j)P(E_1|H_j), \quad j = 1,\ldots,n$$

Therefore,

$$\begin{aligned}
P(H_i|E_1E_2) &= \frac{P(E_2|H_i)P(E_1|H_i)P(H_i)}{P(E_1E_2)} \\
&= \frac{P(E_2|H_i)P(E_1H_i)}{P(E_1E_2)} \\
&= \frac{P(E_2|H_i)P(H_i|E_1)P(E_1)}{P(E_1E_2)} \\
&= \frac{P(E_2|H_i)P(H_i|E_1)}{Q(1,2)}
\end{aligned}$$

where $Q(1,2) = \frac{P(E_1E_2)}{P(E_1)}$. Since the preceding equation is valid for all i, we obtain, upon summing,

$$1 = \sum_{i=1}^{n} P(H_i|E_1E_2) = \sum_{i=1}^{n} \frac{P(E_2|H_i)P(H_i|E_1)}{Q(1,2)}$$

showing that

$$Q(1,2) = \sum_{i=1}^{n} P(E_2|H_i)P(H_i|E_1)$$

and yielding the result

$$P(H_i|E_1E_2) = \frac{P(E_2|H_i)P(H_i|E_1)}{\sum_{i=1}^{n} P(E_2|H_i)P(H_i|E_1)}$$

For instance, suppose that one of two coins is chosen to be flipped. Let H_i be the event that coin i, $i = 1, 2$, is chosen, and suppose that when coin i is flipped, it lands on heads with probability p_i, $i = 1, 2$. Then, the preceding equations show that to sequentially update the probability that coin 1 is the one being flipped, given the results of the previous flips, all that must be saved after each new flip is the conditional probability that coin 1 is the coin being used. That is, it is not necessary to keep track of all earlier results. ∎

Summary

For events E and F, the conditional probability of E given that F has occurred is denoted by $P(E|F)$ and is defined by

$$P(E|F) = \frac{P(EF)}{P(F)}$$

The identity

$$P(E_1E_2 \cdots E_n) = P(E_1)P(E_2|E_1) \cdots P(E_n|E_1 \cdots E_{n-1})$$

is known as the *multiplication rule* of probability.

A valuable identity is

$$P(E) = P(E|F)P(F) + P(E|F^c)P(F^c)$$

which can be used to compute $P(E)$ by "conditioning" on whether F occurs.

$P(H)/P(H^c)$ is called the *odds* of the event H. The identity

$$\frac{P(H|E)}{P(H^c|E)} = \frac{P(H)}{P(H^c)} \frac{P(E|H)}{P(E|H^c)}$$

shows that when new evidence E is obtained, the value of the odds of H becomes its old value multiplied by the ratio of the conditional probability of the new evidence when H is true to the conditional probability when H is not true.

Let F_i, $i = 1, \ldots, n$, be mutually exclusive events whose union is the entire sample space. The identity

$$P(F_j|E) = \frac{P(E|F_j)P(F_j)}{\sum_{i=1}^{n} P(E|F_i)P(F_i)}$$

is known as *Bayes's formula*. If the events F_i, $i = 1, \ldots, n$, are competing hypotheses, then Bayes's formula shows how to compute the conditional probabilities of these hypotheses when additional evidence E becomes available.

The denominator of Bayes's formula uses that

$$P(E) = \sum_{i=1}^{n} P(E|F_i)P(F_i)$$

which is called the *law of total probability*.

If $P(EF) = P(E)P(F)$, then we say that the events E and F are *independent*. This condition is equivalent to $P(E|F) = P(E)$ and to $P(F|E) = P(F)$. Thus, the events E and F are independent if knowledge of the occurrence of one of them does not affect the probability of the other.

The events $E_1, \ldots, E_n$ are said to be independent if, for any subset $E_{i_1}, \ldots, E_{i_r}$ of them,

$$P(E_{i_1} \cdots E_{i_r}) = P(E_{i_1}) \cdots P(E_{i_r})$$

For a fixed event F, $P(E|F)$ can be considered to be a probability function on the events E of the sample space.

Problems

3.1. Two fair dice are rolled. What is the conditional probability that at least one lands on 6 given that the dice land on different numbers?

3.2. A bag contains blue and red balls. Two balls are drawn randomly without replacement. The probability of selecting a red and then a blue ball is 0.4. The probability of selecting a red ball in the first draw is 0.5. What is the probability of drawing a blue ball, given that the first ball drawn was red?

3.3. We roll an unbiased die and let A be the event that die shows either 3 or 4. Also let B be the event that the even number appears.
(a) Obtain $P(A|B)$
(b) Are A and B independent?

3.4. What is the probability that at least one of a pair of fair dice lands on 6, given that the sum of the dice is i, $i = 2, 3, \ldots, 12$?

3.5. An urn contains 6 white and 9 black balls. If 4 balls are to be randomly selected without replacement, what is the probability that the first 2 selected are white and the last 2 black?

3.6. Consider an urn containing 12 balls, of which 8 are white. A sample of size 4 is to be drawn with replacement (without replacement). What is the conditional probability (in each case) that the first and third balls drawn will be white given that the sample drawn contains exactly 3 white balls?

3.7. The king comes from a family of 2 children. What is the probability that the other child is his sister?

3.8. Consider a deck of fifty two cards. We draw two cards without replacement and let A be the event that first card is ace and B be the event that both the cards are ace. What is the conditional probability of B given A?

3.9. Consider 3 urns. Urn A contains 2 white and 4 red balls, urn B contains 8 white and 4 red balls, and urn C contains 1 white and 3 red balls. If 1 ball is selected from each urn, what is the probability that the ball chosen from urn A was white given that exactly 2 white balls were selected?

3.10. Three cards are randomly selected, without replacement, from an ordinary deck of 52 playing cards. Compute the conditional probability that the first card selected is a spade given that the second and third cards are spades.

3.11. Two cards are randomly chosen without replacement from an ordinary deck of 52 cards. Let B be the event that both cards are aces, let A_s be the event that the ace of spades is chosen, and let A be the event that at least one ace is chosen. Find

(a) $P(B|A_s)$

(b) $P(B|A)$

3.12. A recent college graduate is planning to take the first three actuarial examinations in the coming summer. She will take the first actuarial exam in June. If she passes that exam, then she will take the second exam in July, and if she also passes that one, then she will take the third exam in September. If she fails an exam, then she is not allowed to take any others. The probability that she passes the first exam is .9. If she passes the first exam, then the conditional probability that she passes the second one is .8, and if she passes both the first and the second exams, then the conditional probability that she passes the third exam is .7.

(a) What is the probability that she passes all three exams?

(b) Given that she did not pass all three exams, what is the conditional probability that she failed the second exam?

3.13. Suppose that an ordinary deck of 52 cards (which contains 4 aces) is randomly divided into 4 hands of 13 cards each. We are interested in determining p, the probability that each hand has an ace. Let E_i be the event that the ith hand has exactly one ace. Determine $p = P(E_1 E_2 E_3 E_4)$ by using the multiplication rule.

3.14. Consider a deck of fifty two cards. We draw four cards without replacement. What is the probability that all are from different suits?

3.15. Suppose the frequency of the disease in a particular population is 0.2. A laboratory test is highly accurate with a 0.05 false positive probability and a false 0.1 negative probability. If ones test is positive what is the probability that he has the no disease?

3.16. Consider a deck of fifty two cards. We draw three cards without replacement. Find the probability of obtaining at least one ace if

(a) all the card are from different suits.

(b) all are from same suit.

3.17. Probability of 2 children to be twins is given as 2% and probability of them being identical twins is 0.16%. If both genders are equally likely and identical twins always belong to the same gender, then find the probability that the children are identical twins given that they are both twin boys?

3.18. A total of 46 percent of the voters in a certain city classify themselves as Independents, whereas 30 percent classify themselves as Liberals and 24 percent say that they are Conservatives. In a recent local election, 35 percent of the Independents, 62 percent of the Liberals, and 58 percent of the Conservatives voted. A voter is chosen at random. Given that this person voted in the local election, what is the probability that he or she is

(a) an Independent?

(b) a Liberal?

(c) a Conservative?

(d) What percent of voters participated in the local election?

3.19. A lie detector catches 90% of lies, but it also has the defect that it wrongly classify a truth as a lie with probability 0.05. 100 persons are taken for testing this detector of which half of them are told to tell a lie and the other half the truth.

(a) If a person is randomly selected from the group and the detector says he is telling the truth. What is the probability that it is actually telling the truth?

(b) If the machine claims he lied, what is the probability that he indeed lied?

3.20. In a multiple choice examination with four optional answers for each question, student knows the answer with probability 4/5. And make a random guess with probability 1/5. If a particular question was found to be correct, what is the probability that he actually new the answer?

3.21. A total of 500 married working couples were polled about their annual salaries, with the following information resulting:

Wife	Husband	
	Less than $25,000	More than $25,000
Less than $25,000	212	198
More than $25,000	36	54

For instance, in 36 of the couples, the wife earned more and the husband earned less than $25,000. If one of the couples is randomly chosen, what is

(a) the probability that the husband earns less than $25,000?

(b) the conditional probability that the wife earns more than $25,000 given that the husband earns more than this amount?

(c) the conditional probability that the wife earns more than $25,000 given that the husband earns less than this amount?

3.22. A red die, a blue die, and a yellow die (all six sided) are rolled. We are interested in the probability that the number appearing on the blue die is less than that appearing on the yellow die, which is less than that appearing on the red die. That is, with B, Y, and R denoting, respectively, the number appearing on the blue, yellow, and red die, we are interested in $P(B < Y < R)$.

(a) What is the probability that no two of the dice land on the same number?

(b) Given that no two of the dice land on the same number, what is the conditional probability that $B < Y < R$?

(c) What is $P(B < Y < R)$?

3.23. A player was told that in a casino there are two slot machines $M1$ and $M2$ with different pay-offs. One machine had a winning chance of 30% and another had a 20% chance for winning. But, the player forgot to ask which was the machines having these pay offs and he went ahead and played $M1$. If he won the prize what is the probability that $M1$ was the machine with higher pay off? Would it be different if he lost the prize?

3.24. Consider a game between two players A and B where each player toss an unbiased coin. Whoever first obtain the head wins the game. If the player A starts the game, what is the probability that he will win it?

3.25. The following method was proposed to estimate the number of people over the age of 50 who reside in a town of known population 100,000: "As you walk along the streets, keep a running count of the percentage of people you encounter who are over 50. Do this for a few days; then multiply the percentage you obtain by 100,000 to obtain the estimate." Comment on this method.

Hint: Let p denote the proportion of people in the town who are over 50. Furthermore, let α_1 denote the proportion of time that a person under the age of 50 spends in the streets, and let α_2 be the corresponding value for those over 50. What quantity does the method suggested estimate? When is the estimate approximately equal to p?

3.26. In a random experiment of rolling a fair die, Let A and B be the event of obtaining an even number and odd number, respectively. Let C be the event of obtaining either 5 or 6.

(a) What is the probability of obtaining A given C

(b) Are B and C independent?

(c) Are A, B and C independent?

3.27. Consider a game between two players A and B. The player A starts the game by tossing a coin once and he wins the game if head appears. If tails appears the player B tosses the coin two times and he wins the game if the toss results in least one head. What is the probability that

(a) the player A will win the game?

(b) the player B will win the game?

3.28. Suppose that an ordinary deck of 52 cards is shuffled and the cards are then turned over one at a time until the first ace appears. Given that the first ace is the 20th card to appear, what is the conditional probability that the card following it is the

(a) ace of spades?

(b) two of clubs?

3.29. What is the probability of obtaining a sum of 13 when rolling a three fair dice given that the first roll resulted in a six?

3.30. Probability of detecting a cancer in laboratory test is 0.95. Probability of incorrectly diagnosing that a person has cancer is 0.1. If there are 100 number of cancer patients in a population of two thousand people, find the probability that a person diagnosed with cancer is actually suffering from cancer?

3.31. Ms. Aquina has just had a biopsy on a possibly cancerous tumor. Not wanting to spoil a weekend family event, she does not want to hear any bad news in the next few days. But if she tells the doctor to call only if the news is good, then if the doctor does not call, Ms. Aquina can conclude that the news is bad. So, being a student of probability, Ms. Aquina instructs the doctor to flip a coin. If it comes up heads, the doctor is to call if the news is good and not call if the news is bad. If the coin comes up tails, the doctor is not to call. In this way, even if the doctor doesn't call, the news is not necessarily bad. Let α be the probability that the tumor is cancerous; let β be the conditional probability that the tumor is cancerous given that the doctor does not call.

(a) Which should be larger, α or β?

(b) Find β in terms of α, and prove your answer in part (a).

3.32. A family has j children with probability p_j, where $p_1 = .1, p_2 = .25, p_3 = .35, p_4 = .3$. A child from this family is randomly chosen. Given that this child is the eldest child in the family, find the conditional probability that the family has

(a) only 1 child;

(b) 4 children.

Redo (a) and (b) when the randomly selected child is the youngest child of the family.

3.33. Meteorology department predict the rain correctly with probability 4/5. When rain is predicted Amit travels by his car. When rain is not forecasted, he travels with his car with probability 0.5. Assuming that it rains in a day with probability 1/2. Find the probability that Amit does not travel by car given it rains?

3.34. In an archery championship, a competitor hits the target at the first attempt with probability 0.8. If he hits the target, his confidence increases and the probability that he hits the target again in the next attempt is 0.9. If he misses an attempt, he loses confidence and in the next attempt he only has a 0.5 chance of hinting the target. Find the probability that in 3 attempts,

(a) the target is hit all the 3 times.

(b) the target is only hit once.

3.35. With probability .6, the present was hidden by mom; with probability .4, it was hidden by dad. When mom hides the present, she hides it upstairs 70 percent of the time and downstairs 30 percent of the time. Dad is equally likely to hide it upstairs or downstairs.

(a) What is the probability that the present is upstairs?

(b) Given that it is downstairs, what is the probability it was hidden by dad?

3.36. In a random experiment of rolling a fair die, Let A and B be the event of obtaining an even number and odd number, respectively. Let C be the event of obtaining a number greater than 3.

(a) What is the probability of obtaining A given C?

(b) What is the probability of obtaining B given C?

(c) Are A, B and C independent?

3.37. (a) A gambler has a fair coin and a two-headed coin in his pocket. He selects one of the coins at random; when he flips it, it shows heads. What is the probability that it is the fair coin?

(b) Suppose that he flips the same coin a second time and, again, it shows heads. Now what is the probability that it is the fair coin?

(c) Suppose that he flips the same coin a third time and it shows tails. Now what is the probability that it is the fair coin?

3.38. Urn A has 5 white and 7 black balls. Urn B has 3 white and 12 black balls. We flip a fair coin. If the outcome is heads, then a ball from urn A is selected, whereas if the outcome is tails, then a ball from urn B is selected. Suppose that a white ball is selected. What is the probability that the coin landed tails?

3.39. In Example 3a, what is the probability that someone has an accident in the second year given that he or she had no accidents in the first year?

3.40. Consider a sample of size 3 drawn in the following manner: We start with an urn containing 5 white and 7 red balls. At each stage, a ball is drawn and its color is noted. The ball is then returned to the urn, along with an additional ball of the same color. Find the probability that the sample will contain exactly

(a) 0 white balls;

(b) 1 white ball;

(c) 3 white balls;

(d) 2 white balls.

3.41. A deck of cards is shuffled and then divided into two halves of 26 cards each. A card is drawn from one of the halves; it turns out to be an ace. The ace is then placed in the second half-deck. The half is then shuffled, and a card is drawn from it. Compute the probability that this drawn card is an ace.

Hint: Condition on whether or not the interchanged card is selected.

3.42. Twelve percent of all U.S. households are in California. A total of 1.3 percent of all U.S. households earn more than $250,000 per year, while a total of 3.3 percent of all California households earn more than $250,000 per year.

(a) What proportion of all non-California households earn more than $250,000 per year?

(b) Given that a randomly chosen U.S. household earns more than $250,000 per year, what is the probability it is a California household?

3.43. Consider a random experiment of tossing a coin and rolling a die. If the toss resulted in head, then we roll the die once. If it resulted in tail, then we rolled the die twice. If the die shows at least one six, what is the probability that the coin toss resulted in head?

3.44. A fair die is rolled and if it shows a multiple of 3, a white ball is placed in an empty box. Otherwise a black ball is placed in the box. If the die is rolled five times, find the probability that the box contain exactly two white balls, given that the first roll resulted in a 6.

3.45. Suppose we have 10 coins such that if the ith coin is flipped, heads will appear with probability $i/10, i = 1, 2, \ldots, 10$. When one of the coins is randomly selected and flipped, it shows heads. What is the conditional probability that it was the fifth coin?

3.46. In any given year, a male automobile policyholder will make a claim with probability p_m and a female policyholder will make a claim with probability p_f, where $p_f \neq p_m$. The fraction of the policyholders that are male is $\alpha, 0 < \alpha < 1$. A policyholder is randomly chosen. If A_i denotes the event that this policyholder will make a claim in year i, show that

$$P(A_2|A_1) > P(A_1)$$

Give an intuitive explanation of why the preceding inequality is true.

3.47. An urn contains 5 white and 10 black balls. A fair die is rolled and that number of balls is randomly chosen from the urn. What is the probability that all of the balls selected are white? What is the conditional probability that the die landed on 3 if all the balls selected are white?

3.48. A box contains 10 red balls and 20 blue balls. A ball is drawn at random and its color is noted and return it to the box for the next draw.
(a) Find the probability that first red ball is drawn on the third draw.
(b) What is the probability in if the ball once drawn is not replaced?

3.49. Prostate cancer is the most common type of cancer found in males. As an indicator of whether a male has prostate cancer, doctors often perform a test that measures the level of the prostate-specific antigen (PSA) that is produced only by the prostate gland. Although PSA levels are indicative of cancer, the test is notoriously unreliable. Indeed, the probability that a noncancerous man will have an elevated PSA level is approximately .135, increasing to approximately .268 if the man does have cancer. If, on the basis of other factors, a physician is 70 percent certain that a male has prostate cancer, what is the conditional probability that he has the cancer given that

(a) the test indicated an elevated PSA level?
(b) the test did not indicate an elevated PSA level?

Repeat the preceding calculation, this time assuming that the physician initially believes that there is a 30 percent chance that the man has prostate cancer.

3.50. Suppose that an insurance company classifies people into one of three classes: good risks, average risks, and bad risks. The company's records indicate that the probabilities that good-, average-, and bad-risk persons will be involved

in an accident over a 1-year span are, respectively, .05, .15, and .30. If 20 percent of the population is a good risk, 50 percent an average risk, and 30 percent a bad risk, what proportion of people have accidents in a fixed year? If policyholder A had no accidents in 2012, what is the probability that he or she is a good risk? is an average risk?

3.51. The city of Mumbai has just two seasons, Wet and Dry. The Wet season lasts for 1/3 of the year, and the Dry season for 2/3 of the year. During the Wet season, the probability that it is raining is 3/4; during the Dry season, the probability that it is raining is 1/6.
(a) Sam visited Mumbai on a random day of the year. What is the probability that it was raining when he arrived?
(b) Sam visited Mumbai on a random day, and it was raining when he arrived. Given this information, what is the probability that his visit was during the Wet season?
(c) Sam visited Mumbai on a random day, and it was raining when he arrived. Given this information, what is the probability that it will be raining when he return to Mumbai same time next year?

3.52. A high school student is anxiously waiting to receive mail telling her whether she has been accepted to a certain college. She estimates that the conditional probabilities of receiving notification on each day of next week, given that she is accepted and that she is rejected, are as follows:

Day	P(mail|accepted)	P(mail|rejected)
Monday	.15	.05
Tuesday	.20	.10
Wednesday	.25	.10
Thursday	.15	.15
Friday	.10	.20

She estimates that her probability of being accepted is .6.
(a) What is the probability that she receives mail on Monday?
(b) What is the conditional probability that she receives mail on Tuesday given that she does not receive mail on Monday?
(c) If there is no mail through Wednesday, what is the conditional probability that she will be accepted?
(d) What is the conditional probability that she will be accepted if mail comes on Thursday?
(e) What is the conditional probability that she will be accepted if no mail arrives that week?

3.53. A parallel system functions whenever at least one of its components works. Consider a parallel system of n components, and suppose that each component works independently with probability $\frac{1}{2}$. Find the conditional probability that component 1 works given that the system is functioning.

3.54. If you had to construct a mathematical model for events E and F, as described in parts (a) through (e), would you assume that they were independent events? Explain your reasoning.

(a) E is the event that a businesswoman has blue eyes, and F is the event that her secretary has blue eyes.

(b) E is the event that a professor owns a car, and F is the event that he is listed in the telephone book.

(c) E is the event that a man is under 6 feet tall, and F is the event that he weighs more than 200 pounds.

(d) E is the event that a woman lives in the United States, and F is the event that she lives in the Western Hemisphere.

(e) E is the event that it will rain tomorrow, and F is the event that it will rain the day after tomorrow.

3.55. In a jewelery store counter, there are 8 diamond rings, 20 diamond bangles, 10 gold rings and an unknown number of gold bangles. When an item is selected at random from the counter, the type and material of the item are independent. Determine the number of gold bangles.

3.56. Suppose that you continually collect coupons and that there are m different types. Suppose also that each time a new coupon is obtained, it is a type i coupon with probability $p_i, i = 1, \ldots, m$. Suppose that you have just collected your nth coupon. What is the probability that it is a new type?

Hint: Condition on the type of this coupon.

3.57. A 10 g packet of Cadbury Gems had 3 Blue, 2 Yellow, 2 Red, 2 Green, and 1 Orange Chocolates. A larger 25 gram pack had 4 Blue, 10 Green, 6 Yellow, and 5 Red chocolates. If chocolates from both packets are mixed in a bowl and a person picks a green chocolate randomly what is the probability that it belong to the 10 g packet? What is the probability of not picking same colour chocolate in first two pickings, if the chocolate picked first belong to the 25 gm pack?

3.58. Suppose that we want to generate the outcome of the flip of a fair coin, but that all we have at our disposal is a biased coin that lands on heads with some unknown probability p that need not be equal to $\frac{1}{2}$. Consider the following procedure for accomplishing our task:

1. Flip the coin.
2. Flip the coin again.
3. If both flips land on heads or both land on tails, return to step 1.
4. Let the result of the last flip be the result of the experiment.

(a) Show that the result is equally likely to be either heads or tails.

(b) Could we use a simpler procedure that continues to flip the coin until the last two flips are different and then lets the result be the outcome of the final flip?

3.59. Independent flips of a coin that lands on heads with probability p are made. What is the probability that the first four outcomes are

(a) H, H, H, H?

(b) T, H, H, H?

(c) What is the probability that the pattern T, H, H, H occurs before the pattern H, H, H, H?

Hint for part (c): How can the pattern H, H, H, H occur first?

3.60. The color of a person's eyes is determined by a single pair of genes. If they are both blue-eyed genes, then the person will have blue eyes; if they are both brown-eyed genes, then the person will have brown eyes; and if one of them is a blue-eyed gene and the other a brown-eyed gene, then the person will have brown eyes. (Because of the latter fact, we say that the brown-eyed gene is *dominant* over the blue-eyed one.) A newborn child independently receives one eye gene from each of its parents, and the gene it receives from a parent is equally likely to be either of the two eye genes of that parent. Suppose that Smith and both of his parents have brown eyes, but Smith's sister has blue eyes.

(a) What is the probability that Smith possesses a blue-eyed gene?

(b) Suppose that Smith's wife has blue eyes. What is the probability that their first child will have blue eyes?

(c) If their first child has brown eyes, what is the probability that their next child will also have brown eyes?

3.61. Genes relating to albinism are denoted by A and a. Only those people who receive the a gene from both parents will be albino. Persons having the gene pair A, a are normal in appearance and, because they can pass on the trait to their offspring, are called carriers. Suppose that a normal couple has two children, exactly one of whom is an albino. Suppose that the nonalbino child mates with a person who is known to be a carrier for albinism.

(a) What is the probability that their first offspring is an albino?

(b) What is the conditional probability that their second offspring is an albino given that their firstborn is not?

3.62. Barbara and Dianne go target shooting. Suppose that each of Barbara's shots hits a wooden duck target with probability p_1, while each shot of Dianne's hits it with probability p_2. Suppose that they shoot simultaneously at the same target. If the wooden duck is knocked over (indicating that it was hit), what is the probability that

(a) both shots hit the duck?

(b) Barbara's shot hit the duck?

What independence assumptions have you made?

3.63. A and B are involved in a duel. The rules of the duel are that they are to pick up their guns and shoot at each other simultaneously. If one or both are hit, then the duel is over. If both shots miss, then they repeat the process. Suppose that the results of the shots are independent and that each shot of A will hit B with probability p_A, and each shot of B will hit A with probability p_B. What is

(a) the probability that A is not hit?

(b) the probability that both duelists are hit?

(c) the probability that the duel ends after the nth round of shots?

(d) the conditional probability that the duel ends after the nth round of shots given that A is not hit?

(e) the conditional probability that the duel ends after the nth round of shots given that both duelists are hit?

3.64. A true–false question is to be posed to a husband-and-wife team on a quiz show. Both the husband and the wife will independently give the correct answer with probability p. Which of the following is a better strategy for the couple?

(a) Choose one of them and let that person answer the question.

(b) Have them both consider the question, and then either give the common answer if they agree or, if they disagree, flip a coin to determine which answer to give.

3.65. Ramu and Balu roll a die simultaneously. What is the probability that the number appearing on the die rolled by Ramu is greater than that of Balu?

3.66. The probability of the closing of the ith relay in the circuits shown in Figure 3.4 is given by $p_i, i = 1, 2, 3, 4, 5$. If all relays function independently, what is the probability

that a current flows between A and B for the respective circuits?

Hint for (b): Condition on whether relay 3 closes.

3.67. An engineering system consisting of n components is said to be a k-out-of-n system ($k \le n$) if the system functions if and only if at least k of the n components function. Suppose that all components function independently of one another.

(a) If the ith component functions with probability $P_i, i = 1, 2, 3, 4$, compute the probability that a 2-out-of-4 system functions.

(b) Repeat part (a) for a 3-out-of-5 system.

(c) Repeat for a k-out-of-n system when all the P_i equal p (that is, $P_i = p, i = 1, 2, \ldots, n$).

3.68. If two people throw a fair coin n times each. What is the probability that they will both get the same number of heads?

3.69. A certain organism possesses a pair of each of 5 different genes (which we will designate by the first 5 letters of the English alphabet). Each gene appears in 2 forms (which we designate by lowercase and capital letters). The capital letter will be assumed to be the dominant gene, in the sense that if an organism possesses the gene pair xX, then it will outwardly have the appearance of the X gene. For instance, if X stands for brown eyes and x for blue eyes, then an individual having either gene pair XX or xX will have brown eyes, whereas one having gene pair xx will have blue eyes. The characteristic appearance of an organism is called its phenotype, whereas its genetic constitution is called its genotype. (Thus, 2 organisms with respective genotypes aA, bB, cc, dD, ee and AA, BB, cc,

(a)

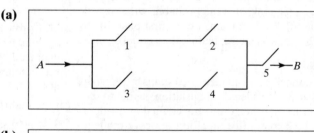

(b)

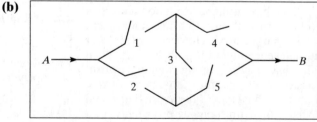

Figure 3.4 Circuits for Problem 3.66.

DD, ee would have different genotypes but the same phenotype.) In a mating between 2 organisms, each one contributes, at random, one of its gene pairs of each type. The 5 contributions of an organism (one of each of the 5 types) are assumed to be independent and are also independent of the contributions of the organism's mate. In a mating between organisms having genotypes *aA, bB, cC, dD, eE* and *aa, bB, cc, Dd, ee* what is the probability that the progeny will (i) phenotypically and (ii) genotypically resemble

(a) the first parent?

(b) the second parent?

(c) either parent?

(d) neither parent?

3.70. There is a 50–50 chance that the queen carries the gene for hemophilia. If she is a carrier, then each prince has a 50–50 chance of having hemophilia. If the queen has had three princes without the disease, what is the probability that the queen is a carrier? If there is a fourth prince, what is the probability that he will have hemophilia?

3.71. On the morning of September 30, 1982, the won–lost records of the three leading baseball teams in the Western Division of the National League were as follows:

Team	Won	Lost
Atlanta Braves	87	72
San Francisco Giants	86	73
Los Angeles Dodgers	86	73

Each team had 3 games remaining. All 3 of the Giants' games were with the Dodgers, and the 3 remaining games of the Braves were against the San Diego Padres. Suppose that the outcomes of all remaining games are independent and each game is equally likely to be won by either participant. For each team, what is the probability that it will win the division title? If two teams tie for first place, they have a playoff game, which each team has an equal chance of winning.

3.72. A town council of 7 members contains a steering committee of size 3. New ideas for legislation go first to the steering committee and then on to the council as a whole if at least 2 of the 3 committee members approve the legislation. Once at the full council, the legislation requires a majority vote (of at least 4) to pass. Consider a new piece of legislation, and suppose that each town council member will approve it, independently, with probability *p*. What is the probability that a given steering committee member's vote is decisive in the sense that if that person's vote were reversed, then the final fate of the legislation would be reversed? What is the corresponding probability for a given council member not on the steering committee?

3.73. Suppose that each child born to a couple is equally likely to be a boy or a girl, independently of the sex distribution of the other children in the family. For a couple having 5 children, compute the probabilities of the following events:

(a) All children are of the same sex.

(b) The 3 eldest are boys and the others girls.

(c) Exactly 3 are boys.

(d) The 2 oldest are girls.

(e) There is at least 1 girl.

3.74. *A* and *B* play a game of rolling the dice in which the player who rolls an even sum is said to be the winner and the game is stopped. If a player gets an odd number, the other player gets to throw the dice one more time than the previous player and the game continuous alternatively among the two players till a winner is found. Player *A* wants to start the game with a single die, does this increase his winning probability rather than going second?

3.75. In a certain village, it is traditional for the eldest son (or the older son in a two-son family) and his wife to be responsible for taking care of his parents as they age. In recent years, however, the women of this village, not wanting that responsibility, have not looked favorably upon marrying an eldest son.

(a) If every family in the village has two children, what proportion of all sons are older sons?

(b) If every family in the village has three children, what proportion of all sons are eldest sons?
Assume that each child is, independently, equally likely to be either a boy or a girl.

3.76. Suppose that *E* and *F* are mutually exclusive events of an experiment. Show that if independent trials of this experiment are performed, then *E* will occur before *F* with probability $P(E)/[P(E) + P(F)]$.

3.77. Consider an unending sequence of independent trials, where each trial is equally likely to result in any of the outcomes 1, 2, or 3. Given that outcome 3 is the last of the three outcomes to occur, find the conditional probability that

(a) the first trial results in outcome 1;

(b) the first two trials both result in outcome 1.

3.78. *A* and *B* play a series of games. Each game is independently won by *A* with probability *p* and by *B* with probability $1 - p$. They stop when the total number of wins of one of the players is two greater than that of the other player. The player with the greater number of total wins is declared the winner of the series.

(a) Find the probability that a total of 4 games are played.

(b) Find the probability that A is the winner of the series.

3.79. A pair of fair dice rolled successively. What is the probability of getting an even number before getting two fives?

3.80. In a certain contest, the players are of equal skill and the probability is $\frac{1}{2}$ that a specified one of the two contestants will be the victor. In a group of 2^n players, the players are paired off against each other at random. The 2^{n-1} winners are again paired off randomly, and so on, until a single winner remains. Consider two specified contestants, A and B, and define the events $A_i, i \le n, E$ by

$$A_i: \quad A \text{ plays in exactly } i \text{ contests}$$
$$E: \quad A \text{ and } B \text{ never play each other}$$

(a) Find $P(A_i), i = 1, \ldots, n$.
(b) Find $P(E)$.
(c) Let $P_n = P(E)$. Show that

$$P_n = \frac{1}{2^n - 1} + \frac{2^n - 2}{2^n - 1}\left(\frac{1}{2}\right)^2 P_{n-1}$$

and use this formula to check the answer you obtained in part (b).
Hint: Find $P(E)$ by conditioning on which of the events $A_i, i = 1, \ldots, n$ occur. In simplifying your answer, use the algebraic identity

$$\sum_{i=1}^{n-1} i x^{i-1} = \frac{1 - nx^{n-1} + (n-1)x^n}{(1-x)^2}$$

For another approach to solving this problem, note that there are a total of $2^n - 1$ games played.
(d) Explain why $2^n - 1$ games are played.
Number these games, and let B_i denote the event that A and B play each other in game $i, i = 1, \ldots, 2^n - 1$.
(e) What is $P(B_i)$?
(f) Use part (e) to find $P(E)$.

3.81. An investor owns shares in a stock whose present value is 25. She has decided that she must sell her stock if it goes either down to 10 or up to 40. If each change of price is either up 1 point with probability .55 or down 1 point with probability .45, and the successive changes are independent, what is the probability that the investor retires a winner?

3.82. A and B flip coins. A starts and continues flipping until a tail occurs, at which point B starts flipping and continues until there is a tail. Then A takes over, and so on. Let P_1 be the probability of the coin landing on heads when A flips and P_2 when B flips. The winner of the game is the first one to get

(a) 2 heads in a row;
(b) a total of 2 heads;
(c) 3 heads in a row;
(d) a total of 3 heads.
In each case, find the probability that A wins.

3.83. Die A has 4 red and 2 white faces, whereas die B has 2 red and 4 white faces. A fair coin is flipped once. If it lands on heads, the game continues with die A; if it lands on tails, then die B is to be used.

(a) Show that the probability of red at any throw is $\frac{1}{2}$.
(b) If the first two throws result in red, what is the probability of red at the third throw?
(c) If red turns up at the first two throws, what is the probability that it is die A that is being used?

3.84. We randomly select a child from a two-child family and we observe that the child is a boy. Compute the probability that the other child in the same family is a girl. In next turn, we randomly select a two-child family and we observe that at least one of the children is a boy. Compute the probability that the other child in the family is a girl. Are the probabilities the same?

3.85. Three prisoners, A, B and C, are in separate cells and sentenced to death. The governor has selected one of them at random to be pardoned. The warden knows which one is pardoned, but is not allowed to tell. Prisoner A begs the warden to let him know the identity of one of the others who are going to be executed and asks him to give C's name if B is to be pardoned B's name if C is to be pardoned And if A is to be pardoned, flip a coin to decide whether to name B or C.

The warden tells A that B is to be executed. Prisoner A is pleased because he believes that his probability of surviving has gone up from 1/3 to 1/2, as it is now between him and C. Prisoner A secretly tells C the news, who is also pleased, because he reasons that A still has a chance of 1/3 to be the pardoned one, but his chance has gone up to 2/3. Who among A and C got it correct?

3.86. Let $S = \{1, 2, \ldots, n\}$ and suppose that A and B are, independently, equally likely to be any of the 2^n subsets (including the null set and S itself) of S.
(a) Show that

$$P\{A \subset B\} = \left(\frac{3}{4}\right)^n$$

Hint: Let $N(B)$ denote the number of elements in B. Use

$$P\{A \subset B\} = \sum_{i=0}^{n} P\{A \subset B | N(B) = i\}P\{N(B) = i\}$$

Show that $P\{AB = \emptyset\} = \left(\frac{3}{4}\right)^n$.

3.87. Consider Example 2a, but now suppose that when the key is in a certain pocket, there is a 10 percent chance that a search of that pocket will not find the key. Let R and L be, respectively, the events that the key is in the right-hand pocket of the jacket and that it is in the left-hand pocket. Also, let S_R be the event that a search of the right-hand jacket pocket will be successful in finding the key, and let U_L be the event that a search of the left-hand jacket pocket will be unsuccessful and, thus, not find the key. Find $P(S_R|U_L)$, the conditional probability that a search of the right-hand pocket will find the key given that a search of the left-hand pocket did not, by

(a) using the identity

$$P(S_R|U_L) = \frac{P(S_R U_L)}{P(U_L)}$$

determining $P(S_R U_L)$ by conditioning on whether or not the key is in the right-hand pocket, and determining $P(U_L)$ by conditioning on whether or not the key is in the left-hand pocket;

(b) using the identity

$$P(S_R|U_L) = P(S_R|R U_L)P(R|U_L)$$
$$+ P(S_R|R^c U_L)P(R^c|U_L)$$

3.88. In Example 5e, what is the conditional probability that the ith coin was selected given that the first n trials all result in heads?

3.89. In Laplace's rule of succession (Example 5e), are the outcomes of the successive flips independent? Explain.

3.90. A person tried by a 3-judge panel is declared guilty if at least 2 judges cast votes of guilty. Suppose that when the defendant is in fact guilty, each judge will independently vote guilty with probability .7, whereas when the defendant is in fact innocent, this probability drops to .2. If 70 percent of defendants are guilty, compute the conditional probability that judge number 3 votes guilty given that

(a) judges 1 and 2 vote guilty;
(b) judges 1 and 2 cast 1 guilty and 1 not guilty vote;
(c) judges 1 and 2 both cast not guilty votes.

Let $E_i, i = 1, 2, 3$ denote the event that judge i casts a guilty vote. Are these events independent? Are they conditionally independent? Explain.

3.91. Suppose that n independent trials, each of which results in any of the outcomes 0, 1, or 2, with respective probabilities p_0, p_1, and $p_2, \sum_{i=0}^{2} p_i = 1$, are performed. Find the probability that outcomes 1 and 2 both occur at least once.

Theoretical Exercises

3.1. Let A, B and C be such that $P(B \cap C) > 0$ and A and B are independent. Check whether,

$$P(A \cap B|C) = P(A|C)P(B|C).$$

3.2. Consider an experiment of tossing an unbiased coin n times. Show that the conditional probability of a head on any specified trial, given a total of m heads over the n trials is m/n.

3.3. Let A_1, A_2, and A_3 be events. Also let B_i represent either A_i or its complement. Prove that the events A_1, A_2 and A_3 are independent if and only if

$$P(B_1 B_2 B_3) = P(B_1)P(B_2)P(B_3).$$

3.4. A ball is in any one of n boxes and is in the ith box with probability P_i. If the ball is in box i, a search of that box will uncover it with probability α_i. Show that the conditional probability that the ball is in box j, given that a search of box i did not uncover it, is

$$\frac{P_j}{1 - \alpha_i P_i} \quad \text{if } j \neq i$$

$$\frac{(1 - \alpha_i)P_i}{1 - \alpha_i P_i} \quad \text{if } j = i$$

3.5. Let $E1, E2$ and $E3$ be three events such that $P(E1|E2) \leq P(E1)$ and $P(E2|E3) \leq P(E2)$. Then can we say that $P(E1|E3) \leq P(E1)$?

3.6. Prove that if $E_1, E_2, \ldots, E_n$ are independent events, then

$$P(E_1 \cup E_2 \cup \cdots \cup E_n) = 1 - \prod_{i=1}^{n}[1 - P(E_i)]$$

3.7. (a) An urn contains n white and m black balls. The balls are withdrawn one at a time until only those of the same color are left. Show that with probability $n/(n + m)$, they are all white.

Hint: Imagine that the experiment continues until all the balls are removed, and consider the last ball withdrawn.

(b) A pond contains 3 distinct species of fish, which we will call the Red, Blue, and Green fish. There are r Red, b Blue, and g Green fish. Suppose that the fish are removed from the pond in a random order. (That is, each selection is equally likely to be any of the remaining fish.) What is the probability that the Red fish are the first species to become extinct in the pond?

Hint: Write $P\{R\} = P\{RBG\} + P\{RGB\}$, and compute the probabilities on the right by first conditioning on the last species to be removed.

3.8. *Monty Hall problem.* Suppose we are participating in a game show. Given the choice of three doors: behind one door is a car; behind the others, goats. You are asked to pick a door, say you choose No. 1, and the host, who knows what's behind the doors, opens another door, say No. 3, which has a goat. He then says to you, "Do you want to pick door No. 2?". Does the probability of winning the car will change if we switch our choice? Justify.

3.9. A fair die is rolled independently n times. At each roll i ($i = 2, 3, ..., n$) we get a reward at time $k + 1$ if ith roll resulted in an odd numbered face odd and the previous roll resulted in an even numbered face. Let E_i be the event that a reward is obtained at time i.
(a) Are events E_i and E_{i+1} independent?
(b) Are events E_i and E_{i+2} independent?

3.10. Two percent of women age 45 who participate in routine screening have breast cancer. Ninety percent of those with breast cancer have positive mammographies. Eight percent of the women who do not have breast cancer will also have positive mammographies. Given that a woman has a positive mammography, what is the probability she has breast cancer?

3.11. A drawer contains two coins. One is an unbiased coin, which when tossed, is equally likely to turn up heads or tails. The other is a biased coin, which will turn up heads with probability p and tails with probability $1 - p$. One coin is selected at random from the drawer. Two experiments are performed:
(a) The selected coin is tossed n times. Given that the coin turns up heads k times and tails $n - k$ times, what is the probability that the coin is biased?
(b) The selected coin is toss repeatedly until it turns up heads k times. Given that the coin is tossed n times in total, what is the probability that the coin is biased?

3.12. Show that $0 \le a_i \le 1, i = 1, 2, \ldots$, then

$$\sum_{i=1}^{\infty} \left[a_i \prod_{j=1}^{i-1}(1 - a_j) \right] + \prod_{i=1}^{\infty}(1 - a_i) = 1$$

Hint: Suppose that an infinite number of coins are to be flipped. Let a_i be the probability that the ith coin lands on heads, and consider when the first head occurs.

3.13. The probability of getting a head on a single toss of a coin is p. Suppose that A starts and continues to flip the coin until a tail shows up, at which point B starts flipping. Then B continues to flip until a tail comes up, at which point A takes over, and so on. Let $P_{n,m}$ denote the probability that A accumulates a total of n heads before B accumulates m. Show that

$$P_{n,m} = pP_{n-1,m} + (1 - p)(1 - P_{m,n})$$

*3.14. Suppose that you are gambling against an infinitely rich adversary and at each stage you either win or lose 1 unit with respective probabilities p and $1 - p$. Show that the probability that you eventually go broke is

$$\begin{array}{ll} 1 & \text{if } p \le \frac{1}{2} \\ (q/p)^i & \text{if } p > \frac{1}{2} \end{array}$$

where $q = 1 - p$ and where i is your initial fortune.

3.15. Independent trials that result in a success with probability p are successively performed until a total of r successes is obtained. Show that the probability that exactly n trials are required is

$$\binom{n - 1}{r - 1} p^r (1 - p)^{n-r}$$

Use this result to solve the problem of the points (Example 4j).

Hint: In order for it to take n trials to obtain r successes, how many successes must occur in the first $n - 1$ trials?

3.16. Independent trials that result in a success with probability p and a failure with probability $1 - p$ are called *Bernoulli trials*. Let P_n denote the probability that n Bernoulli trials result in an even number of successes (0 being considered an even number). Show that

$$P_n = p(1 - P_{n-1}) + (1 - p)P_{n-1} \quad n \ge 1$$

and use this formula to prove (by induction) that

$$P_n = \frac{1 + (1 - 2p)^n}{2}$$

3.17. Suppose that n independent trials are performed, with trial i being a success with probability $1/(2i + 1)$. Let P_n denote the probability that the total number of successes that result is an odd number.
(a) Find P_n for $n = 1, 2, 3, 4, 5$.
(b) Conjecture a general formula for P_n.
(c) Derive a formula for P_n in terms of P_{n-1}.
(d) Verify that your conjecture in part (b) satisfies the recursive formula in part (c). Because the recursive formula has a unique solution, this then proves that your conjecture is correct.

3.18. Let Q_n denote the probability that no run of 3 consecutive heads appears in n tosses of a fair coin. Show that

$$Q_n = \frac{1}{2}Q_{n-1} + \frac{1}{4}Q_{n-2} + \frac{1}{8}Q_{n-3}$$
$$Q_0 = Q_1 = Q_2 = 1$$

Find Q_8.

Hint: Condition on the first tail.

3.19. Consider the gambler's ruin problem, with the exception that A and B agree to play no more than n games. Let $P_{n,i}$ denote the probability that A winds up with all the money when A starts with i and B starts with $N - i$. Derive an equation for $P_{n,i}$ in terms of $P_{n-1, i+1}$ and $P_{n-1, i-1}$, and compute $P_{7,3}$, $N = 5$.

3.20. *Polya's urn Problem.* At time $t = 0$ an urn contains two balls, one black and one red. At time $t = 1$ you draw one ball at random and replace it together with a new ball of the same color. You repeat this procedure at every integer time (so that at time $t = n$ there are $n + 2$ balls). Calculate

$$P_{n,r} = P(\text{there are } r \text{ red balls at time } n) \text{ for } n = 1,2,...,\text{and}$$
$$r = 1,2,...,n+1.$$

What can you say about the proportion of red balls as $n \to \infty$?

3.21. *The Ballot Problem.* In an election, candidate A receives n votes and candidate B receives m votes, where $n > m$. Assuming that all of the $(n + m)!/n!\, m!$ orderings of the votes are equally likely, let $P_{n,m}$ denote the probability that A is always ahead in the counting of the votes.

(a) Compute $P_{2,1}, P_{3,1}, P_{3,2}, P_{4,1}, P_{4,2}, P_{4,3}$.
(b) Find $P_{n,1}, P_{n,2}$.
(c) On the basis of your results in parts (a) and (b), conjecture the value of $P_{n,m}$.
(d) Derive a recursion for $P_{n,m}$ in terms of $P_{n-1,m}$ and $P_{n,m-1}$ by conditioning on who receives the last vote.
(e) Use part (d) to verify your conjecture in part (c) by an induction proof on $n + m$.

3.22. As a simplified model for weather forecasting, suppose that the weather (either wet or dry) tomorrow will be the same as the weather today with probability p. Show that the weather is dry on January 1, then P_n, the probability that it will be dry n days later, satisfies

$$P_n = (2p - 1)P_{n-1} + (1 - p) \qquad n \geq 1$$
$$P_0 = 1$$

Prove that

$$P_n = \frac{1}{2} + \frac{1}{2}(2p - 1)^n \qquad n \geq 0$$

3.23. In the gambler ruin problem [*Example 4l*], consider the case were the gambler wins with probability $p = 1/3$ and looses with probability $q = 2/3$. Suppose the gambler adopts the strategy that he will quit if he leads by 2 points or otherwise will play till goes bankrupt. Show that irrespective of his initial capital i, the probability that he will ever be ahead by 2 points is less than 1/4.

*3.24. A round-robin tournament of n contestants is a tournament in which each of the $\binom{n}{2}$ pairs of contestants play each other exactly once, with the outcome of any play being that one of the contestants wins and the other loses. For a fixed integer k, $k < n$, a question of interest is whether it is possible that the tournament outcome is such that for every set of k players, there is a player who beat each member of that set. Show that if

$$\binom{n}{k}\left[1 - \left(\frac{1}{2}\right)^k\right]^{n-k} < 1$$

then such an outcome is possible.

Hint: Suppose that the results of the games are independent and that each game is equally likely to be won by either contestant. Number the $\binom{n}{k}$ sets of k contestants, and let B_i denote the event that no contestant beat all of the k players in the ith set. Then use Boole's inequality to bound $P\left(\bigcup_i B_i\right)$.

3.25. Prove directly that

$$P(E|F) = P(E|FG)P(G|F) + P(E|FG^c)P(G^c|F)$$

3.26. Two events A and B are said to be conditionally independent, given another event C with $P(C) > 0$, if

$$P(A \cap B|C) = P(A|C)P(B|C).$$

Prove that independence doesn't imply conditional independence and vice versa.

3.27. Extend the definition of conditional independence to more than 2 events.

3.28. Prove or give a counterexample. If E_1 and E_2 are independent, then they are conditionally independent given F.

3.29. In Laplace's rule of succession (Example 5e), show that if the first n flips all result in heads, then the conditional probability that the next m flips also result in all heads is $(n + 1)/(n + m + 1)$.

3.30. In Laplace's rule of succession (Example 5e), suppose that the first n flips resulted in r heads and $n - r$ tails. Show that the probability that the $(n + 1)$ flip turns up heads is $(r + 1)/(n + 2)$. To do so, you will have to prove and use the identity

$$\int_0^1 y^n(1 - y)^m dy = \frac{n!\,m!}{(n + m + 1)!}$$

Hint: To prove the identity, let $C(n, m) = \int_0^1 y^n (1 - y)^m dy$. Integrating by parts yields

$$C(n, m) = \frac{m}{n + 1} C(n + 1, m - 1)$$

Starting with $C(n, 0) = 1/(n + 1)$, prove the identity by induction on m.

3.31. Suppose that a nonmathematical, but philosophically minded, friend of yours claims that Laplace's rule of succession must be incorrect because it can lead to ridiculous conclusions. "For instance," says he, "the rule states that if a boy is 10 years old, having lived 10 years, the boy has probability $\frac{11}{12}$ of living another year. On the other hand, if the boy has an 80-year-old grandfather, then, by Laplace's rule, the grandfather has probability $\frac{81}{82}$ of surviving another year. However, this is ridiculous. Clearly, the boy is more likely to survive an additional year than the grandfather is." How would you answer your friend?

Self-Test Problems and Exercises

3.1. In a game of bridge, West has no aces. What is the probability of his partner's having (a) no aces? (b) 2 or more aces? (c) What would the probabilities be if West had exactly 1 ace?

3.2. The probability that a new car battery functions for more than 10,000 miles is .8, the probability that it functions for more than 20,000 miles is .4, and the probability that it functions for more than 30,000 miles is .1. If a new car battery is still working after 10,000 miles, what is the probability that

(a) its total life will exceed 20,000 miles?

(b) its additional life will exceed 20,000 miles?

3.3. There are four machines M_i, $i = 1, 2, 3, 4$. M_1 produces a binary code zero with probability 1/2 and code one with probability 1/2 and passes it to machine M_2. M_2 either leaves the code alone or change its compliment before passing in to M_3. M_3 and M_4 repeats the same procedure before producing the final output. It is known that M_2, M_3 and M_4 changes the binary code with probability 1/3. If the final output is given as zero, find the probability that M_1 produce the code zero?

3.4. A couple goes to a consultation to learn about their chances of having healthy/sick children due to a recessive genetic trait, because the mother has a brother who suffers from this disease. Her 2 parents are healthy, and she is healthy as well. The husband is healthy, and has no history of disease in the family. What is the chance of them having a sick child?

3.5. Suppose that A and B are events such that $P(A \mid B) = P(B \mid A)$ and $P(A \text{ or } B) = 1$ and $P(AB) > 0$. Prove that $P(A) > 1/2$.

3.6. An urn contains b black balls and r red balls. One of the balls is drawn at random, but when it is put back in the urn, c additional balls of the same color are put in with it. Now, suppose that we draw another ball. Show that the probability that the first ball was black, given that the second ball drawn was red, is $b/(b + r + c)$.

3.7. A friend randomly chooses two cards, without replacement, from an ordinary deck of 52 playing cards. In each of the following situations, determine the conditional probability that both cards are aces.

(a) You ask your friend if one of the cards is the ace of spades, and your friend answers in the affirmative.

(b) You ask your friend if the first card selected is an ace, and your friend answers in the affirmative.

(c) You ask your friend if the second card selected is an ace, and your friend answers in the affirmative.

(d) You ask your friend if either of the cards selected is an ace, and your friend answers in the affirmative.

3.8. Show that

$$\frac{P(H \mid E)}{P(G \mid E)} = \frac{P(H)}{P(G)} \frac{P(E \mid H)}{P(E \mid G)}$$

Suppose that, before new evidence is observed, the hypothesis H is three times as likely to be true as is hypothesis G. If the new evidence is twice as likely when G is true than it is when H is true, which hypothesis is more likely after the evidence has been observed?

3.9. A, B and C tell the truth with probability 1/3. A makes a statement and B tells C whether A statement was true or not. C tells us that B confirm that A was telling the truth. What is the probability that A was actually telling the truth?

3.10. Two urns contain coloured balls. Urn 1 contains 4 blue, 3 green and 5 red balls. Urn 2 contains 6 blue, 2 green and 3 red balls. A ball is selected at random from urn 1 and transferred to urn 2. A ball is then selected at random from urn 2. If the ball selected from urn 2 is red, what is the probability that the ball transferred from urn 1 was

(a) red?

(b) green?

(c) blue?

3.11. A type C battery is in working condition with probability .7, whereas a type D battery is in working condition with probability .4. A battery is randomly chosen from a bin consisting of 8 type C and 6 type D batteries.

(a) What is the probability that the battery works?

(b) Given that the battery does not work, what is the conditional probability that it was a type C battery?

3.12. Maria will take two books with her on a trip. Suppose that the probability that she will like book 1 is .6, the probability that she will like book 2 is .5, and the probability that she will like both books is .4. Find the conditional probability that she will like book 2 given that she did not like book 1.

3.13. Balls are randomly removed from an urn that initially contains 20 red and 10 blue balls.

(a) What is the probability that all of the red balls are removed before all of the blue ones have been removed? Now suppose that the urn initially contains 20 red, 10 blue, and 8 green balls.

(b) Now what is the probability that all of the red balls are removed before all of the blue ones have been removed?

(c) What is the probability that the colors are depleted in the order blue, red, green?

(d) What is the probability that the group of blue balls is the first of the three groups to be removed?

3.14. A dice $D1$ has four red faces and two blue faces. A dice $D2$ has two red faces and four blue faces. You flip a coin once, if heads the game continues with dice $D1$, otherwise it continues with dice $D2$.

(a) On rolling the dice for first time, what is the probability that a red face appears on the dice?

(b) If the first two rolling show a red face, what is the probability that also on the third rolling is red?

(c) If the first n rolling show a red face, what is the probability that you are using dice A?

3.15. In a certain species of rats, black dominates over brown. Suppose that a black rat with two black parents has a brown sibling.

(a) What is the probability that this rat is a pure black rat (as opposed to being a hybrid with one black and one brown gene)?

(b) Suppose that when the black rat is mated with a brown rat, all 5 of their offspring are black. Now what is the probability that the rat is a pure black rat?

3.16. Drawn a card from a deck of 52 cards, verify whether the following events are independent:

(a) $A =$ drawing of a picture card; $B =$ drawing of a spade

(b) What if the king of spade is missing from the deck?

(c) What if a card, at random, is missing from the deck?

3.17. For the k-out-of-n system described in Problem 3.67, assume that each component independently works with probability $\frac{1}{2}$. Find the conditional probability that component 1 is working, given that the system works, when

(a) $k = 1, n = 2$;

(b) $k = 2, n = 3$.

3.18. A person is trying to quit smoking, if he smokes today, there's an 90% chance that he'll smoke tomorrow If he skipped smoking today, there's a 30% chance that he'll smoke tomorrow. If he smokes today, what is the probability that he smokes 10 days from now?

3.19. Three players simultaneously toss coins. The coin tossed by $A(B)[C]$ turns up heads with probability $P_1(P_2)[P_3]$. If one person gets an outcome different from those of the other two, then he is the odd man out. If there is no odd man out, the players flip again and continue to do so until they get an odd man out. What is the probability that A will be the odd man?

3.20. Suppose that there are n possible outcomes of a trial, with outcome i resulting with probability $p_i, i = 1, \ldots, n, \sum_{i=1}^{n} p_i = 1$. If two independent trials are observed, what is the probability that the result of the second trial is larger than that of the first?

3.21. If A flips $n + 1$ and B flips n fair coins, show that the probability that A gets more heads than B is $\frac{1}{2}$.

Hint: Condition on which player has more heads after each has flipped n coins. (There are three possibilities.)

3.22. Prove or give counterexamples to the following statements:

(a) If E is independent of F and E is independent of G, then E is independent of $F \cup G$.

(b) If E is independent of F, and E is independent of G, and $FG = \emptyset$, then E is independent of $F \cup G$.

(c) If E is independent of F, and F is independent of G, and E is independent of FG, then G is independent of EF.

3.23. Let A and B be events having positive probability. State whether each of the following statements is (i) necessarily true, (ii) necessarily false, or (iii) possibly true.

(a) If A and B are mutually exclusive, then they are independent.

(b) If A and B are independent, then they are mutually exclusive.

(c) $P(A) = P(B) = .6$, and A and B are mutually exclusive.

(d) $P(A) = P(B) = .6$, and A and B are independent.

3.24. Rank the following from most likely to least likely to occur:

(a) A fair die is cast and result in a prime number.

(b) Three dice were cast and their sum was a prime number.

(c) The sum of three dice is a prime given the first die resulted in a prime number.

3.25. Two local factories, A and B, produce radios. Each radio produced at factory A is defective with probability .05, whereas each one produced at factory B is defective with probability .01. Suppose you purchase two radios that were produced at the same factory, which is equally likely to have been either factory A or factory B. If the first radio that you check is defective, what is the conditional probability that the other one is also defective?

3.26. Show that if $P(A|B) = 1$, then $P(B^c|A^c) = 1$.

3.27. An urn initially contains 1 red and 1 blue ball. At each stage, a ball is randomly withdrawn and replaced by two other balls of the same color. (For instance, if the red ball is initially chosen, then there would be 2 red and 1 blue balls in the urn when the next selection occurs.) Show by mathematical induction that the probability that there are exactly i red balls in the urn after n stages have been completed is $\frac{1}{n+1}, 1 \le i \le n + 1$.

3.28. Two teams are playing a best of $2n + 1$ game where the team who wins $n + 1$ games first will be declared the winner. Both teams have a probability to win of 50%. However, as Team 1 was playing with a player short , they made an agreement that they only have to win n games to be the winner (team 2 still has to win $n + 1$ games). What is the probability that Team 1 will be the winner?

3.29. There are n distinct types of coupons, and each coupon obtained is, independently of prior types collected, of type i with probability p_i, $\sum_{i=1}^{n} p_i = 1$.

(a) If n coupons are collected, what is the probability that one of each type is obtained?

(b) Now suppose that $p_1 = p_2 = \cdots = p_n = 1/n$. Let E_i be the event that there are no type i coupons among the n collected. Apply the inclusion–exclusion identity for the probability of the union of events to $P(\cup_i E_i)$ to prove the identity

$$n! = \sum_{k=0}^{n} (-1)^k \binom{n}{k} (n - k)^n$$

3.30. Show that for any events E and F,

$$P(E|E \cup F) \ge P(E|F)$$

Hint: Compute $P(E|E \cup F)$ by conditioning on whether F occurs.

3.31. There is a 60 percent chance that event A will occur. If A does not occur, then there is a 10 percent chance that B will occur.

What is the probability that at least one of the events A or B will occur?

RANDOM VARIABLES

Chapter

4

Contents

4.1 Random Variables
4.2 Discrete Random Variables
4.3 Expected Value
4.4 Expectation of a Function of a Random Variable
4.5 Variance
4.6 The Bernoulli and Binomial Random Variables

4.7 The Poisson Random Variable
4.8 Other Discrete Probability Distributions
4.9 Expected Value of Sums of Random Variables
4.10 Properties of the Cumulative Distribution Function

4.1 Random Variables

When an experiment is performed, we are frequently interested mainly in some function of the outcome as opposed to the actual outcome itself. For instance, in tossing dice, we are often interested in the sum of the two dice and are not really concerned about the separate values of each die. That is, we may be interested in knowing that the sum is 7 and may not be concerned over whether the actual outcome was $(1, 6)$, $(2, 5)$, $(3, 4)$, $(4, 3)$, $(5, 2)$, or $(6, 1)$. Also, in flipping a coin, we may be interested in the total number of heads that occur and not care at all about the actual head–tail sequence that results. These quantities of interest, or, more formally, these real-valued functions defined on the sample space, are known as *random variables*.

Because the value of a random variable is determined by the outcome of the experiment, we may assign probabilities to the possible values of the random variable.

Example 1a

Suppose that our experiment consists of tossing 3 fair coins. If we let Y denote the number of heads that appear, then Y is a random variable taking on one of the values $0, 1, 2$, and 3 with respective probabilities

$$P\{Y = 0\} = P\{(T, T, T)\} = \frac{1}{8}$$

$$P\{Y = 1\} = P\{(T, T, H), (T, H, T), (H, T, T)\} = \frac{3}{8}$$

$$P\{Y = 2\} = P\{(T, H, H), (H, T, H), (H, H, T)\} = \frac{3}{8}$$

$$P\{Y = 3\} = P\{(H, H, H)\} = \frac{1}{8}$$

Since Y must take on one of the values 0 through 3, we must have

$$1 = P\left(\bigcup_{i=0}^{3}\{Y = i\}\right) = \sum_{i=0}^{3} P\{Y = i\}$$

which, of course, is in accord with the preceding probabilities. ∎

Example 1b

A life insurance agent has 2 elderly clients, each of whom has a life insurance policy that pays \$100,000 upon death. Let Y be the event that the younger one dies in the following year, and let O be the event that the older one dies in the following year. Assume that Y and O are independent, with respective probabilities $P(Y) = .05$ and $P(O) = .10$. If X denotes the total amount of money (in units of \$100,000) that will be paid out this year to any of these clients' beneficiaries, then X is a random variable that takes on one of the possible values $0, 1, 2$ with respective probabilities

$$P\{X = 0\} = P(Y^c O^c) = P(Y^c)P(O^c) = (.95)(.9) = .855$$
$$P\{X = 1\} = P(YO^c) + P(Y^c O) = (.05)(.9) + (.95)(.1) = .140$$
$$P\{X = 2\} = P(YO) = (.05)(.1) = .005$$
∎

Example 1c

Four balls are to be randomly selected, without replacement, from an urn that contains 20 balls numbered 1 through 20. If X is the largest numbered ball selected, then X is a random variable that takes on one of the values $4, 5, \ldots, 20$. Because each of the $\binom{20}{4}$ possible selections of 4 of the 20 balls is equally likely, the probability that X takes on each of its possible values is

$$P\{X = i\} = \frac{\binom{i-1}{3}}{\binom{20}{4}}, \quad i = 4, \ldots, 20$$

This is so because the number of selections that result in $X = i$ is the number of selections that result in ball numbered i and three of the balls numbered 1 through $i - 1$ being selected. As there are $\binom{1}{1}\binom{i-1}{3}$ such selections, the preceding equation follows.

Suppose now that we want to determine $P\{X > 10\}$. One way, of course, is to just use the preceding to obtain

$$P\{X > 10\} = \sum_{i=11}^{20} P\{X = i\} = \sum_{i=11}^{20} \frac{\binom{i-1}{3}}{\binom{20}{4}}$$

However, a more direct approach for determining $P(X > 10)$ would be to use

$$P\{X > 10\} = 1 - P\{X \le 10\} = 1 - \frac{\binom{10}{4}}{\binom{20}{4}}$$

where the preceding results because X will be less than or equal to 10 when the 4 balls chosen are among balls numbered 1 through 10. ∎

Example 1d

Independent trials consisting of the flipping of a coin having probability p of coming up heads are continually performed until either a head occurs or a total of n flips is made. If we let X denote the number of times the coin is flipped, then X is a random variable taking on one of the values $1, 2, 3, \ldots, n$ with respective probabilities

$$P\{X = 1\} = P\{H\} = p$$

$$P\{X = 2\} = P\{(T, H)\} = (1 - p)p$$

$$P\{X = 3\} = P\{(T, T, H)\} = (1 - p)^2 p$$

$$\vdots$$

$$P\{X = n - 1\} = P\{(\underbrace{T, T, \ldots, T}_{n-2}, H)\} = (1 - p)^{n-2} p$$

$$P\{X = n\} = P\{(\underbrace{T, T, \ldots, T}_{n-1}, T), (\underbrace{T, T, \ldots, T}_{n-1}, H)\} = (1 - p)^{n-1}$$

As a check, note that

$$P\left(\bigcup_{i=1}^{n} \{X = i\}\right) = \sum_{i=1}^{n} P\{X = i\}$$

$$= \sum_{i=1}^{n-1} p(1 - p)^{i-1} + (1 - p)^{n-1}$$

$$= p\left[\frac{1 - (1 - p)^{n-1}}{1 - (1 - p)}\right] + (1 - p)^{n-1}$$

$$= 1 - (1 - p)^{n-1} + (1 - p)^{n-1}$$

$$= 1 \qquad \blacksquare$$

Example 1e

Suppose that there are N distinct types of coupons and that each time one obtains a coupon, it is, independently of previous selections, equally likely to be any one of the N types. One random variable of interest is T, the number of coupons that need to be collected until one obtains a complete set of at least one of each type. Rather than derive $P\{T = n\}$ directly, let us start by considering the probability that T is greater than n. To do so, fix n and define the events $A_1, A_2, \ldots, A_N$ as follows: A_j is the event that no type j coupon is contained among the first n coupons collected, $j = 1, \ldots, N$. Hence,

$$P\{T > n\} = P\left(\bigcup_{j=1}^{N} A_j\right)$$

$$= \sum_{j} P(A_j) - \sum_{j_1 < j_2} \sum P(A_{j_1} A_{j_2}) + \cdots$$

$$+ (-1)^{k+1} \sum_{j_1 < j_2 < \cdots < j_k} \sum \sum P(A_{j_1} A_{j_2} \cdots A_{j_k}) \cdots$$

$$+ (-1)^{N+1} P(A_1 A_2 \cdots A_N)$$

Now, A_j will occur if each of the n coupons collected is not of type j. Since each of the coupons will not be of type j with probability $(N - 1)/N$, we have, by the assumed independence of the types of successive coupons,

$$P(A_j) = \left(\frac{N - 1}{N}\right)^n$$

Also, the event $A_{j_1}A_{j_2}$ will occur if none of the first n coupons collected is of either type j_1 or type j_2. Thus, again using independence, we see that

$$P(A_{j_1}A_{j_2}) = \left(\frac{N - 2}{N}\right)^n$$

The same reasoning gives

$$P(A_{j_1}A_{j_2}\cdots A_{j_k}) = \left(\frac{N - k}{N}\right)^n$$

and we see that for $n > 0$,

$$P\{T > n\} = N\left(\frac{N - 1}{N}\right)^n - \binom{N}{2}\left(\frac{N - 2}{N}\right)^n + \binom{N}{3}\left(\frac{N - 3}{N}\right)^n - \cdots$$
$$+ (-1)^N\binom{N}{N - 1}\left(\frac{1}{N}\right)^n$$
$$= \sum_{i=1}^{N-1}\binom{N}{i}\left(\frac{N - i}{N}\right)^n (-1)^{i+1} \tag{1.1}$$

The probability that T equals n can now be obtained from the preceding formula by the use of

$$P\{T > n - 1\} = P\{T = n\} + P\{T > n\}$$

or, equivalently,

$$P\{T = n\} = P\{T > n - 1\} - P\{T > n\}$$

Another random variable of interest is the number of distinct types of coupons that are contained in the first n selections—call this random variable D_n. To compute $P\{D_n = k\}$, let us start by fixing attention on a particular set of k distinct types, and let us then determine the probability that this set constitutes the set of distinct types obtained in the first n selections. Now, in order for this to be the situation, it is necessary and sufficient that of the first n coupons obtained,

A: each is one of these k types

B: each of these k types is represented

Now, each coupon selected will be one of the k types with probability k/N, so the probability that A will be valid is $(k/N)^n$. Also, given that a coupon is of one of the k types under consideration, it is easy to see that it is equally likely to be of any one of these k types. Hence, the conditional probability of B given that A occurs is the same as the probability that a set of n coupons, each equally likely to be any of k possible types, contains a complete set of all k types. But this is just the probability that the number needed to amass a complete set, when choosing among k types, is less than or equal to n and is thus obtainable from Equation (1.1) with k replacing N. Thus, we have

$$P(A) = \left(\frac{k}{N}\right)^n$$

$$P(B|A) = 1 - \sum_{i=1}^{k-1} \binom{k}{i} \left(\frac{k-i}{k}\right)^n (-1)^{i+1}$$

Finally, as there are $\binom{N}{k}$ possible choices for the set of k types, we arrive at

$$P\{D_n = k\} = \binom{N}{k} P(AB)$$

$$= \binom{N}{k} \left(\frac{k}{N}\right)^n \left[1 - \sum_{i=1}^{k-1} \binom{k}{i} \left(\frac{k-i}{k}\right)^n (-1)^{i+1} \right]$$

Remark Since one must collect at least N coupons to obtain a complete set, it follows that $P\{T > n\} = 1$ if $n < N$. Therefore, from Equation (1.1), we obtain the interesting combinatorial identity that for integers $1 \le n < N$,

$$\sum_{i=1}^{N-1} \binom{N}{i} \left(\frac{N-i}{N}\right)^n (-1)^{i+1} = 1$$

which can be written as

$$\sum_{i=0}^{N-1} \binom{N}{i} \left(\frac{N-i}{N}\right)^n (-1)^{i+1} = 0$$

or, upon multiplying by $(-1)^N N^n$ and letting $j = N - i$,

$$\sum_{j=1}^{N} \binom{N}{j} j^n (-1)^{j-1} = 0 \qquad 1 \le n < N \qquad \blacksquare$$

For a random variable X, the function F defined by

$$F(x) = P\{X \le x\} \qquad -\infty < x < \infty$$

is called the *cumulative distribution function* or, more simply, the *distribution function* of X. Thus, the distribution function specifies, for all real values x, the probability that the random variable is less than or equal to x.

Now, suppose that $a \le b$. Then, because the event $\{X \le a\}$ is contained in the event $\{X \le b\}$, it follows that $F(a)$, the probability of the former, is less than or equal to $F(b)$, the probability of the latter. In other words, $F(x)$ is a nondecreasing function of x. Other general properties of the distribution function are given in Section 4.10.

4.2 Discrete Random Variables

A random variable that can take on at most a countable number of possible values is said to be discrete. For a discrete random variable X, we define the *probability mass function $p(a)$* of X by

$$p(a) = P\{X = a\}$$

The probability mass function $p(a)$ is positive for at most a countable number of values of a. That is, if X must assume one of the values $x_1, x_2, \ldots$, then

$$p(x_i) \geq 0 \quad \text{for } i = 1, 2, \ldots$$
$$p(x) = 0 \quad \text{for all other values of } x$$

Since X must take on one of the values x_i, we have

$$\sum_{i=1}^{\infty} p(x_i) = 1$$

It is often instructive to present the probability mass function in a graphical format by plotting $p(x_i)$ on the y-axis against x_i on the x-axis. For instance, if the probability mass function of X is

$$p(0) = \frac{1}{4} \qquad p(1) = \frac{1}{2} \qquad p(2) = \frac{1}{4}$$

we can represent this function graphically as shown in Figure 4.1. Similarly, a graph of the probability mass function of the random variable representing the sum when two dice are rolled looks like Figure 4.2.

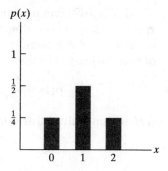

Figure 4.1

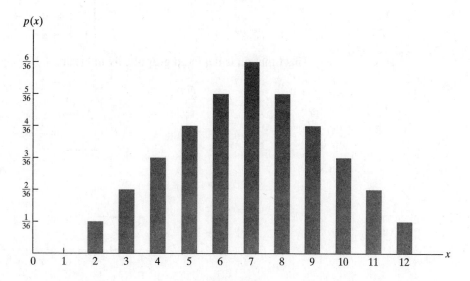

Figure 4.2

Example 2a

The probability mass function of a random variable X is given by $p(i) = c\lambda^i/i!$, $i = 0, 1, 2, \ldots$, where λ is some positive value. Find (a) $P\{X = 0\}$ and (b) $P\{X > 2\}$.

Solution Since $\sum_{i=0}^{\infty} p(i) = 1$, we have

$$c \sum_{i=0}^{\infty} \frac{\lambda^i}{i!} = 1$$

which, because $e^x = \sum_{i=0}^{\infty} x^i/i!$, implies that

$$ce^\lambda = 1 \quad \text{or} \quad c = e^{-\lambda}$$

Hence,

(a) $P\{X = 0\} = e^{-\lambda}\lambda^0/0! = e^{-\lambda}$

(b) $P\{X > 2\} = 1 - P\{X \leq 2\} = 1 - P\{X = 0\} - P\{X = 1\}$
$$- P\{X = 2\}$$
$$= 1 - e^{-\lambda} - \lambda e^{-\lambda} - \frac{\lambda^2 e^{-\lambda}}{2} \qquad \blacksquare$$

The cumulative distribution function F can be expressed in terms of $p(a)$ by

$$F(a) = \sum_{\text{all } x \leq a} p(x)$$

If X is a discrete random variable whose possible values are $x_1, x_2, x_3, \ldots$, where $x_1 < x_2 < x_3 < \cdots$, then the distribution function F of X is a step function. That is, the value of F is constant in the intervals (x_{i-1}, x_i) and then takes a step (or jump) of size $p(x_i)$ at x_i. For instance, if X has a probability mass function given by

$$p(1) = \frac{1}{4} \qquad p(2) = \frac{1}{2} \qquad p(3) = \frac{1}{8} \qquad p(4) = \frac{1}{8}$$

then its cumulative distribution function is

$$F(a) = \begin{cases} 0 & a < 1 \\ \frac{1}{4} & 1 \leq a < 2 \\ \frac{3}{4} & 2 \leq a < 3 \\ \frac{7}{8} & 3 \leq a < 4 \\ 1 & 4 \leq a \end{cases}$$

This function is depicted graphically in Figure 4.3.

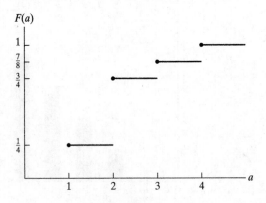

Figure 4.3

Note that the size of the step at any of the values 1, 2, 3, and 4 is equal to the probability that X assumes that particular value.

4.3 Expected Value

One of the most important concepts in probability theory is that of the expectation of a random variable. If X is a discrete random variable having a probability mass function $p(x)$, then the *expectation*, or the *expected value*, of X, denoted by $E[X]$, is defined by

$$E[X] = \sum_{x:p(x)>0} xp(x)$$

In words, the expected value of X is a weighted average of the possible values that X can take on, each value being weighted by the probability that X assumes it. For instance, on the one hand, if the probability mass function of X is given by

$$p(0) = \frac{1}{2} = p(1)$$

then

$$E[X] = 0\left(\frac{1}{2}\right) + 1\left(\frac{1}{2}\right) = \frac{1}{2}$$

is just the ordinary average of the two possible values, 0 and 1, that X can assume. On the other hand, if

$$p(0) = \frac{1}{3} \qquad p(1) = \frac{2}{3}$$

then

$$E[X] = 0\left(\frac{1}{3}\right) + 1\left(\frac{2}{3}\right) = \frac{2}{3}$$

is a weighted average of the two possible values 0 and 1, where the value 1 is given twice as much weight as the value 0, since $p(1) = 2p(0)$.

Another motivation of the definition of expectation is provided by the frequency interpretation of probabilities. This interpretation (partially justified by the strong law of large numbers, to be presented in Chapter 8) assumes that if an infinite sequence of independent replications of an experiment is performed, then, for any event E, the proportion of time that E occurs will be $P(E)$. Now, consider a random variable X that must take on one of the values $x_1, x_2, \ldots x_n$ with respective probabilities $p(x_1), p(x_2), \ldots, p(x_n)$, and think of X as representing our winnings in a single game of chance. That is, with probability $p(x_i)$, we shall win x_i units $i = 1, 2, \ldots, n$. By the frequency interpretation, if we play this game continually, then the proportion of time that we win x_i will be $p(x_i)$. Since this is true for all $i, i = 1, 2, \ldots, n$, it follows that our average winnings per game will be

$$\sum_{i=1}^{n} x_i p(x_i) = E[X]$$

Example 3a

Find $E[X]$, where X is the outcome when we roll a fair die.

Solution Since $p(1) = p(2) = p(3) = p(4) = p(5) = p(6) = \frac{1}{6}$, we obtain

$$E[X] = 1\left(\frac{1}{6}\right) + 2\left(\frac{1}{6}\right) + 3\left(\frac{1}{6}\right) + 4\left(\frac{1}{6}\right) + 5\left(\frac{1}{6}\right) + 6\left(\frac{1}{6}\right) = \frac{7}{2} \qquad \blacksquare$$

Example 3b

We say that I is an indicator variable for the event A if

$$I = \begin{cases} 1 & \text{if } A \text{ occurs} \\ 0 & \text{if } A^c \text{ occurs} \end{cases}$$

Find $E[I]$.

Solution Since $p(1) = P(A), p(0) = 1 - P(A)$, we have

$$E[I] = P(A)$$

That is, the expected value of the indicator variable for the event A is equal to the probability that A occurs. ∎

Example 3c

A contestant on a quiz show is presented with two questions, questions 1 and 2, which he is to attempt to answer in some order he chooses. If he decides to try question i first, then he will be allowed to go on to question $j, j \neq i$, only if his answer to question i is correct. If his initial answer is incorrect, he is not allowed to answer the other question. The contestant is to receive V_i dollars if he answers question i correctly, $i = 1, 2$. For instance, he will receive $V_1 + V_2$ dollars if he answers both questions correctly. If the probability that he knows the answer to question i is $P_i, i = 1, 2$, which question should he attempt to answer first so as to maximize his expected winnings? Assume that the events $E_i, i = 1, 2$, that he knows the answer to question i are independent events.

Solution On the one hand, if he attempts to answer question 1 first, then he will win

$$\begin{array}{ll} 0 & \text{with probability } 1 - P_1 \\ V_1 & \text{with probability } P_1(1 - P_2) \\ V_1 + V_2 & \text{with probability } P_1 P_2 \end{array}$$

Hence, his expected winnings in this case will be

$$V_1 P_1(1 - P_2) + (V_1 + V_2)P_1 P_2$$

On the other hand, if he attempts to answer question 2 first, his expected winnings will be

$$V_2 P_2(1 - P_1) + (V_1 + V_2)P_1 P_2$$

Therefore, it is better to try question 1 first if

$$V_1 P_1(1 - P_2) \geq V_2 P_2(1 - P_1)$$

or, equivalently, if

$$\frac{V_1 P_1}{1 - P_1} \geq \frac{V_2 P_2}{1 - P_2}$$

For example, if he is 60 percent certain of answering question 1, worth \$200, correctly and he is 80 percent certain of answering question 2, worth \$100, correctly, then he should attempt to answer question 2 first because

$$400 = \frac{(100)(.8)}{.2} > \frac{(200)(.6)}{.4} = 300$$ ∎

Example 3d

A school class of 120 students is driven in 3 buses to a symphonic performance. There are 36 students in one of the buses, 40 in another, and 44 in the third bus. When the buses arrive, one of the 120 students is randomly chosen. Let X denote the number of students on the bus of that randomly chosen student, and find $E[X]$.

Solution Since the randomly chosen student is equally likely to be any of the 120 students, it follows that

$$P\{X = 36\} = \frac{36}{120} \quad P\{X = 40\} = \frac{40}{120} \quad P\{X = 44\} = \frac{44}{120}$$

Hence,

$$E[X] = 36\left(\frac{3}{10}\right) + 40\left(\frac{1}{3}\right) + 44\left(\frac{11}{30}\right) = \frac{1208}{30} = 40.2667$$

However, the average number of students on a bus is $120/3 = 40$, showing that the expected number of students on the bus of a randomly chosen student is larger than the average number of students on a bus. This is a general phenomenon, and it occurs because the more students there are on a bus, the more likely it is that a randomly chosen student would have been on that bus. As a result, buses with many students are given more weight than those with fewer students. (See Self-Test Problem 4.4) ∎

Remark The probability concept of expectation is analogous to the physical concept of the *center of gravity* of a distribution of mass. Consider a discrete random variable X having probability mass function $p(x_i), i \geq 1$. If we now imagine a weightless rod in which weights with mass $p(x_i), i \geq 1$, are located at the points $x_i, i \geq 1$ (see Figure 4.4), then the point at which the rod would be in balance is known as the center of gravity. For those readers acquainted with elementary statics, it is now a simple matter to show that this point is at $E[X]$.[†] ∎

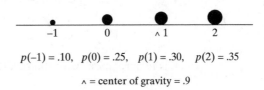

$$p(-1) = .10, \quad p(0) = .25, \quad p(1) = .30, \quad p(2) = .35$$

$$\wedge = \text{center of gravity} = .9$$

Figure 4.4

4.4 Expectation of a Function of a Random Variable

Suppose that we are given a discrete random variable along with its probability mass function and that we want to compute the expected value of some function of X, say, $g(X)$. How can we accomplish this? One way is as follows: Since $g(X)$ is itself a discrete random variable, it has a probability mass function, which can be determined from the probability mass function of X. Once we have determined the probability mass function of $g(X)$, we can compute $E[g(X)]$ by using the definition of expected value.

[†] To prove this, we must show that the sum of the torques tending to turn the point around $E[X]$ is equal to 0. That is, we must show that $0 = \sum_i (x_i - E[X])p(x_i)$, which is immediate.

Example 4a

Let X denote a random variable that takes on any of the values -1, 0, and 1 with respective probabilities

$$P\{X = -1\} = .2 \quad P\{X = 0\} = .5 \quad P\{X = 1\} = .3$$

Compute $E[X^2]$.

Solution Let $Y = X^2$. Then the probability mass function of Y is given by

$$P\{Y = 1\} = P\{X = -1\} + P\{X = 1\} = .5$$
$$P\{Y = 0\} = P\{X = 0\} = .5$$

Hence,

$$E[X^2] = E[Y] = 1(.5) + 0(.5) = .5$$

Note that

$$.5 = E[X^2] \neq (E[X])^2 = .01 \qquad \blacksquare$$

Although the preceding procedure will always enable us to compute the expected value of any function of X from a knowledge of the probability mass function of X, there is another way of thinking about $E[g(X)]$: Since $g(X)$ will equal $g(x)$ whenever X is equal to x, it seems reasonable that $E[g(X)]$ should just be a weighted average of the values $g(x)$, with $g(x)$ being weighted by the probability that X is equal to x. That is, the following result is quite intuitive.

Proposition 4.1

If X is a discrete random variable that takes on one of the values $x_i, i \geq 1$, with respective probabilities $p(x_i)$, then, for any real-valued function g,

$$E[g(X)] = \sum_i g(x_i)p(x_i)$$

Before proving this proposition, let us check that it is in accord with the results of Example 4a. Applying it to that example yields

$$E\{X^2\} = (-1)^2(.2) + 0^2(.5) + 1^2(.3)$$
$$= 1(.2 + .3) + 0(.5)$$
$$= .5$$

which is in agreement with the result given in Example 4a.

Proof of Proposition 4.1 The proof of Proposition 4.1 proceeds, as in the preceding verification, by grouping together all the terms in $\sum_i g(x_i)p(x_i)$ having the same value of $g(x_i)$. Specifically, suppose that $y_j, j \geq 1$, represent the different values of $g(x_i), i \geq 1$. Then, grouping all the $g(x_i)$ having the same value gives

$$\sum_i g(x_i)p(x_i) = \sum_j \sum_{i:g(x_i)=y_j} g(x_i)p(x_i)$$
$$= \sum_j \sum_{i:g(x_i)=y_j} y_j p(x_i)$$
$$= \sum_j y_j \sum_{i:g(x_i)=y_j} p(x_i)$$
$$= \sum_j y_j P\{g(X) = y_j\}$$
$$= E[g(X)] \qquad \square$$

Example 4b

A product that is sold seasonally yields a net profit of b dollars for each unit sold and a net loss of ℓ dollars for each unit left unsold when the season ends. The number of units of the product that are ordered at a specific department store during any season is a random variable having probability mass function $p(i), i \geq 0$. If the store must stock this product in advance, determine the number of units the store should stock so as to maximize its expected profit.

Solution Let X denote the number of units ordered. If s units are stocked, then the profit—call it $P(s)$—can be expressed as

$$P(s) = bX - (s - X)\ell \quad \text{if } X \leq s$$
$$= sb \qquad\qquad\quad \text{if } X > s$$

Hence, the expected profit equals

$$E[P(s)] = \sum_{i=0}^{s}[bi - (s - i)\ell]p(i) + \sum_{i=s+1}^{\infty} sbp(i)$$

$$= (b + \ell)\sum_{i=0}^{s} ip(i) - s\ell\sum_{i=0}^{s} p(i) + sb\left[1 - \sum_{i=0}^{s} p(i)\right]$$

$$= (b + \ell)\sum_{i=0}^{s} ip(i) - (b + \ell)s\sum_{i=0}^{s} p(i) + sb$$

$$= sb + (b + \ell)\sum_{i=0}^{s}(i - s)p(i)$$

To determine the optimum value of s, let us investigate what happens to the profit when we increase s by 1 unit. By substitution, we see that the expected profit in this case is given by

$$E[P(s + 1)] = b(s + 1) + (b + \ell)\sum_{i=0}^{s+1}(i - s - 1)p(i)$$

$$= b(s + 1) + (b + \ell)\sum_{i=0}^{s}(i - s - 1)p(i)$$

Therefore,

$$E[P(s + 1)] - E[P(s)] = b - (b + \ell)\sum_{i=0}^{s} p(i)$$

Thus, stocking $s + 1$ units will be better than stocking s units whenever

$$\sum_{i=0}^{s} p(i) < \frac{b}{b + \ell} \tag{4.1}$$

Because the left-hand side of Equation (4.1) is increasing in s while the right-hand side is constant, the inequality will be satisfied for all values of $s \leq s^*$, where s^* is the largest value of s satisfying Equation (4.1). Since

$$E[P(0)] < \cdots < E[P(s^*)] < E[P(s^* + 1)] > E[P(s^* + 2)] > \cdots$$

it follows that stocking $s^* + 1$ items will lead to a maximum expected profit. ∎

Example 4c

Utility

Suppose that you must choose one of two possible actions, each of which can result in any of n consequences, denoted as $C_1, \ldots, C_n$. Suppose that if the first action is chosen, then consequence C_i will result with probability $p_i, i = 1, \ldots, n$, whereas if the second action is chosen, then consequence C_i will result with probability q_i, $i = 1, \ldots, n$, where $\sum_{i=1}^{n} p_i = \sum_{i=1}^{n} q_i = 1$. The following approach can be used to determine which action to choose: Start by assigning numerical values to the different consequences. First, identify the least and the most desirable consequences—call them c and C, respectively; give consequence c the value 0 and give C the value 1. Now consider any of the other $n - 2$ consequences, say, C_i. To value this consequence, imagine that you are given the choice between either receiving C_i or taking part in a random experiment that either earns you consequence C with probability u or consequence c with probability $1 - u$. Clearly, your choice will depend on the value of u. On the one hand, if $u = 1$, then the experiment is certain to result in consequence C, and since C is the most desirable consequence, you will prefer participating in the experiment to receiving C_i. On the other hand, if $u = 0$, then the experiment will result in the least desirable consequence—namely, c—so in this case you will prefer the consequence C_i to participating in the experiment. Now, as u decreases from 1 to 0, it seems reasonable that your choice will at some point switch from participating in the experiment to the certain return of C_i, and at that critical switch point you will be indifferent between the two alternatives. Take that indifference probability u as the value of the consequence C_i. In other words, the value of C_i is that probability u such that you are indifferent between either receiving the consequence C_i or taking part in an experiment that returns consequence C with probability u or consequence c with probability $1 - u$. We call this indifference probability the *utility* of the consequence C_i, and we designate it as $u(C_i)$.

To determine which action is superior, we need to evaluate each one. Consider the first action, which results in consequence C_i with probability $p_i, i = 1, \ldots, n$. We can think of the result of this action as being determined by a two-stage experiment. In the first stage, one of the values $1, \ldots, n$ is chosen according to the probabilities $p_1, \ldots, p_n$; if value i is chosen, you receive consequence C_i. However, since C_i is equivalent to obtaining consequence C with probability $u(C_i)$ or consequence c with probability $1 - u(C_i)$, it follows that the result of the two-stage experiment is equivalent to an experiment in which either consequence C or consequence c is obtained, with C being obtained with probability

$$\sum_{i=1}^{n} p_i u(C_i)$$

Similarly, the result of choosing the second action is equivalent to taking part in an experiment in which either consequence C or consequence c is obtained, with C being obtained with probability

$$\sum_{i=1}^{n} q_i u(C_i)$$

Since C is preferable to c, it follows that the first action is preferable to the second action if

$$\sum_{i=1}^{n} p_i u(C_i) > \sum_{i=1}^{n} q_i u(C_i)$$

In other words, the worth of an action can be measured by the expected value of the utility of its consequence, and the action with the largest expected utility is the most preferable. ∎

A simple logical consequence of Proposition 4.1 is Corollary 4.1.

Corollary 4.1

If a and b are constants, then

$$E[aX + b] = aE[X] + b$$

Proof

$$E[aX + b] = \sum_{x:p(x)>0} (ax + b)p(x)$$

$$= a \sum_{x:p(x)>0} xp(x) + b \sum_{x:p(x)>0} p(x)$$

$$= aE[X] + b \qquad \square$$

The expected value of a random variable X, $E[X]$, is also referred to as the *mean* or the *first moment of X*. The quantity $E[X^n]$, $n \geq 1$, is called the *nth moment of X*. By Proposition 4.1, we note that

$$E[X^n] = \sum_{x:p(x)>0} x^n p(x)$$

4.5 Variance

Given a random variable X along with its distribution function F, it would be extremely useful if we were able to summarize the essential properties of F by certain suitably defined measures. One such measure would be $E[X]$, the expected value of X. However, although $E[X]$ yields the weighted average of the possible values of X, it does not tell us anything about the variation, or spread, of these values. For instance, although random variables W, Y, and Z having probability mass functions determined by

$$W = 0 \quad \text{with probability 1}$$

$$Y = \begin{cases} -1 & \text{with probability } \frac{1}{2} \\ +1 & \text{with probability } \frac{1}{2} \end{cases}$$

$$Z = \begin{cases} -100 & \text{with probability } \frac{1}{2} \\ +100 & \text{with probability } \frac{1}{2} \end{cases}$$

all have the same expectation—namely, 0—there is a much greater spread in the possible values of Y than in those of W (which is a constant) and in the possible values of Z than in those of Y.

Because we expect X to take on values around its mean $E[X]$, it would appear that a reasonable way of measuring the possible variation of X would be to look at how far apart X would be from its mean, on the average. One possible way to measure this variation would be to consider the quantity $E[|X - \mu|]$, where $\mu = E[X]$. However, it turns out to be mathematically inconvenient to deal with this quantity, so a more tractable quantity is usually considered—namely, the expectation of the square of the difference between X and its mean. We thus have the following definition.

Definition

If X is a random variable with mean μ, then the variance of X, denoted by $\mathrm{Var}(X)$, is defined by
$$\mathrm{Var}(X) = E[(X - \mu)^2]$$

An alternative formula for $\mathrm{Var}(X)$ is derived as follows:

$$
\begin{aligned}
\mathrm{Var}(X) &= E[(X - \mu)^2]\\
&= \sum_x (x - \mu)^2 p(x)\\
&= \sum_x (x^2 - 2\mu x + \mu^2) p(x)\\
&= \sum_x x^2 p(x) - 2\mu \sum_x x p(x) + \mu^2 \sum_x p(x)\\
&= E[X^2] - 2\mu^2 + \mu^2\\
&= E[X^2] - \mu^2
\end{aligned}
$$

That is,

$$\boxed{\mathrm{Var}(X) = E[X^2] - (E[X])^2}$$

In words, the variance of X is equal to the expected value of X^2 minus the square of its expected value. In practice, this formula frequently offers the easiest way to compute $\mathrm{Var}(X)$.

Example 5a

Calculate $\mathrm{Var}(X)$ if X represents the outcome when a fair die is rolled.

Solution It was shown in Example 3a that $E[X] = \frac{7}{2}$. Also,

$$E[X^2] = 1^2\left(\frac{1}{6}\right) + 2^2\left(\frac{1}{6}\right) + 3^2\left(\frac{1}{6}\right) + 4^2\left(\frac{1}{6}\right) + 5^2\left(\frac{1}{6}\right) + 6^2\left(\frac{1}{6}\right)$$
$$= \left(\frac{1}{6}\right)(91)$$

Hence,
$$\mathrm{Var}(X) = \frac{91}{6} - \left(\frac{7}{2}\right)^2 = \frac{35}{12} \qquad \blacksquare$$

A useful identity is that for any constants a and b,

$$\mathrm{Var}(aX + b) = a^2 \mathrm{Var}(X)$$

To prove this equality, let $\mu = E[X]$ and note from Corollary 4.1 that $E[aX + b] = a\mu + b$. Therefore,

$$
\begin{aligned}
\mathrm{Var}(aX + b) &= E[(aX + b - a\mu - b)^2]\\
&= E[a^2(X - \mu)^2]\\
&= a^2 E[(X - \mu)^2]\\
&= a^2 \mathrm{Var}(X)
\end{aligned}
$$

Remarks (a) Analogous to the means being the center of gravity of a distribution of mass, the variance represents, in the terminology of mechanics, the moment of inertia.

(b) The square root of the Var(X) is called the *standard deviation* of X, and we denote it by SD(X). That is,

$$SD(X) = \sqrt{Var(X)}$$

Discrete random variables are often classified according to their probability mass functions. In the next few sections, we consider some of the more common types.

4.6 The Bernoulli and Binomial Random Variables

Suppose that a trial, or an experiment, whose outcome can be classified as either a *success* or a *failure* is performed. If we let $X = 1$ when the outcome is a success and $X = 0$ when it is a failure, then the probability mass function of X is given by

$$p(0) = P\{X = 0\} = 1 - p$$
$$p(1) = P\{X = 1\} = p$$

(6.1)

where $p, 0 \leq p \leq 1$, is the probability that the trial is a success.

A random variable X is said to be a *Bernoulli random variable* (after the Swiss mathematician James Bernoulli) if its probability mass function is given by Equations (6.1) for some $p \in (0, 1)$.

Suppose now that n independent trials, each of which results in a success with probability p or in a failure with probability $1 - p$, are to be performed. If X represents the number of successes that occur in the n trials, then X is said to be a *binomial random variable* with parameters (n, p). Thus, a Bernoulli random variable is just a binomial random variable with parameters $(1, p)$.

The probability mass function of a binomial random variable having parameters (n, p) is given by

$$p(i) = \binom{n}{i} p^i (1 - p)^{n-i} \qquad i = 0, 1, \ldots, n$$

(6.2)

The validity of Equation (6.2) may be verified by first noting that the probability of any particular sequence of n outcomes containing i successes and $n - i$ failures is, by the assumed independence of trials, $p^i (1 - p)^{n-i}$. Equation (6.2) then follows, since there are $\binom{n}{i}$ different sequences of the n outcomes leading to i successes and $n - i$ failures. This perhaps can most easily be seen by noting that there are $\binom{n}{i}$ different choices of the i trials that result in successes. For instance, if $n = 4, i = 2$, then there are $\binom{4}{2} = 6$ ways in which the four trials can result in two successes, namely, any of the outcomes $(s, s, f, f), (s, f, s, f), (s, f, f, s), (f, s, s, f), (f, s, f, s)$, and (f, f, s, s), where the outcome (s, s, f, f) means, for instance, that the first two trials are successes and the last two failures. Since each of these outcomes has probability $p^2 (1 - p)^2$ of occurring, the desired probability of two successes in the four trials is $\binom{4}{2} p^2 (1 - p)^2$.

Note that, by the binomial theorem, the probabilities sum to 1; that is,

$$\sum_{i=0}^{\infty} p(i) = \sum_{i=0}^{n} \binom{n}{i} p^i (1-p)^{n-i} = [p + (1-p)]^n = 1$$

Example 6a

Five fair coins are flipped. If the outcomes are assumed independent, find the probability mass function of the number of heads obtained.

Solution If we let X equal the number of heads (successes) that appear, then X is a binomial random variable with parameters $\left(n = 5, p = \frac{1}{2}\right)$. Hence, by Equation (6.2),

$$P\{X = 0\} = \binom{5}{0} \left(\frac{1}{2}\right)^0 \left(\frac{1}{2}\right)^5 = \frac{1}{32}$$

$$P\{X = 1\} = \binom{5}{1} \left(\frac{1}{2}\right)^1 \left(\frac{1}{2}\right)^4 = \frac{5}{32}$$

$$P\{X = 2\} = \binom{5}{2} \left(\frac{1}{2}\right)^2 \left(\frac{1}{2}\right)^3 = \frac{10}{32}$$

$$P\{X = 3\} = \binom{5}{3} \left(\frac{1}{2}\right)^3 \left(\frac{1}{2}\right)^2 = \frac{10}{32}$$

$$P\{X = 4\} = \binom{5}{4} \left(\frac{1}{2}\right)^4 \left(\frac{1}{2}\right)^1 = \frac{5}{32}$$

$$P\{X = 5\} = \binom{5}{5} \left(\frac{1}{2}\right)^5 \left(\frac{1}{2}\right)^0 = \frac{1}{32}$$

∎

Example 6b

It is known that screws produced by a certain company will be defective with probability .01, independently of one another. The company sells the screws in packages of 10 and offers a money-back guarantee that at most 1 of the 10 screws is defective. What proportion of packages sold must the company replace?

Solution If X is the number of defective screws in a package, then X is a binomial random variable with parameters (10, .01). Hence, the probability that a package will have to be replaced is

$$1 - P\{X = 0\} - P\{X = 1\} = 1 - \binom{10}{0}(.01)^0(.99)^{10} - \binom{10}{1}(.01)^1(.99)^9$$

$$\approx .004$$

Thus, only .4 percent of the packages will have to be replaced. ∎

Example 6c

The following gambling game, known as the wheel of fortune (or chuck-a-luck), is quite popular at many carnivals and gambling casinos: A player bets on one of the numbers 1 through 6. Three dice are then rolled, and if the number bet by the player appears i times, $i = 1, 2, 3$, then the player wins i units; if the number bet by the player does not appear on any of the dice, then the player loses 1 unit. Is this game fair to the player? (Actually, the game is played by spinning a wheel that comes to rest on a slot labeled by three of the numbers 1 through 6, but this variant is mathematically equivalent to the dice version.)

Solution If we assume that the dice are fair and act independently of one another, then the number of times that the number bet appears is a binomial random variable with parameters $\left(3, \frac{1}{6}\right)$. Hence, letting X denote the player's winnings in the game, we have

$$P\{X = -1\} = \binom{3}{0} \left(\frac{1}{6}\right)^0 \left(\frac{5}{6}\right)^3 = \frac{125}{216}$$

$$P\{X = 1\} = \binom{3}{1} \left(\frac{1}{6}\right)^1 \left(\frac{5}{6}\right)^2 = \frac{75}{216}$$

$$P\{X = 2\} = \binom{3}{2} \left(\frac{1}{6}\right)^2 \left(\frac{5}{6}\right)^1 = \frac{15}{216}$$

$$P\{X = 3\} = \binom{3}{3} \left(\frac{1}{6}\right)^3 \left(\frac{5}{6}\right)^0 = \frac{1}{216}$$

In order to determine whether or not this is a fair game for the player, let us calculate $E[X]$. From the preceding probabilities, we obtain

$$E[X] = \frac{-125 + 75 + 30 + 3}{216}$$
$$= \frac{-17}{216}$$

Hence, in the long run, the player will lose 17 units per every 216 games he plays. ∎

In the next example, we consider the simplest form of the theory of inheritance as developed by Gregor Mendel (1822–1884).

Example 6d

Suppose that a particular trait (such as eye color or left-handedness) of a person is classified on the basis of one pair of genes, and suppose also that d represents a dominant gene and r a recessive gene. Thus, a person with dd genes is purely dominant, one with rr is purely recessive, and one with rd is hybrid. The purely dominant and the hybrid individuals are alike in appearance. Children receive 1 gene from each parent. If, with respect to a particular trait, 2 hybrid parents have a total of 4 children, what is the probability that 3 of the 4 children have the outward appearance of the dominant gene?

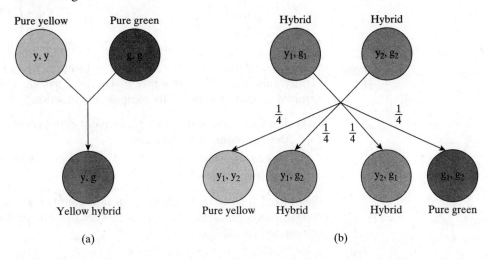

Figure 4.5 (a) Crossing pure yellow seeds with pure green seeds; (b) Crossing hybrid first-generation seeds.

The preceding Figure 4.5a and b shows what can happen when hybrid yellow (dominant) and green (recessive) seeds are crossed.

Solution If we assume that each child is equally likely to inherit either of 2 genes from each parent, the probabilities that the child of 2 hybrid parents will have *dd*, *rr*, and *rd* pairs of genes are, respectively, $\frac{1}{4}, \frac{1}{4}$, and $\frac{1}{2}$. Hence, since an offspring will have the outward appearance of the dominant gene if its gene pair is either *dd* or *rd*, it follows that the number of such children is binomially distributed with parameters $\left(4, \frac{3}{4}\right)$. Thus, the desired probability is

$$\binom{4}{3}\left(\frac{3}{4}\right)^3\left(\frac{1}{4}\right)^1 = \frac{27}{64} \qquad \blacksquare$$

Example 6e

Consider a jury trial in which it takes 8 of the 12 jurors to convict the defendant; that is, in order for the defendant to be convicted, at least 8 of the jurors must vote him guilty. If we assume that jurors act independently and that whether or not the defendant is guilty, each makes the right decision with probability θ, what is the probability that the jury renders a correct decision?

Solution The problem, as stated, is incapable of solution, for there is not yet enough information. For instance, if the defendant is innocent, the probability of the jury rendering a correct decision is

$$\sum_{i=5}^{12}\binom{12}{i}\theta^i(1-\theta)^{12-i}$$

whereas, if he is guilty, the probability of a correct decision is

$$\sum_{i=8}^{12}\binom{12}{i}\theta^i(1-\theta)^{12-i}$$

Therefore, if α represents the probability that the defendant is guilty, then, by conditioning on whether or not he is guilty, we obtain the probability that the jury renders a correct decision:

$$\alpha\sum_{i=8}^{12}\binom{12}{i}\theta^i(1-\theta)^{12-i} + (1-\alpha)\sum_{i=5}^{12}\binom{12}{i}\theta^i(1-\theta)^{12-i} \qquad \blacksquare$$

Example 6f

A communication system consists of n components, each of which will, independently, function with probability p. The total system will be able to operate effectively if at least one-half of its components function.

(a) For what values of p is a 5-component system more likely to operate effectively than a 3-component system?

(b) In general, when is a $(2k + 1)$-component system better than a $(2k - 1)$-component system?

Solution (a) Because the number of functioning components is a binomial random variable with parameters (n, p), it follows that the probability that a 5-component system will be effective is

$$\binom{5}{3}p^3(1-p)^2 + \binom{5}{4}p^4(1-p) + p^5$$

whereas the corresponding probability for a 3-component system is

$$\binom{3}{2} p^2(1 - p) + p^3$$

Hence, the 5-component system is better if

$$10p^3(1 - p)^2 + 5p^4(1 - p) + p^5 > 3p^2(1 - p) + p^3$$

which reduces to

$$3(p - 1)^2(2p - 1) > 0$$

or

$$p > \frac{1}{2}$$

(b) In general, a system with $2k + 1$ components will be better than one with $2k - 1$ components if (and only if) $p > \frac{1}{2}$. To prove this, consider a system of $2k + 1$ components and let X denote the number of the first $2k - 1$ that function. Then

$$P_{2k+1}(\text{effective}) = P\{X \geq k + 1\} + P\{X = k\}(1 - (1 - p)^2) + P\{X = k - 1\}p^2$$

which follows because the $(2k + 1)$-component system will be effective if either

(i) $X \geq k + 1$;
(ii) $X = k$ and at least one of the remaining 2 components function; or
(iii) $X = k - 1$ and both of the next 2 components function.

Since

$$P_{2k-1}(\text{effective}) = P\{X \geq k\}$$
$$= P\{X = k\} + P\{X \geq k + 1\}$$

we obtain

$$P_{2k+1}(\text{effective}) - P_{2k-1}(\text{effective})$$
$$= P\{X = k - 1\}p^2 - (1 - p)^2 P\{X = k\}$$
$$= \binom{2k - 1}{k - 1} p^{k-1}(1 - p)^k p^2 - (1 - p)^2 \binom{2k - 1}{k} p^k(1 - p)^{k-1}$$
$$= \binom{2k - 1}{k} p^k(1 - p)^k[p - (1 - p)] \text{ since } \binom{2k - 1}{k - 1} = \binom{2k - 1}{k}$$
$$> 0 \Leftrightarrow p > \frac{1}{2}$$

∎

4.6.1 Properties of Binomial Random Variables

We will now examine the properties of a binomial random variable with parameters n and p. To begin, let us compute its expected value and variance. To begin, note that

$$E[X^k] = \sum_{i=0}^{n} i^k \binom{n}{i} p^i(1 - p)^{n-i}$$
$$= \sum_{i=1}^{n} i^k \binom{n}{i} p^i(1 - p)^{n-i}$$

Using the identity

$$i \binom{n}{i} = n \binom{n-1}{i-1}$$

gives

$$E[X^k] = np \sum_{i=1}^{n} i^{k-1} \binom{n-1}{i-1} p^{i-1}(1-p)^{n-i}$$

$$= np \sum_{j=0}^{n-1} (j+1)^{k-1} \binom{n-1}{j} p^j (1-p)^{n-1-j} \quad \text{by letting} \atop j = i-1$$

$$= npE[(Y+1)^{k-1}]$$

where Y is a binomial random variable with parameters $n-1, p$. Setting $k = 1$ in the preceding equation yields

$$E[X] = np$$

That is, the expected number of successes that occur in n independent trials when each is a success with probability p is equal to np. Setting $k = 2$ in the preceding equation and using the preceding formula for the expected value of a binomial random variable yields

$$E[X^2] = npE[Y+1]$$
$$= np[(n-1)p + 1]$$

Since $E[X] = np$, we obtain

$$\text{Var}(X) = E[X^2] - (E[X])^2$$
$$= np[(n-1)p + 1] - (np)^2$$
$$= np(1-p)$$

Summing up, we have shown the following:

If X is a binomial random variable with parameters n and p, then

$$E[X] = np$$
$$\text{Var}(X) = np(1-p)$$

The following proposition details how the binomial probability mass function first increases and then decreases.

Proposition 6.1 If X is a binomial random variable with parameters (n, p), where $0 < p < 1$, then as k goes from 0 to $n, P\{X = k\}$ first increases monotonically and then decreases monotonically, reaching its largest value when k is the largest integer less than or equal to $(n+1)p$.

Proof We prove the proposition by considering $P\{X = k\}/P\{X = k-1\}$ and determining for what values of k it is greater or less than 1. Now,

$$\frac{P\{X = k\}}{P\{X = k-1\}} = \frac{\dfrac{n!}{(n-k)!k!}p^k(1-p)^{n-k}}{\dfrac{n!}{(n-k+1)!(k-1)!}p^{k-1}(1-p)^{n-k+1}}$$

$$= \frac{(n-k+1)p}{k(1-p)}$$

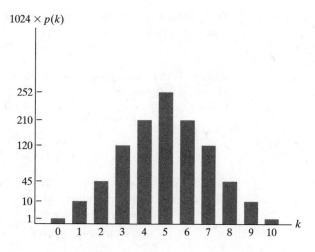

Figure 4.6 Graph of $p(k) = \binom{10}{k}\left(\frac{1}{2}\right)^{10}$.

Hence, $P\{X = k\} \geq P\{X = k - 1\}$ if and only if

$$(n - k + 1)p \geq k(1 - p)$$

or, equivalently, if and only if

$$k \leq (n + 1)p$$

and the proposition is proved. $\qquad\qquad\square$

As an illustration of Proposition 6.1, consider Figure 4.6, the graph of the probability mass function of a binomial random variable with parameters $(10, \frac{1}{2})$.

Example 6g

In a U.S. presidential election, the candidate who gains the maximum number of votes in a state is awarded the total number of electoral college votes allocated to that state. The number of electoral college votes of a given state is roughly proportional to the population of that state—that is, a state with population n has roughly nc electoral votes. (Actually, it is closer to $nc + 2$, as a state is given an electoral vote for each member it has in the House of Representatives, with the number of such representatives being roughly proportional to the population of the state, and one electoral college vote for each of its two senators.) Let us determine the average power of a citizen in a state of size n in a close presidential election, where, by *average power in a close election*, we mean that a voter in a state of size $n = 2k + 1$ will be decisive if the other $n - 1$ voters split their votes evenly between the two candidates. (We are assuming here that n is odd, but the case where n is even is quite similar.) Because the election is close, we shall suppose that each of the other $n - 1 = 2k$ voters acts independently and is equally likely to vote for either candidate. Hence, the probability that a voter in a state of size $n = 2k + 1$ will make a difference to the outcome is the same as the probability that $2k$ tosses of a fair coin land heads and tails an equal number of times. That is,

$$P\{\text{voter in state of size } 2k + 1 \text{ makes a difference}\}$$

$$= \binom{2k}{k}\left(\frac{1}{2}\right)^k\left(\frac{1}{2}\right)^k$$

$$= \frac{(2k)!}{k!k!2^{2k}}$$

To approximate the preceding equality, we make use of Stirling's approximation, which says that for k large,

$$k! \sim k^{k+1/2}e^{-k}\sqrt{2\pi}$$

where we say that $a_k \sim b_k$ when the ratio a_k/b_k approaches 1 as k approaches ∞. Hence, it follows that

$$P\{\text{voter in state of size } 2k + 1 \text{ makes a difference}\}$$

$$\sim \frac{(2k)^{2k+1/2}e^{-2k}\sqrt{2\pi}}{k^{2k+1}e^{-2k}(2\pi)2^{2k}} = \frac{1}{\sqrt{k\pi}}$$

Because such a voter (if he or she makes a difference) will affect nc electoral votes, the expected number of electoral votes a voter in a state of size n will affect—or the voter's average power—is given by

$$\text{average power} = ncP\{\text{makes a difference}\}$$

$$\sim \frac{nc}{\sqrt{n\pi/2}}$$

$$= c\sqrt{2n/\pi}$$

Thus, the average power of a voter in a state of size n is proportional to the square root of n, showing that in presidential elections, voters in large states have more power than do those in smaller states. ∎

4.6.2 Computing the Binomial Distribution Function

Suppose that X is binomial with parameters (n, p). The key to computing its distribution function

$$P\{X \le i\} = \sum_{k=0}^{i}\binom{n}{k}p^k(1 - p)^{n-k} \qquad i = 0, 1, \ldots, n$$

is to utilize the following relationship between $P\{X = k + 1\}$ and $P\{X = k\}$, which was established in the proof of Proposition 6.1:

$$P\{X = k + 1\} = \frac{p}{1 - p}\frac{n - k}{k + 1}P\{X = k\} \tag{6.3}$$

Example 6h

Let X be a binomial random variable with parameters $n = 6$, $p = .4$. Then, starting with $P\{X = 0\} = (.6)^6$ and recursively employing Equation (6.3), we obtain

$$P\{X = 0\} = (.6)^6 \approx .0467$$

$$P\{X = 1\} = \frac{4}{6}\frac{6}{1}P\{X = 0\} \approx .1866$$

$$P\{X = 2\} = \frac{4}{6}\frac{5}{2}P\{X = 1\} \approx .3110$$

$$P\{X = 3\} = \frac{4}{6}\frac{4}{3}P\{X = 2\} \approx .2765$$

$$P\{X = 4\} = \frac{4}{6}\frac{3}{4}P\{X = 3\} \approx .1382$$

$$P\{X = 5\} = \frac{4}{6}\frac{2}{5}P\{X = 4\} \approx .0369$$

$$P\{X = 6\} = \frac{4}{6}\frac{1}{6}P\{X = 5\} \approx .0041$$ ∎

A computer program that utilizes the recursion (6.3) to compute the binomial distribution function is easily written. To compute $P\{X \le i\}$, the program should first compute $P\{X = i\}$ and then use the recursion to successively compute $P\{X = i - 1\}, P\{X = i - 2\}$, and so on.

Historical note

Independent trials having a common probability of success p were first studied by the Swiss mathematician Jacques Bernoulli (1654–1705). In his book *Ars Conjectandi (The Art of Conjecturing)*, published by his nephew Nicholas eight years after his death in 1713, Bernoulli showed that if the number of such trials were large, then the proportion of them that were successes would be close to p with a probability near 1.

Jacques Bernoulli was from the first generation of the most famous mathematical family of all time. Altogether, there were between 8 and 12 Bernoullis, spread over three generations, who made fundamental contributions to probability, statistics, and mathematics. One difficulty in knowing their exact number is the fact that several had the same name. (For example, two of the sons of Jacques's brother Jean were named Jacques and Jean.) Another difficulty is that several of the Bernoullis were known by different names in different places. Our Jacques (sometimes written Jaques) was, for instance, also known as Jakob (sometimes written Jacob) and as James Bernoulli. But whatever their number, their influence and output were prodigious. Like the Bachs of music, the Bernoullis of mathematics were a family for the ages!

Example 6i

If X is a binomial random variable with parameters $n = 100$ and $p = .75$, find $P\{X = 70\}$ and $P\{X \le 70\}$.

Solution A binomial calculator can be used to obtain the following solutions:

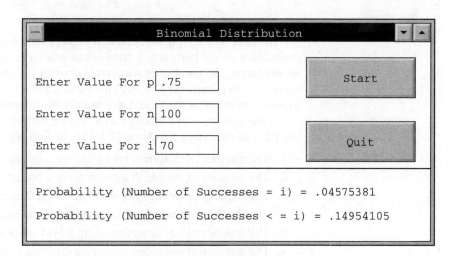

Figure 4.7

4.7 The Poisson Random Variable

A random variable X that takes on one of the values $0, 1, 2, \ldots$ is said to be a *Poisson* random variable with parameter λ if, for some $\lambda > 0$,

$$p(i) = P\{X = i\} = e^{-\lambda}\frac{\lambda^i}{i!} \quad i = 0, 1, 2, \ldots \tag{7.1}$$

Equation (7.1) defines a probability mass function, since

$$\sum_{i=0}^{\infty} p(i) = e^{-\lambda} \sum_{i=0}^{\infty} \frac{\lambda^i}{i!} = e^{-\lambda}e^{\lambda} = 1$$

The Poisson probability distribution was introduced by Siméon Denis Poisson in a book he wrote regarding the application of probability theory to lawsuits, criminal trials, and the like. This book, published in 1837, was entitled *Recherches sur la probabilité des jugements en matière criminelle et en matière civile (Investigations into the Probability of Verdicts in Criminal and Civil Matters)*.

The Poisson random variable has a tremendous range of applications in diverse areas because it may be used as an approximation for a binomial random variable with parameters (n, p) when n is large and p is small enough so that np is of moderate size. To see this, suppose that X is a binomial random variable with parameters (n, p), and let $\lambda = np$. Then

$$P\{X = i\} = \frac{n!}{(n-i)!i!}p^i(1-p)^{n-i}$$

$$= \frac{n!}{(n-i)!i!}\left(\frac{\lambda}{n}\right)^i\left(1-\frac{\lambda}{n}\right)^{n-i}$$

$$= \frac{n(n-1)\cdots(n-i+1)}{n^i}\frac{\lambda^i}{i!}\frac{(1-\lambda/n)^n}{(1-\lambda/n)^i}$$

Now, for n large and λ moderate,

$$\left(1-\frac{\lambda}{n}\right)^n \approx e^{-\lambda} \quad \frac{n(n-1)\cdots(n-i+1)}{n^i} \approx 1 \quad \left(1-\frac{\lambda}{n}\right)^i \approx 1$$

Hence, for n large and λ moderate,

$$P\{X = i\} \approx e^{-\lambda}\frac{\lambda^i}{i!}$$

In other words, if n independent trials, each of which results in a success with probability p, are performed, then when n is large and p is small enough to make np moderate, the number of successes occurring is approximately a Poisson random variable with parameter $\lambda = np$. This value λ (which will later be shown to equal the expected number of successes) will usually be determined empirically.

Some examples of random variables that generally obey the Poisson probability law [that is, they obey Equation (7.1)] are as follows:

1. The number of misprints on a page (or a group of pages) of a book
2. The number of people in a community who survive to age 100
3. The number of wrong telephone numbers that are dialed in a day
4. The number of packages of dog biscuits sold in a particular store each day
5. The number of customers entering a post office on a given day
6. The number of vacancies occurring during a year in the federal judicial system
7. The number of α-particles discharged in a fixed period of time from some radioactive material

Each of the preceding and numerous other random variables are approximately Poisson for the same reason—namely, because of the Poisson approximation to the binomial. For instance, we can suppose that there is a small probability p that each letter typed on a page will be misprinted. Hence, the number of misprints on a page will be approximately Poisson with $\lambda = np$, where n is the number of letters on a page. Similarly, we can suppose that each person in a community has some small probability of reaching age 100. Also, each person entering a store may be thought of as having some small probability of buying a package of dog biscuits, and so on.

Example 7a

Suppose that the number of typographical errors on a single page of this book has a Poisson distribution with parameter $\lambda = \frac{1}{2}$. Calculate the probability that there is at least one error on this page.

Solution Letting X denote the number of errors on this page, we have

$$P\{X \geq 1\} = 1 - P\{X = 0\} = 1 - e^{-1/2} \approx .393 \qquad \blacksquare$$

Example 7b

Suppose that the probability that an item produced by a certain machine will be defective is .1. Find the probability that a sample of 10 items will contain at most 1 defective item.

Solution The desired probability is $\binom{10}{0}(.1)^0(.9)^{10} + \binom{10}{1}(.1)^1(.9)^9 = .7361$, whereas the Poisson approximation yields the value $e^{-1} + e^{-1} \approx .7358$. $\qquad \blacksquare$

Example 7c

Consider an experiment that consists of counting the number of α particles given off in a 1-second interval by 1 gram of radioactive material. If we know from past experience that on the average, 3.2 such α particles are given off, what is a good approximation to the probability that no more than 2 α particles will appear?

Solution If we think of the gram of radioactive material as consisting of a large number n of atoms, each of which has probability of $3.2/n$ of disintegrating and sending off an α particle during the second considered, then we see that to a very close approximation, the number of α particles given off will be a Poisson random variable with parameter $\lambda = 3.2$. Hence, the desired probability is

$$P\{X \leq 2\} = e^{-3.2} + 3.2e^{-3.2} + \frac{(3.2)^2}{2}e^{-3.2}$$
$$\approx .3799 \qquad \blacksquare$$

Before computing the expected value and variance of the Poisson random variable with parameter λ, recall that this random variable approximates a binomial random variable with parameters n and p when n is large, p is small, and $\lambda = np$. Since such a binomial random variable has expected value $np = \lambda$ and variance $np(1 - p) = \lambda(1 - p) \approx \lambda$ (since p is small), it would seem that both the expected value and the variance of a Poisson random variable would equal its parameter λ. We now verify this result:

$$E[X] = \sum_{i=0}^{\infty} \frac{ie^{-\lambda}\lambda^i}{i!}$$
$$= \lambda \sum_{i=1}^{\infty} \frac{e^{-\lambda}\lambda^{i-1}}{(i-1)!}$$
$$= \lambda e^{-\lambda} \sum_{j=0}^{\infty} \frac{\lambda^j}{j!} \quad \begin{array}{l}\text{by letting}\\ j = i - 1\end{array}$$
$$= \lambda \quad \text{since } \sum_{j=0}^{\infty} \frac{\lambda^j}{j!} = e^{\lambda}$$

Thus, the expected value of a Poisson random variable X is indeed equal to its parameter λ. To determine its variance, we first compute $E[X^2]$:

$$
\begin{aligned}
E[X^2] &= \sum_{i=0}^{\infty} \frac{i^2 e^{-\lambda} \lambda^i}{i!} \\
&= \lambda \sum_{i=1}^{\infty} \frac{i e^{-\lambda} \lambda^{i-1}}{(i-1)!} \\
&= \lambda \sum_{j=0}^{\infty} \frac{(j+1) e^{-\lambda} \lambda^j}{j!} \quad \begin{array}{l} \text{by letting} \\ j = i - 1 \end{array} \\
&= \lambda \left[\sum_{j=0}^{\infty} \frac{j e^{-\lambda} \lambda^j}{j!} + \sum_{j=0}^{\infty} \frac{e^{-\lambda} \lambda^j}{j!} \right] \\
&= \lambda(\lambda + 1)
\end{aligned}
$$

where the final equality follows because the first sum is the expected value of a Poisson random variable with parameter λ and the second is the sum of the probabilities of this random variable. Therefore, since we have shown that $E[X] = \lambda$, we obtain

$$
\begin{aligned}
\text{Var}(X) &= E[X^2] - (E[X])^2 \\
&= \lambda
\end{aligned}
$$

Hence, the expected value and variance of a Poisson random variable are both equal to its parameter λ.

We have shown that the Poisson distribution with parameter np is a very good approximation to the distribution of the number of successes in n independent trials when each trial has probability p of being a success, provided that n is large and p small. In fact, it remains a good approximation even when the trials are not independent, provided that their dependence is weak. For instance, recall the matching problem (Example 5m of Chapter 2) in which n men randomly select hats from a set consisting of one hat from each person. From the point of view of the number of men who select their own hat, we may regard the random selection as the result of n trials where we say that trial i is a success if person i selects his own hat, $i = 1, \ldots, n$. Defining the events $E_i, i = 1, \ldots, n$, by

$$
E_i = \{\text{trial } i \text{ is a success}\}
$$

it is easy to see that

$$
P\{E_i\} = \frac{1}{n} \quad \text{and} \quad P\{E_i | E_j\} = \frac{1}{n-1}, \quad j \neq i
$$

Thus, we see that although the events $E_i, i = 1, \ldots, n$ are not independent, their dependence, for large n, appears to be weak. Because of this, it seems reasonable to expect that the number of successes will approximately have a Poisson distribution with parameter $n \times 1/n = 1$ and indeed this is verified in Example 5m of Chapter 2.

For a second illustration of the strength of the Poisson approximation when the trials are weakly dependent, let us consider again the birthday problem presented in Example 5i of Chapter 2. In this example, we suppose that each of n people is equally likely to have any of the 365 days of the year as his or her birthday, and the problem is to determine the probability that a set of n independent people all have different birthdays. A combinatorial argument was used to determine this probability, which was shown to be less than $\frac{1}{2}$ when $n = 23$.

We can approximate the preceding probability by using the Poisson approximation as follows: Imagine that we have a trial for each of the $\binom{n}{2}$ pairs of individuals i and $j, i \neq j$, and say that trial i, j is a success if persons i and j have the same birthday. If we let E_{ij} denote the event that trial i, j is a success, then, whereas the $\binom{n}{2}$ events $E_{ij}, 1 \leq i < j \leq n$, are not independent (see Theoretical Exercise 21), their dependence appears to be rather weak. (Indeed, these events are even *pairwise independent*, in that any 2 of the events E_{ij} and E_{kl} are independent—again, see Theoretical Exercise 21). Since $P(E_{ij}) = 1/365$, it is reasonable to suppose that the number of successes should approximately have a Poisson distribution with mean $\binom{n}{2} \Big/ 365 = n(n - 1)/730$. Therefore,

$$P\{\text{no 2 people have the same birthday}\} = P\{0 \text{ successes}\}$$
$$\approx \exp\left\{\frac{-n(n - 1)}{730}\right\}$$

To determine the smallest integer n for which this probability is less than $\frac{1}{2}$, note that

$$\exp\left\{\frac{-n(n - 1)}{730}\right\} \leq \frac{1}{2}$$

is equivalent to

$$\exp\left\{\frac{n(n - 1)}{730}\right\} \geq 2$$

Taking logarithms of both sides, we obtain

$$n(n - 1) \geq 730 \log 2$$
$$\approx 505.997$$

which yields the solution $n = 23$, in agreement with the result of Example 5i of Chapter 2.

Suppose now that we wanted the probability that among the n people, no 3 of them have their birthday on the same day. Whereas this now becomes a difficult combinatorial problem, it is a simple matter to obtain a good approximation. To begin, imagine that we have a trial for each of the $\binom{n}{3}$ triplets i, j, k, where $1 \leq i < j < k \leq n$, and call the i, j, k trial a success if persons i, j, and k all have their birthday on the same day. As before, we can then conclude that the number of successes is approximately a Poisson random variable with parameter

$$\binom{n}{3} P\{i, j, k \text{ have the same birthday}\} = \binom{n}{3}\left(\frac{1}{365}\right)^2$$
$$= \frac{n(n - 1)(n - 2)}{6 \times (365)^2}$$

Hence,

$$P\{\text{no 3 have the same birthday}\} \approx \exp\left\{\frac{-n(n-1)(n-2)}{799350}\right\}$$

This probability will be less than $\frac{1}{2}$ when n is such that

$$n(n-1)(n-2) \geq 799350 \log 2 \approx 554067.1$$

which is equivalent to $n \geq 84$. Thus, the approximate probability that at least 3 people in a group of size 84 or larger will have the same birthday exceeds $\frac{1}{2}$.

For the number of events to occur to approximately have a Poisson distribution, it is not essential that all the events have the same probability of occurrence, but only that all of these probabilities be small. The following is referred to as the *Poisson paradigm*.

Poisson Paradigm. Consider n events, with p_i equal to the probability that event i occurs, $i = 1, \ldots, n$. If all the p_i are "small" and the trials are either independent or at most "weakly dependent," then the number of these events that occur approximately has a Poisson distribution with mean $\sum_{i=1}^{n} p_i$.

Our next example not only makes use of the Poisson paradigm, but also illustrates a variety of the techniques we have studied so far.

Example 7d

Length of the longest run

A coin is flipped n times. Assuming that the flips are independent, with each one coming up heads with probability p, what is the probability that there is a string of k consecutive heads?

Solution We will first use the Poisson paradigm to approximate this probability. Now, if for $i = 1, \ldots, n - k + 1$, we let H_i denote the event that flips $i, i+1, \ldots, i + k - 1$ all land on heads, then the desired probability is that at least one of the events H_i occur. Because H_i is the event that starting with flip i, the next k flips all land on heads, it follows that $P(H_i) = p^k$. Thus, when p^k is small, we might think that the number of the H_i that occur should have an approximate Poisson distribution. However, such is not the case, because, although the events all have small probabilities, some of their dependencies are too great for the Poisson distribution to be a good approximation. For instance, because the conditional probability that flips $2, \ldots, k + 1$ are all heads given that flips $1, \ldots, k$ are all heads is equal to the probability that flip $k + 1$ is a head, it follows that

$$P(H_2|H_1) = p$$

which is far greater than the unconditional probability of H_2.

The trick that enables us to use a Poisson approximation is to note that there will be a string of k consecutive heads either if there is such a string that is immediately followed by a tail or if the final k flips all land on heads. Consequently, for $i = 1, \ldots, n - k$, let E_i be the event that flips $i, \ldots, i + k - 1$ are all heads and flip $i + k$ is a tail; also, let E_{n-k+1} be the event that flips $n - k + 1, \ldots, n$ are all heads. Note that

$$P(E_i) = p^k(1-p), \quad i \leq n - k$$
$$P(E_{n-k+1}) = p^k$$

Thus, when p^k is small, each of the events E_i has a small probability of occurring. Moreover, for $i \neq j$, if the events E_i and E_j refer to nonoverlapping sequences of flips, then $P(E_i|E_j) = P(E_i)$; if they refer to overlapping sequences, then $P(E_i|E_j) = 0$. Hence, in both cases, the conditional probabilities are close to the unconditional ones, indicating that N, the number of the events E_i that occur, should have an approximate Poisson distribution with mean

$$E[N] = \sum_{i=1}^{n-k+1} P(E_i) = (n - k)p^k(1 - p) + p^k$$

Because there will not be a run of k heads if (and only if) $N = 0$, thus the preceding gives

$$P(\text{no head strings of length } k) = P(N = 0) \approx \exp\{-(n - k)p^k(1 - p) - p^k\}$$

If we let L_n denote the largest number of consecutive heads in the n flips, then, because L_n will be less than k if (and only if) there are no head strings of length k, the preceding equation can be written as

$$P\{L_n < k\} \approx \exp\{-(n - k)p^k(1 - p) - p^k\}$$

Now, let us suppose that the coin being flipped is fair; that is, suppose that $p = 1/2$. Then the preceding gives

$$P\{L_n < k\} \approx \exp\left\{-\frac{n - k + 2}{2^{k+1}}\right\} \approx \exp\left\{-\frac{n}{2^{k+1}}\right\}$$

where the final approximation supposes that $e^{\frac{k-2}{2^{k+1}}} \approx 1$ (that is, that $\frac{k-2}{2^{k+1}} \approx 0$). Let $j = \log_2 n$, and assume that j is an integer. For $k = j + i$,

$$\frac{n}{2^{k+1}} = \frac{n}{2^j 2^{i+1}} = \frac{1}{2^{i+1}}$$

Consequently,

$$P\{L_n < j + i\} \approx \exp\{-(1/2)^{i+1}\}$$

which implies that

$$P\{L_n = j + i\} = P\{L_n < j + i + 1\} - P\{L_n < j + i\}$$
$$\approx \exp\{-(1/2)^{i+2}\} - \exp\{-(1/2)^{i+1}\}$$

For instance,

$$P\{L_n < j - 3\} \approx e^{-4} \approx .0183$$
$$P\{L_n = j - 3\} \approx e^{-2} - e^{-4} \approx .1170$$
$$P\{L_n = j - 2\} \approx e^{-1} - e^{-2} \approx .2325$$
$$P\{L_n = j - 1\} \approx e^{-1/2} - e^{-1} \approx .2387$$
$$P\{L_n = j\} \approx e^{-1/4} - e^{-1/2} \approx .1723$$
$$P\{L_n = j + 1\} \approx e^{-1/8} - e^{-1/4} \approx .1037$$
$$P\{L_n = j + 2\} \approx e^{-1/16} - e^{-1/8} \approx .0569$$
$$P\{L_n = j + 3\} \approx e^{-1/32} - e^{-1/16} \approx .0298$$
$$P\{L_n \geq j + 4\} \approx 1 - e^{-1/32} \approx .0308$$

Thus, we observe the rather interesting fact that no matter how large n is, the length of the longest run of heads in a sequence of n flips of a fair coin will be within 2 of $\log_2(n) - 1$ with a probability approximately equal to .86.

We now derive an exact expression for the probability that there is a string of k consecutive heads when a coin that lands on heads with probability p is flipped n times. With the events $E_i, i = 1, \ldots, n - k + 1$, as defined earlier, and with L_n denoting, as before, the length of the longest run of heads,

$$P(L_n \geq k) = P(\text{there is a string of } k \text{ consecutive heads}) = P(\cup_{i=1}^{n-k+1} E_i)$$

The inclusion–exclusion identity for the probability of a union can be written as

$$P(\cup_{i=1}^{n-k+1} E_i) = \sum_{r=1}^{n-k+1} (-1)^{r+1} \sum_{i_1 < \cdots < i_r} P(E_{i_1} \cdots E_{i_r})$$

Let S_i denote the set of flip numbers to which the event E_i refers. (So, for instance, $S_1 = \{1, \ldots, k + 1\}$.) Now, consider one of the r-way intersection probabilities that does not include the event E_{n-k+1}. That is, consider $P(E_{i_1} \cdots E_{i_r})$ where $i_1 < \cdots < i_r < n - k + 1$. On the one hand, if there is any overlap in the sets $S_{i_1}, \ldots, S_{i_r}$, then this probability is 0. On the other hand, if there is no overlap, then the events $E_{i_1}, \ldots, E_{i_r}$ are independent. Therefore,

$$P(E_{i_1} \cdots E_{i_r}) = \begin{cases} 0, & \text{if there is any overlap in } S_{i_1}, \ldots, S_{i_r} \\ p^{rk}(1 - p)^r, & \text{if there is no overlap} \end{cases}$$

We must now determine the number of different choices of $i_1 < \cdots < i_r < n - k + 1$ for which there is no overlap in the sets $S_{i_1}, \ldots, S_{i_r}$. To do so, note first that each of the $S_{i_j}, j = 1, \ldots, r$, refer to $k + 1$ flips, so, without any overlap, they together refer to $r(k + 1)$ flips. Now consider any permutation of r identical letters a and of $n - r(k + 1)$ identical letters b. Interpret the number of b's before the first a as the number of flips before S_{i_1}, the number of b's between the first and second a as the number of flips between S_{i_1} and S_{i_2}, and so on, with the number of b's after the final a representing the number of flips after S_{i_r}. Because there are $\binom{n-rk}{r}$ permutations of r letters a and of $n - r(k + 1)$ letters b, with every such permutation corresponding (in a one-to-one fashion) to a different nonoverlapping choice, it follows that

$$\sum_{i_1 < \cdots < i_r < n-k+1} P(E_{i_1} \cdots E_{i_r}) = \binom{n - rk}{r} p^{rk}(1 - p)^r$$

We must now consider r-way intersection probabilities of the form

$$P(E_{i_1} \cdots E_{i_{r-1}} E_{n-k+1}),$$

where $i_1 < \cdots < i_{r-1} < n - k + 1$. Now, this probability will equal 0 if there is any overlap in $S_{i_1}, \ldots, S_{i_{r-1}}, S_{n-k}$; if there is no overlap, then the events of the intersection will be independent, so

$$P(E_{i_1} \cdots E_{i_{r-1}} E_{n-k+1}) = [p^k(1 - p)]^{r-1} p^k = p^{kr}(1 - p)^{r-1}$$

By a similar argument as before, the number of nonoverlapping sets $S_{i_1}, \ldots, S_{i_{r-1}}$, S_{n-k} will equal the number of permutations of $r - 1$ letters a (one for each of the sets $S_{i_1}, \ldots, S_{i_{r-1}}$) and of $n - (r - 1)(k + 1) - k = n - rk - (r - 1)$ letters b (one for each of the trials that are not part of any of $S_{i_1}, \ldots, S_{i_{r-1}}, S_{n-k+1}$). Since there are $\binom{n-rk}{r-1}$ permutations of $r - 1$ letters a and of $n - rk - (r - 1)$ letters b, we have

$$\sum_{i_1 < \ldots < i_{r-1} < n-k+1} P(E_{i_1} \cdots E_{i_{r-1}} E_{n-k+1}) = \binom{n - rk}{r - 1} p^{kr} (1 - p)^{r-1}$$

Putting it all together yields the exact expression, namely,

$$P(L_n \geq k) = \sum_{r=1}^{n-k+1} (-1)^{r+1} \left[\binom{n - rk}{r} + \frac{1}{p} \binom{n - rk}{r - 1} \right] p^{kr} (1 - p)^r$$

where we utilize the convention that $\binom{m}{j} = 0$ if $m < j$.

From a computational point of view, a more efficient method for computing the desired probability than the use of the preceding identity is to derive a set of recursive equations. To do so, let A_n be the event that there is a string of k consecutive heads in a sequence of n flips of a fair coin, and let $P_n = P(A_n)$. We will derive a set of recursive equations for P_n by conditioning on when the first tail appears. For $j = 1, \ldots, k$, let F_j be the event that the first tail appears on flip j, and let H be the event that the first k flips are all heads. Because the events $F_1, \ldots, F_k, H$ are mutually exclusive and exhaustive (that is, exactly one of these events must occur), we have

$$P(A_n) = \sum_{j=1}^{k} P(A_n|F_j)P(F_j) + P(A_n|H)P(H)$$

Now, given that the first tail appears on flip j, where $j < k$, it follows that those j flips are wasted as far as obtaining a string of k heads in a row; thus, the conditional probability of this event is the probability that such a string will occur among the remaining $n - j$ flips. Therefore,

$$P(A_n|F_j) = P_{n-j}$$

Because $P(A_n|H) = 1$, the preceding equation gives

$$P_n = P(A_n)$$
$$= \sum_{j=1}^{k} P_{n-j} P(F_j) + P(H)$$
$$= \sum_{j=1}^{k} P_{n-j} p^{j-1}(1 - p) + p^k$$

Starting with $P_j = 0, j < k$, and $P_k = p^k$, we can use the latter formula to recursively compute P_{k+1}, P_{k+2}, and so on, up to P_n. For instance, suppose we want the probability that there is a run of 2 consecutive heads when a fair coin is flipped 4 times. Then, with $k = 2$, we have $P_1 = 0, P_2 = (1/2)^2$. Because, when $p = 1/2$, the recursion becomes

$$P_n = \sum_{j=1}^{k} P_{n-j} (1/2)^j + (1/2)^k$$

we obtain

$$P_3 = P_2(1/2) + P_1(1/2)^2 + (1/2)^2 = 3/8$$

and

$$P_4 = P_3(1/2) + P_2(1/2)^2 + (1/2)^2 = 1/2$$

which is clearly true because there are 8 outcomes that result in a string of 2 consecutive heads: *hhhh, hhht, hhth, hthh, thhh, hhtt, thht,* and *tthh*. Each of these outcomes occurs with probability 1/16. ∎

Another use of the Poisson probability distribution arises in situations where "events" occur at certain points in time. One example is to designate the occurrence of an earthquake as an event; another possibility would be for events to correspond to people entering a particular establishment (bank, post office, gas station, and so on); and a third possibility is for an event to occur whenever a war starts. Let us suppose that events are indeed occurring at certain (random) points of time, and let us assume that for some positive constant λ, the following assumptions hold true:

1. The probability that exactly 1 event occurs in a given interval of length h is equal to $\lambda h + o(h)$, where $o(h)$ stands for any function $f(h)$ for which $\lim_{h \to 0} f(h)/h = 0$. [For instance, $f(h) = h^2$ is $o(h)$, whereas $f(h) = h$ is not.]
2. The probability that 2 or more events occur in an interval of length h is equal to $o(h)$.
3. For any integers $n, j_1, j_2, \ldots, j_n$ and any set of n nonoverlapping intervals, if we define E_i to be the event that exactly j_i of the events under consideration occur in the ith of these intervals, then events $E_1, E_2, \ldots, E_n$ are independent.

Loosely put, assumptions 1 and 2 state that for small values of h, the probability that exactly 1 event occurs in an interval of size h equals λh plus something that is small compared with h, whereas the probability that 2 or more events occur is small compared with h. Assumption 3 states that whatever occurs in one interval has no (probability) effect on what will occur in other, nonoverlapping intervals.

We now show that under assumptions 1, 2, and 3, the number of events occurring in any interval of length t is a Poisson random variable with parameter λt. To be precise, let us call the interval $[0, t]$ and denote the number of events occurring in that interval by $N(t)$. To obtain an expression for $P\{N(t) = k\}$, we start by breaking the interval $[0, t]$ into n nonoverlapping subintervals, each of length t/n (Figure 4.8).

Figure 4.8

Now,

$$P\{N(t) = k\} = P\{k \text{ of the } n \text{ subintervals contain exactly 1 event}$$
$$\text{and the other } n - k \text{ contain 0 events}\} \quad (7.2)$$
$$+ P\{N(t) = k \text{ and at least 1 subinterval contains}$$
$$2 \text{ or more events}\}$$

The preceding equation holds because the event on the left side of Equation (7.2), that is, $\{N(t) = k\}$, is clearly equal to the union of the two mutually exclusive events on the right side of the equation. Letting A and B denote the two mutually exclusive events on the right side of Equation (7.2), we have

$$P(B) \le P\{\text{at least one subinterval contains 2 or more events}\}$$

$$= P\left(\bigcup_{i=1}^{n}\{i\text{th subinterval contains 2 or more events}\}\right)$$

$$\le \sum_{i=1}^{n} P\{i\text{th subinterval contains 2 or more events}\} \qquad \text{by Boole's inequality}$$

$$= \sum_{i=1}^{n} o\left(\frac{t}{n}\right) \qquad \text{by assumption 2}$$

$$= no\left(\frac{t}{n}\right)$$

$$= t\left[\frac{o(t/n)}{t/n}\right]$$

Now, in addition, for any t, $t/n \to 0$ as $n \to \infty$, so $o(t/n)/(t/n) \to 0$ as $n \to \infty$, by the definition of $o(h)$. Hence,

$$P(B) \to 0 \quad \text{as} \quad n \to \infty \tag{7.3}$$

Moreover, since assumptions 1 and 2 imply that[†]

$$P\{0 \text{ events occur in an interval of length } h\}$$
$$= 1 - [\lambda h + o(h) + o(h)] = 1 - \lambda h - o(h)$$

we see from the independence assumption (number 3) that

$$P(A) = P\{k \text{ of the subintervals contain exactly 1 event and the other}$$
$$n - k \text{ contain 0 events}\}$$

$$= \binom{n}{k}\left[\frac{\lambda t}{n} + o\left(\frac{t}{n}\right)\right]^{k}\left[1 - \left(\frac{\lambda t}{n}\right) - o\left(\frac{t}{n}\right)\right]^{n-k}$$

However, since

$$n\left[\frac{\lambda t}{n} + o\left(\frac{t}{n}\right)\right] = \lambda t + t\left[\frac{o(t/n)}{t/n}\right] \to \lambda t \quad \text{as} \quad n \to \infty$$

it follows, by the same argument that verified the Poisson approximation to the binomial, that

$$P(A) \to e^{-\lambda t}\frac{(\lambda t)^{k}}{k!} \quad \text{as} \quad n \to \infty \tag{7.4}$$

Thus, from Equations (7.2), (7.3), and (7.4), by letting $n \to \infty$, we obtain

$$P\{N(t) = k\} = e^{-\lambda t}\frac{(\lambda t)^{k}}{k!} \quad k = 0, 1, \ldots \tag{7.5}$$

Hence, if assumptions 1, 2, and 3 are satisfied, then the number of events occurring in any fixed interval of length t is a Poisson random variable with mean λt, and we say that the events occur in accordance with a Poisson process having rate λ. The value λ, which can be shown to equal the rate per unit time at which events occur, is a constant that must be empirically determined.

[†] The sum of two functions, both of which are $o(h)$, is also $o(h)$. This is so because if $\lim_{h \to 0} f(h)/h = \lim_{h \to 0} g(h)/h = 0$, then $\lim_{h \to 0}[f(h) + g(h)]/h = 0$.

The preceding discussion explains why a Poisson random variable is usually a good approximation for such diverse phenomena as the following:

1. The number of earthquakes occurring during some fixed time span
2. The number of wars per year
3. The number of electrons emitted from a heated cathode during a fixed time period
4. The number of deaths, in a given period of time, of the policyholders of a life insurance company

Example 7e

Suppose that earthquakes occur in the western portion of the United States in accordance with assumptions 1, 2, and 3, with $\lambda = 2$ and with 1 week as the unit of time. (That is, earthquakes occur in accordance with the three assumptions at a rate of 2 per week.)

(a) Find the probability that at least 3 earthquakes occur during the next 2 weeks.

(b) Find the probability distribution of the time, starting from now, until the next earthquake.

Solution (a) From Equation (7.5), we have

$$P\{N(2) \geq 3\} = 1 - P\{N(2) = 0\} - P\{N(2) = 1\} - P\{N(2) = 2\}$$

$$= 1 - e^{-4} - 4e^{-4} - \frac{4^2}{2}e^{-4}$$

$$= 1 - 13e^{-4}$$

(b) Let X denote the amount of time (in weeks) until the next earthquake. Because X will be greater than t if and only if no events occur within the next t units of time, we have, from Equation (7.5),

$$P\{X > t\} = P\{N(t) = 0\} = e^{-\lambda t}$$

so the probability distribution function F of the random variable X is given by

$$F(t) = P\{X \leq t\} = 1 - P\{X > t\} = 1 - e^{-\lambda t}$$

$$= 1 - e^{-2t} \qquad \blacksquare$$

4.7.1 Computing the Poisson Distribution Function

If X is Poisson with parameter λ, then

$$\frac{P\{X = i + 1\}}{P\{X = i\}} = \frac{e^{-\lambda}\lambda^{i+1}/(i+1)!}{e^{-\lambda}\lambda^i/i!} = \frac{\lambda}{i+1} \qquad (7.6)$$

Starting with $P\{X = 0\} = e^{-\lambda}$, we can use (7.6) to compute successively

$$P\{X = 1\} = \lambda P\{X = 0\}$$

$$P\{X = 2\} = \frac{\lambda}{2}P\{X = 1\}$$

$$\vdots$$

$$P\{X = i + 1\} = \frac{\lambda}{i+1}P\{X = i\}$$

We can use a module to compute the Poisson probabilities for Equation (7.6).

Example 7f

(a) Determine $P\{X \le 90\}$ when X is Poisson with mean 100.

(b) Determine $P\{Y \le 1075\}$ when Y is Poisson with mean 1000.

Solution Using the Poisson calculator of StatCrunch yields the solutions:

(a) $P\{X \le 90\} = .17138$

(b) $P\{Y \le 1075\} = .99095$ ∎

4.8 Other Discrete Probability Distributions

4.8.1 The Geometric Random Variable

Suppose that independent trials, each having a probability $p, 0 < p < 1$, of being a success, are performed until a success occurs. If we let X equal the number of trials required, then

$$P\{X = n\} = (1 - p)^{n-1}p \qquad n = 1, 2, \ldots \qquad (8.1)$$

Equation (8.1) follows because, in order for X to equal n, it is necessary and sufficient that the first $n - 1$ trials are failures and the nth trial is a success. Equation (8.1) then follows, since the outcomes of the successive trials are assumed to be independent.

Since

$$\sum_{n=1}^{\infty} P\{X = n\} = p \sum_{n=1}^{\infty} (1 - p)^{n-1} = \frac{p}{1 - (1 - p)} = 1$$

it follows that with probability 1, a success will eventually occur. Any random variable X whose probability mass function is given by Equation (8.1) is said to be a *geometric* random variable with parameter p.

Example 8a

An urn contains N white and M black balls. Balls are randomly selected, one at a time, until a black one is obtained. If we assume that each ball selected is replaced before the next one is drawn, what is the probability that

(a) exactly n draws are needed?

(b) at least k draws are needed?

Solution If we let X denote the number of draws needed to select a black ball, then X satisfies Equation (8.1) with $p = M/(M + N)$. Hence,

(a)

$$P\{X = n\} = \left(\frac{N}{M + N}\right)^{n-1} \frac{M}{M + N} = \frac{MN^{n-1}}{(M + N)^n}$$

(b)

$$P\{X \ge k\} = \frac{M}{M + N} \sum_{n=k}^{\infty} \left(\frac{N}{M + N}\right)^{n-1}$$

$$= \left(\frac{M}{M + N}\right)\left(\frac{N}{M + N}\right)^{k-1} \Big/ \left[1 - \frac{N}{M + N}\right]$$

$$= \left(\frac{N}{M + N}\right)^{k-1}$$

Of course, part (b) could have been obtained directly, since the probability that at least k trials are necessary to obtain a success is equal to the probability that the first $k - 1$ trials are all failures. That is, for a geometric random variable,

$$P\{X \geq k\} = (1 - p)^{k-1}$$ ∎

Example 8b

Find the expected value of a geometric random variable.

Solution With $q = 1 - p$, we have

$$E[X] = \sum_{i=1}^{\infty} iq^{i-1}p$$

$$= \sum_{i=1}^{\infty} (i - 1 + 1)q^{i-1}p$$

$$= \sum_{i=1}^{\infty} (i - 1)q^{i-1}p + \sum_{i=1}^{\infty} q^{i-1}p$$

$$= \sum_{j=0}^{\infty} jq^{j}p + 1$$

$$= q\sum_{j=1}^{\infty} jq^{j-1}p + 1$$

$$= qE[X] + 1$$

Hence,

$$pE[X] = 1$$

yielding the result

$$E[X] = \frac{1}{p}$$

In other words, if independent trials having a common probability p of being successful are performed until the first success occurs, then the expected number of required trials equals $1/p$. For instance, the expected number of rolls of a fair die that it takes to obtain the value 1 is 6. ∎

Example 8c

Find the variance of a geometric random variable.

Solution To determine $\text{Var}(X)$, let us first compute $E[X^2]$. With $q = 1 - p$, we have

$$E[X^2] = \sum_{i=1}^{\infty} i^2 q^{i-1}p$$

$$= \sum_{i=1}^{\infty} (i - 1 + 1)^2 q^{i-1}p$$

$$= \sum_{i=1}^{\infty} (i - 1)^2 q^{i-1}p + \sum_{i=1}^{\infty} 2(i - 1)q^{i-1}p + \sum_{i=1}^{\infty} q^{i-1}p$$

$$= \sum_{j=0}^{\infty} j^2 q^{j}p + 2\sum_{j=1}^{\infty} jq^{j}p + 1$$

$$= qE[X^2] + 2qE[X] + 1$$

Using $E[X] = 1/p$, the equation for $E[X^2]$ yields

$$pE[X^2] = \frac{2q}{p} + 1$$

Hence,

$$E[X^2] = \frac{2q + p}{p^2} = \frac{q + 1}{p^2}$$

giving the result

$$\text{Var}(X) = \frac{q + 1}{p^2} - \frac{1}{p^2} = \frac{q}{p^2} = \frac{1 - p}{p^2}$$
∎

4.8.2 The Negative Binomial Random Variable

Suppose that independent trials, each having probability $p, 0 < p < 1$, of being a success are performed until a total of r successes is accumulated. If we let X equal the number of trials required, then

$$P\{X = n\} = \binom{n - 1}{r - 1} p^r (1 - p)^{n-r} \quad n = r, r + 1, \ldots \tag{8.2}$$

Equation (8.2) follows because, in order for the rth success to occur at the nth trial, there must be $r - 1$ successes in the first $n - 1$ trials and the nth trial must be a success. The probability of the first event is

$$\binom{n - 1}{r - 1} p^{r-1} (1 - p)^{n-r}$$

and the probability of the second is p; thus, by independence, Equation (8.2) is established. To verify that a total of r successes must eventually be accumulated, either we can prove analytically that

$$\sum_{n=r}^{\infty} P\{X = n\} = \sum_{n=r}^{\infty} \binom{n - 1}{r - 1} p^r (1 - p)^{n-r} = 1 \tag{8.3}$$

or we can give a probabilistic argument as follows: The number of trials required to obtain r successes can be expressed as $Y_1 + Y_2 + \cdots + Y_r$, where Y_1 equals the number of trials required for the first success, Y_2 the number of additional trials after the first success until the second success occurs, Y_3 the number of additional trials until the third success, and so on. Because the trials are independent and all have the same probability of success, it follows that $Y_1, Y_2, \ldots, Y_r$ are all geometric random variables. Hence, each is finite with probability 1, so $\sum_{i=1}^{r} Y_i$ must also be finite, establishing Equation (8.3).

Any random variable X whose probability mass function is given by Equation (8.2) is said to be a *negative binomial* random variable with parameters (r, p). Note that a geometric random variable is just a negative binomial with parameter $(1, p)$.

In the next example, we use the negative binomial to obtain another solution of the problem of the points.

Example 8d

If independent trials, each resulting in a success with probability p, are performed, what is the probability of r successes occurring before m failures?

Solution The solution will be arrived at by noting that r successes will occur before m failures if and only if the rth success occurs no later than the $(r + m - 1)$ trial. This follows because if the rth success occurs before or at the $(r + m - 1)$ trial, then it must have occurred before the mth failure, and conversely. Hence, from Equation (8.2), the desired probability is

$$\sum_{n=r}^{r+m-1} \binom{n-1}{r-1} p^r (1-p)^{n-r}$$ ∎

Example 8e

The Banach match problem

At all times, a pipe-smoking mathematician carries 2 matchboxes—1 in his left-hand pocket and 1 in his right-hand pocket. Each time he needs a match, he is equally likely to take it from either pocket. Consider the moment when the mathematician first discovers that one of his matchboxes is empty. If it is assumed that both matchboxes initially contained N matches, what is the probability that there are exactly k matches, $k = 0, 1, \ldots, N$, in the other box?

Solution Let E denote the event that the mathematician first discovers that the right-hand matchbox is empty and that there are k matches in the left-hand box at the time. Now, this event will occur if and only if the $(N + 1)$ choice of the right-hand matchbox is made at the $(N + 1 + N - k)$ trial. Hence, from Equation (8.2) (with $p = \frac{1}{2}, r = N + 1,$ and $n = 2N - k + 1$), we see that

$$P(E) = \binom{2N - k}{N} \left(\frac{1}{2}\right)^{2N-k+1}$$

Since there is an equal probability that it is the left-hand box that is first discovered to be empty and there are k matches in the right-hand box at that time, the desired result is

$$2P(E) = \binom{2N - k}{N} \left(\frac{1}{2}\right)^{2N-k}$$ ∎

Example 8f

Compute the expected value and the variance of a negative binomial random variable with parameters r and p.

Solution We have

$$E[X^k] = \sum_{n=r}^{\infty} n^k \binom{n-1}{r-1} p^r (1-p)^{n-r}$$

$$= \frac{r}{p} \sum_{n=r}^{\infty} n^{k-1} \binom{n}{r} p^{r+1} (1-p)^{n-r} \quad \text{since} \quad n\binom{n-1}{r-1} = r\binom{n}{r}$$

$$= \frac{r}{p} \sum_{m=r+1}^{\infty} (m-1)^{k-1} \binom{m-1}{r} p^{r+1} (1-p)^{m-(r+1)} \quad \begin{array}{l}\text{by setting}\\ m = n + 1\end{array}$$

$$= \frac{r}{p} E[(Y-1)^{k-1}]$$

where Y is a negative binomial random variable with parameters $r + 1, p$. Setting $k = 1$ in the preceding equation yields

$$E[X] = \frac{r}{p}$$

Setting $k = 2$ in the equation for $E[X^k]$ and using the formula for the expected value of a negative binomial random variable gives

$$E[X^2] = \frac{r}{p} E[Y - 1]$$
$$= \frac{r}{p} \left(\frac{r + 1}{p} - 1 \right)$$

Therefore,

$$\text{Var}(X) = \frac{r}{p} \left(\frac{r + 1}{p} - 1 \right) - \left(\frac{r}{p} \right)^2$$
$$= \frac{r(1 - p)}{p^2}$$ ∎

Thus, from Example 8f, if independent trials, each of which is a success with probability p, are performed, then the expected value and variance of the number of trials that it takes to amass r successes is r/p and $r(1 - p)/p^2$, respectively.

Since a geometric random variable is just a negative binomial with parameter $r = 1$, it follows from the preceding example that the variance of a geometric random variable with parameter p is equal to $(1 - p)/p^2$, which checks with the result of Example 8c.

Example 8g

Find the expected value and the variance of the number of times one must throw a die until the outcome 1 has occurred 4 times.

Solution Since the random variable of interest is a negative binomial with parameters $r = 4$ and $p = \frac{1}{6}$, it follows that

$$E[X] = 24$$

$$\text{Var}(X) = \frac{4 \left(\frac{5}{6} \right)}{\left(\frac{1}{6} \right)^2} = 120$$ ∎

4.8.3 The Hypergeometric Random Variable

Suppose that a sample of size n is to be chosen randomly (without replacement) from an urn containing N balls, of which m are white and $N - m$ are black. If we let X denote the number of white balls selected, then

$$P\{X = i\} = \frac{\dbinom{m}{i} \dbinom{N - m}{n - i}}{\dbinom{N}{n}} \quad i = 0, 1, \dots, n \tag{8.4}$$

A random variable X whose probability mass function is given by Equation (8.4) for some values of n, N, m is said to be a *hypergeometric* random variable.

Remark Although we have written the hypergeometric probability mass function with i going from 0 to n, $P\{X = i\}$ will actually be 0, unless i satisfies the inequalities $n - (N - m) \leq i \leq \min(n, m)$. However, Equation (8.4) is always valid because of our convention that $\binom{r}{k}$ is equal to 0 when either $k < 0$ or $r < k$. ■

Example 8h

An unknown number, say, N, of animals inhabit a certain region. To obtain some information about the size of the population, ecologists often perform the following experiment: They first catch a number, say, m, of these animals, mark them in some manner, and release them. After allowing the marked animals time to disperse throughout the region, a new catch of size, say, n, is made. Let X denote the number of marked animals in this second capture. If we assume that the population of animals in the region remained fixed between the time of the two catches and that each time an animal was caught it was equally likely to be any of the remaining uncaught animals, it follows that X is a hypergeometric random variable such that

$$P\{X = i\} = \frac{\binom{m}{i}\binom{N - m}{n - i}}{\binom{N}{n}} \equiv P_i(N)$$

Suppose now that X is observed to equal i. Then, since $P_i(N)$ represents the probability of the observed event when there are actually N animals present in the region, it would appear that a reasonable estimate of N would be the value of N that maximizes $P_i(N)$. Such an estimate is called a *maximum likelihood* estimate. (See Theoretical Exercises 13 and 18 for other examples of this type of estimation procedure.)

The maximization of $P_i(N)$ can be done most simply by first noting that

$$\frac{P_i(N)}{P_i(N - 1)} = \frac{(N - m)(N - n)}{N(N - m - n + i)}$$

Now, the preceding ratio is greater than 1 if and only if

$$(N - m)(N - n) \geq N(N - m - n + i)$$

or, equivalently, if and only if

$$N \leq \frac{mn}{i}$$

Thus, $P_i(N)$ is first increasing and then decreasing and reaches its maximum value at the largest integral value not exceeding mn/i. This value is the maximum likelihood estimate of N. For example, suppose that the initial catch consisted of $m = 50$ animals, which are marked and then released. If a subsequent catch consists of $n = 40$ animals of which $i = 4$ are marked, then we would estimate that there are some 500 animals in the region. (Note that the preceding estimate could also have been obtained by assuming that the proportion of marked animals in the region, m/N, is approximately equal to the proportion of marked animals in our second catch, i/n.) ■

Example 8i

A purchaser of electrical components buys them in lots of size 10. It is his policy to inspect 3 components randomly from a lot and to accept the lot only if all 3 are nondefective. If 30 percent of the lots have 4 defective components and 70 percent have only 1, what proportion of lots does the purchaser reject?

Solution Let A denote the event that the purchaser accepts a lot. Now,

$$P(A) = P(A|\text{lot has 4 defectives})\frac{3}{10} + P(A|\text{lot has 1 defective})\frac{7}{10}$$

$$= \frac{\binom{4}{0}\binom{6}{3}}{\binom{10}{3}}\left(\frac{3}{10}\right) + \frac{\binom{1}{0}\binom{9}{3}}{\binom{10}{3}}\left(\frac{7}{10}\right)$$

$$= \frac{54}{100}$$

Hence, 46 percent of the lots are rejected. ∎

If n balls are randomly chosen without replacement from a set of N balls of which the fraction $p = m/N$ is white, then the number of white balls selected is hypergeometric. Now, it would seem that when m and N are large in relation to n, it shouldn't make much difference whether the selection is being done with or without replacement, because, no matter which balls have previously been selected, when m and N are large, each additional selection will be white with a probability approximately equal to p. In other words, it seems intuitive that when m and N are large in relation to n, the probability mass function of X should approximately be that of a binomial random variable with parameters n and p. To verify this intuition, note that if X is hypergeometric, then, for $i \leq n$,

$$P\{X = i\} = \frac{\binom{m}{i}\binom{N-m}{n-i}}{\binom{N}{n}}$$

$$= \frac{m!}{(m-i)!\,i!}\frac{(N-m)!}{(N-m-n+i)!\,(n-i)!}\frac{(N-n)!\,n!}{N!}$$

$$= \binom{n}{i}\frac{m}{N}\frac{m-1}{N-1}\cdots\frac{m-i+1}{N-i+1}\frac{N-m}{N-i}\frac{N-m-1}{N-i-1}$$

$$\cdots\frac{N-m-(n-i-1)}{N-i-(n-i-1)}$$

$$\approx \binom{n}{i}p^i(1-p)^{n-i} \qquad \begin{array}{l} \text{when } p = m/N \text{ and } m \text{ and } N \text{ are} \\ \text{large in relation to } n \text{ and } i \end{array}$$

Example 8j Determine the expected value and the variance of X, a hypergeometric random variable with parameters n, N, and m.

Solution

$$E[X^k] = \sum_{i=0}^{n} i^k P\{X = i\}$$

$$= \sum_{i=1}^{n} i^k \binom{m}{i}\binom{N-m}{n-i} \Big/ \binom{N}{n}$$

Using the identities

$$i\binom{m}{i} = m\binom{m-1}{i-1} \quad \text{and} \quad n\binom{N}{n} = N\binom{N-1}{n-1}$$

we obtain

$$E[X^k] = \frac{nm}{N} \sum_{i=1}^{n} i^{k-1} \binom{m-1}{i-1}\binom{N-m}{n-i} \Big/ \binom{N-1}{n-1}$$

$$= \frac{nm}{N} \sum_{j=0}^{n-1} (j+1)^{k-1} \binom{m-1}{j}\binom{N-m}{n-1-j} \Big/ \binom{N-1}{n-1}$$

$$= \frac{nm}{N} E[(Y+1)^{k-1}]$$

where Y is a hypergeometric random variable with parameters $n-1$, $N-1$, and $m-1$. Hence, upon setting $k = 1$, we have

$$E[X] = \frac{nm}{N}$$

In words, if n balls are randomly selected from a set of N balls, of which m are white, then the expected number of white balls selected is nm/N.

Upon setting $k = 2$ in the equation for $E[X^k]$, we obtain

$$E[X^2] = \frac{nm}{N} E[Y+1]$$

$$= \frac{nm}{N} \left[\frac{(n-1)(m-1)}{N-1} + 1 \right]$$

where the final equality uses our preceding result to compute the expected value of the hypergeometric random variable Y.

Because $E[X] = nm/N$, we can conclude that

$$\text{Var}(X) = \frac{nm}{N} \left[\frac{(n-1)(m-1)}{N-1} + 1 - \frac{nm}{N} \right]$$

Letting $p = m/N$ and using the identity

$$\frac{m-1}{N-1} = \frac{Np-1}{N-1} = p - \frac{1-p}{N-1}$$

shows that

$$\text{Var}(X) = np[(n-1)p - (n-1)\frac{1-p}{N-1} + 1 - np]$$

$$= np(1-p)\left(1 - \frac{n-1}{N-1}\right)$$ ■

Remark We have shown in Example 8j that if n balls are randomly selected without replacement from a set of N balls, of which the fraction p are white, then the expected number of white balls chosen is np. In addition, if N is large in relation to n [so that $(N-n)/(N-1)$ is approximately equal to 1], then

$$\text{Var}(X) \approx np(1-p)$$

In other words, $E[X]$ is the same as when the selection of the balls is done with replacement (so that the number of white balls is binomial with parameters n and p), and if the total collection of balls is large, then $\text{Var}(X)$ is approximately equal to what it would be if the selection were done with replacement. This is, of course, exactly what we would have guessed, given our earlier result that when the number of balls in the urn is large, the number of white balls chosen approximately has the mass function of a binomial random variable. ■

4.8.4 The Zeta (or Zipf) Distribution

A random variable is said to have a zeta (sometimes called the Zipf) distribution if its probability mass function is given by

$$P\{X = k\} = \frac{C}{k^{\alpha+1}} \quad k = 1, 2, \ldots$$

for some value of $\alpha > 0$. Since the sum of the foregoing probabilities must equal 1, it follows that

$$C = \left[\sum_{k=1}^{\infty} \left(\frac{1}{k} \right)^{\alpha+1} \right]^{-1}$$

The zeta distribution owes its name to the fact that the function

$$\zeta(s) = 1 + \left(\frac{1}{2} \right)^s + \left(\frac{1}{3} \right)^s + \cdots + \left(\frac{1}{k} \right)^s + \cdots$$

is known in mathematical disciplines as the Riemann zeta function (after the German mathematician G. F. B. Riemann).

The zeta distribution was used by the Italian economist V. Pareto to describe the distribution of family incomes in a given country. However, it was G. K. Zipf who applied zeta distribution to a wide variety of problems in different areas and, in doing so, popularized its use.

4.9 Expected Value of Sums of Random Variables

A very important property of expectations is that the expected value of a sum of random variables is equal to the sum of their expectations. In this section, we will prove this result under the assumption that the set of possible values of the probability experiment—that is, the sample space S—is either finite or countably infinite. Although the result is true without this assumption (and a proof is outlined in the theoretical exercises), not only will the assumption simplify the argument, but it will also result in an enlightening proof that will add to our intuition about expectations. So, for the remainder of this section, suppose that the sample space S is either a finite or a countably infinite set.

For a random variable X, let $X(s)$ denote the value of X when $s \in S$ is the outcome of the experiment. Now, if X and Y are both random variables, then so is their sum. That is, $Z = X + Y$ is also a random variable. Moreover, $Z(s) = X(s) + Y(s)$.

Example 9a

Suppose that the experiment consists of flipping a coin 5 times, with the outcome being the resulting sequence of heads and tails. Suppose X is the number of heads in the first 3 flips and Y is the number of heads in the final 2 flips. Let $Z = X + Y$. Then, for instance, for the outcome $s = (h, t, h, t, h)$,

$$X(s) = 2$$
$$Y(s) = 1$$
$$Z(s) = X(s) + Y(s) = 3$$

meaning that the outcome (h, t, h, t, h) results in 2 heads in the first three flips, 1 head in the final two flips, and a total of 3 heads in the five flips. ∎

Let $p(s) = P(\{s\})$ be the probability that s is the outcome of the experiment. Because we can write any event A as the finite or countably infinite union of the mutually exclusive events $\{s\}, s \in A$, it follows by the axioms of probability that

$$P(A) = \sum_{s \in A} p(s)$$

When $A = S$, the preceding equation gives

$$1 = \sum_{s \in S} p(s)$$

Now, let X be a random variable, and consider $E[X]$. Because $X(s)$ is the value of X when s is the outcome of the experiment, it seems intuitive that $E[X]$—the weighted average of the possible values of X, with each value weighted by the probability that X assumes that value—should equal a weighted average of the values $X(s), s \in S$, with $X(s)$ weighted by the probability that s is the outcome of the experiment. We now prove this intuition.

Proposition 9.1

$$E[X] = \sum_{s \in S} X(s)\, p(s)$$

Proof Suppose that the distinct values of X are $x_i, i \geq 1$. For each i, let S_i be the event that X is equal to x_i. That is, $S_i = \{s : X(s) = x_i\}$. Then,

$$E[X] = \sum_i x_i P\{X = x_i\}$$

$$= \sum_i x_i P(S_i)$$

$$= \sum_i x_i \sum_{s \in S_i} p(s)$$

$$= \sum_i \sum_{s \in S_i} x_i p(s)$$

$$= \sum_i \sum_{s \in S_i} X(s) p(s)$$

$$= \sum_{s \in S} X(s) p(s)$$

where the final equality follows because $S_1, S_2, \ldots$ are mutually exclusive events whose union is S. $\qquad \square$

Example 9b

Suppose that two independent flips of a coin that comes up heads with probability p are made, and let X denote the number of heads obtained. Because

$$P(X = 0) = P(t, t) = (1 - p)^2,$$
$$P(X = 1) = P(h, t) + P(t, h) = 2p(1 - p)$$
$$P(X = 2) = P(h, h) = p^2$$

it follows from the definition of expected value that

$$E[X] = 0 \cdot (1 - p)^2 + 1 \cdot 2p(1 - p) + 2 \cdot p^2 = 2p$$

which agrees with

$$E[X] = X(h,h)p^2 + X(h,t)p(1-p) + X(t,h)(1-p)p + X(t,t)(1-p)^2$$
$$= 2p^2 + p(1-p) + (1-p)p$$
$$= 2p$$

We now prove the important and useful result that the expected value of a sum of random variables is equal to the sum of their expectations.

Corollary 9.2 For random variables $X_1, X_2, \ldots, X_n$,

$$E\left[\sum_{i=1}^{n} X_i\right] = \sum_{i=1}^{n} E[X_i]$$

Proof Let $Z = \sum_{i=1}^{n} X_i$. Then, by Proposition 9.1,

$$E[Z] = \sum_{s \in S} Z(s)p(s)$$
$$= \sum_{s \in S} \left(X_1(s) + X_2(s) + \ldots + X_n(s)\right)p(s)$$
$$= \sum_{s \in S} X_1(s)p(s) + \sum_{s \in S} X_2(s)p(s) + \ldots + \sum_{s \in S} X_n(s)p(s)$$
$$= E[X_1] + E[X_2] + \ldots + E[X_n]$$

Example 9c Find the expected value of the sum obtained when n fair dice are rolled.

Solution Let X be the sum. We will compute $E[X]$ by using the representation

$$X = \sum_{i=1}^{n} X_i$$

where X_i is the upturned value on die i. Because X_i is equally likely to be any of the values from 1 to 6, it follows that

$$E[X_i] = \sum_{i=1}^{6} i(1/6) = 21/6 = 7/2$$

which yields the result

$$E[X] = E\left[\sum_{i=1}^{n} X_i\right] = \sum_{i=1}^{n} E[X_i] = 3.5 n$$

Example 9d Find the expected total number of successes that result from n trials when trial i is a success with probability p_i, $i = 1, \ldots, n$.

Solution Letting

$$X_i = \begin{cases} 1, & \text{if trial } i \text{ is a success} \\ 0, & \text{if trial } i \text{ is a failure} \end{cases}$$

we have the representation

$$X = \sum_{i=1}^{n} X_i$$

Consequently,

$$E[X] = \sum_{i=1}^{n} E[X_i] = \sum_{i=1}^{n} p_i$$

Note that this result does not require that the trials be independent. It includes as a special case the expected value of a binomial random variable, which assumes independent trials and all $p_i = p$, and thus has mean np. It also gives the expected value of a hypergeometric random variable representing the number of white balls selected when n balls are randomly selected, without replacement, from an urn of N balls of which m are white. We can interpret the hypergeometric as representing the number of successes in n trials, where trial i is said to be a success if the ith ball selected is white. Because the ith ball selected is equally likely to be any of the N balls and thus has probability m/N of being white, it follows that the hypergeometric is the number of successes in n trials in which each trial is a success with probability $p = m/N$. Hence, even though these hypergeometric trials are dependent, it follows from the result of Example 9d that the expected value of the hypergeometric is $np = nm/N$. ■

Example 9e

Derive an expression for the variance of the number of successful trials in Example 9d, and apply it to obtain the variance of a binomial random variable with parameters n and p, and of a hypergeometric random variable equal to the number of white balls chosen when n balls are randomly chosen from an urn containing N balls of which m are white.

Solution Letting X be the number of successful trials, and using the same representation for X—namely, $X = \sum_{i=1}^{n} X_i$—as in the previous example, we have

$$E[X^2] = E\left[\left(\sum_{i=1}^{n} X_i\right)\left(\sum_{j=1}^{n} X_j\right)\right]$$

$$= E\left[\sum_{i=1}^{n} X_i\left(X_i + \sum_{j \neq i} X_j\right)\right]$$

$$= E\left[\sum_{i=1}^{n} X_i^2 + \sum_{i=1}^{n}\sum_{j \neq i} X_i X_j\right]$$

$$= \sum_{i=1}^{n} E[X_i^2] + \sum_{i=1}^{n}\sum_{j \neq i} E[X_i X_j]$$

$$= \sum_{i} p_i + \sum_{i=1}^{n}\sum_{j \neq i} E[X_i X_j] \tag{9.1}$$

where the final equation used that $X_i^2 = X_i$. However, because the possible values of both X_i and X_j are 0 or 1, it follows that

$$X_i X_j = \begin{cases} 1, & \text{if } X_i = 1, X_j = 1 \\ 0, & \text{otherwise} \end{cases}$$

Hence,

$$E[X_i X_j] = P\{X_i = 1, X_j = 1\} = P(\text{trials } i \text{ and } j \text{ are successes})$$

Now, on the one hand, if X is binomial, then, for $i \neq j$, the results of trial i and trial j are independent, with each being a success with probability p. Therefore,

$$E[X_i X_j] = p^2, \qquad i \neq j$$

Together with Equation (9.1), the preceding equation shows that for a binomial random variable X,

$$E[X^2] = np + n(n-1)p^2$$

implying that

$$\text{Var}(X) = E[X^2] - (E[X])^2 = np + n(n-1)p^2 - n^2 p^2 = np(1-p)$$

On the other hand, if X is hypergeometric, then, given that a white ball is chosen in trial i, each of the other $N-1$ balls, of which $m-1$ are white, is equally likely to be the jth ball chosen, for $j \neq i$. Consequently, for $j \neq i$,

$$P\{X_i = 1, X_j = 1\} = P\{X_i = 1\}P\{X_j = 1 | X_i = 1\} = \frac{m}{N}\frac{m-1}{N-1}$$

Using $p_i = m/N$, we now obtain, from Equation (9.1),

$$E[X^2] = \frac{nm}{N} + n(n-1)\frac{m}{N}\frac{m-1}{N-1}$$

Consequently,

$$\text{Var}(X) = \frac{nm}{N} + n(n-1)\frac{m}{N}\frac{m-1}{N-1} - \left(\frac{nm}{N}\right)^2$$

which, as shown in Example 8j, can be simplified to yield

$$\text{Var}(X) = np(1-p)\left(1 - \frac{n-1}{N-1}\right)$$

where $p = m/N$. ∎

4.10 Properties of the Cumulative Distribution Function

Recall that for the distribution function F of X, $F(b)$ denotes the probability that the random variable X takes on a value that is less than or equal to b. Following are some properties of the cumulative distribution function (c.d.f.) F:

1. F is a nondecreasing function; that is, if $a < b$, then $F(a) \leq F(b)$.
2. $\lim_{b \to \infty} F(b) = 1$.
3. $\lim_{b \to -\infty} F(b) = 0$.
4. F is right continuous. That is, for any b and any decreasing sequence $b_n, n \geq 1$, that converges to b, $\lim_{n \to \infty} F(b_n) = F(b)$.

Property 1 follows, as was noted in Section 4.1, because, for $a < b$, the event $\{X \leq a\}$ is contained in the event $\{X \leq b\}$ and so cannot have a larger probability. Properties 2, 3, and 4 all follow from the continuity property of probabilities (Section 2.6). For instance, to prove property 2, we note that if b_n increases to ∞, then the events $\{X \le b_n\}, n \ge 1$, are increasing events whose union is the event $\{X < \infty\}$. Hence, by the continuity property of probabilities,

$$\lim_{n \to \infty} P\{X \le b_n\} = P\{X < \infty\} = 1$$

which proves property 2.

The proof of property 3 is similar and is left as an exercise. To prove property 4, we note that if b_n decreases to b, then $\{X \le b_n\}, n \ge 1$, are decreasing events whose intersection is $\{X \le b\}$. The continuity property then, yields

$$\lim_{n \to \infty} P\{X \le b_n\} = P\{X \le b\}$$

which verifies property 4.

All probability questions about X can be answered in terms of the c.d.f., F. For example,

$$P\{a < X \le b\} = F(b) - F(a) \quad \text{for all } a < b \tag{10.1}$$

This equation can best be seen to hold if we write the event $\{X \le b\}$ as the union of the mutually exclusive events $\{X \le a\}$ and $\{a < X \le b\}$. That is,

$$\{X \le b\} = \{X \le a\} \cup \{a < X \le b\}$$

so

$$P\{X \le b\} = P\{X \le a\} + P\{a < X \le b\}$$

which establishes Equation (10.1).

If we want to compute the probability that X is strictly less than b, we can again apply the continuity property to obtain

$$P\{X < b\} = P\left(\lim_{n \to \infty} \left\{X \le b - \frac{1}{n}\right\}\right)$$
$$= \lim_{n \to \infty} P\left(X \le b - \frac{1}{n}\right)$$
$$= \lim_{n \to \infty} F\left(b - \frac{1}{n}\right)$$

Note that $P\{X < b\}$ does not necessarily equal $F(b)$, since $F(b)$ also includes the probability that X equals b.

Example 10a

The distribution function of the random variable X is given by

$$F(x) = \begin{cases} 0 & x < 0 \\ \dfrac{x}{2} & 0 \le x < 1 \\ \dfrac{2}{3} & 1 \le x < 2 \\ \dfrac{11}{12} & 2 \le x < 3 \\ 1 & 3 \le x \end{cases}$$

A graph of $F(x)$ is presented in Figure 4.9. Compute (a) $P\{X < 3\}$, (b) $P\{X = 1\}$, (c) $P\{X > \frac{1}{2}\}$, and (d) $P\{2 < X \le 4\}$.

Solution (a) $P\{X < 3\} = \lim_n P\left\{X \le 3 - \dfrac{1}{n}\right\} = \lim_n F\left(3 - \dfrac{1}{n}\right) = \dfrac{11}{12}$

(b)
$$P\{X = 1\} = P\{X \le 1\} - P\{X < 1\}$$
$$= F(1) - \lim_n F\left(1 - \dfrac{1}{n}\right) = \dfrac{2}{3} - \dfrac{1}{2} = \dfrac{1}{6}$$

(c)
$$P\left\{X > \dfrac{1}{2}\right\} = 1 - P\left\{X \le \dfrac{1}{2}\right\}$$
$$= 1 - F\left(\dfrac{1}{2}\right) = \dfrac{3}{4}$$

(d)
$$P\{2 < X \le 4\} = F(4) - F(2)$$
$$= \dfrac{1}{12}$$

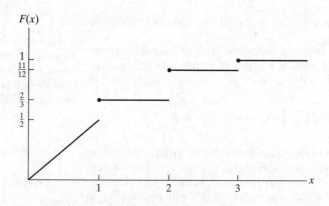

Figure 4.9 Graph of $F(x)$.

Summary

A real-valued function defined on the outcome of a probability experiment is called a *random variable*.

If X is a random variable, then the function $F(x)$ defined by

$$F(x) = P\{X \leq x\}$$

is called the *distribution function* of X. All probabilities concerning X can be stated in terms of F.

A random variable whose set of possible values is either finite or countably infinite is called *discrete*. If X is a discrete random variable, then the function

$$p(x) = P\{X = x\}$$

is called the *probability mass function* of X. Also, the quantity $E[X]$ defined by

$$E[X] = \sum_{x:p(x)>0} xp(x)$$

is called the *expected value* of X. $E[X]$ is also commonly called the *mean* or the *expectation* of X.

A useful identity states that for a function g,

$$E[g(X)] = \sum_{x:p(x)>0} g(x)p(x)$$

The *variance* of a random variable X, denoted by $\text{Var}(X)$, is defined by

$$\text{Var}(X) = E[(X - E[X])^2]$$

The variance, which is equal to the expected square of the difference between X and its expected value, is a measure of the spread of the possible values of X. A useful identity is

$$\text{Var}(X) = E[X^2] - (E[X])^2$$

The quantity $\sqrt{\text{Var}(X)}$ is called the *standard deviation* of X.

We now note some common types of discrete random variables. The random variable X whose probability mass function is given by

$$p(i) = \binom{n}{i} p^i (1 - p)^{n-i} \quad i = 0, \ldots, n$$

is said to be a *binomial* random variable with parameters n and p. Such a random variable can be interpreted as being the number of successes that occur when n independent trials, each of which results in a success with probability p, are performed. Its mean and variance are given by

$$E[X] = np \quad \text{Var}(X) = np(1 - p)$$

The random variable X whose probability mass function is given by

$$p(i) = \frac{e^{-\lambda} \lambda^i}{i!} \quad i \geq 0$$

is said to be a *Poisson* random variable with parameter λ. If a large number of (approximately) independent trials are performed, each having a small probability of being successful, then the number of successful trials that result will have a distribution that is approximately that of a Poisson random variable. The mean and variance of a Poisson random variable are both equal to its parameter λ. That is,

$$E[X] = \text{Var}(X) = \lambda$$

The random variable X whose probability mass function is given by

$$p(i) = p(1 - p)^{i-1} \quad i = 1, 2, \ldots$$

is said to be a *geometric* random variable with parameter p. Such a random variable represents the trial number of the first success when each trial is independently a success with probability p. Its mean and variance are given by

$$E[X] = \frac{1}{p} \quad \text{Var}(X) = \frac{1 - p}{p^2}$$

The random variable X whose probability mass function is given by

$$p(i) = \binom{i - 1}{r - 1} p^r (1 - p)^{i-r} \quad i \geq r$$

is said to be a *negative binomial* random variable with parameters r and p. Such a random variable represents the trial number of the rth success when each trial is independently a success with probability p. Its mean and variance are given by

$$E[X] = \frac{r}{p} \quad \text{Var}(X) = \frac{r(1 - p)}{p^2}$$

A *hypergeometric* random variable X with parameters n, N, and m represents the number of white balls selected when n balls are randomly chosen from an urn that contains N balls of which m are white. The probability mass function of this random variable is given by

$$p(i) = \frac{\binom{m}{i} \binom{N - m}{n - i}}{\binom{N}{n}} \quad i = 0, \ldots, m$$

With $p = m/N$, its mean and variance are

$$E[X] = np \quad \text{Var}(X) = \frac{N - n}{N - 1} np(1 - p)$$

An important property of the expected value is that the expected value of a sum of random variables is equal to the sum of their expected values. That is,

$$E\left[\sum_{i=1}^{n} X_i\right] = \sum_{i=1}^{n} E[X_i]$$

Problems

4.1. Two balls are chosen randomly from an urn containing 8 white, 4 black, and 2 orange balls. Suppose that we win $2 for each black ball selected and we lose $1 for each white ball selected. Let X denote our winnings. What are the possible values of X, and what are the probabilities associated with each value?

4.2. Two fair dice are rolled. Let X be equal to the absolute difference between the value obtained by the first die and the second die. What are the possible values that X can take? Also Compute the probabilities attached to it.

4.3. Three dice are rolled. By assuming that each of the $6^3 = 216$ possible outcomes is equally likely, find the probabilities attached to the possible values that X can take on, where X is the sum of the 3 dice.

4.4. 5 goals were recorded in a Hockey match played between India and Britain. If the goals are assumed to be equally likely to be scored by both the teams, find the probabilities associated with different values of X, where X denotes the number of goals scored by India?

4.5. Let X represent the difference between the number of heads and the number of tails obtained when a coin is tossed n times. What are the possible values of X?

4.6. In Problem 4.5, for $n = 3$, if the coin is assumed fair, what are the probabilities associated with the values that X can take on?

4.7. Suppose that a die is rolled twice. What are the possible values that the following random variables can take on:

(a) the maximum value to appear in the two rolls;

(b) the minimum value to appear in the two rolls;

(c) the sum of the two rolls;

(d) the value of the first roll minus the value of the second roll?

4.8. If the die in Problem 4.7 is assumed fair, calculate the probabilities associated with the random variables in parts (a) through (d).

4.9. Repeat Example 1c when the balls are selected with replacement.

4.10. Let X be the winnings of a gambler. Let $p(i) = P(X = i)$ and suppose that

$$p(0) = 1/3; p(1) = p(-1) = 13/55;$$
$$p(2) = p(-2) = 1/11; p(3) = p(-3) = 1/165$$

Compute the conditional probability that the gambler wins i, $i = 1, 2, 3$, given that he wins a positive amount.

4.11. (a) An integer N is to be selected at random from $\{1, 2, \ldots, (10)^3\}$ in the sense that each integer has the same probability of being selected. What is the probability that N will be divisible by 3? by 5? by 7? by 15? by 105? How would your answer change if $(10)^3$ is replaced by $(10)^k$ as k became larger and larger?

(b) An important function in number theory—one whose properties can be shown to be related to what is probably the most important unsolved problem of mathematics, the Riemann hypothesis—is the Möbius function $\mu(n)$, defined for all positive integral values n as follows: Factor n into its prime factors. If there is a repeated prime factor, as in $12 = 2 \cdot 2 \cdot 3$ or $49 = 7 \cdot 7$, then $\mu(n)$ is defined to equal 0. Now let N be chosen at random from $\{1, 2, \ldots (10)^k\}$, where k is large. Determine $P\{\mu(N) = 0\}$ as $k \to \infty$. *Hint*: To compute $P\{\mu(N) \neq 0\}$, use the identity

$$\prod_{i=1}^{\infty} \frac{P_i^2 - 1}{P_i^2} = \left(\frac{3}{4}\right)\left(\frac{8}{9}\right)\left(\frac{24}{25}\right)\left(\frac{48}{49}\right)\cdots = \frac{6}{\pi^2}$$

where P_i is the ith-smallest prime. (The number 1 is not a prime.)

4.12. In the game of Two-Finger Morra, 2 players show 1 or 2 fingers and simultaneously guess the number of fingers their opponent will show. If only one of the players guesses correctly, he wins an amount (in dollars) equal to the sum of the fingers shown by him and his opponent. If both players guess correctly or if neither guesses correctly, then no money is exchanged. Consider a specified player, and denote by X the amount of money he wins in a single game of Two-Finger Morra.

(a) If each player acts independently of the other, and if each player makes his choice of the number of fingers he will hold up and the number he will guess that his opponent will hold up in such a way that each of the 4 possibilities is equally likely, what are the possible values of X and what are their associated probabilities?

(b) Suppose that each player acts independently of the other. If each player decides to hold up the same number of fingers that he guesses his opponent will hold up, and if each player is equally likely to hold up 1 or 2 fingers, what are the possible values of X and their associated probabilities?

4.13. An airline operates a flight having 50 seats. As they expect some passenger to not show up, they overbook the flight by selling 51 tickets. The probability that an individual passenger will not show up is 0.01, independent of all other tourists. Each ticket costs Rs.10 thousand, and is non-refundable if a tourist fails to show up . If a tourist shows up and a seat is not available, the airline has to pay a compensation of Rs. 1 lakh to that passenger. What is the expected revenue of the airline ?

4.14. Five distinct numbers are randomly distributed to players numbered 1 through 5. Whenever two players compare their numbers, the one with the higher one is declared the winner. Initially, players 1 and 2 compare their numbers; the winner then compares her number with that of player 3, and so on. Let X denote the number of times player 1 is a winner. Find $P\{X = i\}, i = 0, 1, 2, 3, 4$.

4.15. The National Basketball Association (NBA) draft lottery involves the 11 teams that had the worst won–lost records during the year. A total of 66 balls are placed in an urn. Each of these balls is inscribed with the name of a team: Eleven have the name of the team with the worst record, 10 have the name of the team with the second-worst record, 9 have the name of the team with the third-worst record, and so on (with 1 ball having the name of the team with the 11th-worst record). A ball is then chosen at random, and the team whose name is on the ball is given the first pick in the draft of players about to enter the league. Another ball is then chosen, and if it "belongs" to a team different from the one that received the first draft pick, then the team to which it belongs receives the second draft pick. (If the ball belongs to the team receiving the first pick, then it is discarded and another one is chosen; this continues until the ball of another team is chosen.) Finally, another ball is chosen, and the team named on the ball (provided that it is different from the previous two teams) receives the third draft pick. The remaining draft picks 4 through 11 are then awarded to the 8 teams that did not "win the lottery," in inverse order of their won–lost records. For instance, if the team with the worst record did not receive any of the 3 lottery picks, then that team would receive the fourth draft pick. Let X denote the draft pick of the team with the worst record. Find the probability mass function of X.

4.16. In Problem 4.15, let team number 1 be the team with the worst record, let team number 2 be the team with the second-worst record, and so on. Let Y_i denote the team that gets draft pick number i. (Thus, $Y_1 = 3$ if the first ball chosen belongs to team number 3.) Find the probability mass function of (a) Y_1, (b) Y_2, and (c) Y_3.

4.17. Let the distribution function of X be given by

$$F(x) = \begin{cases} 0, & x < 1 \\ 1/12, & 1 \le x < 2 \\ 1/3, & 2 \le x < 3 \\ 1/2, & 3 \le x < 4 \\ 1, & x \ge 4 \end{cases}$$

(a) Obtain the probability mass function of X.

(b) Find $P(0 < X < 3)$.

4.18. Three fair dice are rolled. Let X be the number of dice in which an even number comes up. Find the probability mass function and plot it. Also obtain its distribution function.

4.19. If the distribution function of X is given by

$$F(b) = \begin{cases} 0 & b < 0 \\ \dfrac{1}{2} & 0 \le b < 1 \\ \dfrac{3}{5} & 1 \le b < 2 \\ \dfrac{4}{5} & 2 \le b < 3 \\ \dfrac{9}{10} & 3 \le b < 3.5 \\ 1 & b \ge 3.5 \end{cases}$$

calculate the probability mass function of X.

4.20. A lottery consists 10 tickets of which two are prize winning. Tom is asked to pick three tickets without replacement. Let X be the number of prize winning tickets Tom picks.

(a) Find $P(X = i)$ for all possible values of i.

(b) Determine $E(X)$.

(c) Tom wins Rs. 3 for a prize wining ticket and losses Rs. 1 for the other tickets. If the r.v Y denotes his winnings, find $E(Y)$.

4.21. One box contain 4 red balls and 6 green balls and another box contain 6 red balls and 4 green balls. Let X be the number of red balls obtained when any one of the boxes is chosen randomly and two balls are picked from it without replacement. Let Y be the number of red balls obtained if one ball is picked randomly from each box. Which of the random variable has a higher expectation? Explain.

4.22. Suppose that two teams play a series of games that ends when one of them has won i games. Suppose that each game played is, independently, won by team A with probability p. Find the expected number of games that are played when (a) $i = 2$ and (b) $i = 3$. Also, show in both cases that this number is maximized when $p = \frac{1}{2}$.

4.23. You have $1000, and a certain commodity presently sells for $2 per ounce. Suppose that after one week the commodity will sell for either $1 or $4 an ounce, with these two possibilities being equally likely.

(a) If your objective is to maximize the expected amount of money that you possess at the end of the week, what strategy should you employ?

(b) If your objective is to maximize the expected amount of the commodity that you possess at the end of the week, what strategy should you employ?

4.24. A and B play the following game: A writes down either number 1 or number 2, and B must guess which one. If the number that A has written down is i and B has guessed correctly, B receives i units from A. If B makes a wrong guess, B pays $\frac{3}{4}$ unit to A. If B randomizes his decision by guessing 1 with probability p and 2 with probability $1 - p$, determine his expected gain if (a) A has written down number 1 and (b) A has written down number 2.

What value of p maximizes the minimum possible value of B's expected gain, and what is this maximin value? (Note that B's expected gain depends not only on p, but also on what A does.)

Consider now player A. Suppose that she also randomizes her decision, writing down number 1 with probability q. What is A's expected loss if (c) B chooses number 1 and (d) B chooses number 2?

What value of q minimizes A's maximum expected loss? Show that the minimum of A's maximum expected loss is equal to the maximum of B's minimum expected gain. This result, known as the *minimax theorem*, was first established in generality by the mathematician John von Neumann and is the fundamental result in the mathematical discipline known as the theory of games. The common value is called the value of the game to player B.

4.25. A box containing a dozen eggs are examined. The probability that an egg would be broken is 0.1 and is independent of whether the other eggs are broken or not. If X denotes the number of broken eggs in the box,

(a) Find $P(X = 0)$.

(b) If a box containing more than 1 broken egg is rejected, calculate the probability that a given box will be rejected.

(c) Find $E(X)$.

4.26. One of the numbers 1 through 10 is randomly chosen. You are to try to guess the number chosen by asking questions with "yes–no" answers. Compute the expected number of questions you will need to ask in each of the following two cases:

(a) Your ith question is to be "Is it i?" $i = 1, 2, 3, 4, 5, 6, 7, 8, 9, 10$.

(b) With each question you try to eliminate one-half of the remaining numbers, as nearly as possible.

4.27. A person pays Rs. 2 to play a certain game of rolling a fair die. If 1 or 2 appears the player gets no rewards and if the number appearing is greater than or equal to 3, he gets the difference between the number on the die and Rs. 2. Is the game fair? Justify.

4.28. Consider a game where the player rolls a fair six-sided die. If 6 comes up, then the player gets Rs. 36. If any other face i ($i = 1, 2, 3, 4, 5$) comes, he losses Rs. k^2. What amount can the player expect to win at this game?

4.29. There are two possible causes for a breakdown of a machine. To check the first possibility would cost C_1 dollars, and, if that were the cause of the breakdown, the trouble could be repaired at a cost of R_1 dollars. Similarly, there are costs C_2 and R_2 associated with the second possibility. Let p and $1 - p$ denote, respectively, the probabilities that the breakdown is caused by the first and second possibilities. Under what conditions on $p, C_i, R_i, i = 1, 2$, should we check the first possible cause of breakdown and then the second, as opposed to reversing the checking order, so as to minimize the expected cost involved in returning the machine to working order?
Note: If the first check is negative, we must still check the other possibility.

4.30. A person tosses a fair coin until a tail appears for the first time. If the tail appears on the nth flip, the person wins 2^n dollars. Let X denote the player's winnings. Show that $E[X] = +\infty$. This problem is known as the St. Petersburg paradox.

(a) Would you be willing to pay \$1 million to play this game once?

(b) Would you be willing to pay \$1 million for each game if you could play for as long as you liked and only had to settle up when you stopped playing?

4.31. Each night different meteorologists give us the probability that it will rain the next day. To judge how well these people predict, we will score each of them as follows: If a meteorologist says that it will rain with probability p, then he or she will receive a score of

$$\begin{array}{ll} 1 - (1 - p)^2 & \text{if it does rain} \\ 1 - p^2 & \text{if it does not rain} \end{array}$$

We will then keep track of scores over a certain time span and conclude that the meteorologist with the highest average score is the best predictor of weather. Suppose now that a given meteorologist is aware of our scoring mechanism and wants to maximize his or her expected score. If this person truly believes that it will rain tomorrow with probability p^*, what value of p should he or she assert so as to maximize the expected score?

4.32. To determine whether they have a certain disease, 100 people are to have their blood tested. However, rather than testing each individual separately, it has been decided first to place the people into groups of 10. The blood samples of the 10 people in each group will be pooled and analyzed together. If the test is negative, one test will suffice for the 10 people, whereas if the test is positive, each of the 10 people will also be individually tested and, in all, 11 tests will be made on this group. Assume that the probability that a person has the disease is .1 for all people, independently of one another, and compute the expected number of tests necessary for each group. (Note that we are assuming that the pooled test will be positive if at least one person in the pool has the disease.)

4.33. The daily demand for cake made at a small bakery is given by the random variable X, where X takes the value 1 with probability 0.2, 2 with probability 0.4, 3 with probability 0.3 and 0 with probability 0.1. The the cost of making the cake is Rs. 100 and he sells them at Rs. 150. If the leftover cakes are thrown away daily, how many cakes should the baker bake to maximize his expected daily profit?

4.34. In Example 4b, suppose that the department store incurs an additional cost of c for each unit of unmet demand. (This type of cost is often referred to as a goodwill cost because the store loses the goodwill of those customers whose demands it cannot meet.) Compute the expected profit when the store stocks s units, and determine the value of s that maximizes the expected profit.

4.35. A box contains 5 red and 5 blue marbles. Two marbles are withdrawn randomly. If they are the same color, then you win \$1.10; if they are different colors, then you win −\$1.00. (That is, you lose \$1.00.) Calculate

(a) the expected value of the amount you win;

(b) the variance of the amount you win.

4.36. Consider Problem 4.22 with $i = 2$. Find the variance of the number of games played, and show that this number is maximized when $p = \frac{1}{2}$.

4.37. Find $Var(X)$ and $Var(Y)$ for X and Y as given in Problem 4.21.

4.38. If $E[X] = -2$ and $Var(X) = 1$, obtain

(a) $E(1 - X)^2$

(b) $Var(2 - 5X)$.

4.39. A ball is drawn from an urn containing 3 white and 3 black balls. After the ball is drawn, it is replaced and another ball is drawn. This process goes on indefinitely. What is the probability that of the first 4 balls drawn, exactly 2 are white?

4.40. A department of 10 employees has a Wifi facility which connects a maximum of 3 devices at a time. If there is a 30% chance that an employee will need internet at a particular time, find the probability that the Wifi is not enough at a certain time?

4.41. 40% of the customers use Credit cards while paying for their groceries at a local supermarket, if 4 customers are there at the supermarket at given time, find the probability that at least one of them will use a Credit Card for payment?

4.42. In a restaurant, 3 out of 5 people order a dessert with dinner. A random sample of 10 people is selected, then find the probability that more than 8 people order a dessert?

4.43. A carnival swing ride swings to the left with probability 0.4 and to the right with probability. If the ride stops after 10 swings, what is the probability that it is exactly at the place it started?

4.44. A satellite system consists of n components and functions on any given day if at least k of the n components function on that day. On a rainy day, each of the components independently functions with probability p_1, whereas on a dry day, each independently functions with probability p_2. If the probability of rain tomorrow is α, what is the probability that the satellite system will function?

4.45. A student is getting ready to take an important oral examination and is concerned about the possibility of having an "on" day or an "off" day. He figures that if he has an on day, then each of his examiners will pass him, independently of one another, with probability .8, whereas if he has an off day, this probability will be reduced to .4. Suppose that the student will pass the examination if a majority of the examiners pass him. If the student believes that he is twice as likely to have an off day as he is to have an on day, should he request an examination with 3 examiners or with 5 examiners?

4.46. Suppose that it takes at least 9 votes from a 12-member jury to convict a defendant. Suppose also that the probability that a juror votes a guilty person innocent is .2, whereas the probability that the juror votes an innocent person guilty is .1. If each juror acts independently and if 65 percent of the defendants are guilty, find the probability that the jury renders a correct decision. What percentage of defendants is convicted?

4.47. In some military courts, 9 judges are appointed. However, both the prosecution and the defense attorneys are entitled to a peremptory challenge of any judge, in which case that judge is removed from the case and is not replaced. A defendant is declared guilty if the majority of judges cast votes of guilty, and he or she is declared innocent otherwise. Suppose that when the defendant is, in fact, guilty, each judge will (independently) vote guilty with probability .7, whereas when the defendant is, in fact, innocent, this probability drops to .3.

(a) What is the probability that a guilty defendant is declared guilty when there are (i) 9, (ii) 8, and (iii) 7 judges?

(b) Repeat part (a) for an innocent defendant.

(c) If the prosecuting attorney does not exercise the right to a peremptory challenge of a judge, and if the defense is limited to at most two such challenges, how many challenges should the defense attorney make if he or she is 60 percent certain that the client is guilty?

4.48. It is known that diskettes produced by a certain company will be defective with probability .01, independently of one another. The company sells the diskettes in packages of size 10 and offers a money-back guarantee that at most 1 of the 10 diskettes in the package will be defective. The guarantee is that the customer can return the entire package of diskettes if he or she finds more than 1 defective diskette in it. If someone buys 3 packages, what is the probability that he or she will return exactly 1 of them?

4.49. When coin 1 is flipped, it lands on heads with probability .4; when coin 2 is flipped, it lands on heads with probability .7. One of these coins is randomly chosen and flipped 10 times.

(a) What is the probability that the coin lands on heads on exactly 7 of the 10 flips?

(b) Given that the first of these 10 flips lands heads, what is the conditional probability that exactly 7 of the 10 flips land on heads?

4.50. Suppose that a biased coin that lands on heads with probability p is flipped 10 times. Given that a total of 6 heads results, find the conditional probability that the first 3 outcomes are

(a) h, t, t (meaning that the first flip results in heads, the second in tails, and the third in tails);

(b) t, h, t.

4.51. If a student copies his assignments from his friend he would get 80 marks. If he had done the assignments independently he would have scored 50 marks out of 100 and if the teacher finds he is cheating he will be penalized and will be given 0 marks. The probability that the teacher catches his cheating is 0.3. If he copies 10 such assignments, what is the probability that he will lose more marks with copying than by doing his independent work independently?

4.52. The monthly worldwide average number of airplane crashes of commercial airlines is 3.5. What is the probability that there will be

(a) at least 2 such accidents in the next month;

(b) at most 1 accident in the next month?
Explain your reasoning!

4.53. Approximately 80,000 marriages took place in the state of New York last year. Estimate the probability that for at least one of these couples,

(a) both partners were born on April 30;

(b) both partners celebrated their birthday on the same day of the year.
State your assumptions.

4.54. Suppose that the average number of cars abandoned weekly on a certain highway is 2.2. Approximate the probability that there will be

(a) no abandoned cars in the next week;

(b) at least 2 abandoned cars in the next week.

4.55. A certain typing agency employs 2 typists. The average number of errors per article is 3 when typed by the first typist and 4.2 when typed by the second. If your article is equally likely to be typed by either typist, approximate the probability that it will have no errors.

4.56. How many people are needed so that the probability that at least one of them has the same birthday as you is greater than $\frac{1}{2}$?

4.57. Suppose that the number of accidents occurring on a highway each day is a Poisson random variable with parameter $\lambda = 3$.

(a) Find the probability that 3 or more accidents occur today.

(b) Repeat part (a) under the assumption that at least 1 accident occurs today.

4.58. Compare the Poisson approximation with the correct binomial probability for the following cases:

(a) $P\{X = 2\}$ when $n = 8, p = .1$;

(b) $P\{X = 9\}$ when $n = 10, p = .95$;

(c) $P\{X = 0\}$ when $n = 10, p = .1$;

(d) $P\{X = 4\}$ when $n = 9, p = .2$.

4.59. The number of policies an Insurance Salesman sells in a week, is a Poisson random variable with mean 3 per week. Find,

(a) the probability that he sell at least one policy in a week?

(b) the probability that the number of policies sold is more than two but less than 5?

4.60. In an express highway toll-booth, on average 120 cars pass a specified point in any given hour. It is estimated if more than 3 cars arrive at any given minute, there will be a congestion at the toll booth. Find the probability that the toll booth will be congested at some specified minute?

4.61. Consider a raffle in which two numbers out of 10 are selected at random and a person holding exactly those two numbers is the winner. Suppose the person plays for a large number of times (n), using Poisson approximation obtain the probability that he will win at least twice?

4.62. Consider n independent trials, each of which results in one of the outcomes $1, \ldots, k$ with respective probabilities $p_1, \ldots, p_k$, $\sum_{i=1}^{k} p_i = 1$. Show that if all the p_i are small, then the probability that no trial outcome occurs more than once is approximately equal to $\exp(-n(n-1) \sum_i p_i^2/2)$.

4.63. The average number of accidents happening at a busy intersection during the a day is 1 per 3 hours.

(a) Find the probability that there are no accidents during the time 9:00 am to 2:00 pm there were no accidents?

(b) Find the probability that there should be exactly 2 ambulances available at the above time slot, if one ambulance is needed for each accident case?

4.64. The weekly demand for a refrigerator in a shop is said to be poisson random variable with mean 3.

(a) What is the probability that there will be a demand for at least 5 refrigerators in a week?

(b) What is the probability that the demand is less than 20 a month?

(c) What is the minimum number of stocks to be kept if it is to ensure that the shop meets at least 90% of the demands made in a month?

4.65. Each of 500 soldiers in an army company independently has a certain disease with probability $1/10^3$. This disease will show up in a blood test, and to facilitate matters, blood samples from all 500 soldiers are pooled and tested.

(a) What is the (approximate) probability that the blood test will be positive (that is, at least one person has the disease)?

Suppose now that the blood test yields a positive result.

(b) What is the probability, under this circumstance, that more than one person has the disease?

Now, suppose one of the 500 people is Jones, who knows that he has the disease.

(c) What does Jones think is the probability that more than one person has the disease?

Because the pooled test was positive, the authorities have decided to test each individual separately. The first $i - 1$ of these tests were negative, and the ith one—which was on Jones—was positive.

(d) Given the preceding scenario, what is the probability, as a function of i, that any of the remaining people have the disease?

4.66. A total of $2n$ people, consisting of n married couples, are randomly seated (all possible orderings being equally likely) at a round table. Let C_i denote the event that the members of couple i are seated next to each other, $i = 1, \ldots, n$.

(a) Find $P(C_i)$.

(b) For $j \neq i$, find $P(C_j | C_i)$.

(c) Approximate the probability, for n large, that there are no married couples who are seated next to each other.

4.67. Repeat the preceding problem when the seating is random but subject to the constraint that the men and women alternate.

4.68. In response to an attack of 10 missiles, 500 antiballistic missiles are launched. The missile targets of the antiballistic missiles are independent, and each antiballistic missile is equally likely to go towards any of the target missiles. If each antiballistic missile independently hits its target with probability .1, use the Poisson paradigm to approximate the probability that all missiles are hit.

4.69. A fair coin is flipped 10 times. Find the probability that there is a string of 4 consecutive heads by

(a) using the formula derived in the text;

(b) using the recursive equations derived in the text.

(c) Compare your answer with that given by the Poisson approximation.

4.70. At time 0, a coin that comes up heads with probability p is flipped and falls to the ground. Suppose it lands on heads. At times chosen according to a Poisson process with rate λ, the coin is picked up and flipped. (Between these times, the coin remains on the ground.) What is the probability that the coin is on its head side at time t?

Hint: What would be the conditional probability if there were no additional flips by time t, and what would it be if there were additional flips by time t?

4.71. Footballer Cristiano Ronaldo misses 10% of the the penalty kicks he takes
(a) Find the probability that he will miss the first 3 shots he takes?

(b) Find the probability that his 2nd shot resulted in his first goal?

(c) Find the expected number of goals he scores before his first miss?

4.72. Two athletic teams play a series of games; the first team to win 4 games is declared the overall winner. Suppose that one of the teams is stronger than the other and wins each game with probability .6, independently of the outcomes of the other games. Find the probability, for $i = 4, 5, 6, 7$, that the stronger team wins the series in exactly i games. Compare the probability that the stronger team wins with the probability that it would win a 2-out-of-3 series.

4.73. In a university 10 out of every 100 students take a Maths 101 course. A person who needs help in solving a mathematical problem comes to the university. If any student who has taken the Maths 101 course can help to solve the persons problem and none others can solve it, what is the expected number of students the person asks for help?

4.74. An interviewer is given a list of people she can interview. If the interviewer needs to interview 5 people, and if each person (independently) agrees to be interviewed with probability $\frac{2}{3}$, what is the probability that her list of people will enable her to obtain her necessary number of interviews if the list consists of (a) 5 people and (b) 8 people? For part (b), what is the probability that the interviewer will speak to exactly (c) 6 people and (d) 7 people on the list?

4.75. A survey is to be conducted among teens who smokes cigarettes. If the probability that a cigarette smoking person agrees to be part of the survey is 0.1, what is the probability that 16 persons are asked to obtain 3 willing participants?

4.76. Solve the Banach match problem (Example 8e) when the left-hand matchbox originally contained N_1 matches and the right-hand box contained N_2 matches.

4.77. In the Banach matchbox problem, find the probability that at the moment when the first box is emptied (as opposed to being found empty), the other box contains exactly k matches.

4.78. From a class having 20 boys and 15 girls, a committee of 6 members had to be formed for conducting the annual day programme. The committee was picked by picking 6 students randomly. The randomly selected committee will be rejected if the number of boys and girls were not equal and again a random selection of 6 would be made from all the 35 students. What is the probability that a committee was approved on the the third random selection?

4.79. Five cards are selected from a well-shuffled deck of 52 cards.
(a) If X be the number of diamonds in the selected sample, then find $P(X > 0)$.
(b) Let Y be the number of aces selected, then obtain $P(Y \le 3)$.

4.80. A game popular in Nevada gambling casinos is Keno, which is played as follows: Twenty numbers are selected at random by the casino from the set of numbers 1 through 80. A player can select from 1 to 15 numbers; a win occurs if some fraction of the player's chosen subset matches any of the 20 numbers drawn by the house. The payoff is a function of the number of elements in the player's selection and the number of matches. For instance, if the player selects only 1 number, then he or she wins if this number is among the set of 20, and the payoff is $2.20 won for every dollar bet. (As the player's probability of winning in this case is $\frac{1}{4}$, it is clear that the "fair" payoff should be $3 won for every $1 bet.) When the player selects 2 numbers, a payoff (of odds) of $12 won for every $1 bet is made when both numbers are among the 20.

(a) What would be the fair payoff in this case?
Let $P_{n,k}$ denote the probability that exactly k of the n numbers chosen by the player are among the 20 selected by the house.

(b) Compute $P_{n,k}$
(c) The most typical wager at Keno consists of selecting 10 numbers. For such a bet, the casino pays off as shown in the following table. Compute the expected payoff:

Keno Payoffs in 10 Number Bets	
Number of matches	Dollars won for each $1 bet
0–4	−1
5	1
6	17
7	179
8	1,299
9	2,599
10	24,999

4.81. In Example 8i, what percentage of i defective lots does the purchaser reject? Find it for $i = 1, 4$. Given that a lot is rejected, what is the conditional probability that it contained 4 defective components?

4.82. A purchaser of transistors buys them in lots of 20. It is his policy to randomly inspect 4 components from a lot and to accept the lot only if all 4 are nondefective. If each component in a lot is, independently, defective with probability .1, what proportion of lots is rejected?

4.83. In an IT company, the number of computer servers that breaks down during a month follows a poisson distribution with rate 2. The cost of repairing a single server is 2 thousand rupees and also there is a fixed overhead cost of Rs. 10000 kept as salary for the technician. If X denote the total cost incurred due to server maintenance in a month, obtain the expected value and variance for X.

4.84. Suppose that 10 balls are put into 5 boxes, with each ball independently being put in box i with probability p_i, $\sum_{i=1}^{5} p_i = 1$.

(a) Find the expected number of boxes that do not have any balls.
(b) Find the expected number of boxes that have exactly 1 ball.

4.85. There are k types of coupons. Independently of the types of previously collected coupons, each new coupon collected is of type i with probability p_i, $\sum_{i=1}^{k} p_i = 1$. If n coupons are collected, find the expected number of distinct types that appear in this set. (That is, find the expected number of types of coupons that appear at least once in the set of n coupons.)

Theoretical Exercises

4.1. There are N distinct types of coupons, and each time one is obtained it will, independently of past choices, be of type i with probability $P_i, i = 1, \ldots, N$. Let T denote the number one need select to obtain at least one of each type. Compute $P\{T = n\}$.

Hint: Use an argument similar to the one used in Example 1e.

4.2. Let X have a distribution function denoted by F. Obtain the distribution function of $Y = \log X$.

4.3. Let X be a binomial distributed random variable with parameter n and p. Find the p.m.f of $Y_1 = n - X$ and $Y_2 = X_2$.

4.4. The random variable X is said to have the *Yule-Simons distribution* if

$$P\{X = n\} = \frac{4}{n(n + 1)(n + 2)}, \quad n \geq 1$$

(a) Show that the preceding is actually a probability mass function. That is, show that $\sum_{n=1}^{\infty} P\{X = n\} = 1$.

(b) Show that $E[X] = 2$.

(c) Show that $E[X^2] = \infty$.

Hint: For (a), first use that $\frac{1}{n(n+1)(n+2)} = \frac{1}{n(n+1)} - \frac{1}{n(n+2)}$, then use that $\frac{k}{n(n+k)} = \frac{1}{n} - \frac{1}{n+k}$.

4.5. Let N be a nonnegative integer-valued random variable. For nonnegative values $a_j, j \geq 1$, show that

$$\sum_{j=1}^{\infty}(a_1 + \ldots + a_j)P\{N = j\} = \sum_{i=1}^{\infty} a_i P\{N \geq i\}$$

Then show that

$$E[N] = \sum_{i=1}^{\infty} P\{N \geq i\}$$

and

$$E[N(N + 1)] = 2\sum_{i=1}^{\infty} iP\{N \geq i\}$$

4.6. Let X be such that

$$P\{X = 1\} = p = 1 - P\{X = -1\}$$

Find $c \neq 1$ such that $E[c^X] = 1$.

4.7. Let the random variable X denote the number of heads appearing in 4 independent tosses of an unbiased coin. Find the mean and variance of $Y = 1 - 2X^2$.

4.8. Let X be a binomial random variable. Prove that $P(X$ is even$) = 1 - \frac{(1-2p)^n}{2}$.

4.9. Show how the derivation of the binomial probabilities

$$P\{X = i\} = \binom{n}{i}p^i(1 - p)^{n-i}, \quad i = 0, \ldots, n$$

leads to a proof of the binomial theorem

$$(x + y)^n = \sum_{i=0}^{n}\binom{n}{i}x^i y^{n-i}$$

when x and y are nonnegative.

Hint: Let $p = \frac{x}{x+y}$.

4.10. Let X_1 be a binomial distributed random variable with parameter n_1 and p and X_2 be a binomial distributed random variable with parameter n_2 and p. Find the conditional distribution of $X_1 / X_1 + X_2$.

$$E\left[\frac{1}{X + 1}\right] = \frac{1 - (1 - p)^{n+1}}{(n + 1)p}$$

4.11. Consider n independent sequential trials, each of which is successful with probability p. If there is a total of k successes, show that each of the $n!/[k!(n - k)!]$ possible arrangements of the k successes and $n - k$ failures is equally likely.

4.12. Using the result in Theoretical Exercise 4.8 show that $P(X$ is even$)$ is larger than $1/2$ for any n if $p < 1/2$ but is larger than $1/2$ only for even values of n if $p > 1/2$.

4.13. Let X be a binomial random variable with parameters (n, p). What value of p maximizes $P\{X = k\}, k = 0, 1, \ldots, n$? This is an example of a statistical method used to estimate p when a binomial (n, p) random variable is observed to equal k. If we assume that n is known, then we estimate p by choosing that value of p that maximizes $P\{X = k\}$. This is known as the *method of maximum likelihood estimation*.

4.14. A family has n children with probability $\alpha p^n, n \geq 1$, where $\alpha \leq (1 - p)/p$.

(a) What proportion of families has no children?

(b) If each child is equally likely to be a boy or a girl (independently of each other), what proportion of families consists of k boys (and any number of girls)?

4.15. Suppose that n independent tosses of a coin having probability p of coming up heads are made. Show that the probability that an even number of heads results is $\frac{1}{2}[1 + (q - p)^n]$, where $q = 1 - p$. Do this by proving and then utilizing the identity

$$\sum_{i=0}^{[n/2]}\binom{n}{2i}p^{2i}q^{n-2i} = \frac{1}{2}\left[(p + q)^n + (q - p)^n\right]$$

where $[n/2]$ is the largest integer less than or equal to $n/2$. Compare this exercise with Theoretical Exercise 3.5 of Chapter 3.

4.16. Let X and Y be any two independent poisson distribution with parameters λ and μ. Then show that for any $n = 0, 1, 2\ldots$

$$P(x) = \frac{e^{-(\lambda+\mu)}(\lambda+\mu)^n}{n!}$$

4.17. Let X be a Poisson random variable with parameter λ.

(a) Show that

$$P\{X \text{ is even}\} = \frac{1}{2}\left[1 + e^{-2\lambda}\right]$$

by using the result of Theoretical Exercise 4.15 and the relationship between Poisson and binomial random variables.

(b) Verify the formula in part (a) directly by making use of the expansion of $e^{-\lambda} + e^{\lambda}$.

4.18. Let X be a Poisson random variable with parameter λ. What value of λ maximizes $P\{X = k\}, k \geq 0$?

4.19. Let X be a Poisson random variable with parameter λ which denote the number of eggs laid by a hen in a month. Each egg has a probability of hatching into a chick with probability p. Obtain the distribution for Y, the number of chicks that hatch from the eggs.

4.20. Consider n coins, each of which independently comes up heads with probability p. Suppose that n is large and p is small, and let $\lambda = np$. Suppose that all n coins are tossed; if at least one comes up heads, the experiment ends; if not, we again toss all n coins, and so on. That is, we stop the first time that at least one of the n coins come up heads. Let X denote the total number of heads that appear. Which of the following reasonings concerned with approximating $P\{X = 1\}$ is correct (in all cases, Y is a Poisson random variable with parameter λ)?

(a) Because the total number of heads that occur when all n coins are rolled is approximately a Poisson random variable with parameter λ,

$$P\{X = 1\} \approx P\{Y = 1\} = \lambda e^{-\lambda}$$

(b) Because the total number of heads that occur when all n coins are rolled is approximately a Poisson random variable with parameter λ, and because we stop only when this number is positive,

$$P\{X = 1\} \approx P\{Y = 1 | Y > 0\} = \frac{\lambda e^{-\lambda}}{1 - e^{-\lambda}}$$

(c) Because at least one coin comes up heads, X will equal 1 if none of the other $n - 1$ coins come up heads. Because the number of heads resulting from these $n - 1$ coins is approximately Poisson with mean $(n - 1)p \approx \lambda$,

$$P\{X = 1\} \approx P\{Y = 0\} = e^{-\lambda}$$

4.21. Consider X and Y given as in Theoretical Exercise 4.16. Then prove that for any whole numbers $m, n = 0, 1, 2..., m \leq n$, we have

$$P(X = m / X + Y = n) = \binom{n}{m} \left(\frac{\lambda}{\lambda + \mu}\right)^m \left(\frac{\mu}{\lambda + \mu}\right)^{n-m}$$

4.22. An urn contains $2n$ balls, of which 2 are numbered 1, 2 are numbered 2, $\ldots$, and 2 are numbered n. Balls are successively withdrawn 2 at a time without replacement. Let

T denote the first selection in which the balls withdrawn have the same number (and let it equal infinity if none of the pairs withdrawn has the same number). We want to show that, for $0 < \alpha < 1$,

$$\lim_n P\{T > \alpha n\} = e^{-\alpha/2}$$

To verify the preceding formula, let M_k denote the number of pairs withdrawn in the first k selections, $k = 1, \ldots, n$.

(a) Argue that when n is large, M_k can be regarded as the number of successes in k (approximately) independent trials.

(b) Approximate $P\{M_k = 0\}$ when n is large.

(c) Write the event $\{T > \alpha n\}$ in terms of the value of one of the variables M_k.

(d) Verify the limiting probability given for $P\{T > \alpha n\}$.

4.23. Consider a random collection of n individuals. In approximating the probability that no 3 of these individuals share the same birthday, a better Poisson approximation than that obtained in the text (at least for values of n between 80 and 90) is obtained by letting E_i be the event that there are at least 3 birthdays on day $i, i = 1, \ldots, 365$.

(a) Find $P(E_i)$.

(b) Give an approximation for the probability that no 3 individuals share the same birthday.

(c) Evaluate the preceding when $n = 88$ (which can be shown to be the smallest value of n for which the probability exceeds .5).

4.24. Here is another way to obtain a set of recursive equations for determining P_n, the probability that there is a string of k consecutive heads in a sequence of n flips of a fair coin that comes up heads with probability p:

(a) Argue that for $k < n$, there will be a string of k consecutive heads if either

1. there is a string of k consecutive heads within the first $n - 1$ flips, or
2. there is no string of k consecutive heads within the first $n - k - 1$ flips, flip $n - k$ is a tail, and flips $n - k + 1, \ldots, n$ are all heads.

(b) Using the preceding, relate P_n to P_{n-1}. Starting with $P_k = p^k$, the recursion can be used to obtain P_{k+1}, then P_{k+2}, and so on, up to P_n.

4.25. Suppose that the number of events that occur in a specified time is a Poisson random variable with parameter λ. If each event is counted with probability p, independently of every other event, show that the number of events that are counted is a Poisson random variable with parameter λp. Also, give an intuitive argument as to why this should be so. As an application of the preceding result, suppose that the number of distinct uranium deposits in a given area is a Poisson random variable with parameter $\lambda = 10$. If, in a fixed period of time, each deposit is discovered independently with probability $\frac{1}{50}$, find the probability that (a) exactly 1, (b) at least 1, and (c) at most 1 deposit is discovered during that time.

4.26. Prove

$$\sum_{i=0}^{n} e^{-\lambda} \frac{\lambda^i}{i!} = \frac{1}{n!} \int_{\lambda}^{\infty} e^{-x} x^n dx$$

Hint: Use integration by parts.

4.27. If X is a geometric random variable, show analytically that

$$P\{X = n + k | X > n\} = P\{X = k\}$$

Using the interpretation of a geometric random variable, give a verbal argument as to why the preceding equation is true.

4.28. Let X be a negative binomial random variable with parameters r and p, and let Y be a binomial random variable with parameters n and p. Show that

$$P\{X > n\} = P\{Y < r\}$$

Hint: Either one could attempt an analytical proof of the preceding equation, which is equivalent to proving the identity

$$\sum_{i=n+1}^{\infty} \binom{i-1}{r-1} p^r (1-p)^{i-r} = \sum_{i=0}^{r-1} \binom{n}{i}$$
$$\times p^i (1-p)^{n-i}$$

or one could attempt a proof that uses the probabilistic interpretation of these random variables. That is, in the latter case, start by considering a sequence of independent trials having a common probability p of success. Then try to express the events $\{X > n\}$ and $\{Y < r\}$ in terms of the outcomes of this sequence.

4.29. Let X be a geometric random variable with parameter p and Y be a binomial distribution with parameters n and p. show that

$$P(Y = 0) = P(X > n)$$

4.30. Balls numbered 1 through N are in an urn. Suppose that $n, n \leq N$, of them are randomly selected without replacement. Let Y denote the largest number selected.

(a) Find the probability mass function of Y.

(b) Derive an expression for $E[Y]$ and then use Fermat's combinatorial identity (see Theoretical Exercise 11 of Chapter 1) to simplify the expression.

4.31. Let X be a hypergeometric random variable X with parameters n, N, and m such that as $N \to \infty$, $m/N \to p$, for $0 < p < 1$. Then show that for any fixed n,

$$P(X = x) = \frac{\binom{m}{x}\binom{N-m}{n-x}}{\binom{N}{m}} \to \binom{n}{x} p^x (1-p)^{n-x} \text{ as } N \to \infty.$$

Hint: use sterling's approximation.

4.32. A jar contains n chips. Suppose that a boy successively draws a chip from the jar, each time replacing the one drawn before drawing another. The process continues until the boy draws a chip that he has previously drawn. Let X denote the number of draws, and compute its probability mass function.

4.33. An urn contain M black and n white balls. At each turn a ball is picked randomly and if it is black nothing is done and if it is white it is removed from the urn. Let X be random variable that denote the number of balls to be taken before the urn contains only black balls. Compute the probability mass function of X and also its expectation.

4.34. From a set of n elements, a nonempty subset is chosen at random in the sense that all of the nonempty subsets are equally likely to be selected. Let X denote the number of elements in the chosen subset. Using the identities given in Theoretical Exercise 12 of Chapter 1, show that

$$E[X] = \frac{n}{2 - \left(\frac{1}{2}\right)^{n-1}}$$

$$\text{Var}(X) = \frac{n \cdot 2^{2n-2} - n(n+1)2^{n-2}}{(2^n - 1)^2}$$

Show also that for n large,

$$\text{Var}(X) \backsim \frac{n}{4}$$

in the sense that the ratio $\text{Var}(X)$ to $n/4$ approaches 1 as n approaches ∞. Compare this formula with the limiting form of $\text{Var}(Y)$ when $P\{Y = i\} = 1/n, i = 1, \ldots, n$.

4.35. An urn initially contains one red and one blue ball. At each stage, a ball is randomly chosen and then replaced along with another of the same color. Let X denote the selection number of the first chosen ball that is blue. For instance, if the first selection is red and the second blue, then X is equal to 2.

(a) Find $P\{X > i\}, i \geq 1$.

(b) Show that with probability 1, a blue ball is eventually chosen. (That is, show that $P\{X < \infty\} = 1$.)

(c) Find $E[X]$.

4.36. Suppose the possible values of X are $\{x_i\}$, the possible values of Y are $\{y_j\}$, and the possible values of $X + Y$ are $\{z_k\}$. Let A_k denote the set of all pairs of indices (i, j) such that $x_i + y_j = z_k$; that is, $A_k = \{(i, j) : x_i + y_j = z_k\}$.

(a) Argue that

$$P\{X + Y = z_k\} = \sum_{(i,j) \in A_k} P\{X = x_i, Y = y_j\}$$

(b) Show that

$$E[X + Y] = \sum_k \sum_{(i,j)\in A_k} (x_i + y_j)P\{X = x_i, Y = y_j\}$$

(c) Using the formula from part (b), argue that

$$E[X + Y] = \sum_i \sum_j (x_i + y_j)P\{X = x_i, Y = y_j\}$$

(d) Show that

$$P(X = x_i) = \sum_j P(X = x_i, Y = y_j),$$

$$P(Y = y_j) = \sum_i P\{X = x_i, Y = y_j\}$$

(e) Prove that

$$E[X + Y] = E[X] + E[Y]$$

Self-Test Problems and Exercises

4.1. Suppose that the random variable X is equal to the number of hits obtained by a certain baseball player in his next 3 at bats. If $P\{X = 1\} = .3, P\{X = 2\} = .2$, and $P\{X = 0\} = 3P\{X = 3\}$, find $E[X]$.

4.2. Suppose that X takes on one of the values 0, 1, and 2. If for some constant $c, P\{X = i\} = cP\{X = i - 1\}, i = 1, 2$, find $E[X]$.

4.3. A fair die is cast till two similar numbers appear on successive rolls. Find the expected number of rolls.

4.4. A certain community is composed of m families, n_i of which have i children, $\sum_{i=1}^{r} n_i = m$. If one of the families is randomly chosen, let X denote the number of children in that family. If one of the $\sum_{i=1}^{r} in_i$ children is randomly chosen, let Y denote the total number of children in the family of that child. Show that $E[Y] \geq E[X]$.

4.5. Suppose that $P\{X = 0\} = 1 - P\{X = 1\}$. If $E[X] = 3\text{Var}(X)$, find $P\{X = 0\}$.

4.6. There are 2 coins in a bin. When one of them is flipped, it lands on heads with probability .6, and when the other is flipped, it lands on heads with probability .3. One of these coins is to be randomly chosen and then flipped. Without knowing which coin is chosen, you can bet any amount up to $10, and you then either win that amount if the coin comes up heads or lose it if it comes up tails. Suppose, however, that an insider is willing to sell you, for an amount C, the information as to which coin was selected. What is your expected payoff if you buy this information? Note that if you buy it and then bet x, you will end up either winning $x - C$ or $-x - C$ (that is, losing $x + C$ in the latter case). Also, for what values of C does it pay to purchase the information?

4.7. A philanthropist writes a positive number x on a piece of red paper, shows the paper to an impartial observer, and then turns it face down on the table. The observer then flips a fair coin. If it shows heads, she writes the value $2x$ and, if tails, the value $x/2$, on a piece of blue paper, which she then turns face down on the table. Without knowing either the value x or the result of the coin flip, you have the option of turning over either the red or the blue piece of paper. After doing so and observing the number written on that paper, you may elect to receive as a reward either that amount or the (unknown) amount written on the other piece of paper. For instance, if you elect to turn over the blue paper and observe the value 100, then you can elect either to accept 100 as your reward or to take the amount (either 200 or 50) on the red paper. Suppose that you would like your expected reward to be large.

(a) Argue that there is no reason to turn over the red paper first, because if you do so, then no matter what value you observe, it is always better to switch to the blue paper.

(b) Let y be a fixed nonnegative value, and consider the following strategy: Turn over the blue paper, and if its value is at least y, then accept that amount. If it is less than y, then switch to the red paper. Let $R_y(x)$ denote the reward obtained if the philanthropist writes the amount x and you employ this strategy. Find $E[R_y(x)]$. Note that $E[R_0(x)]$ is the expected reward if the philanthropist writes the amount x when you employ the strategy of always choosing the blue paper.

4.8. Let $B(n, p)$ represent a binomial random variable with parameters n and p. Argue that

$$P\{B(n, p) \leq i\} = 1 - P\{B(n, 1 - p) \leq n - i - 1\}$$

Hint: The number of successes less than or equal to i is equivalent to what statement about the number of failures?

4.9. For a binomial distribution with mean 4 and variance 3. Find $P(X \leq 2)$.

4.10. An urn contains n balls numbered 1 through n. If you withdraw m balls randomly in sequence, each time replacing the ball selected previously, find $P\{X = k\}, k =$

$1, \ldots, m$, where X is the maximum of the m chosen numbers.

Hint: First find $P\{X \leq k\}$.

4.11. Teams A and B play a series of games, with the first team to win 3 games being declared the winner of the series. Suppose that team A independently wins each game with probability p. Find the conditional probability that team A wins

(a) the series given that it wins the first game;

(b) the first game given that it wins the series.

4.12. A local soccer team has 5 more games left to play. If it wins its game this weekend, then it will play its final 4 games in the upper bracket of its league, and if it loses, then it will play its final games in the lower bracket. If it plays in the upper bracket, then it will independently win each of its games in this bracket with probability .4, and if it plays in the lower bracket, then it will independently win each of its games with probability .7. If the probability that the team wins its game this weekend is .5, what is the probability that it wins at least 3 of its final 4 games?

4.13. A box contains P blue balls and Q red balls. From the box, n balls are taken with replacement. Find the expected number of blue balls in the sample.

4.14. A policyholder of a certain health insurance policy is six times more likely to file two claims as to file exactly three claims. Assuming that the number of claims X is Poisson distributed. What is $E(X^2)$?

4.15. The number of eggs laid on a tree leaf by an insect of a certain type is a Poisson random variable with parameter λ. However, such a random variable can be observed only if it is positive, since if it is 0, then we cannot know that such an insect was on the leaf. If we let Y denote the observed number of eggs, then

$$P\{Y = i\} = P\{X = i | X > 0\}$$

where X is Poisson with parameter λ. Find $E[Y]$.

4.16. Each of n boys and n girls, independently and randomly, chooses a member of the other sex. If a boy and girl choose each other, they become a couple. Number the girls, and let G_i be the event that girl number i is part of a couple. Let $P_0 = 1 - P(\cup_{i=1}^{n} G_i)$ be the probability that no couples are formed.

(a) What is $P(G_i)$?

(b) What is $P(G_i | G_j)$?

(c) When n is large, approximate P_0.

(d) When n is large, approximate P_k, the probability that exactly k couples are formed.

(e) Use the inclusion–exclusion identity to evaluate P_0.

4.17. A total of $2n$ people, consisting of n married couples, are randomly divided into n pairs. Arbitrarily number the women, and let W_i denote the event that woman i is paired with her husband.

(a) Find $P(W_i)$.

(b) For $i \neq j$, find $P(W_i | W_j)$.

(c) When n is large, approximate the probability that no wife is paired with her husband.

(d) If each pairing must consist of a man and a woman, what does the problem reduce to?

4.18. A fair die in the form of a dodecahedron has faces with numbers one to twelve. How many throws does a player need to make at least 90% sure that he gets a 12?

4.19. A ceramic pot manufacturer supplies pottery in a lot of 100. A shop owner, test a random sample of 10 items and if all are good, he accept a lot otherwise he refuse it.

(a) What is the probability that he will accept a lot containing 5 defective items ?

(b) What is the probability that he will reject a lot containing only two defective items?

4.20. Show that if X is a geometric random variable with parameter p, then

$$E[1/X] = \frac{-p \log(p)}{1 - p}$$

Hint: You will need to evaluate an expression of the form $\sum_{i=1}^{\infty} a^i / i$. To do so, write $a^i / i = \int_0^a x^{i-1} dx$, and then interchange the sum and the integral.

4.21. Suppose that

$$P\{X = a\} = p, \quad P\{X = b\} = 1 - p$$

(a) Show that $\frac{X-b}{a-b}$ is a Bernoulli random variable.

(b) Find $\text{Var}(X)$.

4.22. A person buy 10 lottery tickets with each having a winning probability p. If he wins a prize in at least one of the tickets, he gets addicted and will keep on buying tickets till he wins again.

(a) Find the expected number of tickets he buys.

(b) Find the expected number of winning tickets.

(c) Find the expected number of unsuccessful attempts.

4.23. An urn contains M white and N black balls. n random selections without replacement are made. What is the probability of

(a) getting a black ball on i th selection?

(b) getting a black ball on i th selection and white on j th selection, with $j > i$?

(c) obtaining balls of different colours in adjacent selections?

4.24. Ten balls are to be distributed among 5 urns, with each ball going into urn i with probability p_i, $\sum_{i=1}^{5} p_i = 1$.

Let X_i denote the number of balls that go into urn i. Assume that events corresponding to the locations of different balls are independent.

(a) What type of random variable is X_i? Be as specific as possible.

(b) For $i \neq j$, what type of random variable is $X_i + X_j$?

(c) Find $P\{X_1 + X_2 + X_3 = 7\}$.

4.25. For the match problem (Example 5m in Chapter 2), find

(a) the expected number of matches.

(b) the variance of the number of matches.

4.26. Let α be the probability that a geometric random variable X with parameter p is an even number.

(a) Find α by using the identity $\alpha = \sum_{i=1}^{\infty} P\{X = 2i\}$.

(b) Find α by conditioning on whether $X = 1$ or $X > 1$.

4.27. The National Basketball Association championship series is a best of 7 series, meaning that the first team to win 4 games is declared the champion. In its history, no team has ever come back to win the championship series after being behind 3 games to 1. Assuming that each of the games played in this year's series is equally likely to be won by either team, independent of the results of earlier games, what is the probability that the upcoming championship series will result in a team coming back from a 3 games to 1 deficit to win the series?

4.28. An urn has n white and m black balls. Balls are randomly withdrawn, without replacement, until a total of $k, k \leq n$ white balls have been withdrawn. The random variable X equal to the total number of balls that are withdrawn is said to be a *negative hypergeometric* random variable.

(a) Explain how such a random variable differs from a negative binomial random variable.

(b) Find $P\{X = r\}$.

Hint for (b): In order for $X = r$ to happen, what must be the results of the first $r - 1$ withdrawals?

Chapter 5

CONTINUOUS RANDOM VARIABLES

Contents

5.1 Introduction
5.2 Expectation and Variance of Continuous Random Variables
5.3 The Uniform Random Variable
5.4 Normal Random Variables
5.5 Exponential Random Variables
5.6 Other Continuous Distributions
5.7 The Distribution of a Function of a Random Variable

5.1   Introduction

In Chapter 4, we considered discrete random variables—that is, random variables whose set of possible values is either finite or countably infinite. However, there also exist random variables whose set of possible values is uncountable. Two examples are the time that a train arrives at a specified stop and the lifetime of a transistor. Let X be such a random variable. We say that X is a *continuous*[†] random variable if there exists a nonnegative function f, defined for all real $x \in (-\infty, \infty)$, having the property that for any set B of real numbers,[‡]

$$P\{X \in B\} = \int_B f(x)\, dx \tag{1.1}$$

The function f is called the *probability density function* of the random variable X. (See Figure 5.1.)

In words, Equation (1.1) states that the probability that X will be in B may be obtained by integrating the probability density function over the set B. Since X must assume some value, f must satisfy

$$1 = P\{X \in (-\infty, \infty)\} = \int_{-\infty}^{\infty} f(x)\, dx$$

All probability statements about X can be answered in terms of f. For instance, from Equation (1.1), letting $B = [a, b]$, we obtain

$$P\{a \le X \le b\} = \int_a^b f(x)\, dx \tag{1.2}$$

[†] Sometimes called *absolutely continuous*.

[‡] Actually, for technical reasons, Equation (1.1) is true only for the *measurable* sets B, which, fortunately, include all sets of practical interest.

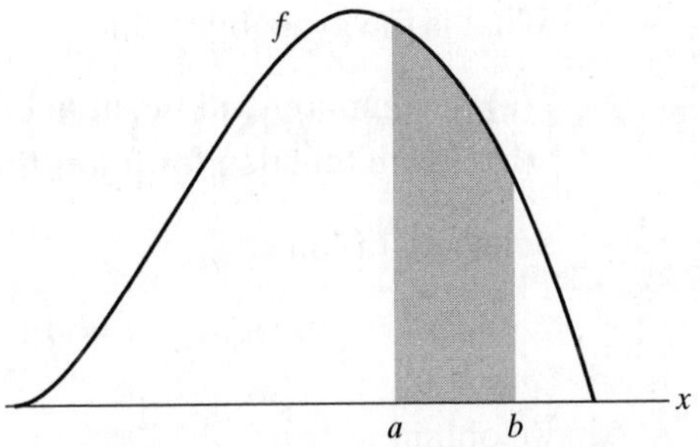

$P(a \le X \le b)$ = area of shaded region

Figure 5.1 Probability density function f.

If we let $a = b$ in Equation (1.2), we get

$$P\{X = a\} = \int_a^a f(x)\,dx = 0$$

In words, this equation states that the probability that a continuous random variable will assume any fixed value is zero. Hence, for a continuous random variable,

$$P\{X < a\} = P\{X \le a\} = F(a) = \int_{-\infty}^a f(x)\,dx$$

Example 1a

Suppose that X is a continuous random variable whose probability density function is given by

$$f(x) = \begin{cases} C(4x - 2x^2) & 0 < x < 2 \\ 0 & \text{otherwise} \end{cases}$$

(a) What is the value of C?

(b) Find $P\{X > 1\}$.

Solution (a) Since f is a probability density function, we must have $\int_{-\infty}^\infty f(x)\,dx = 1$, implying that

$$C \int_0^2 (4x - 2x^2)\,dx = 1$$

or

$$C \left[2x^2 - \frac{2x^3}{3} \right]\Bigg|_{x=0}^{x=2} = 1$$

or

$$C = \frac{3}{8}$$

Hence,

(b) $P\{X > 1\} = \int_1^\infty f(x)\,dx = \frac{3}{8} \int_1^2 (4x - 2x^2)\,dx = \frac{1}{2}$ ∎

Example 1b

The amount of time in hours that a computer functions before breaking down is a continuous random variable with probability density function given by

$$f(x) = \begin{cases} \lambda e^{-x/100} & x \ge 0 \\ 0 & x < 0 \end{cases}$$

What is the probability that

(a) a computer will function between 50 and 150 hours before breaking down?
(b) it will function for fewer than 100 hours?

Solution (a) Since

$$1 = \int_{-\infty}^{\infty} f(x)\,dx = \lambda \int_{0}^{\infty} e^{-x/100}\,dx$$

we obtain

$$1 = -\lambda(100)e^{-x/100}\big|_{0}^{\infty} = 100\lambda \quad or \quad \lambda = \frac{1}{100}$$

Hence, the probability that a computer will function between 50 and 150 hours before breaking down is given by

$$P\{50 < X < 150\} = \int_{50}^{150} \frac{1}{100} e^{-x/100}\,dx = -e^{-x/100}\big|_{50}^{150}$$
$$= e^{-1/2} - e^{-3/2} \approx .383$$

(b) Similarly,

$$P\{X < 100\} = \int_{0}^{100} \frac{1}{100} e^{-x/100}\,dx = -e^{-x/100}\big|_{0}^{100} = 1 - e^{-1} \approx .632$$

In other words, approximately 63.2 percent of the time, a computer will fail before registering 100 hours of use. ∎

Example 1c

The lifetime in hours of a certain kind of radio tube is a random variable having a probability density function given by

$$f(x) = \begin{cases} 0 & x \leq 100 \\ \dfrac{100}{x^2} & x > 100 \end{cases}$$

What is the probability that exactly 2 of 5 such tubes in a radio set will have to be replaced within the first 150 hours of operation? Assume that the events $E_i, i = 1, 2, 3, 4, 5$, that the ith such tube will have to be replaced within this time are independent.

Solution From the statement of the problem, we have

$$P(E_i) = \int_{0}^{150} f(x)\,dx$$
$$= 100 \int_{100}^{150} x^{-2}\,dx$$
$$= \frac{1}{3}$$

Hence, from the independence of the events E_i, it follows that the desired probability is

$$\binom{5}{2}\left(\frac{1}{3}\right)^2 \left(\frac{2}{3}\right)^3 = \frac{80}{243} \qquad \blacksquare$$

The relationship between the cumulative distribution F and the probability density f is expressed by

$$F(a) = P\{X \in (-\infty, a]\} = \int_{-\infty}^{a} f(x)\,dx$$

Differentiating both sides of the preceding equation yields

$$\frac{d}{da}F(a) = f(a)$$

That is, the density is the derivative of the cumulative distribution function. A somewhat more intuitive interpretation of the density function may be obtained from Equation (1.2) as follows:

$$P\left\{a - \frac{\varepsilon}{2} \le X \le a + \frac{\varepsilon}{2}\right\} = \int_{a-\varepsilon/2}^{a+\varepsilon/2} f(x)\,dx \approx \varepsilon f(a)$$

when ε is small and when $f(\cdot)$ is continuous at $x = a$. In other words, the probability that X will be contained in an interval of length ε around the point a is approximately $\varepsilon f(a)$. From this result, we see that $f(a)$ is a measure of how likely it is that the random variable will be near a.

Example 1d

If X is continuous with distribution function F_X and density function f_X, find the density function of $Y = 2X$.

Solution We will determine f_Y in two ways. The first way is to derive, and then differentiate, the distribution function of Y:

$$\begin{aligned}
F_Y(a) &= P\{Y \le a\} \\
&= P\{2X \le a\} \\
&= P\{X \le a/2\} \\
&= F_X(a/2)
\end{aligned}$$

Differentiation gives

$$f_Y(a) = \frac{1}{2}f_X(a/2)$$

Another way to determine f_Y is to note that

$$\begin{aligned}
\epsilon f_Y(a) &\approx P\left\{a - \frac{\epsilon}{2} \le Y \le a + \frac{\epsilon}{2}\right\} \\
&= P\left\{a - \frac{\epsilon}{2} \le 2X \le a + \frac{\epsilon}{2}\right\} \\
&= P\left\{\frac{a}{2} - \frac{\epsilon}{4} \le X \le \frac{a}{2} + \frac{\epsilon}{4}\right\} \\
&\approx \frac{\epsilon}{2}f_X(a/2)
\end{aligned}$$

Dividing through by ϵ gives the same result as before. ∎

5.2 Expectation and Variance of Continuous Random Variables

In Chapter 4, we defined the expected value of a discrete random variable X by

$$E[X] = \sum_x x P\{X = x\}$$

If X is a continuous random variable having probability density function $f(x)$, then, because

$$f(x)\,dx \approx P\{x \leq X \leq x + dx\} \quad \text{for } dx \text{ small}$$

it is easy to see that the analogous definition is to define the expected value of X by

$$E[X] = \int_{-\infty}^{\infty} xf(x)\,dx$$

Example 2a

Find $E[X]$ when the density function of X is

$$f(x) = \begin{cases} 2x & \text{if } 0 \leq x \leq 1 \\ 0 & \text{otherwise} \end{cases}$$

Solution

$$\begin{aligned} E[X] &= \int xf(x)\,dx \\ &= \int_0^1 2x^2\,dx \\ &= \frac{2}{3} \end{aligned}$$

∎

Example 2b

The density function of X is given by

$$f(x) = \begin{cases} 1 & \text{if } 0 \leq x \leq 1 \\ 0 & \text{otherwise} \end{cases}$$

Find $E[e^X]$.

Solution Let $Y = e^X$. We start by determining F_Y, the cumulative distribution function of Y. Now, for $1 \leq x \leq e$,

$$\begin{aligned} F_Y(x) &= P\{Y \leq x\} \\ &= P\{e^X \leq x\} \\ &= P\{X \leq \log(x)\} \\ &= \int_0^{\log(x)} f(y)\,dy \\ &= \log(x) \end{aligned}$$

By differentiating $F_Y(x)$, we can conclude that the probability density function of Y is given by

$$f_Y(x) = \frac{1}{x} \quad 1 \leq x \leq e$$

Hence,

$$\begin{aligned} E[e^X] = E[Y] &= \int_{-\infty}^{\infty} xf_Y(x)\,dx \\ &= \int_1^e dx \\ &= e - 1 \end{aligned}$$

∎

Although the method employed in Example 2b to compute the expected value of a function of X is always applicable, there is, as in the discrete case, an alternative way of proceeding. The following is a direct analog of Proposition 4.1 of Chapter 4.

Proposition 2.1

If X is a continuous random variable with probability density function $f(x)$, then, for any real-valued function g,

$$E[g(X)] = \int_{-\infty}^{\infty} g(x)f(x)\,dx$$

An application of Proposition 2.1 to Example 2b yields

$$E[e^X] = \int_0^1 e^x\,dx \qquad \text{since } f(x) = 1, \quad 0 < x < 1$$
$$= e - 1$$

which is in accord with the result obtained in that example.

The proof of Proposition 2.1 is more involved than that of its discrete random variable analog. We will present such a proof under the provision that the random variable $g(X)$ is nonnegative. (The general proof, which follows the argument in the case we present, is indicated in Theoretical Exercises 5.2 and 5.3.) We will need the following lemma, which is of independent interest.

Lemma 2.1

For a nonnegative random variable Y,

$$E[Y] = \int_0^{\infty} P\{Y > y\}\,dy$$

Proof We present a proof when Y is a continuous random variable with probability density function f_Y. We have

$$\int_0^{\infty} P\{Y > y\}\,dy = \int_0^{\infty} \int_y^{\infty} f_Y(x)\,dx\,dy$$

where we have used the fact that $P\{Y > y\} = \int_y^{\infty} f_Y(x)\,dx$. Interchanging the order of integration in the preceding equation yields

$$\int_0^{\infty} P\{Y > y\}\,dy = \int_0^{\infty} \left(\int_0^x dy \right) f_Y(x)\,dx$$
$$= \int_0^{\infty} x f_Y(x)\,dx$$
$$= E[Y] \qquad \blacksquare$$

Proof of Proposition 2.1 From Lemma 2.1, for any function g for which $g(x) \geq 0$,

$$E[g(X)] = \int_0^{\infty} P\{g(X) > y\}\,dy$$
$$= \int_0^{\infty} \int_{x:g(x)>y} f(x)\,dx\,dy$$
$$= \int_{x:g(x)>0} \int_0^{g(x)} dy\,f(x)\,dx$$
$$= \int_{x:g(x)>0} g(x)f(x)\,dx$$

which completes the proof.

Example 2c

A stick of length 1 is split at a point U having density function $f(u) = 1, 0 < u < 1$. Determine the expected length of the piece that contains the point $p, 0 \leq p \leq 1$.

Solution Let $L_p(U)$ denote the length of the substick that contains the point p, and note that

$$L_p(U) = \begin{cases} 1 - U & U < p \\ U & U > p \end{cases}$$

(See Figure 5.2.) Hence, from Proposition 2.1,

$$
\begin{aligned}
E[L_p(U)] &= \int_0^1 L_p(u)\, du \\
&= \int_0^p (1 - u)\, du + \int_p^1 u\, du \\
&= \frac{1}{2} - \frac{(1 - p)^2}{2} + \frac{1}{2} - \frac{p^2}{2} \\
&= \frac{1}{2} + p(1 - p)
\end{aligned}
$$

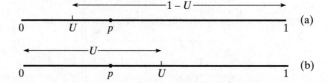

Figure 5.2 Substick containing point p: (a) $U < p$; (b) $U > p$.

Since $p(1 - p)$ is maximized when $p = \frac{1}{2}$, it is interesting to note that the expected length of the substick containing the point p is maximized when p is the midpoint of the original stick. ∎

Example 2d

Suppose that if you are s minutes early for an appointment, then you incur the cost cs, and if you are s minutes late, then you incur the cost ks. Suppose also that the travel time from where you presently are to the location of your appointment is a continuous random variable having probability density function f. Determine the time at which you should depart if you want to minimize your expected cost.

Solution Let X denote the travel time. If you leave t minutes before your appointment, then your cost—call it $C_t(X)$—is given by

$$C_t(X) = \begin{cases} c(t - X) & \text{if } X \leq t \\ k(X - t) & \text{if } X \geq t \end{cases}$$

Therefore,

$$
\begin{aligned}
E[C_t(X)] &= \int_0^\infty C_t(x) f(x)\, dx \\
&= \int_0^t c(t - x) f(x)\, dx + \int_t^\infty k(x - t) f(x)\, dx \\
&= ct \int_0^t f(x)\, dx - c \int_0^t x f(x)\, dx + k \int_t^\infty x f(x)\, dx - kt \int_t^\infty f(x)\, dx
\end{aligned}
$$

The value of t that minimizes $E[C_t(X)]$ can now be obtained by calculus. Differentiation yields

$$\frac{d}{dt}E[C_t(X)] = ctf(t) + cF(t) - ctf(t) - ktf(t) + ktf(t) - k[1 - F(t)]$$
$$= (k + c)F(t) - k$$

Equating the rightmost side to zero shows that the minimal expected cost is obtained when you leave t^* minutes before your appointment, where t^* satisfies

$$F(t^*) = \frac{k}{k + c}$$ ∎

As in Chapter 4, we can use Proposition 2.1 to show the following.

Corollary 2.1

If a and b are constants, then

$$E[aX + b] = aE[X] + b$$

The proof of Corollary 2.1 for a continuous random variable X is the same as the one given for a discrete random variable. The only modification is that the sum is replaced by an integral and the probability mass function by a probability density function.

The variance of a continuous random variable is defined exactly as it is for a discrete random variable, namely, if X is a random variable with expected value μ, then the variance of X is defined (for any type of random variable) by

$$\text{Var}(X) = E[(X - \mu)^2]$$

The alternative formula,

$$\text{Var}(X) = E[X^2] - (E[X])^2$$

is established in a manner similar to its counterpart in the discrete case.

Example 2e

Find $\text{Var}(X)$ for X as given in Example 2a.

Solution We first compute $E[X^2]$.

$$E[X^2] = \int_{-\infty}^{\infty} x^2 f(x)\, dx$$
$$= \int_{0}^{1} 2x^3\, dx$$
$$= \frac{1}{2}$$

Hence, since $E[X] = \frac{2}{3}$, we obtain

$$\text{Var}(X) = \frac{1}{2} - \left(\frac{2}{3}\right)^2 = \frac{1}{18}$$ ∎

It can be shown that, for constants a and b,

$$\text{Var}(aX + b) = a^2\text{Var}(X)$$

The proof mimics the one given for discrete random variables.

There are several important classes of continuous random variables that appear frequently in applications of probability; the next few sections are devoted to a study of some of them.

5.3 The Uniform Random Variable

A random variable is said to be *uniformly* distributed over the interval (0, 1) if its probability density function is given by

$$f(x) = \begin{cases} 1 & 0 < x < 1 \\ 0 & \text{otherwise} \end{cases} \tag{3.1}$$

Note that Equation (3.1) is a density function, since $f(x) \geq 0$ and $\int_{-\infty}^{\infty} f(x)\,dx = \int_0^1 dx = 1$. Because $f(x) > 0$ only when $x \in (0,1)$, it follows that X must assume a value in interval (0, 1). Also, since $f(x)$ is constant for $x \in (0,1)$, X is just as likely to be near any value in (0, 1) as it is to be near any other value. To verify this statement, note that for any $0 < a < b < 1$,

$$P\{a \leq X \leq b\} = \int_a^b f(x)\,dx = b - a$$

In other words, the probability that X is in any particular subinterval of (0, 1) equals the length of that subinterval.

In general, we say that X is a uniform random variable on the interval (α, β) if the probability density function of X is given by

$$f(x) = \begin{cases} \dfrac{1}{\beta - \alpha} & \text{if } \alpha < x < \beta \\ 0 & \text{otherwise} \end{cases} \tag{3.2}$$

Since $F(a) = \int_{-\infty}^a f(x)\,dx$, it follows from Equation (3.2) that the distribution function of a uniform random variable on the interval (α, β) is given by

$$F(a) = \begin{cases} 0 & a \leq \alpha \\ \dfrac{a - \alpha}{\beta - \alpha} & \alpha < a < \beta \\ 1 & a \geq \beta \end{cases}$$

Figure 5.3 presents a graph of $f(a)$ and $F(a)$.

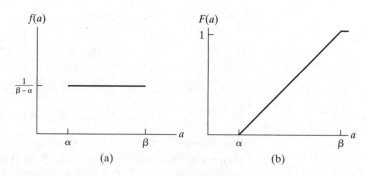

Figure 5.3 Graph of (a) $f(a)$ and (b) $F(a)$ for a uniform (α, β) random variable.

Example 3a

Let X be uniformly distributed over (α, β). Find (a) $E[X]$ and (b) $Var(X)$.

Solution   (a)

$$E[X] = \int_{-\infty}^{\infty} xf(x)\,dx$$

$$= \int_{\alpha}^{\beta} \frac{x}{\beta - \alpha}\,dx$$

$$= \frac{\beta^2 - \alpha^2}{2(\beta - \alpha)}$$

$$= \frac{\beta + \alpha}{2}$$

In words, the expected value of a random variable that is uniformly distributed over some interval is equal to the midpoint of that interval.

(b) To find $Var(X)$, we first calculate $E[X^2]$.

$$E[X^2] = \int_{\alpha}^{\beta} \frac{1}{\beta - \alpha} x^2\,dx$$

$$= \frac{\beta^3 - \alpha^3}{3(\beta - \alpha)}$$

$$= \frac{\beta^2 + \alpha\beta + \alpha^2}{3}$$

Hence,

$$Var(X) = \frac{\beta^2 + \alpha\beta + \alpha^2}{3} - \frac{(\alpha + \beta)^2}{4}$$

$$= \frac{(\beta - \alpha)^2}{12}$$

Therefore, the variance of a random variable that is uniformly distributed over some interval is the square of the length of that interval divided by 12. ∎

Example 3b

If X is uniformly distributed over $(0, 10)$, calculate the probability that (a) $X < 3$, (b) $X > 6$, and (c) $3 < X < 8$.

Solution   (a) $P\{X < 3\} = \int_0^3 \frac{1}{10}\,dx = \frac{3}{10}$

(b) $P\{X > 6\} = \int_6^{10} \frac{1}{10}\,dx = \frac{4}{10}$

(c) $P\{3 < X < 8\} = \int_3^8 \frac{1}{10}\,dx = \frac{1}{2}$ ∎

Example 3c

Buses arrive at a specified stop at 15-minute intervals starting at 7 A.M. That is, they arrive at 7, 7:15, 7:30, 7:45, and so on. If a passenger arrives at the stop at a time that is uniformly distributed between 7 and 7:30, find the probability that he waits

(a) less than 5 minutes for a bus;

(b) more than 10 minutes for a bus.

Solution Let X denote the number of minutes past 7 that the passenger arrives at the stop. Since X is a uniform random variable over the interval $(0, 30)$, it follows that the passenger will have to wait less than 5 minutes if (and only if) he arrives between 7:10 and 7:15 or between 7:25 and 7:30. Hence, the desired probability for part (a) is

$$P\{10 < X < 15\} + P\{25 < X < 30\} = \int_{10}^{15} \frac{1}{30}\, dx + \int_{25}^{30} \frac{1}{30}\, dx = \frac{1}{3}$$

Similarly, he would have to wait more than 10 minutes if he arrives between 7 and 7:05 or between 7:15 and 7:20, so the probability for part (b) is

$$P\{0 < X < 5\} + P\{15 < X < 20\} = \frac{1}{3} \qquad \blacksquare$$

The next example was first considered by the French mathematician Joseph L. F. Bertrand in 1889 and is often referred to as *Bertrand's paradox*. It represents our initial introduction to a subject commonly referred to as *geometrical probability*.

Example 3d

Consider a random chord of a circle. What is the probability that the length of the chord will be greater than the side of the equilateral triangle inscribed in that circle?

Solution As stated, the problem is incapable of solution because it is not clear what is meant by a random chord. To give meaning to this phrase, we shall reformulate the problem in two distinct ways.

The first formulation is as follows: The position of the chord can be determined by its distance from the center of the circle. This distance can vary between 0 and r, the radius of the circle. Now, the length of the chord will be greater than the side of the equilateral triangle inscribed in the circle if the distance from the chord to the center of the circle is less than $r/2$. Hence, by assuming that a random chord is a chord whose distance D from the center of the circle is uniformly distributed between 0 and r, we see that the probability that the length of the chord is greater than the side of an inscribed equilateral triangle is

$$P\left\{D < \frac{r}{2}\right\} = \frac{r/2}{r} = \frac{1}{2}$$

For our second formulation of the problem, consider an arbitrary chord of the circle; through one end of the chord, draw a tangent. The angle θ between the chord and the tangent, which can vary from $0°$ to $180°$, determines the position of the chord. (See Figure 5.4.) Furthermore, the length of the chord will be greater than the side of the inscribed equilateral triangle if the angle θ is between $60°$ and $120°$. Hence, assuming that a random chord is a chord whose angle θ is uniformly distributed between $0°$ and $180°$, we see that the desired answer in this formulation is

$$P\{60 < \theta < 120\} = \frac{120 - 60}{180} = \frac{1}{3}$$

Note that random experiments could be performed in such a way that $\frac{1}{2}$ or $\frac{1}{3}$ would be the correct probability. For instance, if a circular disk of radius r is thrown on a table ruled with parallel lines a distance $2r$ apart, then one and only one of these lines would cross the disk and form a chord. All distances from this chord to the

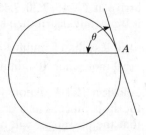

Figure 5.4

center of the disk would be equally likely, so that the desired probability that the chord's length will be greater than the side of an inscribed equilateral triangle is $\frac{1}{2}$. In contrast, if the experiment consisted of rotating a needle freely about a point A on the edge (see Figure 5.4) of the circle, the desired answer would be $\frac{1}{3}$. ∎

5.4   Normal Random Variables

We say that X is a normal random variable, or simply that X is normally distributed, with parameters μ and σ^2 if the density of X is given by

$$f(x) = \frac{1}{\sqrt{2\pi}\,\sigma}e^{-(x-\mu)^2/2\sigma^2} \qquad -\infty < x < \infty$$

This density function is a bell-shaped curve that is symmetric about μ. (See Figure 5.5.)

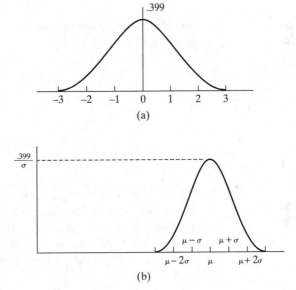

Figure 5.5 Normal density function: (a) $\mu = 0, \sigma = 1$; (b) arbitrary μ, σ^2.

The normal distribution was introduced by the French mathematician Abraham DeMoivre in 1733, who used it to approximate probabilities associated with binomial random variables when the binomial parameter n is large. This result was later extended by Laplace and others and is now encompassed in a probability theorem known as the central limit theorem, which is discussed in Chapter 8. The *central limit theorem*, one of the two most important results in probability theory,[†] gives a theoretical base to the often noted empirical observation that, in practice, many random phenomena obey, at least approximately, a normal probability distribution. Some examples of random phenomena obeying this behavior are the height of a man or woman, the velocity in any direction of a molecule in gas, and the error made in measuring a physical quantity.

[†]The other is the strong law of large numbers.

To prove that $f(x)$ is indeed a probability density function, we need to show that

$$\frac{1}{\sqrt{2\pi}\sigma} \int_{-\infty}^{\infty} e^{-(x-\mu)^2/2\sigma^2} \, dx = 1$$

Making the substitution $y = (x - \mu)/\sigma$, we see that

$$\frac{1}{\sqrt{2\pi}\sigma} \int_{-\infty}^{\infty} e^{-(x-\mu)^2/2\sigma^2} \, dx = \frac{1}{\sqrt{2\pi}} \int_{-\infty}^{\infty} e^{-y^2/2} \, dy$$

Hence, we must show that

$$\int_{-\infty}^{\infty} e^{-y^2/2} \, dy = \sqrt{2\pi}$$

Toward this end, let $I = \int_{-\infty}^{\infty} e^{-y^2/2} \, dy$. Then

$$I^2 = \int_{-\infty}^{\infty} e^{-y^2/2} \, dy \int_{-\infty}^{\infty} e^{-x^2/2} \, dx$$

$$= \int_{-\infty}^{\infty} \int_{-\infty}^{\infty} e^{-(y^2+x^2)/2} \, dy \, dx$$

We now evaluate the double integral by means of a change of variables to polar coordinates. (That is, let $x = r \cos\theta, y = r \sin\theta$, and $dy \, dx = r \, d\theta \, dr$.) Thus,

$$I^2 = \int_0^{\infty} \int_0^{2\pi} e^{-r^2/2} r \, d\theta \, dr$$

$$= 2\pi \int_0^{\infty} r e^{-r^2/2} dr$$

$$= -2\pi e^{-r^2/2} \big|_0^{\infty}$$

$$= 2\pi$$

Hence, $I = \sqrt{2\pi}$, and the result is proved.

An important fact about normal random variables is that if X is normally distributed with parameters μ and σ^2, then $Y = aX + b$ is normally distributed with parameters $a\mu + b$ and $a^2\sigma^2$. To prove this statement, suppose that $a > 0$. (The proof when $a < 0$ is similar.) Let F_Y denote the cumulative distribution function of Y. Then

$$F_Y(x) = P\{Y \le x\}$$

$$= P\{aX + b \le x\}$$

$$= P\left\{X \le \frac{x - b}{a}\right\}$$

$$= F_X\left(\frac{x - b}{a}\right)$$

where F_X is the cumulative distribution function of X. By differentiation, the density function of Y is then

$$f_Y(x) = \frac{1}{a} f_X\left(\frac{x - b}{a}\right)$$

$$= \frac{1}{\sqrt{2\pi}a\sigma} \exp\left\{-\left(\frac{x - b}{a} - \mu\right)^2 \Big/ 2\sigma^2\right\}$$

$$= \frac{1}{\sqrt{2\pi}a\sigma} \exp\{-(x - b - a\mu)^2/2(a\sigma)^2\}$$

which shows that Y is normal with parameters $a\mu + b$ and $a^2\sigma^2$.

An important implication of the preceding result is that if X is normally distributed with parameters μ and σ^2, then $Z = (X - \mu)/\sigma$ is normally distributed with parameters 0 and 1. Such a random variable is said to be a *standard*, or a *unit*, normal random variable.

We now show that the parameters μ and σ^2 of a normal random variable represent, respectively, its expected value and variance.

Example 4a

Find $E[X]$ and $\text{Var}(X)$ when X is a normal random variable with parameters μ and σ^2.

Solution Let us start by finding the mean and variance of the standard normal random variable $Z = (X - \mu)/\sigma$. We have

$$E[Z] = \int_{-\infty}^{\infty} x f_Z(x) \, dx$$
$$= \frac{1}{\sqrt{2\pi}} \int_{-\infty}^{\infty} x e^{-x^2/2} \, dx$$
$$= -\frac{1}{\sqrt{2\pi}} e^{-x^2/2} \Big|_{-\infty}^{\infty}$$
$$= 0$$

Thus,

$$\text{Var}(Z) = E[Z^2]$$
$$= \frac{1}{\sqrt{2\pi}} \int_{-\infty}^{\infty} x^2 e^{-x^2/2} \, dx$$

Integration by parts (with $u = x$ and $dv = x e^{-x^2/2}$) now gives

$$\text{Var}(Z) = \frac{1}{\sqrt{2\pi}} \left(-x e^{-x^2/2} \Big|_{-\infty}^{\infty} + \int_{-\infty}^{\infty} e^{-x^2/2} \, dx \right)$$
$$= \frac{1}{\sqrt{2\pi}} \int_{-\infty}^{\infty} e^{-x^2/2} \, dx$$
$$= 1$$

Because $X = \mu + \sigma Z$, the preceding yields the results

$$E[X] = \mu + \sigma E[Z] = \mu$$

and

$$\text{Var}(X) = \sigma^2 \text{Var}(Z) = \sigma^2 \qquad \blacksquare$$

It is customary to denote the cumulative distribution function of a standard normal random variable by $\Phi(x)$. That is,

$$\Phi(x) = \frac{1}{\sqrt{2\pi}} \int_{-\infty}^{x} e^{-y^2/2} \, dy$$

Table 5.1 Area $\Phi(x)$ Under the Standard Normal Curve to the Left of X.

X	.00	.01	.02	.03	.04	.05	.06	.07	.08	.09
.0	.5000	.5040	.5080	.5120	.5160	.5199	.5239	.5279	.5319	.5359
.1	.5398	.5438	.5478	.5517	.5557	.5596	.5636	.5675	.5714	.5753
.2	.5793	.5832	.5871	.5910	.5948	.5987	.6026	.6064	.6103	.6141
.3	.6179	.6217	.6255	.6293	.6331	.6368	.6406	.6443	.6480	.6517
.4	.6554	.6591	.6628	.6664	.6700	.6736	.6772	.6808	.6844	.6879
.5	.6915	.6950	.6985	.7019	.7054	.7088	.7123	.7157	.7190	.7224
.6	.7257	.7291	.7324	.7357	.7389	.7422	.7454	.7486	.7517	.7549
.7	.7580	.7611	.7642	.7673	.7704	.7734	.7764	.7794	.7823	.7852
.8	.7881	.7910	.7939	.7967	.7995	.8023	.8051	.8078	.8106	.8133
.9	.8159	.8186	.8212	.8238	.8264	.8289	.8315	.8340	.8365	.8389
1.0	.8413	.8438	.8461	.8485	.8508	.8531	.8554	.8577	.8599	.8621
1.1	.8643	.8665	.8686	.8708	.8729	.8749	.8770	.8790	.8810	.8830
1.2	.8849	.8869	.8888	.8907	.8925	.8944	.8962	.8980	.8997	.9015
1.3	.9032	.9049	.9066	.9082	.9099	.9115	.9131	.9147	.9162	.9177
1.4	.9192	.9207	.9222	.9236	.9251	.9265	.9279	.9292	.9306	.9319
1.5	.9332	.9345	.9357	.9370	.9382	.9394	.9406	.9418	.9429	.9441
1.6	.9452	.9463	.9474	.9484	.9495	.9505	.9515	.9525	.9535	.9545
1.7	.9554	.9564	.9573	.9582	.9591	.9599	.9608	.9616	.9625	.9633
1.8	.9641	.9649	.9656	.9664	.9671	.9678	.9686	.9693	.9699	.9706
1.9	.9713	.9719	.9726	.9732	.9738	.9744	.9750	.9756	.9761	.9767
2.0	.9772	.9778	.9783	.9788	.9793	.9798	.9803	.9808	.9812	.9817
2.1	.9821	.9826	.9830	.9834	.9838	.9842	.9846	.9850	.9854	.9857
2.2	.9861	.9864	.9868	.9871	.9875	.9878	.9881	.9884	.9887	.9890
2.3	.9893	.9896	.9898	.9901	.9904	.9906	.9909	.9911	.9913	.9916
2.4	.9918	.9920	.9922	.9925	.9927	.9929	.9931	.9932	.9934	.9936
2.5	.9938	.9940	.9941	.9943	.9945	.9946	.9948	.9949	.9951	.9952
2.6	.9953	.9955	.9956	.9957	.9959	.9960	.9961	.9962	.9963	.9964
2.7	.9965	.9966	.9967	.9968	.9969	.9970	.9971	.9972	.9973	.9974
2.8	.9974	.9975	.9976	.9977	.9977	.9978	.9979	.9979	.9980	.9981
2.9	.9981	.9982	.9982	.9983	.9984	.9984	.9985	.9985	.9986	.9986
3.0	.9987	.9987	.9987	.9988	.9988	.9989	.9989	.9989	.9990	.9990
3.1	.9990	.9991	.9991	.9991	.9992	.9992	.9992	.9992	.9993	.9993
3.2	.9993	.9993	.9994	.9994	.9994	.9994	.9994	.9995	.9995	.9995
3.3	.9995	.9995	.9995	.9996	.9996	.9996	.9996	.9996	.9996	.9997
3.4	.9997	.9997	.9997	.9997	.9997	.9997	.9997	.9997	.9997	.9998

The values of $\Phi(x)$ for nonnegative x are given in Table 5.1. For negative values of x, $\Phi(x)$ can be obtained from the relationship

$$\Phi(-x) = 1 - \Phi(x) \qquad -\infty < x < \infty \qquad (4.1)$$

The proof of Equation (4.1), which follows from the symmetry of the standard normal density, is left as an exercise. This equation states that if Z is a standard normal random variable, then

$$P\{Z \le -x\} = P\{Z > x\} \qquad -\infty < x < \infty$$

Since $Z = (X - \mu)/\sigma$ is a standard normal random variable whenever X is normally distributed with parameters μ and σ^2, it follows that the distribution function of X can be expressed as

$$F_X(a) = P\{X \leq a\} = P\left(\frac{X - \mu}{\sigma} \leq \frac{a - \mu}{\sigma}\right) = \Phi\left(\frac{a - \mu}{\sigma}\right)$$

Example 4b

If X is a normal random variable with parameters $\mu = 3$ and $\sigma^2 = 9$, find (a) $P\{2 < X < 5\}$; (b) $P\{X > 0\}$; (c) $P\{|X - 3| > 6\}$.

Solution (a)

$$P\{2 < X < 5\} = P\left\{\frac{2 - 3}{3} < \frac{X - 3}{3} < \frac{5 - 3}{3}\right\}$$

$$= P\left\{-\frac{1}{3} < Z < \frac{2}{3}\right\}$$

$$= \Phi\left(\frac{2}{3}\right) - \Phi\left(-\frac{1}{3}\right)$$

$$= \Phi\left(\frac{2}{3}\right) - \left[1 - \Phi\left(\frac{1}{3}\right)\right] \approx .3779$$

(b)

$$P\{X > 0\} = P\left\{\frac{X - 3}{3} > \frac{0 - 3}{3}\right\} = P\{Z > -1\}$$

$$= 1 - \Phi(-1)$$

$$= \Phi(1)$$

$$\approx .8413$$

(c)

$$P\{|X - 3| > 6\} = P\{X > 9\} + P\{X < -3\}$$

$$= P\left\{\frac{X - 3}{3} > \frac{9 - 3}{3}\right\} + P\left\{\frac{X - 3}{3} < \frac{-3 - 3}{3}\right\}$$

$$= P\{Z > 2\} + P\{Z < -2\}$$

$$= 1 - \Phi(2) + \Phi(-2)$$

$$= 2[1 - \Phi(2)]$$

$$\approx .0456$$

Example 4c

An examination is frequently regarded as being good (in the sense of determining a valid grade spread for those taking it) if the test scores of those taking the examination can be approximated by a normal density function. (In other words, a graph of the frequency of grade scores should have approximately the bell-shaped form of the normal density.) The instructor often uses the test scores to estimate the normal parameters μ and σ^2 and then assigns the letter grade A to those whose test score is greater than $\mu + \sigma$, B to those whose score is between μ and $\mu + \sigma$, C to those whose score is between $\mu - \sigma$ and μ, D to those whose score is between $\mu - 2\sigma$ and $\mu - \sigma$, and F to those getting a score below $\mu - 2\sigma$. (This strategy is sometimes referred to as grading "on the curve.") Since

$$P\{X > \mu + \sigma\} = P\left\{\frac{X - \mu}{\sigma} > 1\right\} = 1 - \Phi(1) \approx .1587$$

$$P\{\mu < X < \mu + \sigma\} = P\left\{0 < \frac{X - \mu}{\sigma} < 1\right\} = \Phi(1) - \Phi(0) \approx .3413$$

$$P\{\mu - \sigma < X < \mu\} = P\left\{-1 < \frac{X - \mu}{\sigma} < 0\right\}$$

$$= \Phi(0) - \Phi(-1) \approx .3413$$

$$P\{\mu - 2\sigma < X < \mu - \sigma\} = P\left\{-2 < \frac{X - \mu}{\sigma} < -1\right\}$$

$$= \Phi(2) - \Phi(1) \approx .1359$$

$$P\{X < \mu - 2\sigma\} = P\left\{\frac{X - \mu}{\sigma} < -2\right\} = \Phi(-2) \approx .0228$$

it follows that approximately 16 percent of the class will receive an A grade on the examination, 34 percent a B grade, 34 percent a C grade, and 14 percent a D grade; 2 percent will fail. ∎

Example 4d

An expert witness in a paternity suit testifies that the length (in days) of human gestation is approximately normally distributed with parameters $\mu = 270$ and $\sigma^2 = 100$. The defendant in the suit is able to prove that he was out of the country during a period that began 290 days before the birth of the child and ended 240 days before the birth. If the defendant was, in fact, the father of the child, what is the probability that the mother could have had the very long or very short gestation indicated by the testimony?

Solution Let X denote the length of the gestation, and assume that the defendant is the father. Then the probability that the birth could occur within the indicated period is

$$P\{X > 290 \text{ or } X < 240\} = P\{X > 290\} + P\{X < 240\}$$

$$= P\left\{\frac{X - 270}{10} > 2\right\} + P\left\{\frac{X - 270}{10} < -3\right\}$$

$$= 1 - \Phi(2) + 1 - \Phi(3)$$

$$\approx .0241 \qquad ∎$$

Example 4e

Suppose that a binary message—either 0 or 1—must be transmitted by wire from location A to location B. However, the data sent over the wire are subject to a channel noise disturbance, so, to reduce the possibility of error, the value 2 is sent over the wire when the message is 1 and the value -2 is sent when the message is 0. If $x, x = \pm 2$, is the value sent at location A, then R, the value received at location B, is given by $R = x + N$, where N is the channel noise disturbance. When the message is received at location B, the receiver decodes it according to the following rule:

If $R \geq .5$, then 1 is concluded.

If $R < .5$, then 0 is concluded.

Because the channel noise is often normally distributed, we will determine the error probabilities when N is a standard normal random variable.

Two types of errors can occur: One is that the message 1 can be incorrectly determined to be 0, and the other is that 0 can be incorrectly determined to be 1.

The first type of error will occur if the message is 1 and $2 + N < .5$, whereas the second will occur if the message is 0 and $-2 + N \geq .5$. Hence,

$$P\{\text{error}|\text{message is }1\} = P\{N < -1.5\}$$
$$= 1 - \Phi(1.5) \approx .0668$$

and

$$P\{\text{error}|\text{message is }0\} = P\{N \geq 2.5\}$$
$$= 1 - \Phi(2.5) \approx .0062 \qquad \blacksquare$$

Example 4f

Value at Risk (VAR) has become a key concept in financial calculations. The VAR of an investment is defined as that value v such that there is only a 1 percent chance that the loss from the investment will be greater than v. If X, the gain from an investment, is a normal random variable with mean μ and variance σ^2, then because the loss is equal to the negative of the gain, the VAR of such an investment is that value v such that

$$.01 = P\{-X > v\}$$

Using that $-X$ is normal with mean $-\mu$ and variance σ^2, we see that

$$.01 = P\left\{\frac{-X + \mu}{\sigma} > \frac{v + \mu}{\sigma}\right\}$$
$$= 1 - \Phi\left(\frac{v + \mu}{\sigma}\right)$$

Because, as indicated by Table 5.1, $\Phi(2.33) = .99$, we see that

$$\frac{v + \mu}{\sigma} = 2.33$$

That is,

$$v = VAR = 2.33\sigma - \mu$$

Consequently, among a set of investments all of whose gains are normally distributed, the investment having the smallest VAR is the one having the largest value of $\mu - 2.33\sigma$. $\qquad \blacksquare$

5.4.1 The Normal Approximation to the Binomial Distribution

An important result in probability theory known as the DeMoivre–Laplace limit theorem states that when n is large, a binomial random variable with parameters n and p will have approximately the same distribution as a normal random variable with the same mean and variance as the binomial. This result was proved originally for the special case of $p = \frac{1}{2}$ by DeMoivre in 1733 and was then extended to general p by Laplace in 1812. It formally states that if we "standardize" the binomial by first subtracting its mean np and then dividing the result by its standard deviation $\sqrt{np(1 - p)}$, then the distribution function of this standardized random variable (which has mean 0 and variance 1) will converge to the standard normal distribution function as $n \rightarrow \infty$.

> **The DeMoivre–Laplace limit theorem**
>
> If S_n denotes the number of successes that occur when n independent trials, each resulting in a success with probability p, are performed, then, for any $a < b$,
>
> $$P\left\{a \le \frac{S_n - np}{\sqrt{np(1-p)}} \le b\right\} \to \Phi(b) - \Phi(a)$$
>
> as $n\to\infty$.

Because the preceding theorem is only a special case of the central limit theorem, which is presented in Chapter 8, we shall not present a proof.

Note that we now have two possible approximations to binomial probabilities: the Poisson approximation, which is good when n is large and p is small, and the normal approximation, which can be shown to be quite good when $np(1-p)$ is large. (See Figure 5.6.) [The normal approximation will, in general, be quite good for values of n satisfying $np(1-p) \ge 10$.]

Example 4g

Let X be the number of times that a fair coin that is flipped 40 times lands on heads. Find the probability that $X = 20$. Use the normal approximation and then compare it with the exact solution.

Solution To employ the normal approximation, note that because the binomial is a discrete integer-valued random variable, whereas the normal is a continuous random variable, it is best to write $P\{X = i\}$ as $P\{i - 1/2 < X < i + 1/2\}$ before

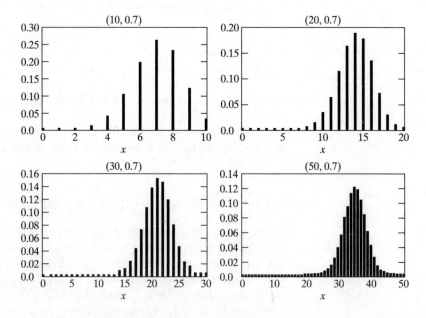

Figure 5.6 The probability mass function of a binomial (n, p) random variable becomes more and more "normal" as n becomes larger and larger.

applying the normal approximation (this is called the *continuity correction*). Doing so gives

$$P\{X = 20\} = P\{19.5 < X < 20.5\}$$

$$= P\left\{\frac{19.5 - 20}{\sqrt{10}} < \frac{X - 20}{\sqrt{10}} < \frac{20.5 - 20}{\sqrt{10}}\right\}$$

$$\approx P\left\{-.16 < \frac{X - 20}{\sqrt{10}} < .16\right\}$$

$$\approx \Phi(.16) - \Phi(-.16) \approx .1272$$

The exact result is

$$P\{X = 20\} = \binom{40}{20}\left(\frac{1}{2}\right)^{40} \approx .1254 \qquad \blacksquare$$

Example 4h

The ideal size of a first-year class at a particular college is 150 students. The college, knowing from past experience that, on the average, only 30 percent of those accepted for admission will actually attend, uses a policy of approving the applications of 450 students. Compute the probability that more than 150 first-year students attend this college.

Solution If X denotes the number of students who attend, then X is a binomial random variable with parameters $n = 450$ and $p = .3$. Using the continuity correction, we see that the normal approximation yields

$$P\{X \geq 150.5\} = P\left\{\frac{X - (450)(.3)}{\sqrt{450(.3)(.7)}} \geq \frac{150.5 - (450)(.3)}{\sqrt{450(.3)(.7)}}\right\}$$

$$\approx 1 - \Phi(1.59)$$

$$\approx .0559$$

Hence, less than 6 percent of the time do more than 150 of the first 450 accepted actually attend. (What independence assumptions have we made?) $\qquad \blacksquare$

Example 4i

To determine the effectiveness of a certain diet in reducing the amount of cholesterol in the bloodstream, 100 people are put on the diet. After they have been on the diet for a sufficient length of time, their cholesterol count will be taken. The nutritionist running this experiment has decided to endorse the diet if at least 65 percent of the people have a lower cholesterol count after going on the diet. What is the probability that the nutritionist endorses the new diet if, in fact, it has no effect on the cholesterol level?

Solution Let us assume that if the diet has no effect on the cholesterol count, then, strictly by chance, each person's count will be lower than it was before the diet with probability $\frac{1}{2}$. Hence, if X is the number of people whose count is lowered, then the probability that the nutritionist will endorse the diet when it actually has no effect on the cholesterol count is

$$\sum_{i=65}^{100}\binom{100}{i}\left(\frac{1}{2}\right)^{100} = P\{X \geq 64.5\}$$

$$= P\left\{\frac{X - (100)(\frac{1}{2})}{\sqrt{100(\frac{1}{2})(\frac{1}{2})}} \geq 2.9\right\}$$

$$\approx 1 - \Phi(2.9)$$

$$\approx .0019 \qquad \blacksquare$$

Example 4j

Fifty-two percent of the residents of New York City are in favor of outlawing cigarette smoking on university campuses. Approximate the probability that more than 50 percent of a random sample of n people from New York are in favor of this prohibition when

(a) $n = 11$

(b) $n = 101$

(c) $n = 1001$

How large would n have to be to make this probability exceed .95?

Solution Let N denote the number of residents of New York City. To answer the preceding question, we must first understand that a *random sample* of size n is a sample such that the n people were chosen in such a manner that each of the $\binom{N}{n}$ subsets of n people had the same chance of being the chosen subset. Consequently, S_n, the number of people in the sample who are in favor of the smoking prohibition, is a hypergeometric random variable. That is, S_n has the same distribution as the number of white balls obtained when n balls are chosen from an urn of N balls, of which $.52N$ are white. But because N and $.52N$ are both large in comparison with the sample size n, it follows from the binomial approximation to the hypergeometric (see Section 4.8.3) that the distribution of S_n is closely approximated by a binomial distribution with parameters n and $p = .52$. The normal approximation to the binomial distribution then shows that

$$P\{S_n > .5n\} = P\left\{ \frac{S_n - .52n}{\sqrt{n(.52)(.48)}} > \frac{.5n - .52n}{\sqrt{n(.52)(.48)}} \right\}$$

$$= P\left\{ \frac{S_n - .52n}{\sqrt{n(.52)(.48)}} > -.04\sqrt{n} \right\}$$

$$\approx \Phi(.04\sqrt{n})$$

Thus,

$$P\{S_n > .5n\} \approx \begin{cases} \Phi(.1328) = .5528, & \text{if } n = 11 \\ \Phi(.4020) = .6562, & \text{if } n = 101 \\ \Phi(1.2665) = .8973, & \text{if } n = 1001 \end{cases}$$

In order for this probability to be at least .95, we would need $\Phi(.04\sqrt{n}) > .95$. Because $\Phi(x)$ is an increasing function and $\Phi(1.645) = .95$, this means that

$$.04\sqrt{n} > 1.645$$

or

$$n \geq 1691.266$$

That is, the sample size would have to be at least 1692. ■

Historical notes concerning the normal distribution

The normal distribution was introduced by the French mathematician Abraham DeMoivre in 1733. DeMoivre, who used this distribution to approximate probabilities connected with coin tossing, called it the exponential bell-shaped curve. Its usefulness, however, became truly apparent only in 1809, when the famous German mathematician Karl Friedrich Gauss used it as an integral part of his approach to predicting the location of astronomical entities. As a result, it became common after this time to call it the *Gaussian distribution*.

During the mid- to late 19th century, however, most statisticians started to believe that the majority of data sets would have histograms conforming to the Gaussian bell-shaped form. Indeed, it came to be accepted that it was "normal" for any well-behaved data set to follow this curve. As a result, following the lead of the British statistician Karl Pearson, people began referring to the Gaussian curve by calling it simply the *normal* curve. (A partial explanation as to why so many data sets conform to the normal curve is provided by the central limit theorem, which is presented in Chapter 8.)

Abraham DeMoivre (1667–1754)

Today there is no shortage of statistical consultants, many of whom ply their trade in the most elegant of settings. However, the first of their breed worked, in the early years of the 18th century, out of a dark, grubby betting shop in Long Acres, London, known as Slaughter's Coffee House. He was Abraham DeMoivre, a Protestant refugee from Catholic France, and, for a price, he would compute the probability of gambling bets in all types of games of chance.

Although DeMoivre, the discoverer of the normal curve, made his living at the coffee shop, he was a mathematician of recognized abilities. Indeed, he was a member of the Royal Society and was reported to be an intimate of Isaac Newton.

Listen to Karl Pearson imagining DeMoivre at work at Slaughter's Coffee House: "*I picture DeMoivre working at a dirty table in the coffee house with a broken-down gambler beside him and Isaac Newton walking through the crowd to his corner to fetch out his friend. It would make a great picture for an inspired artist.*"

Karl Friedrich Gauss

Karl Friedrich Gauss (1777–1855), one of the earliest users of the normal curve, was one of the greatest mathematicians of all time. Listen to the words of the well-known mathematical historian E. T. Bell, as expressed in his 1954 book *Men of Mathematics*: In a chapter entitled "The Prince of Mathematicians," he writes, "*Archimedes, Newton, and Gauss; these three are in a class by themselves among the great mathematicians, and it is not for ordinary mortals to attempt to rank them in order of merit. All three started tidal waves in both pure and applied mathematics. Archimedes esteemed his pure mathematics more highly than its applications;*
Newton appears to have found the chief justification for his mathematical inventions in the scientific uses to which he put them; while Gauss declared it was all one to him whether he worked on the pure or on the applied side."

5.5 Exponential Random Variables

A continuous random variable whose probability density function is given, for some $\lambda > 0$, by

$$f(x) = \begin{cases} \lambda e^{-\lambda x} & \text{if } x \geq 0 \\ 0 & \text{if } x < 0 \end{cases}$$

is said to be an *exponential* random variable (or, more simply, is said to be exponentially distributed) with parameter λ. The cumulative distribution function $F(a)$ of an exponential random variable is given by

$$F(a) = P\{X \le a\}$$

$$= \int_0^a \lambda e^{-\lambda x}\, dx$$

$$= -e^{-\lambda x}\big|_0^a$$

$$= 1 - e^{-\lambda a} \quad a \ge 0$$

Note that $F(\infty) = \int_0^\infty \lambda e^{-\lambda x}\, dx = 1$, as, of course, it must. The parameter λ will now be shown to equal the reciprocal of the expected value.

Example 5a

Let X be an exponential random variable with parameter λ. Calculate (a) $E[X]$ and (b) $\mathrm{Var}(X)$.

Solution (a) Since the density function is given by

$$f(x) = \begin{cases} \lambda e^{-\lambda x} & x \ge 0 \\ 0 & x < 0 \end{cases}$$

we obtain, for $n > 0$,

$$E[X^n] = \int_0^\infty x^n \lambda e^{-\lambda x}\, dx$$

Integrating by parts (with $\lambda e^{-\lambda x} = dv$ and $u = x^n$) yields

$$E[X^n] = -x^n e^{-\lambda x}\big|_0^\infty + \int_0^\infty e^{-\lambda x} n x^{n-1}\, dx$$

$$= 0 + \frac{n}{\lambda} \int_0^\infty \lambda e^{-\lambda x} x^{n-1}\, dx$$

$$= \frac{n}{\lambda} E[X^{n-1}]$$

Letting $n = 1$ and then $n = 2$ gives

$$E[X] = \frac{1}{\lambda}$$

$$E[X^2] = \frac{2}{\lambda} E[X] = \frac{2}{\lambda^2}$$

(b) Hence,

$$\mathrm{Var}(X) = \frac{2}{\lambda^2} - \left(\frac{1}{\lambda}\right)^2 = \frac{1}{\lambda^2}$$

Thus, the mean of the exponential is the reciprocal of its parameter λ, and the variance is the mean squared. ■

In practice, the exponential distribution often arises as the distribution of the amount of time until some specific event occurs. For instance, the amount of time (starting from now) until an earthquake occurs, or until a new war breaks out, or until a telephone call you receive turns out to be a wrong number are all random variables that tend in practice to have exponential distributions. (For a theoretical explanation of this phenomenon, see Section 4.7.)

Example 5b

Suppose that the length of a phone call in minutes is an exponential random variable with parameter $\lambda = \frac{1}{10}$. If someone arrives immediately ahead of you at a public telephone booth, find the probability that you will have to wait

(a) more than 10 minutes;

(b) between 10 and 20 minutes.

Solution Let X denote the length of the call made by the person in the booth. Then the desired probabilities are

(a)

$$P\{X > 10\} = 1 - F(10)$$
$$= e^{-1} \approx .368$$

(b)

$$P\{10 < X < 20\} = F(20) - F(10)$$
$$= e^{-1} - e^{-2} \approx .233 \qquad \blacksquare$$

We say that a nonnegative random variable X is *memoryless* if

$$P\{X > s + t \mid X > t\} = P\{X > s\} \quad \text{for all } s, t \geq 0 \qquad (5.1)$$

If we think of X as being the lifetime of some instrument, Equation (5.1) states that the probability that the instrument survives for at least $s + t$ hours, given that it has survived t hours, is the same as the initial probability that it survives for at least s hours. In other words, if the instrument is alive at age t, the distribution of the remaining amount of time that it survives is the same as the original lifetime distribution. (That is, it is as if the instrument does not "remember" that it has already been in use for a time t.)

Equation (5.1) is equivalent to

$$\frac{P\{X > s + t, X > t\}}{P\{X > t\}} = P\{X > s\}$$

or

$$P\{X > s + t\} = P\{X > s\}P\{X > t\} \qquad (5.2)$$

Since Equation (5.2) is satisfied when X is exponentially distributed (for $e^{-\lambda(s+t)} = e^{-\lambda s}e^{-\lambda t}$), it follows that exponentially distributed random variables are memoryless.

Example 5c

Consider a post office that is staffed by two clerks. Suppose that when Mr. Smith enters the system, he discovers that Ms. Jones is being served by one of the clerks and Mr. Brown by the other. Suppose also that Mr. Smith is told that his service will begin as soon as either Ms. Jones or Mr. Brown leaves. If the amount of time that a clerk spends with a customer is exponentially distributed with parameter λ, what is the probability that of the three customers, Mr. Smith is the last to leave the post office?

Solution The answer is obtained by reasoning as follows: Consider the time at which Mr. Smith first finds a free clerk. At this point, either Ms. Jones or Mr. Brown would have just left, and the other one would still be in service. However, because the exponential is memoryless, it follows that the additional amount of time that this other person (either Ms. Jones or Mr. Brown) would still have to spend in the post office is exponentially distributed with parameter λ. That is, it is the same as if service for that person were just starting at this point. Hence, by symmetry, the probability that the remaining person finishes before Smith leaves must equal $\frac{1}{2}$. $\blacksquare$

It turns out that not only is the exponential distribution memoryless, but it is also the unique distribution possessing this property. To see this, suppose that X is memoryless and let $\overline{F}(x) = P\{X > x\}$. Then, by Equation (5.2),

$$\overline{F}(s + t) = \overline{F}(s)\overline{F}(t)$$

That is, $\overline{F}(\cdot)$ satisfies the functional equation

$$g(s + t) = g(s)g(t)$$

However, it turns out that the only right continuous solution of this functional equation is[†]

$$g(x) = e^{-\lambda x} \qquad (5.3)$$

and, since a distribution function is always right continuous, we must have

$$\overline{F}(x) = e^{-\lambda x} \quad \text{or} \quad F(x) = P\{X \le x\} = 1 - e^{-\lambda x}$$

which shows that X is exponentially distributed.

Example 5d

Suppose that the number of miles that a car can run before its battery wears out is exponentially distributed with an average value of 10,000 miles. If a person desires to take a 5000-mile trip, what is the probability that he or she will be able to complete the trip without having to replace the car battery? What can be said when the distribution is not exponential?

Solution It follows by the memoryless property of the exponential distribution that the remaining lifetime (in thousands of miles) of the battery is exponential with parameter $\lambda = \frac{1}{10}$. Hence, the desired probability is

$$P\{\text{remaining lifetime} > 5\} = 1 - F(5) = e^{-5\lambda} = e^{-1/2} \approx .607$$

However, if the lifetime distribution F is not exponential, then the relevant probability is

$$P\{\text{lifetime} > t + 5 | \text{lifetime} > t\} = \frac{1 - F(t + 5)}{1 - F(t)}$$

where t is the number of miles that the battery had been in use prior to the start of the trip. Therefore, if the distribution is not exponential, additional information is needed (namely, the value of t) before the desired probability can be calculated. ■

A variation of the exponential distribution is the distribution of a random variable that is equally likely to be either positive or negative and whose absolute value is exponentially distributed with parameter $\lambda, \lambda \ge 0$. Such a random variable is said to have a *Laplace* distribution,[‡] and its density is given by

$$f(x) = \frac{1}{2}\lambda e^{-\lambda |x|} \qquad -\infty < x < \infty$$

[†]One can prove Equation (5.3) as follows: If $g(s + t) = g(s)g(t)$, then

$$g\left(\frac{2}{n}\right) = g\left(\frac{1}{n} + \frac{1}{n}\right) = g^2\left(\frac{1}{n}\right)$$

and repeating this yields $g(m/n) = g^m(1/n)$. Also,

$$g(1) = g\left(\frac{1}{n} + \frac{1}{n} + \cdots + \frac{1}{n}\right) = g^n\left(\frac{1}{n}\right) \quad \text{or} \quad g\left(\frac{1}{n}\right) = (g(1))^{1/n}$$

Hence, $g(m/n) = (g(1))^{m/n}$, which, since g is right continuous, implies that $g(x) = (g(1))^x$. Because $g(1) = \left(g\left(\frac{1}{2}\right)\right)^2 \ge 0$, we obtain $g(x) = e^{-\lambda x}$, where $\lambda = -\log(g(1))$.

[‡]It also is sometimes called the double exponential random variable.

Its distribution function is given by

$$
F(x) =
\begin{cases}
\dfrac{1}{2}\displaystyle\int_{-\infty}^{x} \lambda e^{\lambda y}\, dy & x < 0 \\[2ex]
\dfrac{1}{2}\displaystyle\int_{-\infty}^{0} \lambda e^{\lambda y}\, dy + \dfrac{1}{2}\displaystyle\int_{0}^{x} \lambda e^{-\lambda y}\, dy & x > 0
\end{cases}
$$

$$
=
\begin{cases}
\dfrac{1}{2} e^{\lambda x} & x < 0 \\[2ex]
1 - \dfrac{1}{2} e^{-\lambda x} & x > 0
\end{cases}
$$

Example 5e

Consider again Example 4e, which supposes that a binary message is to be transmitted from A to B, with the value 2 being sent when the message is 1 and -2 when it is 0. However, suppose now that rather than being a standard normal random variable, the channel noise N is a Laplacian random variable with parameter $\lambda = 1$. Suppose again that if R is the value received at location B, then the message is decoded as follows:

If $R \geq .5$, then 1 is concluded.

If $R < .5$, then 0 is concluded.

In this case, where the noise is Laplacian with parameter $\lambda = 1$, the two types of errors will have probabilities given by

$$
P\{\text{error}|\text{message 1 is sent}\} = P\{N < -1.5\}
$$
$$
= \frac{1}{2} e^{-1.5}
$$
$$
\approx .1116
$$
$$
P\{\text{error}|\text{message 0 is sent}\} = P\{N \geq 2.5\}
$$
$$
= \frac{1}{2} e^{-2.5}
$$
$$
\approx .041
$$

On comparing this with the results of Example 4e, we see that the error probabilities are higher when the noise is Laplacian with $\lambda = 1$ than when it is a standard normal variable.

5.5.1 Hazard Rate Functions

Consider a positive continuous random variable X that we interpret as being the lifetime of some item. Let X have distribution function F and density f. The *hazard rate* (sometimes called the *failure rate*) function $\lambda(t)$ of F is defined by

$$
\lambda(t) = \frac{f(t)}{\overline{F}(t)}, \quad \text{where } \overline{F} = 1 - F
$$

To interpret $\lambda(t)$, suppose that the item has survived for a time t and we desire the probability that it will not survive for an additional time dt. That is, consider $P\{X \in (t, t + dt)|X > t\}$. Now,

$$P\{X \in (t, t + dt) | X > t\} = \frac{P\{X \in (t, t + dt), X > t\}}{P\{X > t\}}$$

$$= \frac{P\{X \in (t, t + dt)\}}{P\{X > t\}}$$

$$\approx \frac{f(t)}{\bar{F}(t)} \, dt$$

Thus, $\lambda(t)$ represents the conditional probability intensity that a t-unit-old item will fail.

Suppose now that the lifetime distribution is exponential. Then, by the memoryless property, it follows that the distribution of remaining life for a t-year-old item is the same as that for a new item. Hence, $\lambda(t)$ should be constant. In fact, this checks out, since

$$\lambda(t) = \frac{f(t)}{\bar{F}(t)}$$

$$= \frac{\lambda e^{-\lambda t}}{e^{-\lambda t}}$$

$$= \lambda$$

Thus, the failure rate function for the exponential distribution is constant. The parameter λ is often referred to as the *rate* of the distribution.

It turns out that the failure rate function $\lambda(s), s \geq 0$, uniquely determines the distribution function F. To prove this, we integrate $\lambda(s)$ from 0 to t to obtain

$$\int_0^t \lambda(s) \, ds = \int_0^t \frac{f(s)}{1 - F(s)} \, ds$$

$$= -\log(1 - F(s))|_0^t$$

$$= -\log(1 - F(t)) + \log(1 - F(0))$$

$$= -\log(1 - F(t))$$

where the second equality used that $f(s) = \frac{d}{ds} F(s)$ and the final equality used that $F(0) = 0$. Solving the preceding equation for $F(t)$ gives

$$F(t) = 1 - \exp\left\{-\int_0^t \lambda(s) \, ds\right\} \tag{5.4}$$

Hence, a distribution function of a positive continuous random variable can be specified by giving its hazard rate function. For instance, if a random variable has a linear hazard rate function—that is, if

$$\lambda(t) = a + bt$$

then its distribution function is given by

$$F(t) = 1 - e^{-at - bt^2/2}$$

and differentiation yields its density, namely,

$$f(t) = (a + bt)e^{-(at + bt^2/2)} \quad t \geq 0$$

When $a = 0$, the preceding equation is known as the *Rayleigh density function*.

Example 5f

One often hears that the death rate of a person who smokes is, at each age, twice that of a nonsmoker. What does this mean? Does it mean that a nonsmoker has twice the probability of surviving a given number of years as does a smoker of the same age?

Solution If $\lambda_s(t)$ denotes the hazard rate of a smoker of age t and $\lambda_n(t)$ that of a nonsmoker of age t, then the statement at issue is equivalent to the statement that

$$\lambda_s(t) = 2\lambda_n(t)$$

The probability that an A-year-old nonsmoker will survive until age B, $A < B$, is

$$P\{A\text{-year-old nonsmoker reaches age } B\}$$
$$= P\{\text{nonsmoker's lifetime} > B | \text{nonsmoker's lifetime} > A\}$$
$$= \frac{1 - F_{\text{non}}(B)}{1 - F_{\text{non}}(A)}$$
$$= \frac{\exp\left\{-\int_0^B \lambda_n(t)\, dt\right\}}{\exp\left\{-\int_0^A \lambda_n(t)\, dt\right\}} \qquad \text{from (5.4)}$$
$$= \exp\left\{-\int_A^B \lambda_n(t)\, dt\right\}$$

whereas the corresponding probability for a smoker is, by the same reasoning,

$$P\{A\text{-year-old smoker reaches age } B\} = \exp\left\{-\int_A^B \lambda_s(t)\, dt\right\}$$
$$= \exp\left\{-2\int_A^B \lambda_n(t)\, dt\right\}$$
$$= \left[\exp\left\{-\int_A^B \lambda_n(t)\, dt\right\}\right]^2$$

In other words, for two people of the same age, one of whom is a smoker and the other a nonsmoker, the probability that the smoker survives to any given age is the *square* (not one-half) of the corresponding probability for a nonsmoker. For instance, if $\lambda_n(t) = \frac{1}{30}, 50 \le t \le 60$, then the probability that a 50-year-old nonsmoker reaches age 60 is $e^{-1/3} \approx .7165$, whereas the corresponding probability for a smoker is $e^{-2/3} \approx .5134$. ∎

5.6 Other Continuous Distributions

5.6.1 The Gamma Distribution

A random variable is said to have a gamma distribution with parameters $(\alpha, \lambda), \lambda > 0$, $\alpha > 0$, if its density function is given by

$$f(x) = \begin{cases} \dfrac{\lambda e^{-\lambda x}(\lambda x)^{\alpha-1}}{\Gamma(\alpha)} & x \ge 0 \\ 0 & x < 0 \end{cases}$$

where $\Gamma(\alpha)$, called the *gamma function*, is defined as

$$\Gamma(\alpha) = \int_0^\infty e^{-y} y^{\alpha-1}\, dy$$

Integration of $\Gamma(\alpha)$ by parts yields

$$\Gamma(\alpha) = -e^{-y}y^{\alpha-1}\Big|_0^{\infty} + \int_0^{\infty} e^{-y}(\alpha - 1)y^{\alpha-2}\,dy$$

$$= (\alpha - 1)\int_0^{\infty} e^{-y}y^{\alpha-2}\,dy \tag{6.1}$$

$$= (\alpha - 1)\Gamma(\alpha - 1)$$

For integral values of α, say, $\alpha = n$, we obtain, by applying Equation (6.1) repeatedly,

$$\Gamma(n) = (n - 1)\Gamma(n - 1)$$

$$= (n - 1)(n - 2)\Gamma(n - 2)$$

$$= \cdots$$

$$= (n - 1)(n - 2)\cdots 3 \cdot 2\Gamma(1)$$

Since $\Gamma(1) = \int_0^{\infty} e^{-x}\,dx = 1$, it follows that, for integral values of n,

$$\Gamma(n) = (n - 1)!$$

When α is a positive integer, say, $\alpha = n$, the gamma distribution with parameters (α, λ) often arises, in practice as the distribution of the amount of time one has to wait until a total of n events has occurred. More specifically, if events are occurring randomly and in accordance with the three axioms of Section 4.7, then it turns out that the amount of time one has to wait until a total of n events has occurred will be a gamma random variable with parameters (n, λ). To prove this, let T_n denote the time at which the nth event occurs, and note that T_n is less than or equal to t if and only if the number of events that have occurred by time t is at least n. That is, with $N(t)$ equal to the number of events in $[0, t]$,

$$P\{T_n \le t\} = P\{N(t) \ge n\}$$

$$= \sum_{j=n}^{\infty} P\{N(t) = j\}$$

$$= \sum_{j=n}^{\infty} \frac{e^{-\lambda t}(\lambda t)^j}{j!}$$

where the final identity follows because the number of events in $[0, t]$ has a Poisson distribution with parameter λt. Differentiation of the preceding now yields the density function of T_n:

$$f(t) = \sum_{j=n}^{\infty} \frac{e^{-\lambda t}j(\lambda t)^{j-1}\lambda}{j!} - \sum_{j=n}^{\infty} \frac{\lambda e^{-\lambda t}(\lambda t)^j}{j!}$$

$$= \sum_{j=n}^{\infty} \frac{\lambda e^{-\lambda t}(\lambda t)^{j-1}}{(j - 1)!} - \sum_{j=n}^{\infty} \frac{\lambda e^{-\lambda t}(\lambda t)^j}{j!}$$

$$= \frac{\lambda e^{-\lambda t}(\lambda t)^{n-1}}{(n - 1)!}$$

Hence, T_n has the gamma distribution with parameters (n, λ). (This distribution is often referred to in the literature as the *n-Erlang distribution*.) Note that when $n = 1$, this distribution reduces to the exponential distribution.

The gamma distribution with $\lambda = \frac{1}{2}$ and $\alpha = n/2$, n a positive integer, is called the χ_n^2 (read "chi-squared") distribution with n degrees of freedom. The chi-squared distribution often arises in practice as the distribution of the error involved in attempting to hit a target in n-dimensional space when each coordinate error is normally distributed. This distribution will be studied in Chapter 6, where its relation to the normal distribution is detailed.

Example 6a

Let X be a gamma random variable with parameters α and λ. Calculate (a) $E[X]$ and (b) $\text{Var}(X)$.

Solution (a)

$$
\begin{aligned}
E[X] &= \frac{1}{\Gamma(\alpha)} \int_0^\infty \lambda x e^{-\lambda x} (\lambda x)^{\alpha - 1} \, dx \\
&= \frac{1}{\lambda \Gamma(\alpha)} \int_0^\infty \lambda e^{-\lambda x} (\lambda x)^{\alpha} \, dx \\
&= \frac{\Gamma(\alpha + 1)}{\lambda \Gamma(\alpha)} \\
&= \frac{\alpha}{\lambda} \quad \text{by Equation (6.1)}
\end{aligned}
$$

(b) By first calculating $E[X^2]$, we can show that

$$
\text{Var}(X) = \frac{\alpha}{\lambda^2}
$$

The details are left as an exercise. ∎

5.6.2   The Weibull Distribution

The Weibull distribution is widely used in engineering practice due to its versatility. It was originally proposed for the interpretation of fatigue data, but now its use has been extended to many other engineering problems. In particular, it is widely used in the field of life phenomena as the distribution of the lifetime of some object, especially when the "weakest link" model is appropriate for the object. That is, consider an object consisting of many parts, and suppose that the object experiences death (failure) when any of its parts fails. It has been shown (both theoretically and empirically) that under these conditions, a Weibull distribution provides a close approximation to the distribution of the lifetime of the item.

The Weibull distribution function has the form

$$
F(x) = \begin{cases} 0 & x \leq \nu \\ 1 - \exp\left\{ -\left(\dfrac{x - \nu}{\alpha} \right)^{\beta} \right\} & x > \nu \end{cases} \tag{6.2}
$$

A random variable whose cumulative distribution function is given by Equation (6.2) is said to be a *Weibull random variable* with parameters ν, α, and β. Differentiation yields the density:

$$
f(x) = \begin{cases} 0 & x \leq \nu \\ \dfrac{\beta}{\alpha} \left(\dfrac{x - \nu}{\alpha} \right)^{\beta - 1} \exp\left\{ -\left(\dfrac{x - \nu}{\alpha} \right)^{\beta} \right\} & x > \nu \end{cases}
$$

5.6.3 The Cauchy Distribution

A random variable is said to have a Cauchy distribution with parameter θ, $-\infty < \theta < \infty$, if its density is given by

$$f(x) = \frac{1}{\pi} \frac{1}{1 + (x - \theta)^2} \qquad -\infty < x < \infty$$

Example 6b

Suppose that a narrow-beam flashlight is spun around its center, which is located a unit distance from the x-axis. (See Figure 5.7.) Consider the point X at which the beam intersects the x-axis when the flashlight has stopped spinning. (If the beam is not pointing toward the x-axis, repeat the experiment.)

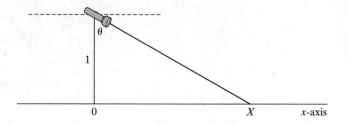

Figure 5.7

As indicated in Figure 5.7, the point X is determined by the angle θ between the flashlight and the y-axis, which, from the physical situation, appears to be uniformly distributed between $-\pi/2$ and $\pi/2$. The distribution function of X is thus given by

$$\begin{aligned}
F(x) &= P\{X \le x\} \\
&= P\{\tan \theta \le x\} \\
&= P\{\theta \le \tan^{-1} x\} \\
&= \frac{1}{2} + \frac{1}{\pi} \tan^{-1} x
\end{aligned}$$

where the last equality follows since θ, being uniform over $(-\pi/2, \pi/2)$, has distribution

$$P\{\theta \le a\} = \frac{a - (-\pi/2)}{\pi} = \frac{1}{2} + \frac{a}{\pi} \qquad -\frac{\pi}{2} < a < \frac{\pi}{2}$$

Hence, the density function of X is given by

$$f(x) = \frac{d}{dx} F(x) = \frac{1}{\pi(1 + x^2)} \qquad -\infty < x < \infty$$

and we see that X has the Cauchy distribution.[†] ∎

[†] That $\frac{d}{dx}(\tan^{-1} x) = 1/(1 + x^2)$ can be seen as follows: If $y = \tan^{-1} x$, then $\tan y = x$, so

$$1 = \frac{d}{dx}(\tan y) = \frac{d}{dy}(\tan y)\frac{dy}{dx} = \frac{d}{dy}\left(\frac{\sin y}{\cos y}\right)\frac{dy}{dx} = \left(\frac{\cos^2 y + \sin^2 y}{\cos^2 y}\right)\frac{dy}{dx}$$

or

$$\frac{dy}{dx} = \frac{\cos^2 y}{\sin^2 y + \cos^2 y} = \frac{1}{\tan^2 y + 1} = \frac{1}{x^2 + 1}$$

5.6.4 The Beta Distribution

A random variable is said to have a beta distribution if its density is given by

$$f(x) = \begin{cases} \dfrac{1}{B(a,b)}x^{a-1}(1-x)^{b-1} & 0 < x < 1 \\ 0 & \text{otherwise} \end{cases}$$

where

$$B(a,b) = \int_0^1 x^{a-1}(1-x)^{b-1}\,dx$$

The beta distribution can be used to model a random phenomenon whose set of possible values is some finite interval $[c, d]$—which, by letting c denote the origin and taking $d - c$ as a unit measurement, can be transformed into the interval $[0, 1]$.

When $a = b$, the beta density is symmetric about $\frac{1}{2}$, giving more and more weight to regions about $\frac{1}{2}$ as the common value a increases. When $a = b = 1$, the beta distribution reduces to the uniform $(0, 1)$ distribution. (See Figure 5.8.) When $b > a$, the density is skewed to the left (in the sense that smaller values become more likely), and it is skewed to the right when $a > b$. (See Figure 5.9.)

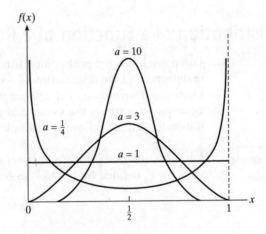

Figure 5.8 Beta densities with parameters (a, b) when $a = b$.

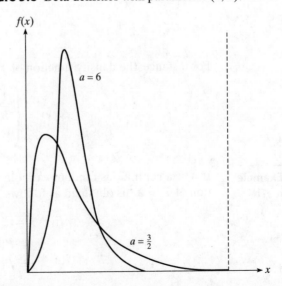

Figure 5.9 Beta densities with parameters (a, b) when $a/(a + b) = 1/20$.

The relationship

$$B(a,b) = \frac{\Gamma(a)\Gamma(b)}{\Gamma(a+b)} \tag{6.3}$$

can be shown to exist between

$$B(a,b) = \int_0^1 x^{a-1}(1-x)^{b-1}\,dx$$

and the gamma function.

Upon using Equation (6.1) along with the identity (6.3), it is an easy matter to show that if X is a beta random variable with parameters a and b, then

$$E[X] = \frac{a}{a+b}$$

$$\text{Var}(X) = \frac{ab}{(a+b)^2(a+b+1)}$$

Remark A verification of Equation (6.3) appears in Example 7c of Chapter 6. ∎

5.7 The Distribution of a Function of a Random Variable

Often, we know the probability distribution of a random variable and are interested in determining the distribution of some function of it. For instance, suppose that we know the distribution of X and want to find the distribution of $g(X)$. To do so, it is necessary to express the event that $g(X) \leq y$ in terms of X being in some set. We illustrate with the following examples.

Example 7a

Let X be uniformly distributed over $(0, 1)$. We obtain the distribution of the random variable Y, defined by $Y = X^n$, as follows: For $0 \leq y \leq 1$,

$$\begin{aligned}
F_Y(y) &= P\{Y \leq y\} \\
&= P\{X^n \leq y\} \\
&= P\{X \leq y^{1/n}\} \\
&= F_X(y^{1/n}) \\
&= y^{1/n}
\end{aligned}$$

For instance, the density function of Y is given by

$$f_Y(y) = \begin{cases} \dfrac{1}{n} y^{1/n-1} & 0 \leq y \leq 1 \\ 0 & \text{otherwise} \end{cases}$$

∎

Example 7b

If X is a continuous random variable with probability density f_X, then the distribution of $Y = X^2$ is obtained as follows: For $y \geq 0$,

$$\begin{aligned}
F_Y(y) &= P\{Y \leq y\} \\
&= P\{X^2 \leq y\} \\
&= P\{-\sqrt{y} \leq X \leq \sqrt{y}\} \\
&= F_X(\sqrt{y}) - F_X(-\sqrt{y})
\end{aligned}$$

Differentiation yields

$$f_Y(y) = \frac{1}{2\sqrt{y}}[f_X(\sqrt{y}) + f_X(-\sqrt{y})] \qquad \blacksquare$$

Example 7c

If X has a probability density f_X, then $Y = |X|$ has a density function that is obtained as follows: For $y \geq 0$,

$$\begin{aligned}
F_Y(y) &= P\{Y \leq y\} \\
&= P\{|X| \leq y\} \\
&= P\{-y \leq X \leq y\} \\
&= F_X(y) - F_X(-y)
\end{aligned}$$

Hence, on differentiation, we obtain

$$f_Y(y) = f_X(y) + f_X(-y) \qquad y \geq 0 \qquad \blacksquare$$

The method employed in Examples 7a through 7c can be used to prove Theorem 7.1.

Theorem 7.1

Let X be a continuous random variable having probability density function f_X. Suppose that $g(x)$ is a strictly monotonic (increasing or decreasing), differentiable (and thus continuous) function of x. Then the random variable Y defined by $Y = g(X)$ has a probability density function given by

$$f_Y(y) = \begin{cases} f_X[g^{-1}(y)]\left|\dfrac{d}{dy}g^{-1}(y)\right| & \text{if } y = g(x) \text{ for some } x \\ 0 & \text{if } y \neq g(x) \text{ for all } x \end{cases}$$

where $g^{-1}(y)$ is defined to equal that value of x such that $g(x) = y$.

We shall prove Theorem 7.1 when $g(x)$ is an increasing function.

Proof Suppose that $y = g(x)$ for some x. Then, with $Y = g(X)$,

$$\begin{aligned}
F_Y(y) &= P\{g(X) \leq y\} \\
&= P\{X \leq g^{-1}(y)\} \\
&= F_X(g^{-1}(y))
\end{aligned}$$

Differentiation gives

$$f_Y(y) = f_X(g^{-1}(y))\frac{d}{dy}g^{-1}(y) \qquad \blacksquare$$

which agrees with Theorem 7.1, since $g^{-1}(y)$ is nondecreasing, so its derivative is nonnegative.

When $y \neq g(x)$ for any x, then $F_Y(y)$ is either 0 or 1, and in either case $f_Y(y) = 0$.

Example 7d

Let X be a continuous nonnegative random variable with density function f, and let $Y = X^n$. Find f_Y, the probability density function of Y.

Solution If $g(x) = x^n$, then

$$g^{-1}(y) = y^{1/n}$$

and

$$\frac{d}{dy}\{g^{-1}(y)\} = \frac{1}{n}y^{1/n-1}$$

Hence, from Theorem 7.1, we obtain, for $y \geq 0$,

$$f_Y(y) = \frac{1}{n} y^{1/n-1} f(y^{1/n})$$

For $n = 2$, this gives

$$f_Y(y) = \frac{1}{2\sqrt{y}} f(\sqrt{y})$$

which (since $X \geq 0$) is in agreement with the result of Example 7b. ∎

Example 7e

The Lognormal Distribution If X is a normal random variable with mean μ and variance σ^2, then the random variable

$$Y = e^X$$

is said to be a *lognormal* random variable with parameters μ and σ^2. Thus, a random variable Y is lognormal if $\log(Y)$ is a normal random variable. The lognormal is often used as the distribution of the ratio of the price of a security at the end of one day to its price at the end of the prior day. That is, if S_n is the price of some security at the end of day n, then it is often supposed that $\frac{S_n}{S_{n-1}}$ is a lognormal random variable, implying that $X \equiv \log\left(\frac{S_n}{S_{n-1}}\right)$ is normal. Thus, to assume that $\frac{S_n}{S_{n-1}}$ is lognormal is to assume that

$$S_n = S_{n-1} e^X$$

where X is normal.

Let us now use Theorem 7.1 to derive the density of a lognormal random variable Y with parameters μ and σ^2. Because $Y = e^X$, where X is normal with mean μ and variance σ^2, we need to determine the inverse of the function $g(x) = e^x$. Because

$$y = g(g^{-1}(y)) = e^{g^{-1}(y)}$$

we obtain upon taking logarithms that

$$g^{-1}(y) = \log(y)$$

Using that $\frac{d}{dy} g^{-1}(y) = 1/y$, Theorem 7.1 yields the density:

$$f_Y(y) = \frac{1}{\sqrt{2\pi}\,\sigma y} \exp\{-(\log(y) - \mu)^2/2\sigma^2\}, \quad y > 0 \qquad ∎$$

Summary

A random variable X is *continuous* if there is a nonnegative function f, called the *probability density function* of X, such that, for any set B,

$$P\{X \in B\} = \int_B f(x)\,dx$$

If X is continuous, then its distribution function F will be differentiable and

$$\frac{d}{dx} F(x) = f(x)$$

The expected value of a continuous random variable X is defined by

$$E[X] = \int_{-\infty}^{\infty} x f(x)\,dx$$

A useful identity is that for any function g,

$$E[g(X)] = \int_{-\infty}^{\infty} g(x) f(x)\,dx$$

As in the case of a discrete random variable, the variance of X is defined by

$$\mathrm{Var}(X) = E[(X - E[X])^2]$$

A random variable X is said to be *uniform* over the interval (a, b) if its probability density function is given by

$$f(x) = \begin{cases} \dfrac{1}{b - a} & a \leq x \leq b \\ 0 & \text{otherwise} \end{cases}$$

Its expected value and variance are

$$E[X] = \frac{a + b}{2} \quad \mathrm{Var}(X) = \frac{(b - a)^2}{12}$$

A random variable X is said to be *normal* with parameters μ and σ^2 if its probability density function is given by

$$f(x) = \frac{1}{\sqrt{2\pi}\sigma} e^{-(x-\mu)^2/2\sigma^2} \quad -\infty < x < \infty$$

It can be shown that

$$\mu = E[X] \quad \sigma^2 = \mathrm{Var}(X)$$

If X is normal with mean μ and variance σ^2, then Z, defined by

$$Z = \frac{X - \mu}{\sigma}$$

is normal with mean 0 and variance 1. Such a random variable is said to be a *standard* normal random variable. Probabilities about X can be expressed in terms of probabilities about the standard normal variable Z, whose probability distribution function can be obtained either from Table 5.1, the normal calculator on StatCrunch, or a website.

When n is large, the probability distribution function of a binomial random variable with parameters n and p can be approximated by that of a normal random variable having mean np and variance $np(1 - p)$.

A random variable whose probability density function is of the form

$$f(x) = \begin{cases} \lambda e^{-\lambda x} & x \geq 0 \\ 0 & \text{otherwise} \end{cases}$$

is said to be an *exponential* random variable with parameter λ. Its expected value and variance are, respectively,

$$E[X] = \frac{1}{\lambda} \quad \mathrm{Var}(X) = \frac{1}{\lambda^2}$$

A key property possessed only by exponential random variables is that they are *memoryless*, in the sense that, for positive s and t,

$$P\{X > s + t | X > t\} = P\{X > s\}$$

If X represents the life of an item, then the memoryless property states that for any t, the remaining life of a t-year-old item has the same probability distribution as the life of a new item. Thus, one need not remember the age of an item to know its distribution of remaining life.

Let X be a nonnegative continuous random variable with distribution function F and density function f. The function

$$\lambda(t) = \frac{f(t)}{1 - F(t)} \quad t \geq 0$$

is called the *hazard rate*, or *failure rate*, function of F. If we interpret X as being the life of an item, then for small values of dt, $\lambda(t)\,dt$ is approximately the probability that a t-unit-old item will fail within an additional time dt. If F is the exponential distribution with parameter λ, then

$$\lambda(t) = \lambda \quad t \geq 0$$

In addition, the exponential is the unique distribution having a constant failure rate.

A random variable is said to have a *gamma* distribution with parameters α and λ if its probability density function is equal to

$$f(x) = \frac{\lambda e^{-\lambda x}(\lambda x)^{\alpha-1}}{\Gamma(\alpha)} \quad x \geq 0$$

and is 0 otherwise. The quantity $\Gamma(\alpha)$ is called the gamma function and is defined by

$$\Gamma(\alpha) = \int_0^\infty e^{-x} x^{\alpha-1}\, dx$$

The expected value and variance of a gamma random variable are, respectively,

$$E[X] = \frac{\alpha}{\lambda} \quad \mathrm{Var}(X) = \frac{\alpha}{\lambda^2}$$

A random variable is said to have a *beta* distribution with parameters (a, b) if its probability density function is equal to

$$f(x) = \frac{1}{B(a,b)} x^{a-1}(1 - x)^{b-1} \quad 0 \leq x \leq 1$$

and is equal to 0 otherwise. The constant $B(a, b)$ is given by

$$B(a,b) = \int_0^1 x^{a-1}(1 - x)^{b-1}\, dx$$

The mean and variance of such a random variable are, respectively,

$$E[X] = \frac{a}{a + b} \quad \mathrm{Var}(X) = \frac{ab}{(a + b)^2(a + b + 1)}$$

Problems

5.1. For a random variable having the following density function,

$$f(x) = \begin{cases} kx^2(1+x), & 0 < x < 1 \\ 0, & \text{otherwise} \end{cases}$$

(a) Obtain the value of k.

(b) Write down the cumulative distribution function of X.

5.2. A system consisting of one original unit plus a spare can function for a random amount of time X. If the density of X is given (in units of months) by

$$f(x) = \begin{cases} Cxe^{-x/2} & x > 0 \\ 0 & x \le 0 \end{cases}$$

what is the probability that the system functions for at least 5 months?

5.3. Consider the function

$$f(x) = \begin{cases} C(2x - x^3) & 0 < x < \frac{5}{2} \\ 0 & \text{otherwise} \end{cases}$$

Could f be a probability density function? If so, determine C. Repeat if $f(x)$ were given by

$$f(x) = \begin{cases} C(2x - x^2) & 0 < x < \frac{5}{2} \\ 0 & \text{otherwise} \end{cases}$$

5.4. The cumulative distribution function of the continuous random variable X is

$$F(x) = \begin{cases} 0, & x \le -2 \\ c(x + 2)^2, & -2 < x \le 2 \\ 1, & x > 2 \end{cases}$$

(a) Obtain the value of c.
(b) Find $P(X > 1)$.
(c) Find a such that $P(X \le a) = 9/16$.

5.5. A filling station is supplied with gasoline once a week. If its weekly volume of sales in thousands of gallons is a random variable with probability density function

$$f(x) = \begin{cases} 5(1 - x)^4 & 0 < x < 1 \\ 0 & \text{otherwise} \end{cases}$$

what must the capacity of the tank be so that the probability of the supply being exhausted in a given week is .01?

5.6. Compute $E[X]$ if X has a density function given by

(a) $f(x) = \begin{cases} \dfrac{1}{4}xe^{-x/2} & x > 0 \\ 0 & \text{otherwise} \end{cases}$;

(b) $f(x) = \begin{cases} c(1 - x^2) & -1 < x < 1 \\ 0 & \text{otherwise} \end{cases}$;

(c) $f(x) = \begin{cases} \dfrac{5}{x^2} & x > 5 \\ 0 & x \le 5 \end{cases}$.

5.7. The density function of the continuous random variable X is given by

$$f(x) = \begin{cases} (x)^2(ux + v), & 0 < x \le 1 \\ 0, & \text{otherwise} \end{cases}$$

Let Var$(1/X)$= 5/36, then obtain the values of u and v.

5.8. The lifetime in hours of an electronic tube is a random variable having a probability density function given by

$$f(x) = xe^{-x} \qquad x \ge 0$$

Compute the expected lifetime of such a tube.

5.9. Consider Example 4b of Chapter 4, but now suppose that the seasonal demand is a continuous random variable having probability density function f. Show that the optimal amount to stock is the value s^* that satisfies

$$F(s^*) = \frac{b}{b + \ell}$$

where b is net profit per unit sale, ℓ is the net loss per unit unsold, and F is the cumulative distribution function of the seasonal demand.

5.10. Trains headed for destination A arrive at the train station at 15-minute intervals starting at 7 A.M., whereas trains headed for destination B arrive at 15-minute intervals starting at 7:05 A.M.

(a) If a certain passenger arrives at the station at a time uniformly distributed between 7 and 8 A.M. and then gets on the first train that arrives, what proportion of time does he or she go to destination A?

(b) What if the passenger arrives at a time uniformly distributed between 7:10 and 8:10 A.M.?

5.11. A point is chosen at random on a line segment of length L. Interpret this statement, and find the probability that the ratio of the shorter to the longer segment is less than $\frac{1}{4}$.

5.12. A bus travels between the two cities A and B, which are 100 miles apart. If the bus has a breakdown, the distance from the breakdown to city A has a uniform distribution over $(0, 100)$. There is a bus service station in city A, in B, and in the center of the route between A and B. It is suggested that it would be more efficient to have the three stations located 25, 50, and 75 miles, respectively, from A. Do you agree? Why?

5.13. A yoga practitioner can hold a particular exercise pose for some time uniformly distributed between 5 to 15 minutes.
(a) What is the probability that he holds the pose for more than 12 minutes?
(b) If he has already held the pose for 10 minutes already, what is the probability that he can hold on for at least 12 minutes?

5.14. Let X be a uniform $(0, 1)$ random variable. Compute $E[X^n]$ by using Proposition 2.1, and then check the result by using the definition of expectation.

5.15. If X is a normal random variable with parameters $\mu = 10$ and $\sigma^2 = 36$, compute

(a) $P\{X > 5\}$;
(b) $P\{4 < X < 16\}$;
(c) $P\{X < 8\}$;
(d) $P\{X < 20\}$;
(e) $P\{X > 16\}$.

5.16. The annual rainfall (in inches) in a certain region is normally distributed with $\mu = 40$ and $\sigma = 4$. What is the probability that starting with this year, it will take more than 10 years before a year occurs having a rainfall of more than 50 inches? What assumptions are you making?

5.17. The salaries of physicians in a certain speciality are approximately normally distributed. If 25 percent of these physicians earn less than $180,000 and 25 percent earn more than $320,000, approximately what fraction earn

(a) less than $200,000?
(b) between $280,000 and $320,000?

5.18. Suppose that X is a normal random variable with mean 5. If $P\{X > 9\} = .2$, approximately what is Var(X)?

5.19. Let X be normal random variable with mean 100 and variance 4. Find the symmetric values a and b such that

$$P(a < X < b) = 0.95$$

5.20. The Top 5 percent students in the class XII examination will get a government scholarship. If the marks in the examination follows a normal distribution with mean 500 and variance 100, how much marks should a student score to ensure a scholarship?

5.21. If in an apartment complex consisting of 45 families, the total drinking water usage for a day was 1350 liters.

If the water usage per family is distributed according to normal distribution with a standard deviation of 5 liter, what percentage of families used more than 35 liters?

5.22. Every day Jo practices her tennis serve by continually serving until she has had a total of 50 successful serves. If each of her serves is, independently of previous ones, successful with probability .4, approximately what is the probability that she will need more than 100 serves to accomplish her goal?
Hint: Imagine even if Jo is successful that she continues to serve until she has served exactly 100 times. What must be true about her first 100 serves if she is to reach her goal?

5.23. One thousand independent rolls of a fair die will be made. Compute an approximation to the probability that the number 6 will appear between 150 and 200 times inclusively. If the number 6 appears exactly 200 times, find the probability that the number 5 will appear less than 150 times.

5.24. The lifetimes of interactive computer chips produced by a certain semiconductor manufacturer are normally distributed with parameters $\mu = 1.4 \times 10^6$ hours and $\sigma = 3 \times 10^5$ hours. What is the approximate probability that a batch of 100 chips will contain at least 20 whose lifetimes are less than 1.8×10^6?

5.25. Each item produced by a certain manufacturer is, independently, of acceptable quality with probability .95. Approximate the probability that at most 10 of the next 150 items produced are unacceptable.

5.26. An entertainment show can accommodate 650 people having free passes. For each free pass they give out, a person attends the event with probability 0.7. If they handed out 900 free passes, what is the probability too many people show up?

5.27. Among 1000 babies born at an IVF facility, 620 turned out to be boys. Assuming that the chances of obtaining a boy or girl using the treatment is the same, how likely was to have 620 or more boys? Explain.

5.28. A study conducted by the Motor Vehicle department showed that 70% of driving test takers clear the test on their first attempt. If 150 people takes the test on a particular day, what is the probability that more than 100 of them qualify the test. State your assumptions.

5.29. A model for the movement of a stock supposes that if the present price of the stock is s, then after one period, it will be either us with probability p or ds with probability $1 - p$. Assuming that successive movements are independent, approximate the probability that the stock's price will be up at least 30 percent after the next 1000 periods if $u = 1.012$, $d = 0.990$, and $p = .52$.

5.30. An image is partitioned into two regions, one white and the other black. A reading taken from a randomly chosen point in the white section will be normally distributed with $\mu = 4$ and $\sigma^2 = 4$, whereas one taken from a randomly chosen point in the black region will have a normally distributed reading with parameters $(6, 9)$. A point is randomly chosen on the image and has a reading of 5. If the fraction of the image that is black is α, for what value of α would the probability of making an error be the same, regardless of whether one concluded that the point was in the black region or in the white region?

5.31. (a) A fire station is to be located along a road of length $A, A < \infty$. If fires occur at points uniformly chosen on $(0, A)$, where should the station be located so as to minimize the expected distance from the fire? That is, choose a so as to

$$\text{minimize } E[|X - a|]$$

when X is uniformly distributed over $(0, A)$.

(b) Now suppose that the road is of infinite length—stretching from point 0 outward to ∞. If the distance of a fire from point 0 is exponentially distributed with rate λ, where should the fire station now be located? That is, we want to minimize $E[|X - a|]$, where X is now exponential with rate λ.

5.32. The time taken by a person (in hours) to solve a Rubik's cube is an exponentially distributed random variable with mean 4 hours. What is
(a) the probability that he solves it within 2 hours?
(b) the conditional probability that he takes more than 4 hours to solve it given that it remains unsolved within the first 2 hours?

5.33. A toy manufacturing company sells a toy train which has a mean lifetime of 10 months. If the lifetime of the toy follows an exponential distribution, what should be the guarantee period offered on the train if they do not want to replace more than 10% of the toys?

5.34. Jones figures that the total number of thousands of miles that an auto can be driven before it would need to be junked is an exponential random variable with parameter $\frac{1}{20}$. Smith has a used car that he claims has been driven only 10,000 miles. If Jones purchases the car, what is the probability that she would get at least 20,000 additional miles out of it? Repeat under the assumption that the lifetime mileage of the car is not exponentially distributed,

but rather is (in thousands of miles) uniformly distributed over $(0, 40)$.

5.35. The lung cancer hazard rate $\lambda(t)$ of a t-year-old male smoker is such that

$$\lambda(t) = .027 + .00025(t - 40)^2 \qquad t \geq 40$$

Assuming that a 40-year-old male smoker survives all other hazards, what is the probability that he survives to (a) age 50 and (b) age 60 without contracting lung cancer?

5.36. The life time distribution of an item has the hazard rate given by $4t^3$, $t > 0$. Obtain the probability that
(a) the item fails within 1 year.
(b) the lifetime is between 1 and 2 years.
(c) given that it survives 1 year it will survive till the second year.

5.37. If X is uniformly distributed over $(-1, 1)$, find
(a) $P\{|X| > \frac{1}{2}\}$;
(b) the density function of the random variable $|X|$.

5.38. If Y is uniformly distributed over $(0, 5)$, what is the probability that the roots of the equation $4x^2 + 4xY + Y + 2 = 0$ are both real?

5.39. If X is an exponential random variable with parameter $\lambda = 1$, compute the probability density function of the random variable Y defined by $Y = \log X$.

5.40. If X follows an exponential distribution with parameter $\lambda = 1$, find the density function of $Y = \sqrt{X}$.

5.41. Find the distribution of $R = A\sin\theta$, where A is a fixed constant and θ is uniformly distributed on $(-\pi/2, \pi/2)$. Such a random variable R arises in the theory of ballistics. If a projectile is fired from the origin at an angle α from the earth with a speed v, then the point R at which it returns to the earth can be expressed as $R = (v^2/g)\sin 2\alpha$, where g is the gravitational constant, equal to 980 centimeters per second squared.

5.42. Let Y be a lognormal random variable (see Example 7e for its definition) and let $c > 0$ be a constant. Answer true or false to the following, and then give an explanation for your answer.

(a) cY is lognormal;
(b) $c + Y$ is lognormal.

Theoretical Exercises

5.1. The speed of a molecule in a uniform gas at equilibrium is a random variable whose probability density function is given by

$$f(x) = \begin{cases} ax^2 e^{-bx^2} & x \geq 0 \\ 0 & x < 0 \end{cases}$$

where $b = m/2kT$ and k, T, and m denote, respectively, Boltzmann's constant, the absolute temperature of the gas, and the mass of the molecule. Evaluate a in terms of b.

5.2. Show that

$$E[Y] = \int_0^\infty P\{Y > y\}\,dy - \int_0^\infty P\{Y < -y\}\,dy$$

Hint: Show that

$$\int_0^\infty P\{Y < -y\}\,dy = -\int_{-\infty}^0 x f_Y(x)\,dx$$
$$\int_0^\infty P\{Y > y\}\,dy = \int_0^\infty x f_Y(x)\,dx$$

5.3. Show that if X has density function f, then

$$E[g(X)] = \int_{-\infty}^\infty g(x)f(x)\,dx$$

Hint: Using Theoretical Exercise 5.2, start with

$$E[g(X)] = \int_0^\infty P\{g(X) > y\}\,dy - \int_0^\infty P\{g(X) < -y\}\,dy$$

and then proceed as in the proof given in the text when $g(X) \geq 0$.

5.4. Prove Corollary 2.1.

5.5. Use the result that for a nonnegative random variable Y,

$$E[Y] = \int_0^\infty P\{Y > t\}\,dt$$

to show that for a nonnegative random variable X,

$$E[X^n] = \int_0^\infty nx^{n-1}P\{X > x\}\,dx$$

Hint: Start with

$$E[X^n] = \int_0^\infty P\{X^n > t\}\,dt$$

and make the change of variables $t = x^n$.

5.6. Define a collection of events $E_a, 0 < a < 1$, having the property that $P(E_a) = 1$ for all a but $P\left(\bigcap_a E_a\right) = 0$.

Hint: Let X be uniform over $(0, 1)$ and define each E_a in terms of X.

5.7. The standard deviation of X, denoted $SD(X)$, is given by $SD(X) = \sqrt{\mathrm{Var}(X)}$

Find $SD(b\text{-}cX)$ if X has variance σ^2 and b and c are some constants.

5.8. Let X be a random variable that takes on values between 0 and c. That is, $P\{0 \leq X \leq c\} = 1$. Show that

$$\mathrm{Var}(X) \leq \frac{c^2}{4}$$

Hint: One approach is to first argue that

$$E[X^2] \leq cE[X]$$

and then use this inequality to show that

$$\mathrm{Var}(X) \leq c^2[\alpha(1 - \alpha)] \quad \text{where } \alpha = \frac{E[X]}{c}$$

5.9. Let Z be a standard normal variable with pdf Φ, then show that

(a) $\Phi(z) + \Phi(-z) = 1$, for any z in R.

(b) Obtain the pdf of the variable $Y = |Z|$ and how it is related with $\Phi(z)$.

5.10. Let $f(x)$ denote the probability density function of a normal random variable with mean μ and variance σ^2. Show that $\mu - \sigma$ and $\mu + \sigma$ are points of inflection of this function. That is, show that $f''(x) = 0$ when $x = \mu - \sigma$ or $x = \mu + \sigma$.

5.11. Let Z be a standard normal random variable Z, and let g be a differentiable function with derivative g'.

(a) Show that $\quad E[g'(Z)] = E[Zg(Z)]$;

(b) Show that $\quad E[Z^{n+1}] = nE[Z^{n-1}]$.

(c) Find $E[Z^4]$.

5.12. Suppose that X has the exponential distribution with rate parameter λ. Then comment on the distribution of $\lfloor X \rfloor$, the largest integer less than X.

5.13. The median of a continuous random variable having distribution function F is that value m such that $F(m) = \frac{1}{2}$. That is, a random variable is just as likely to be larger than its median as it is to be smaller. Find the median of X if X is

(a) uniformly distributed over (a, b);

(b) normal with parameters μ, σ^2;

(c) exponential with rate λ.

5.14. The mode of a continuous random variable having density f is the value of x for which $f(x)$ attains its maximum. Compute the mode of X in cases (a), (b), and (c) of Theoretical Exercise 5.13.

5.15. Let random variable X be uniformly distributed over the interval $(0, 1)$. Compute the pdf of $Y = e^X$.

5.16. Compute the hazard rate function of X when X is uniformly distributed over $(0, a)$.

5.17. If X having a uniform $(0, 1)$ distribution and hazard rate function $\lambda_X(t)$, compute the hazard rate function of $Y = -\log X$.

5.18. Let the cumulative hazard function be defined as $H(t) = \int_0^t h(u)\,du$. Prove $H(t)$ has an exponential distribution with mean one.

5.19. If X is an exponential random variable with mean $1/\lambda$, show that

$$E[X^k] = \frac{k!}{\lambda^k} \qquad k = 1, 2, \dots$$

Hint: Make use of the gamma density function to evaluate the preceding.

5.20. For a normal random variable X with parameters μ and σ^2, show that for some integer $r > 0$,

$$E(X - \mu)^r = \begin{cases} \frac{\sigma^r r!}{2^{r/2}\, r/2!}, & \text{for even } r \\ o, & \text{when } r \text{ is odd} \end{cases}$$

5.21. Show that $\Gamma\left(\frac{1}{2}\right) = \sqrt{\pi}$.

Hint: $\Gamma\left(\frac{1}{2}\right) = \int_0^\infty e^{-x} x^{-1/2}\,dx$. Make the change of variables $y = \sqrt{2x}$ and then relate the resulting expression to the normal distribution.

5.22. Compute the hazard rate function of a gamma random variable with parameters (α, λ) and show it is increasing when $\alpha \geq 1$ and decreasing when $\alpha \leq 1$.

5.23. Compute the hazard rate function of a Weibull random variable and show it is increasing when $\beta \geq 1$ and decreasing when $\beta \leq 1$.

5.24. Show that a plot of $\log(\log(1 - F(x))^{-1})$ against $\log x$ will be a straight line with slope β when $F(\cdot)$ is a Weibull distribution function. Show also that approximately 63.2 percent of all observations from such a distribution will be less than α. Assume that $v = 0$.

5.25. Let

$$Y = \left(\frac{X - v}{\alpha}\right)^\beta$$

Show that if X is a Weibull random variable with parameters v, α, and β, then Y is an exponential random variable with parameter $\lambda = 1$ and vice versa.

5.26. Suppose that X has the gamma distribution with parameters α and λ. Show that if $\alpha > 1$ the mode occurs at $x = \frac{(\alpha - 1)}{\lambda}$.

5.27. Show that if X has a standard uniform distribution ($a = 0$ and $b = 1$), then $X^{1/n}$ is distributed according to a beta distribution with parameters $(1/n, 1)$.

5.28. Consider the beta distribution with parameters (a, b). Show that

(a) when $a > 1$ and $b > 1$, the density is unimodal (that is, it has a unique mode) with mode equal to $(a - 1)/(a + b - 2)$;

(b) when $a \leq 1, b \leq 1$, and $a + b < 2$, the density is either unimodal with mode at 0 or 1 or U-shaped with modes at both 0 and 1;

(c) when $a = 1 = b$, all points in $[0, 1]$ are modes.

5.29. Let X be a continuous random variable having cumulative distribution function F. Define the random variable Y by $Y = F(X)$. Show that Y is uniformly distributed over $(0, 1)$.

5.30. Suppose that X has the gamma distribution with parameters α and λ. Show that if $c > 0$, then cX has the gamma distribution with parameters α and λ/c.

5.31. Find the probability density function of $Y = e^X$ when X is normally distributed with parameters μ and σ^2. The random variable Y is said to have a *lognormal distribution* (since $\log Y$ has a normal distribution) with parameters μ and σ^2.

5.32. Let X and Y be independent random variables that are both equally likely to be either $1, 2, \dots, (10)^N$, where N is very large. Let D denote the greatest common divisor of X and Y, and let $Q_k = P\{D = k\}$.

(a) Give a heuristic argument that $Q_k = \frac{1}{k^2} Q_1$.
Hint: Note that in order for D to equal k, k must divide both X and Y and also X/k, and Y/k must be relatively prime. (That is, X/k, and Y/k must have a greatest common divisor equal to 1.)

(b) Use part (a) to show that

$$Q_1 = P\{X \text{ and } Y \text{ are relatively prime}\}$$
$$= \frac{1}{\sum_{k=1}^\infty 1/k^2}$$

It is a well-known identity that $\sum_1^\infty 1/k^2 = \pi^2/6$, so $Q_1 = 6/\pi^2$. (In number theory, this is known as the Legendre theorem.)

(c) Now argue that

$$Q_1 = \prod_{i=1}^\infty \left(\frac{P_i^2 - 1}{P_i^2}\right)$$

where P_i is the ith-smallest prime greater than 1.
Hint: X and Y will be relatively prime if they have no common prime factors. Hence, from part (b), we see that

$$\prod_{i=1}^{\infty}\left(\frac{P_i^2 - 1}{P_i^2}\right) = \frac{6}{\pi^2}$$

which was noted without explanation in Problem 11 of Chapter 4. (The relationship between this problem and

Self-Test Problems and Exercises

5.1. The number of minutes of playing time of a certain high school basketball player in a randomly chosen game is a random variable whose probability density function is given in the following figure:

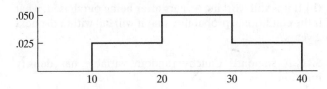

Find the probability that the player plays

(a) more than 15 minutes;

(b) between 20 and 35 minutes;

(c) less than 30 minutes;

(d) more than 36 minutes.

5.2. For some constant c, the random variable X has the probability density function

$$f(x) = \begin{cases} cx^n & 0 < x < 1 \\ 0 & \text{otherwise} \end{cases}$$

Find (a) c and (b) $P\{X > x\}, 0 < x < 1$.

5.3. In a dart throwing game, the target consists of 3 concentric circles with radii $1/\sqrt{3}$, 1, $\sqrt{3}$ each having points $10, 5, 2$ respectively. Let X(feet) be the distance of the dart from the centre having the pdf,

$$f_X(x) = \begin{cases} \frac{c}{(1+x^2)}, & x > 0 \\ 0, & \text{otherwise} \end{cases}$$

Find the value of c and hence obtain the expected number of points that can be scored.

5.4. Twins can be born in different days or even different years when the first-born is born a few minutes before midnight and the second just after midnight. Assuming that the birth of the first child is uniformly distributed and the second birth occurs 10 minutes after the first,
(a) what is the probability the twins will have different birthdays; that is, different days?
(b) what is the probability the twins will be born in different years (assuming non-leap year)?

5.5. The random variable X is said to be a discrete uniform random variable on the integers $1, 2, \ldots, n$ if

Problem 11 of Chapter 4 is that X and Y are relatively prime if XY has no multiple prime factors.)

5.33. If X is a gamma random variable with parameters α and λ, obtain the density function of the Inverse gamma variable Y given by, $Y = 1/X$.

$$P\{X = i\} = \frac{1}{n} \quad i = 1, 2, \ldots, n$$

For any nonnegative real number x, let $\text{Int}(x)$ (sometimes written as $[x]$) be the largest integer that is less than or equal to x. Show that if U is a uniform random variable on $(0, 1)$, then $X = \text{Int}(nU) + 1$ is a discrete uniform random variable on $1, \ldots, n$.

5.6. Your company must make a sealed bid for a construction project. If you succeed in winning the contract (by having the lowest bid), then you plan to pay another firm $100,000 to do the work. If you believe that the minimum bid (in thousands of dollars) of the other participating companies can be modeled as the value of a random variable that is uniformly distributed on $(70, 140)$, how much should you bid to maximize your expected profit?

5.7. To be a winner in a certain game, you must be successful in three successive rounds. The game depends on the value of U, a uniform random variable on $(0, 1)$. If $U > .1$, then you are successful in round 1; if $U > .2$, then you are successful in round 2; and if $U > .3$, then you are successful in round 3.

(a) Find the probability that you are successful in round 1.

(b) Find the conditional probability that you are successful in round 2 given that you were successful in round 1.

(c) Find the conditional probability that you are successful in round 3 given that you were successful in rounds 1 and 2.

(d) Find the probability that you are a winner.

5.8. The monthly salary of employees in an MNC are approximately normally distributed with a mean of Rs. 50,000 and a standard deviation of Rs. 20,000.

(a) What percent of people earn less than Rs. 30,000?
(b) What percent of people earn between Rs. 40,000 and Rs. 75,000?
(c) What percent of people earn more than Rs. 70,000?

5.9. Admission to a University is determined on the basis of an entrance test. The scores on this test are normally distributed with a mean of 300 and a standard deviation of 60. A student is admitted to this university if he score better than at least 70% of the students who took the test. If Rahul takes the test and scores 365 will he be selected?

5.10. The number of calls attended in a call center on a daily basis approximately follows a normal distribution with mean 720 and a standard deviation of 90.
(a) What is the probability that there will be more than 800 calls in a particular day?
(b) What is the probability that the number of daily calls lie between 700 to 750?
(c) Given that there have been 600 calls already what is the probability that there would be another 200 calls?

5.11. The annual rainfall in Cleveland, Ohio, is approximately a normal random variable with mean 40.2 inches and standard deviation 8.4 inches. What is the probability that

(a) next year's rainfall will exceed 44 inches?
(b) the yearly rainfalls in exactly 3 of the next 7 years will exceed 44 inches?

Assume that if A_i is the event that the rainfall exceeds 44 inches in year i (from now), then the events $A_i, i \geq 1$, are independent.

5.12. The following table uses 1992 data concerning the percentages of male and female full-time workers whose annual salaries fall into different ranges:

Earnings range	Percentage of females	Percentage of males
≤9999	8.6	4.4
10,000–19,999	38.0	21.1
20,000–24,999	19.4	15.8
25,000–49,999	29.2	41.5
≥50,000	4.8	17.2

Suppose that random samples of 200 male and 200 female full-time workers are chosen. Approximate the probability that

(a) at least 70 of the women earn $25,000 or more;
(b) at most 60 percent of the men earn $25,000 or more;
(c) at least three-fourths of the men and at least half the women earn $20,000 or more.

5.13. The lifetime of a particular mobile phone follows an exponential distribution with mean 30 months. If a person buys a second hand mobile phone which has been used for some time, what is the probability that it will work for an additional 12 months?

5.14. Suppose that the cumulative distribution function of the random variable X is given by

$$F(x) = 1 - e^{-x^2} \quad x > 0$$

Evaluate (a) $P\{X > 2\}$; (b) $P\{1 < X < 3\}$; (c) the hazard rate function of F; (d) $E[X]$; (e) Var(X).

Hint: For parts (d) and (e), you might want to make use of the results of Theoretical Exercise 5.5.

5.15. The number of years that a washing machine functions is a random variable whose hazard rate function is given by

$$\lambda(t) = \begin{cases} .2 & 0 < t < 2 \\ .2 + .3(t - 2) & 2 \leq t < 5 \\ 1.1 & t > 5 \end{cases}$$

(a) What is the probability that the machine will still be working 6 years after being purchased?
(b) If it is still working 6 years after being purchased, what is the conditional probability that it will fail within the next 2 years?

5.16. A standard Cauchy random variable has density function

$$f(x) = \frac{1}{\pi(1 + x^2)} \quad -\infty < x < \infty$$

Show that if X is a standard Cauchy random variable, then $1/X$ is also a standard Cauchy random variable.

5.17. A roulette wheel has 38 slots, numbered 0, 00, and 1 through 36. If you bet 1 on a specified number, then you either win 35 if the roulette ball lands on that number or lose 1 if it does not. If you continually make such bets, approximate the probability that

(a) you are winning after 34 bets;
(b) you are winning after 1000 bets;
(c) you are winning after 100,000 bets.

Assume that each roll of the roulette ball is equally likely to land on any of the 38 numbers.

5.18. There are two types of batteries in a bin. When in use, type i batteries last (in hours) an exponentially distributed time with rate $\lambda_i, i = 1, 2$. A battery that is randomly chosen from the bin will be a type i battery with probability $p_i, \sum_{i=1}^{2} p_i = 1$. If a randomly chosen battery is still operating after t hours of use, what is the probability that it will still be operating after an additional s hours?

5.19. Evidence concerning the guilt or innocence of a defendant in a criminal investigation can be summarized by the value of an exponential random variable X whose mean μ depends on whether the defendant is guilty. If innocent, $\mu = 1$; if guilty, $\mu = 2$. The deciding judge will rule the defendant guilty if $X > c$ for some suitably chosen value of c.

(a) If the judge wants to be 95 percent certain that an innocent man will not be convicted, what should be the value of c?

(b) Using the value of c found in part (a), what is the probability that a guilty defendant will be convicted?

5.20. For any real number y, define y^+ by

$$y^+ = \begin{cases} y, & \text{if } y \geq 0 \\ 0, & \text{if } y < 0 \end{cases}$$

Let c be a constant.

(a) Show that

$$E[(Z - c)^+] = \frac{1}{\sqrt{2\pi}}e^{-c^2/2} - c(1 - \Phi(c))$$

when Z is a standard normal random variable.

(b) Find $E[(X - c)^+]$ when X is normal with mean μ and variance σ^2.

5.21. With $\Phi(x)$ being the probability that a normal random variable with mean 0 and variance 1 is less than x, which of the following are true:

(a) $\Phi(-x) = \Phi(x)$

(b) $\Phi(x) + \Phi(-x) = 1$

(c) $\Phi(-x) = 1/\Phi(x)$

5.22. Let U be a uniform $(0, 1)$ random variable, and let $a < b$ be constants.

(a) Show that if $b > 0$, then bU is uniformly distributed on $(0, b)$, and if $b < 0$, then bU is uniformly distributed on $(b, 0)$.

(b) Show that $a + U$ is uniformly distributed on $(a, 1 + a)$.

(c) What function of U is uniformly distributed on (a, b)?

(d) Show that $\min(U, 1 - U)$ is a uniform $(0, 1/2)$ random variable.

(e) Show that $\max(U, 1 - U)$ is a uniform $(1/2, 1)$ random variable.

Chapter 6

Jointly Distributed Random Variables

Contents

6.1 Joint Distribution Functions
6.2 Independent Random Variables
6.3 Sums of Independent Random Variables
6.4 Conditional Distributions: Discrete Case

6.5 Conditional Distributions: Continuous Case
6.6 Order Statistics
6.7 Joint Probability Distribution of Functions of Random Variables
6.8 Exchangeable Random Variables

6.1 Joint Distribution Functions

Thus far, we have concerned ourselves only with probability distributions for single random variables. However, we are often interested in probability statements concerning two or more random variables. In order to deal with such probabilities, we define, for any two random variables X and Y, the *joint cumulative probability distribution function* of X and Y by

$$F(a,b) = P\{X \leq a, Y \leq b\} \quad -\infty < a, b < \infty$$

The distribution of X can be obtained from the joint distribution of X and Y as follows:

$$
\begin{aligned}
F_X(a) &= P\{X \leq a\} \\
&= P\{X \leq a, Y < \infty\} \\
&= P\left(\lim_{b \to \infty} \{X \leq a, Y \leq b\}\right) \\
&= \lim_{b \to \infty} P\{X \leq a, Y \leq b\} \\
&= \lim_{b \to \infty} F(a,b) \\
&\equiv F(a,\infty)
\end{aligned}
$$

Note that in the preceding set of equalities, we have once again made use of the fact that probability is a continuous set (that is, event) function. Similarly, the cumulative distribution function of Y is given by

$$
\begin{aligned}
F_Y(b) &= P\{Y \leq b\} \\
&= \lim_{a \to \infty} F(a,b) \\
&\equiv F(\infty,b)
\end{aligned}
$$

The distribution functions F_X and F_Y are sometimes referred to as the *marginal distributions* of X and Y.

All joint probability statements about X and Y can, in theory, be answered in terms of their joint distribution function. For instance, suppose we wanted to compute the joint probability that X is greater than a and Y is greater than b. This could be done as follows:

$$
\begin{aligned}
P\{X > a, Y > b\} &= 1 - P(\{X > a, Y > b\}^c) \\
&= 1 - P(\{X > a\}^c \cup \{Y > b\}^c) \\
&= 1 - P(\{X \le a\} \cup \{Y \le b\}) \\
&= 1 - [P\{X \le a\} + P\{Y \le b\} - P\{X \le a, Y \le b\}] \\
&= 1 - F_X(a) - F_Y(b) + F(a,b)
\end{aligned}
\tag{1.1}
$$

Equation (1.1) is a special case of the following equation, whose verification is left as an exercise:

$$
\begin{aligned}
P\{a_1 < X \le a_2, b_1 < Y \le b_2\} \\
= F(a_2, b_2) + F(a_1, b_1) - F(a_1, b_2) - F(a_2, b_1)
\end{aligned}
\tag{1.2}
$$

whenever $a_1 < a_2, b_1 < b_2$.

In the case when X and Y are both discrete random variables, it is convenient to define the *joint probability mass function* of X and Y by

$$
p(x, y) = P\{X = x, Y = y\}
$$

The probability mass function of X can be obtained from $p(x, y)$ by

$$
\begin{aligned}
p_X(x) &= P\{X = x\} \\
&= \sum_{y : p(x,y) > 0} p(x, y)
\end{aligned}
$$

Similarly,

$$
p_Y(y) = \sum_{x : p(x,y) > 0} p(x, y)
$$

Example 1a

Suppose that 3 balls are randomly selected from an urn containing 3 red, 4 white, and 5 blue balls. If we let X and Y denote, respectively, the number of red and white balls chosen, then the joint probability mass function of X and Y, $p(i, j) = P\{X = i, Y = j\}$, is given by

$$
p(0, 0) = \binom{5}{3} \Big/ \binom{12}{3} = \frac{10}{220}
$$

$$
p(0, 1) = \binom{4}{1} \binom{5}{2} \Big/ \binom{12}{3} = \frac{40}{220}
$$

$$
p(0, 2) = \binom{4}{2} \binom{5}{1} \Big/ \binom{12}{3} = \frac{30}{220}
$$

$$p(0,3) = \binom{4}{3} / \binom{12}{3} = \frac{4}{220}$$

$$p(1,0) = \binom{3}{1}\binom{5}{2} / \binom{12}{3} = \frac{30}{220}$$

$$p(1,1) = \binom{3}{1}\binom{4}{1}\binom{5}{1} / \binom{12}{3} = \frac{60}{220}$$

$$p(1,2) = \binom{3}{1}\binom{4}{2} / \binom{12}{3} = \frac{18}{220}$$

$$p(2,0) = \binom{3}{2}\binom{5}{1} / \binom{12}{3} = \frac{15}{220}$$

$$p(2,1) = \binom{3}{2}\binom{4}{1} / \binom{12}{3} = \frac{12}{220}$$

$$p(3,0) = \binom{3}{3} / \binom{12}{3} = \frac{1}{220}$$

These probabilities can most easily be expressed in tabular form, as in Table 6.1. The reader should note that the probability mass function of X is obtained by computing the row sums, whereas the probability mass function of Y is obtained by computing the column sums. Because the individual probability mass functions of X and Y thus appear in the margin of such a table, they are often referred to as the *marginal probability mass functions* of X and Y, respectively. ∎

Table 6.1 $P\{X = i, Y = j\}$.

i \ j	0	1	2	3	Row sum = $P\{X = i\}$
0	$\frac{10}{220}$	$\frac{40}{220}$	$\frac{30}{220}$	$\frac{4}{220}$	$\frac{84}{220}$
1	$\frac{30}{220}$	$\frac{60}{220}$	$\frac{18}{220}$	0	$\frac{108}{220}$
2	$\frac{15}{220}$	$\frac{12}{220}$	0	0	$\frac{27}{220}$
3	$\frac{1}{220}$	0	0	0	$\frac{1}{220}$
Column sum = $P\{Y = j\}$	$\frac{56}{220}$	$\frac{112}{220}$	$\frac{48}{220}$	$\frac{4}{220}$	

Example 1b

Suppose that 15 percent of the families in a certain community have no children, 20 percent have 1 child, 35 percent have 2 children, and 30 percent have 3. Suppose further that in each family each child is equally likely (independently) to be a boy or a girl. If a family is chosen at random from this community, then B, the number of boys, and G, the number of girls, in this family will have the joint probability mass function shown in Table 6.2.

Table 6.2 $P\{B = i, G = j\}$.

i \ j	0	1	2	3	Row sum = $P\{B = i\}$
0	.15	.10	.0875	.0375	.3750
1	.10	.175	.1125	0	.3875
2	.0875	.1125	0	0	.2000
3	.0375	0	0	0	.0375
Column sum = $P\{G = j\}$	.3750	.3875	.2000	.0375	

The probabilities shown in Table 6.2 are obtained as follows:

$$P\{B = 0, G = 0\} = P\{\text{no children}\} = .15$$
$$P\{B = 0, G = 1\} = P\{\text{1 girl and total of 1 child}\}$$
$$= P\{\text{1 child}\}P\{\text{1 girl}|\text{1 child}\} = (.20)\left(\frac{1}{2}\right)$$
$$P\{B = 0, G = 2\} = P\{\text{2 girls and total of 2 children}\}$$
$$= P\{\text{2 children}\}P\{\text{2 girls}|\text{2 children}\} = (.35)\left(\frac{1}{2}\right)^2$$

We leave the verification of the remaining probabilities in the table to the reader. ∎

We say that X and Y are *jointly continuous* if there exists a function $f(x, y)$, defined for all real x and y, having the property that for every set C of pairs of real numbers (that is, C is a set in the two-dimensional plane),

$$P\{(X, Y) \in C\} = \iint\limits_{(x,y)\in C} f(x, y)\, dx\, dy \qquad (1.3)$$

The function $f(x, y)$ is called the *joint probability density function* of X and Y. If A and B are any sets of real numbers, then by defining $C = \{(x, y) : x \in A, y \in B\}$, we see from Equation (1.3) that

$$P\{X \in A, Y \in B\} = \int_B \int_A f(x, y)\, dx\, dy \qquad (1.4)$$

Because

$$F(a, b) = P\{X \in (-\infty, a], Y \in (-\infty, b]\}$$
$$= \int_{-\infty}^b \int_{-\infty}^a f(x, y)\, dx\, dy$$

it follows, upon differentiation, that

$$f(a, b) = \frac{\partial^2}{\partial a\, \partial b} F(a, b)$$

wherever the partial derivatives are defined. Another interpretation of the joint density function, obtained from Equation (1.4), is

$$P\{a < X < a + da, b < Y < b + db\} = \int_b^{b+db} \int_a^{a+da} f(x, y) \, dx \, dy$$
$$\approx f(a, b) \, da \, db$$

when da and db are small and $f(x, y)$ is continuous at a, b. Hence, $f(a, b)$ is a measure of how likely it is that the random vector (X, Y) will be near (a, b).

If X and Y are jointly continuous, they are individually continuous, and their probability density functions can be obtained as follows:

$$P\{X \in A\} = P\{X \in A, Y \in (-\infty, \infty)\}$$
$$= \int_A \int_{-\infty}^{\infty} f(x, y) \, dy \, dx$$
$$= \int_A f_X(x) \, dx$$

where

$$f_X(x) = \int_{-\infty}^{\infty} f(x, y) \, dy$$

is thus the probability density function of X. Similarly, the probability density function of Y is given by

$$f_Y(y) = \int_{-\infty}^{\infty} f(x, y) \, dx$$

Example 1c

The joint density function of X and Y is given by

$$f(x, y) = \begin{cases} 2e^{-x}e^{-2y} & 0 < x < \infty, \ 0 < y < \infty \\ 0 & \text{otherwise} \end{cases}$$

Compute (a) $P\{X > 1, Y < 1\}$, (b) $P\{X < Y\}$, and (c) $P\{X < a\}$.

Solution

(a)
$$P\{X > 1, Y < 1\} = \int_0^1 \int_1^{\infty} 2e^{-x}e^{-2y} \, dx \, dy$$
$$= \int_0^1 2e^{-2y} \left(-e^{-x} \Big|_1^{\infty} \right) dy$$
$$= e^{-1} \int_0^1 2e^{-2y} \, dy$$
$$= e^{-1}(1 - e^{-2})$$

(b)
$$P\{X < Y\} = \iint_{(x,y):x<y} 2e^{-x}e^{-2y} \, dx \, dy$$
$$= \int_0^{\infty} \int_0^y 2e^{-x}e^{-2y} \, dx \, dy$$
$$= \int_0^{\infty} 2e^{-2y}(1 - e^{-y}) \, dy$$

$$= \int_0^\infty 2e^{-2y}\,dy - \int_0^\infty 2e^{-3y}\,dy$$

$$= 1 - \frac{2}{3}$$

$$= \frac{1}{3}$$

(c)

$$P\{X < a\} = \int_0^a \int_0^\infty 2e^{-2y}e^{-x}\,dy\,dx$$

$$= \int_0^a e^{-x}\,dx$$

$$= 1 - e^{-a} \qquad \blacksquare$$

**Example
Id**

Consider a circle of radius R, and suppose that a point within the circle is randomly chosen in such a manner that all regions within the circle of equal area are equally likely to contain the point. (In other words, the point is uniformly distributed within the circle.) If we let the center of the circle denote the origin and define X and Y to be the coordinates of the point chosen (Figure 6.1), then, since (X, Y) is equally likely to be near each point in the circle, it follows that the joint density function of X and Y is given by

$$f(x, y) = \begin{cases} c & \text{if } x^2 + y^2 \le R^2 \\ 0 & \text{if } x^2 + y^2 > R^2 \end{cases}$$

for some value of c.

(a) Determine c.

(b) Find the marginal density functions of X and Y.

(c) Compute the probability that D, the distance from the origin of the point selected, is less than or equal to a.

(d) Find $E[D]$.

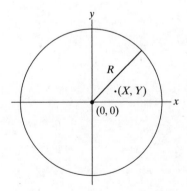

Figure 6.1 Joint probability distribution.

Solution

(a) Because

$$\int_{-\infty}^{\infty} \int_{-\infty}^{\infty} f(x, y)\,dy\,dx = 1$$

it follows that

$$c \iint\limits_{x^2+y^2 \leq R^2} dy\, dx = 1$$

We can evaluate $\iint_{x^2+y^2 \leq R^2} dy\, dx$ either by using polar coordinates or, more simply, by noting that it represents the area of the circle and is thus equal to πR^2. Hence,

$$c = \frac{1}{\pi R^2}$$

(b)
$$
\begin{aligned}
f_X(x) &= \int_{-\infty}^{\infty} f(x, y)\, dy \\
&= \frac{1}{\pi R^2} \int_{x^2+y^2 \leq R^2} dy \\
&= \frac{1}{\pi R^2} \int_{-a}^{a} dy, \quad \text{where } a = \sqrt{R^2 - x^2} \\
&= \frac{2}{\pi R^2} \sqrt{R^2 - x^2} \quad x^2 \leq R^2
\end{aligned}
$$

and it equals 0 when $x^2 > R^2$. By symmetry, the marginal density of Y is given by

$$
\begin{aligned}
f_Y(y) &= \frac{2}{\pi R^2} \sqrt{R^2 - y^2} \quad y^2 \leq R^2 \\
&= 0 \qquad\qquad\qquad y^2 > R^2
\end{aligned}
$$

(c) The distribution function of $D = \sqrt{X^2 + Y^2}$, the distance from the origin, is obtained as follows: For $0 \leq a \leq R$,

$$
\begin{aligned}
F_D(a) &= P\{\sqrt{X^2 + Y^2} \leq a\} \\
&= P\{X^2 + Y^2 \leq a^2\} \\
&= \iint\limits_{x^2+y^2 \leq a^2} f(x, y)\, dy\, dx \\
&= \frac{1}{\pi R^2} \iint\limits_{x^2+y^2 \leq a^2} dy\, dx \\
&= \frac{\pi a^2}{\pi R^2} \\
&= \frac{a^2}{R^2}
\end{aligned}
$$

where we have used the fact that $\iint_{x^2+y^2 \leq a^2} dy\, dx$ is the area of a circle of radius a and thus is equal to πa^2.

(d) From part (c), the density function of D is

$$f_D(a) = \frac{2a}{R^2} \quad 0 \leq a \leq R$$

Hence,

$$E[D] = \frac{2}{R^2} \int_0^R a^2 \, da = \frac{2R}{3}$$ ∎

Example 1e

The joint density of X and Y is given by

$$f(x, y) = \begin{cases} e^{-(x+y)} & 0 < x < \infty, \ 0 < y < \infty \\ 0 & \text{otherwise} \end{cases}$$

Find the density function of the random variable X/Y.

Solution We start by computing the distribution function of X/Y. For $a > 0$,

$$
\begin{aligned}
F_{X/Y}(a) &= P\left\{\frac{X}{Y} \le a\right\} \\
&= \iint\limits_{x/y \le a} e^{-(x+y)} \, dx \, dy \\
&= \int_0^\infty \int_0^{ay} e^{-(x+y)} \, dx \, dy \\
&= \int_0^\infty (1 - e^{-ay}) e^{-y} \, dy \\
&= \left\{ -e^{-y} + \frac{e^{-(a+1)y}}{a+1} \right\} \Bigg|_0^\infty \\
&= 1 - \frac{1}{a+1}
\end{aligned}
$$

Differentiation shows that the density function of X/Y is given by $f_{X/Y}(a) = 1/(a+1)^2, 0 < a < \infty$. ∎

We can also define joint probability distributions for n random variables in exactly the same manner as we did for $n = 2$. For instance, the joint cumulative probability distribution function $F(a_1, a_2, \ldots, a_n)$ of the n random variables $X_1, X_2, \ldots, X_n$ is defined by

$$F(a_1, a_2, \ldots, a_n) = P\{X_1 \le a_1, X_2 \le a_2, \ldots, X_n \le a_n\}$$

Further, the n random variables are said to be *jointly continuous* if there exists a function $f(x_1, x_2, \ldots, x_n)$, called the *joint probability density function*, such that, for any set C in n-space,

$$P\{(X_1, X_2, \ldots, X_n) \in C\} = \iint\limits_{(x_1, \ldots, x_n) \in C} \cdots \int f(x_1, \ldots, x_n) dx_1 dx_2 \cdots dx_n$$

In particular, for any n sets of real numbers $A_1, A_2, \ldots, A_n$,

$$
\begin{aligned}
P\{X_1 \in A_1, X_2, &\in A_2, \ldots, X_n \in A_n\} \\
&= \int_{A_n} \int_{A_{n-1}} \cdots \int_{A_1} f(x_1, \ldots, x_n) \, dx_1 dx_2 \cdots dx_n
\end{aligned}
$$

Example
1f

The multinomial distribution

One of the most important joint distributions is the multinomial distribution, which arises when a sequence of n independent and identical experiments is performed. Suppose that each experiment can result in any one of r possible outcomes, with respective probabilities $p_1, p_2, \ldots, p_r, \sum_{i=1}^{r} p_i = 1$. If we let X_i denote the number of the n experiments that result in outcome number i, then

$$P\{X_1 = n_1, X_2 = n_2, \ldots, X_r = n_r\} = \frac{n!}{n_1! n_2! \cdots n_r!} p_1^{n_1} p_2^{n_2} \cdots p_r^{n_r} \qquad (1.5)$$

whenever $\sum_{i=1}^{r} n_i = n$.

Equation (1.5) is verified by noting that any sequence of outcomes for the n experiments that leads to outcome i occurring n_i times for $i = 1, 2, \ldots, r$ will, by the assumed independence of experiments, have probability $p_1^{n_1} p_2^{n_2} \cdots p_r^{n_r}$ of occurring. Because there are $n!/(n_1! n_2! \ldots n_r!)$ such sequences of outcomes (there are $n!/n_1! \ldots n_r!$ different permutations of n things of which n_1 are alike, n_2 are alike, $\ldots, n_r$ are alike), Equation (1.5) is established. The joint distribution whose joint probability mass function is specified by Equation (1.5) is called the *multinomial distribution*. Note that when $r = 2$, the multinomial reduces to the binomial distribution.

Note also that any sum of a fixed set of the X_i's will have a binomial distribution. That is, if $N \subset \{1, 2, \ldots, r\}$, then $\sum_{i \in N} X_i$ will be a binomial random variable with parameters n and $p = \sum_{i \in N} p_i$. This follows because $\sum_{i \in N} X_i$ represents the number of the n experiments whose outcome is in N, and each experiment will independently have such an outcome with probability $\sum_{i \in N} p_i$.

As an application of the multinomial distribution, suppose that a fair die is rolled 9 times. The probability that 1 appears three times, 2 and 3 twice each, 4 and 5 once each, and 6 not at all is

$$\frac{9!}{3! 2! 2! 1! 1! 0!} \left(\frac{1}{6}\right)^3 \left(\frac{1}{6}\right)^2 \left(\frac{1}{6}\right)^2 \left(\frac{1}{6}\right)^1 \left(\frac{1}{6}\right)^1 \left(\frac{1}{6}\right)^0 = \frac{9!}{3! 2! 2!} \left(\frac{1}{6}\right)^9 \qquad \blacksquare$$

6.2 Independent Random Variables

The random variables X and Y are said to be *independent* if, for any two sets of real numbers A and B,

$$P\{X \in A, Y \in B\} = P\{X \in A\} P\{Y \in B\} \qquad (2.1)$$

In other words, X and Y are independent if, for all A and B, the events $E_A = \{X \in A\}$ and $F_B = \{Y \in B\}$ are independent.

It can be shown by using the three axioms of probability that Equation (2.1) will follow if and only if, for all a, b,

$$P\{X \le a, Y \le b\} = P\{X \le a\} P\{Y \le b\}$$

Hence, in terms of the joint distribution function F of X and Y, X and Y are independent if

$$F(a, b) = F_X(a) F_Y(b) \quad \text{for all } a, b$$

When X and Y are discrete random variables, the condition of independence (2.1) is equivalent to

$$p(x, y) = p_X(x)p_Y(y) \quad \text{for all } x, y \tag{2.2}$$

The equivalence follows because, if Equation (2.1) is satisfied, then we obtain Equation (2.2) by letting A and B be, respectively, the one-point sets $A = \{x\}$ and $B = \{y\}$. Furthermore, if Equation (2.2) is valid, then for any sets A, B,

$$\begin{aligned}
P\{X \in A, Y \in B\} &= \sum_{y \in B} \sum_{x \in A} p(x, y) \\
&= \sum_{y \in B} \sum_{x \in A} p_X(x) p_Y(y) \\
&= \sum_{y \in B} p_Y(y) \sum_{x \in A} p_X(x) \\
&= P\{Y \in B\}P\{X \in A\}
\end{aligned}$$

and Equation (2.1) is established.

In the jointly continuous case, the condition of independence is equivalent to

$$f(x, y) = f_X(x)f_Y(y) \quad \text{for all } x, y$$

Thus, loosely speaking, X and Y are independent if knowing the value of one does not change the distribution of the other. Random variables that are not independent are said to be *dependent*.

Example 2a

Suppose that $n + m$ independent trials having a common probability of success p are performed. If X is the number of successes in the first n trials, and Y is the number of successes in the final m trials, then X and Y are independent, since knowing the number of successes in the first n trials does not affect the distribution of the number of successes in the final m trials (by the assumption of independent trials). In fact, for integral x and y,

$$P\{X = x, Y = y\} = \binom{n}{x} p^x (1 - p)^{n-x} \binom{m}{y} p^y (1 - p)^{m-y} \quad \begin{array}{l} 0 \le x \le n, \\ 0 \le y \le m \end{array}$$

$$= P\{X = x\}P\{Y = y\}$$

In contrast, X and Z will be dependent, where Z is the total number of successes in the $n + m$ trials. (Why?) ∎

Example 2b

Suppose that the number of people who enter a post office on a given day is a Poisson random variable with parameter λ. Show that if each person who enters the post office is a male with probability p and a female with probability $1 - p$, then the number of males and females entering the post office are independent Poisson random variables with respective parameters λp and $\lambda(1 - p)$.

Solution Let X and Y denote, respectively, the number of males and females that enter the post office. We shall show the independence of X and Y by establishing Equation (2.2). To obtain an expression for $P\{X = i, Y = j\}$, we condition on $X + Y$ as follows:

$$\begin{aligned}
P\{X = i, Y = j\} &= P\{X = i, Y = j | X + Y = i + j\}P\{X + Y = i + j\} \\
&\quad + P\{X = i, Y = j | X + Y \ne i + j\}P\{X + Y \ne i + j\}
\end{aligned}$$

[Note that this equation is merely a special case of the formula $P(E) = P(E|F)P(F) + P(E|F^c)P(F^c)$.]

Since $P\{X = i, Y = j | X + Y \neq i + j\}$ is clearly 0, we obtain

$$P\{X = i, Y = j\} = P\{X = i, Y = j | X + Y = i + j\}P\{X + Y = i + j\} \quad (2.3)$$

Now, because $X + Y$ is the total number of people who enter the post office, it follows, by assumption, that

$$P\{X + Y = i + j\} = e^{-\lambda}\frac{\lambda^{i+j}}{(i + j)!} \quad (2.4)$$

Furthermore, given that $i + j$ people do enter the post office, since each person entering will be male with probability p, it follows that the probability that exactly i of them will be male (and thus j of them female) is just the binomial probability $\binom{i + j}{i} p^i(1 - p)^j$. That is,

$$P\{X = i, Y = j | X + Y = i + j\} = \binom{i + j}{i} p^i(1 - p)^j \quad (2.5)$$

Substituting Equations (2.4) and (2.5) into Equation (2.3) yields

$$P\{X = i, Y = j\} = \binom{i + j}{i} p^i(1 - p)^j e^{-\lambda}\frac{\lambda^{i+j}}{(i + j)!}$$

$$= e^{-\lambda}\frac{(\lambda p)^i}{i!j!}[\lambda(1 - p)]^j$$

$$= \frac{e^{-\lambda p}(\lambda p)^i}{i!}e^{-\lambda(1-p)}\frac{[\lambda(1 - p)]^j}{j!} \quad (2.6)$$

Hence,

$$P\{X = i\} = e^{-\lambda p}\frac{(\lambda p)^i}{i!}\sum_j e^{-\lambda(1-p)}\frac{[\lambda(1 - p)]^j}{j!} = e^{-\lambda p}\frac{(\lambda p)^i}{i!} \quad (2.7)$$

and similarly,

$$P\{Y = j\} = e^{-\lambda(1-p)}\frac{[\lambda(1 - p)]^j}{j!} \quad (2.8)$$

Equations (2.6), (2.7), and (2.8) establish the desired result. ∎

Example 2c

A man and a woman decide to meet at a certain location. If each of them independently arrives at a time uniformly distributed between 12 noon and 1 P.M., find the probability that the first to arrive has to wait longer than 10 minutes.

Solution If we let X and Y denote, respectively, the time past 12 that the man and the woman arrive, then X and Y are independent random variables, each of which is uniformly distributed over $(0, 60)$. The desired probability, $P\{X + 10 < Y\} + P\{Y + 10 < X\}$, which, by symmetry, equals $2P\{X + 10 < Y\}$, is obtained as follows:

$$
\begin{aligned}
2P\{X + 10 < Y\} &= 2 \iint\limits_{x+10<y} f(x,y)\, dx\, dy \\
&= 2 \iint\limits_{x+10<y} f_X(x) f_Y(y)\, dx\, dy \\
&= 2 \int_{10}^{60} \int_{0}^{y-10} \left(\frac{1}{60}\right)^2 dx\, dy \\
&= \frac{2}{(60)^2} \int_{10}^{60} (y - 10)\, dy \\
&= \frac{25}{36}
\end{aligned}
$$

∎

Our next example presents the oldest problem dealing with geometrical probabilities. It was first considered and solved by Buffon, a French naturalist of the eighteenth century, and is usually referred to as *Buffon's needle problem*.

Example 2d

Buffon's needle problem

A table is ruled with equidistant parallel lines a distance D apart. A needle of length L, where $L \le D$, is randomly thrown on the table. What is the probability that the needle will intersect one of the lines (the other possibility being that the needle will be completely contained in the strip between two lines)?

Solution Let us determine the position of the needle by specifying (1) the distance X from the middle point of the needle to the nearest parallel line and (2) the angle θ between the needle and the projected line of length X. (See Figure 6.2.) The needle will intersect a line if the hypotenuse of the right triangle in Figure 6.2 is less than $L/2$ — that is, if

$$
\frac{X}{\cos\theta} < \frac{L}{2} \quad \text{or} \quad X < \frac{L}{2}\cos\theta
$$

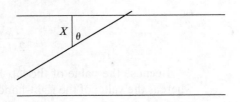

Figure 6.2

As X varies between 0 and $D/2$ and θ between 0 and $\pi/2$, it is reasonable to assume that they are independent, uniformly distributed random variables over these respective ranges. Hence,

$$P\left\{X < \frac{L}{2}\cos\theta\right\} = \iint\limits_{x<L/2\cos y} f_X(x)f_\theta(y)\,dx\,dy$$

$$= \frac{4}{\pi D}\int_0^{\pi/2}\int_0^{L/2\cos y} dx\,dy$$

$$= \frac{4}{\pi D}\int_0^{\pi/2}\frac{L}{2}\cos y\,dy$$

$$= \frac{2L}{\pi D} \qquad \blacksquare$$

*Example 2e

Characterization of the normal distribution

Let X and Y denote the horizontal and vertical miss distances when a bullet is fired at a target, and assume that

1. X and Y are independent continuous random variables having differentiable density functions.
2. The joint density $f(x,y) = f_X(x)f_Y(y)$ of X and Y depends on (x, y) only through $x^2 + y^2$.

Loosely put, assumption 2 states that the probability of the bullet landing on any point of the x–y plane depends only on the distance of the point from the target and not on its angle of orientation. An equivalent way of phrasing this assumption is to say that the joint density function is rotation invariant.

It is a rather interesting fact that assumptions 1 and 2 imply that X and Y are normally distributed random variables. To prove this, note first that the assumptions yield the relation

$$f(x,y) = f_X(x)f_Y(y) = g(x^2 + y^2) \tag{2.9}$$

for some function g. Differentiating Equation (2.9) with respect to x yields

$$f_X'(x)f_Y(y) = 2xg'(x^2 + y^2) \tag{2.10}$$

Dividing Equation (2.10) by Equation (2.9) gives

$$\frac{f_X'(x)}{f_X(x)} = \frac{2xg'(x^2 + y^2)}{g(x^2 + y^2)}$$

or

$$\frac{f_X'(x)}{2xf_X(x)} = \frac{g'(x^2 + y^2)}{g(x^2 + y^2)} \tag{2.11}$$

Because the value of the left-hand side of Equation (2.11) depends only on x, whereas the value of the right-hand side depends on $x^2 + y^2$, it follows that the left-hand side must be the same for all x. To see this, consider any x_1, x_2 and let y_1, y_2 be such that $x_1^2 + y_1^2 = x_2^2 + y_2^2$. Then, from Equation (2.11), we obtain

$$\frac{f_X'(x_1)}{2x_1f_X(x_1)} = \frac{g'(x_1^2 + y_1^2)}{g(x_1^2 + y_1^2)} = \frac{g'(x_2^2 + y_2^2)}{g(x_2^2 + y_2^2)} = \frac{f_X'(x_2)}{2x_2f_X(x_2)}$$

Hence,

$$\frac{f_X'(x)}{xf_X(x)} = c \quad \text{or} \quad \frac{d}{dx}(\log f_X(x)) = cx$$

which implies, upon integration of both sides, that

$$\log f_X(x) = a + \frac{cx^2}{2} \quad \text{or} \quad f_X(x) = ke^{cx^2/2}$$

Since $\int_{-\infty}^{\infty} f_X(x)\,dx = 1$, it follows that c is necessarily negative, and we may write $c = -1/\sigma^2$. Thus,

$$f_X(x) = ke^{-x^2/2\sigma^2}$$

That is, X is a normal random variable with parameters $\mu = 0$ and σ^2. A similar argument can be applied to $f_Y(y)$ to show that

$$f_Y(y) = \frac{1}{\sqrt{2\pi}\,\overline{\sigma}}e^{-y^2/2\overline{\sigma}^2}$$

Furthermore, it follows from assumption 2 that $\sigma^2 = \overline{\sigma}^2$ and that X and Y are thus independent, identically distributed normal random variables with parameters $\mu = 0$ and σ^2. ∎

A necessary and sufficient condition for the random variables X and Y to be independent is for their joint probability density function (or joint probability mass function in the discrete case) $f(x, y)$ to factor into two terms, one depending only on x and the other depending only on y.

Proposition 2.1 The continuous (discrete) random variables X and Y are independent if and only if their joint probability density (mass) function can be expressed as

$$f_{X,Y}(x, y) = h(x)g(y) \qquad -\infty < x < \infty, -\infty < y < \infty$$

Proof Let us give the proof in the continuous case. First, note that independence implies that the joint density is the product of the marginal densities of X and Y, so the preceding factorization will hold when the random variables are independent. Now, suppose that

$$f_{X,Y}(x, y) = h(x)g(y)$$

Then

$$1 = \int_{-\infty}^{\infty}\int_{-\infty}^{\infty} f_{X,Y}(x, y)\,dx\,dy$$
$$= \int_{-\infty}^{\infty} h(x)\,dx \int_{-\infty}^{\infty} g(y)\,dy$$
$$= C_1 C_2$$

where $C_1 = \int_{-\infty}^{\infty} h(x)\,dx$ and $C_2 = \int_{-\infty}^{\infty} g(y)\,dy$. Also,

$$f_X(x) = \int_{-\infty}^{\infty} f_{X,Y}(x, y)\,dy = C_2 h(x)$$
$$f_Y(y) = \int_{-\infty}^{\infty} f_{X,Y}(x, y)\,dx = C_1 g(y)$$

Since $C_1 C_2 = 1$, it follows that

$$f_{X,Y}(x, y) = f_X(x)f_Y(y)$$

and the proof is complete. □

Example 2f

If the joint density function of X and Y is

$$f(x, y) = 6e^{-2x}e^{-3y} \qquad 0 < x < \infty, \ 0 < y < \infty$$

and is equal to 0 outside this region, are the random variables independent? What if the joint density function is

$$f(x, y) = 24xy \qquad 0 < x < 1, 0 < y < 1, \ 0 < x + y < 1$$

and is equal to 0 otherwise?

Solution In the first instance, the joint density function factors, and thus the random variables, are independent (with one being exponential with rate 2 and the other exponential with rate 3). In the second instance, because the region in which the joint density is nonzero cannot be expressed in the form $x \in A, y \in B$, the joint density does not factor, so the random variables are not independent. This can be seen clearly by letting

$$I(x, y) = \begin{cases} 1 & \text{if } 0 < x < 1, \ 0 < y < 1, \ 0 < x + y < 1 \\ 0 & \text{otherwise} \end{cases}$$

and writing

$$f(x, y) = 24xy \, I(x, y)$$

which clearly does not factor into a part depending only on x and another depending only on y. ∎

The concept of independence may, of course, be defined for more than two random variables. In general, the n random variables $X_1, X_2, \ldots, X_n$ are said to be independent if, for all sets of real numbers $A_1, A_2, \ldots, A_n$,

$$P\{X_1 \in A_1, X_2 \in A_2, \ldots, X_n \in A_n\} = \prod_{i=1}^{n} P\{X_i \in A_i\}$$

As before, it can be shown that this condition is equivalent to

$$P\{X_1 \leq a_1, X_2 \leq a_2, \ldots, X_n \leq a_n\}$$

$$= \prod_{i=1}^{n} P\{X_i \leq a_i\} \quad \text{for all } a_1, a_2, \ldots, a_n$$

Finally, we say that an infinite collection of random variables is independent if every finite subcollection of them is independent.

Example 2g

How can a computer choose a random subset?

Most computers are able to generate the value of, or *simulate*, a uniform $(0, 1)$ random variable by means of a built-in subroutine that (to a high degree of approximation) produces such "random numbers." As a result, it is quite easy for a computer to simulate an indicator (that is, a Bernoulli) random variable. Suppose I is an indicator variable such that

$$P\{I = 1\} = p = 1 - P\{I = 0\}$$

The computer can simulate I by choosing a uniform $(0, 1)$ random number U and then letting

$$I = \begin{array}{l} 1 \text{ if } U < p \\ 0 \text{ if } U \geq p \end{array}$$

Suppose that we are interested in having the computer select $k, k \le n$, of the numbers $1, 2, \ldots, n$ in such a way that each of the $\binom{n}{k}$ subsets of size k is equally likely to be chosen. We now present a method that will enable the computer to solve this task. To generate such a subset, we will first simulate, in sequence, n indicator variables $I_1, I_2, \ldots, I_n$, of which exactly k will equal 1. Those i for which $I_i = 1$ will then constitute the desired subset.

To generate the random variables $I_1, \ldots, I_n$, start by simulating n independent uniform $(0, 1)$ random variables $U_1, U_2, \ldots, U_n$. Now define

$$I_1 = \begin{cases} 1 & \text{if } U_1 < \dfrac{k}{n} \\ 0 & \text{otherwise} \end{cases}$$

and then, once $I_1, \ldots, I_i$ are determined, recursively set

$$I_{i+1} = \begin{cases} 1 & \text{if } U_{i+1} < \dfrac{k - (I_1 + \cdots + I_i)}{n - i} \\ 0 & \text{otherwise} \end{cases}$$

In words, at the $(i + 1)$th stage, we set I_{i+1} equal to 1 (and thus put $i + 1$ into the desired subset) with a probability equal to the remaining number of places in the subset $\left(\text{namely, } k - \sum_{j=1}^{i} I_j \right)$, divided by the remaining number of possibilities (namely, $n - i$). Hence, the joint distribution of $I_1, I_2, \ldots, I_n$ is determined from

$$P\{I_1 = 1\} = \frac{k}{n}$$

$$P\{I_{i+1} = 1 | I_1, \ldots, I_i\} = \frac{k - \sum_{j=1}^{i} I_j}{n - i} \quad 1 < i < n$$

The proof that the preceding formula results in all subsets of size k being equally likely to be chosen is by induction on $k + n$. It is immediate when $k + n = 2$ (that is, when $k = 1, n = 1$), so assume it to be true whenever $k + n \le l$. Now, suppose that $k + n = l + 1$, and consider any subset of size k—say, $i_1 \le i_2 \le \cdots \le i_k$—and consider the following two cases.

Case 1: $i_1 = 1$

$$P\{I_1 = I_{i_2} = \cdots = I_{i_k} = 1, I_j = 0 \text{ otherwise}\}$$
$$= P\{I_1 = 1\}P\{I_{i_2} = \cdots = I_{i_k} = 1, I_j = 0 \text{ otherwise} | I_1 = 1\}$$

Now given that $I_1 = 1$, the remaining elements of the subset are chosen as if a subset of size $k - 1$ were to be chosen from the $n - 1$ elements $2, 3, \ldots, n$. Hence, by the induction hypothesis, the conditional probability that this will result in a given subset of size $k - 1$ being selected is $1/\binom{n-1}{k-1}$. Hence,

$$P\{I_1 = I_{i_2} = \cdots = I_{i_k} = 1, I_j = 0 \text{ otherwise}\}$$
$$= \frac{k}{n} \frac{1}{\binom{n-1}{k-1}} = \frac{1}{\binom{n}{k}}$$

Case 2: $i_1 \neq 1$

$$P\{I_{i_1} = I_{i_2} = \cdots = I_{i_k} = 1, I_j = 0 \text{ otherwise}\}$$

$$= P\{I_{i_1} = \cdots = I_{i_k} = 1, I_j = 0 \text{ otherwise}|I_1 = 0\}P\{I_1 = 0\}$$

$$= \frac{1}{\binom{n-1}{k}}\left(1 - \frac{k}{n}\right) = \frac{1}{\binom{n}{k}}$$

where the induction hypothesis was used to evaluate the preceding conditional probability.

Thus, in all cases, the probability that a given subset of size k will be the subset chosen is $1/\binom{n}{k}$. ∎

Remark The foregoing method for generating a random subset has a very low memory requirement. A faster algorithm that requires somewhat more memory is presented in Section 10.1. (The latter algorithm uses the last k elements of a random permutation of $1, 2, \ldots, n$.) ∎

Example 2h

Let X, Y, Z be independent and uniformly distributed over $(0, 1)$. Compute $P\{X \geq YZ\}$.

Solution Since

$$f_{X,Y,Z}(x,y,z) = f_X(x)f_Y(y)f_Z(z) = 1 \quad 0 \leq x \leq 1, 0 \leq y \leq 1, 0 \leq z \leq 1$$

we have

$$P\{X \geq YZ\} = \iiint_{x \geq yz} f_{X,Y,Z}(x,y,z)\, dx\, dy\, dz$$

$$= \int_0^1 \int_0^1 \int_{yz}^1 dx\, dy\, dz$$

$$= \int_0^1 \int_0^1 (1 - yz)\, dy\, dz$$

$$= \int_0^1 \left(1 - \frac{z}{2}\right) dz$$

$$= \frac{3}{4} \qquad ∎$$

Example 2i

Probabilistic interpretation of half-life

Let $N(t)$ denote the number of nuclei contained in a radioactive mass of material at time t. The concept of half-life is often defined in a deterministic fashion by stating this it is an empirical fact that, for some value h, called the *half-life*,

$$N(t) = 2^{-t/h}N(0) \quad t > 0$$

[Note that $N(h) = N(0)/2$.] Since the preceding implies that, for any nonnegative s and t,

$$N(t + s) = 2^{-(s+t)/h}N(0) = 2^{-t/h}N(s)$$

it follows that no matter how much time s has already elapsed, in an additional time t, the number of existing nuclei will decrease by the factor $2^{-t/h}$.

Because the deterministic relationship just given results from observations of radioactive masses containing huge numbers of nuclei, it would seem that it might be consistent with a probabilistic interpretation. The clue to deriving the appropriate probability model for half-life resides in the empirical observation that the proportion of decay in any time interval depends neither on the total number of nuclei at the beginning of the interval nor on the location of this interval [since $N(t + s)/N(s)$ depends neither on $N(s)$ nor on s]. Thus, it appears that the individual nuclei act independently and with a memoryless life distribution. Consequently, since the unique life distribution that is memoryless is the exponential distribution, and since exactly one-half of a given amount of mass decays every h time units, we propose the following probabilistic model for radioactive decay.

Probabilistic interpretation of the half-life h: The lifetimes of the individual nuclei are independent random variables having a life distribution that is exponential with median equal to h. That is, if L represents the lifetime of a given nucleus, then

$$P\{L < t\} = 1 - 2^{-t/h}$$

(Because $P\{L < h\} = \frac{1}{2}$ and the preceding can be written as

$$P\{L < t\} = 1 - \exp\left\{-t\frac{\log 2}{h}\right\}$$

it can be seen that L indeed has an exponential distribution with median h.)

Note that under the probabilistic interpretation of half-life just given, if one starts with $N(0)$ nuclei at time 0, then $N(t)$, the number of nuclei that remain at time t will have a binomial distribution with parameters $n = N(0)$ and $p = 2^{-t/h}$. Results of Chapter 8 will show that this interpretation of half-life is consistent with the deterministic model when considering the proportion of a large number of nuclei that decay over a given time frame. However, the difference between the deterministic and probabilistic interpretation becomes apparent when one considers the actual number of decayed nuclei. We will now indicate this with regard to the question of whether protons decay.

There is some controversy over whether or not protons decay. Indeed, one theory predicts that protons should decay with a half-life of about $h = 10^{30}$ years. To check this prediction empirically, it has been suggested that one follow a large number of protons for, say, one or two years and determine whether any of them decay within that period. (Clearly, it would not be feasible to follow a mass of protons for 10^{30} years to see whether one-half of it decays.) Let us suppose that we are able to keep track of $N(0) = 10^{30}$ protons for c years. The number of decays predicted by the deterministic model would then be given by

$$
\begin{aligned}
N(0) - N(c) &= h(1 - 2^{-c/h}) \\
&= \frac{1 - 2^{-c/h}}{1/h} \\
&\approx \lim_{x \to 0} \frac{1 - 2^{-cx}}{x} \quad \text{since } \frac{1}{h} = 10^{-30} \approx 0 \\
&= \lim_{x \to 0} (c2^{-cx} \log 2) \quad \text{by L'Hôpital's rule} \\
&= c \log 2 \approx .6931c
\end{aligned}
$$

For instance, the deterministic model predicts that in 2 years there should be 1.3863 decays, and it would thus appear to be a serious blow to the hypothesis that protons decay with a half-life of 10^{30} years if no decays are observed over those 2 years.

Let us now contrast the conclusions just drawn with those obtained from the probabilistic model. Again, let us consider the hypothesis that the half-life of protons is $h = 10^{30}$ years, and suppose that we follow h protons for c years. Since there is a huge number of independent protons, each of which will have a very small probability of decaying within this time period, it follows that the number of protons that decay will have (to a very strong approximation) a Poisson distribution with parameter equal to $h(1 - 2^{-c/h}) \approx c \log 2$. Thus,

$$P\{0 \text{ decays}\} = e^{-c \log 2}$$

$$= e^{-\log(2^c)} = \frac{1}{2^c}$$

and, in general,

$$P\{n \text{ decays}\} = \frac{2^{-c}[c \log 2]^n}{n!} \qquad n \geq 0$$

Thus, we see that even though the average number of decays over 2 years is (as predicted by the deterministic model) 1.3863, there is 1 chance in 4 that there will not be any decays, thereby indicating that such a result in no way invalidates the original hypothesis of proton decay. ■

Remark　*Independence is a symmetric relation.* The random variables X and Y are independent if their joint density function (or mass function in the discrete case) is the product of their individual density (or mass) functions. Therefore, to say that X is independent of Y is equivalent to saying that Y is independent of X—or just that X and Y are independent. As a result, in considering whether X is independent of Y in situations where it is not at all intuitive that knowing the value of Y will not change the probabilities concerning X, it can be beneficial to interchange the roles of X and Y and ask instead whether Y is independent of X. The next example illustrates this point. ■

Example 2j

If the initial throw of the dice in the game of craps results in the sum of the dice equaling 4, then the player will continue to throw the dice until the sum is either 4 or 7. If this sum is 4, then the player wins, and if it is 7, then the player loses. Let N denote the number of throws needed until either 4 or 7 appears, and let X denote the value (either 4 or 7) of the final throw. Is N independent of X? That is, does knowing which of 4 or 7 occurs first affect the distribution of the number of throws needed until that number appears? Most people do not find the answer to this question to be intuitively obvious. However, suppose that we turn it around and ask whether X is independent of N. That is, does knowing how many throws it takes to obtain a sum of either 4 or 7 affect the probability that that sum is equal to 4? For instance, suppose we know that it takes n throws of the dice to obtain a sum of either 4 or 7. Does this affect the probability distribution of the final sum? Clearly not, since all that is important is that its value is either 4 or 7, and the fact that none of the first $n - 1$ throws were either 4 or 7 does not change the probabilities for the nth throw. Thus, we can conclude that X is independent of N, or equivalently, that N is independent of X.

As another example, let $X_1, X_2, \ldots$ be a sequence of independent and identically distributed continuous random variables, and suppose that we observe these random variables in sequence. If $X_n > X_i$ for each $i = 1, \ldots, n - 1$, then we say that X_n is a *record value*. That is, each random variable that is larger than all those preceding it is called a record value. Let A_n denote the event that X_n is a record value. Is A_{n+1} independent of A_n? That is, does knowing that the nth random variable is the largest of the first n change the probability that the $(n + 1)$ random variable is the largest of the first $n + 1$? While it is true that A_{n+1} is independent of A_n, this may not be intuitively obvious. However, if we turn the question around and ask whether A_n is independent of A_{n+1}, then the result is more easily understood. For knowing that the $(n + 1)$ value is larger than $X_1, \ldots, X_n$ clearly gives us no information about the relative size of X_n among the first n random variables. Indeed, by symmetry, it is clear that each of these n random variables is equally likely to be the largest of this set, so $P(A_n | A_{n+1}) = P(A_n) = 1/n$. Hence, we can conclude that A_n and A_{n+1} are independent events. ∎

Remark It follows from the identity

$$P\{X_1 \le a_1, \ldots, X_n \le a_n\}$$
$$= P\{X_1 \le a_1\}P\{X_2 \le a_2 | X_1 \le a_1\} \cdots P\{X_n \le a_n | X_1 \le a_1, \ldots, X_{n-1} \le a_{n-1}\}$$

that the independence of $X_1, \ldots, X_n$ can be established sequentially. That is, we can show that these random variables are independent by showing that

$$X_2 \text{ is independent of } X_1$$
$$X_3 \text{ is independent of } X_1, X_2$$
$$X_4 \text{ is independent of } X_1, X_2, X_3$$
$$\vdots$$
$$X_n \text{ is independent of } X_1, \ldots, X_{n-1}$$

6.3   Sums of Independent Random Variables

It is often important to be able to calculate the distribution of $X + Y$ from the distributions of X and Y when X and Y are independent. Suppose that X and Y are independent, continuous random variables having probability density functions f_X and f_Y. The cumulative distribution function of $X + Y$ is obtained as follows:

$$F_{X+Y}(a) = P\{X + Y \le a\}$$
$$= \iint\limits_{x+y \le a} f_X(x)f_Y(y) \, dx \, dy$$
$$= \int_{-\infty}^{\infty} \int_{-\infty}^{a-y} f_X(x)f_Y(y) \, dx \, dy$$
$$= \int_{-\infty}^{\infty} \int_{-\infty}^{a-y} f_X(x) \, dx f_Y(y) \, dy$$
$$= \int_{-\infty}^{\infty} F_X(a - y)f_Y(y) \, dy \tag{3.1}$$

The cumulative distribution function F_{X+Y} is called the *convolution* of the distributions F_X and F_Y (the cumulative distribution functions of X and Y, respectively).

By differentiating Equation (3.1), we find that the probability density function f_{X+Y} of $X + Y$ is given by

$$f_{X+Y}(a) = \frac{d}{da} \int_{-\infty}^{\infty} F_X(a - y) f_Y(y) \, dy$$

$$= \int_{-\infty}^{\infty} \frac{d}{da} F_X(a - y) f_Y(y) \, dy$$

$$= \int_{-\infty}^{\infty} f_X(a - y) f_Y(y) \, dy \tag{3.2}$$

6.3.1 Identically Distributed Uniform Random Variables

It is not difficult to determine the density function of the sum of two independent uniform $(0, 1)$ random variables.

Example 3a

Sum of two independent uniform random variables

If X and Y are independent random variables, both uniformly distributed on $(0, 1)$, calculate the probability density of $X + Y$.

Solution From Equation (3.2), since

$$f_X(a) = f_Y(a) = \begin{cases} 1 & 0 < a < 1 \\ 0 & \text{otherwise} \end{cases}$$

we obtain

$$f_{X+Y}(a) = \int_0^1 f_X(a - y) \, dy$$

For $0 \le a \le 1$, this yields

$$f_{X+Y}(a) = \int_0^a dy = a$$

For $1 < a < 2$, we get

$$f_{X+Y}(a) = \int_{a-1}^1 dy = 2 - a$$

Hence,

$$f_{X+Y}(a) = \begin{cases} a & 0 \le a \le 1 \\ 2 - a & 1 < a < 2 \\ 0 & \text{otherwise} \end{cases}$$

Because of the shape of its density function (see Figure 6.3), the random variable $X + Y$ is said to have a *triangular* distribution. ∎

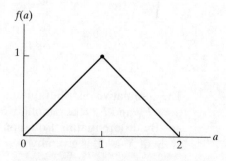

Figure 6.3 Triangular density function.

Now, suppose that $X_1, X_2, \ldots, X_n$ are independent uniform $(0,1)$ random variables, and let

$$F_n(x) = P\{X_1 + \ldots + X_n \le x\}$$

Whereas a general formula for $F_n(x)$ is messy, it has a particularly nice form when $x \le 1$. Indeed, we now use mathematical induction to prove that

$$F_n(x) = x^n/n!, \quad 0 \le x \le 1$$

Because the proceeding equation is true for $n = 1$, assume that

$$F_{n-1}(x) = x^{n-1}/(n-1)!, \quad 0 \le x \le 1$$

Now, writing

$$\sum_{i=1}^{n} X_i = \sum_{i=1}^{n-1} X_i + X_n$$

and using the fact that the X_i are all nonnegative, we see from Equation 3.1 that, for $0 \le x \le 1$,

$$
\begin{aligned}
F_n(x) &= \int_0^1 F_{n-1}(x - y) f_{X_n}(y) dy \\
&= \frac{1}{(n-1)!} \int_0^x (x - y)^{n-1} dy \quad \text{by the induction hypothesis} \\
&= x^n/n!
\end{aligned}
$$

which completes the proof.

For an interesting application of the preceding formula, let us use it to determine the expected number of independent uniform $(0,1)$ random variables that need to be summed to exceed 1. That is, with $X_1, X_2, \ldots$ being independent uniform $(0,1)$ random variables, we want to determine $E[N]$, where

$$N = \min\{n : X_1 + \ldots + X_n > 1\}$$

Noting that N is greater than $n > 0$ if and only if $X_1 + \ldots + X_n \le 1$, we see that

$$P\{N > n\} = F_n(1) = 1/n!, \quad n > 0$$

Because

$$P\{N > 0\} = 1 = 1/0!$$

we see that, for $n > 0$,

$$P\{N = n\} = P\{N > n - 1\} - P\{N > n\} = \frac{1}{(n-1)!} - \frac{1}{n!} = \frac{n-1}{n!}$$

Therefore,

$$
\begin{aligned}
E[N] &= \sum_{n=1}^{\infty} \frac{n(n-1)}{n!} \\
&= \sum_{n=2}^{\infty} \frac{1}{(n-2)!} \\
&= e
\end{aligned}
$$

That is, the mean number of independent uniform $(0,1)$ random variables that must be summed for the sum to exceed 1 is equal to e.

6.3.2 Gamma Random Variables

Recall that a gamma random variable has a density of the form

$$f(y) = \frac{\lambda e^{-\lambda y}(\lambda y)^{t-1}}{\Gamma(t)} \quad 0 < y < \infty$$

An important property of this family of distributions is that for a fixed value of λ, it is closed under convolutions.

Proposition 3.1

If X and Y are independent gamma random variables with respective parameters (s, λ) and (t, λ), then $X + Y$ is a gamma random variable with parameters $(s + t, \lambda)$.

Proof Using Equation (3.2), we obtain

$$f_{X+Y}(a) = \frac{1}{\Gamma(s)\Gamma(t)} \int_0^a \lambda e^{-\lambda(a-y)}[\lambda(a - y)]^{s-1} \lambda e^{-\lambda y}(\lambda y)^{t-1} \, dy$$

$$= Ke^{-\lambda a} \int_0^a (a - y)^{s-1} y^{t-1} dy$$

$$= Ke^{-\lambda a} a^{s+t-1} \int_0^1 (1 - x)^{s-1} x^{t-1} \, dx \quad \text{by letting } x = \frac{y}{a}$$

$$= Ce^{-\lambda a} a^{s+t-1}$$

where C is a constant that does not depend on a. But, as the preceding is a density function and thus must integrate to 1, the value of C is determined, and we have

$$f_{X+Y}(a) = \frac{\lambda e^{-\lambda a}(\lambda a)^{s+t-1}}{\Gamma(s + t)}$$

Hence, the result is proved. ☐

It is now a simple matter to establish, by using Proposition 3.1 and induction, that if $X_i, i = 1, \ldots, n$ are independent gamma random variables with respective parameters $(t_i, \lambda), i = 1, \ldots, n$, then $\sum_{i=1}^n X_i$ is gamma with parameters $\left(\sum_{i=1}^n t_i, \lambda \right)$. We leave the proof of this statement as an exercise.

Example 3b

Let $X_1, X_2, \ldots, X_n$ be n independent exponential random variables, each having parameter λ. Then, since an exponential random variable with parameter λ is the same as a gamma random variable with parameters $(1, \lambda)$, it follows from Proposition 3.1 that $X_1 + X_2 + \cdots + X_n$ is a gamma random variable with parameters (n, λ). ∎

If $Z_1, Z_2, \ldots, Z_n$ are independent standard normal random variables, then $Y \equiv \sum_{i=1}^n Z_i^2$ is said to have the *chi-squared* (sometimes seen as χ^2) distribution with n degrees of freedom. Let us compute the density function of Y. When $n = 1, Y = Z_1^2$, and from Example 7b of Chapter 5, we see that its probability density function is given by

$$f_{Z^2}(y) = \frac{1}{2\sqrt{y}}[f_Z(\sqrt{y}) + f_Z(-\sqrt{y})]$$

$$= \frac{1}{2\sqrt{y}} \frac{2}{\sqrt{2\pi}} e^{-y/2}$$

$$= \frac{\frac{1}{2}e^{-y/2}(y/2)^{1/2-1}}{\sqrt{\pi}}$$

But we recognize the preceding as the gamma distribution with parameters $\left(\frac{1}{2}, \frac{1}{2}\right)$. [A by-product of this analysis is that $\Gamma\left(\frac{1}{2}\right) = \sqrt{\pi}$.] But since each Z_i^2 is gamma $\left(\frac{1}{2}, \frac{1}{2}\right)$, it follows from Proposition 3.1 that the chi-squared distribution with n degrees of freedom is just the gamma distribution with parameters $\left(n/2, \frac{1}{2}\right)$ and hence has a probability density function given by

$$f_Y(y) = \frac{\frac{1}{2}e^{-y/2}\left(\frac{y}{2}\right)^{n/2-1}}{\Gamma\left(\frac{n}{2}\right)} \qquad y > 0$$

$$= \frac{e^{-y/2}y^{n/2-1}}{2^{n/2}\Gamma\left(\frac{n}{2}\right)} \qquad y > 0$$

When n is an even integer, $\Gamma(n/2) = [(n/2) - 1]!$, whereas when n is odd, $\Gamma(n/2)$ can be obtained from iterating the relationship $\Gamma(t) = (t - 1)\Gamma(t - 1)$ and then using the previously obtained result that $\Gamma\left(\frac{1}{2}\right) = \sqrt{\pi}$. [For instance, $\Gamma\left(\frac{5}{2}\right) = \frac{3}{2}\Gamma\left(\frac{3}{2}\right) = \frac{3}{2}\frac{1}{2}\Gamma\left(\frac{1}{2}\right) = \frac{3}{4}\sqrt{\pi}$.]

In practice, the chi-squared distribution often arises as the distribution of the square of the error involved when one attempts to hit a target in n-dimensional space when the coordinate errors are taken to be independent standard normal random variables. It is also important in statistical analysis.

6.3.3 Normal Random Variables

We can also use Equation (3.2) to prove the following important result about normal random variables.

Proposition 3.2 If $X_i, i = 1, \ldots, n$, are independent random variables that are normally distributed with respective parameters $\mu_i, \sigma_i^2, i = 1, \ldots, n$, then $\sum_{i=1}^{n} X_i$ is normally distributed with parameters $\sum_{i=1}^{n} \mu_i$ and $\sum_{i=1}^{n} \sigma_i^2$.

Proof of Proposition 3.2: To begin, let X and Y be independent normal random variables with X having mean 0 and variance σ^2 and Y having mean 0 and variance 1. We will determine the density function of $X + Y$ by utilizing Equation (3.2). Now, with

$$c = \frac{1}{2\sigma^2} + \frac{1}{2} = \frac{1 + \sigma^2}{2\sigma^2}$$

we have

$$f_X(a - y)f_Y(y) = \frac{1}{\sqrt{2\pi}\sigma}\exp\left\{-\frac{(a - y)^2}{2\sigma^2}\right\}\frac{1}{\sqrt{2\pi}}\exp\left\{-\frac{y^2}{2}\right\}$$

$$= \frac{1}{2\pi\sigma}\exp\left\{-\frac{a^2}{2\sigma^2}\right\}\exp\left\{-c\left(y^2 - 2y\frac{a}{1 + \sigma^2}\right)\right\}$$

Hence, from Equation (3.2),

$$f_{X+Y}(a) = \frac{1}{2\pi\sigma} \exp\left\{-\frac{a^2}{2\sigma^2}\right\} \exp\left\{\frac{a^2}{2\sigma^2(1+\sigma^2)}\right\}$$

$$\times \int_{-\infty}^{\infty} \exp\left\{-c\left(y - \frac{a}{1+\sigma^2}\right)^2\right\} dy$$

$$= \frac{1}{2\pi\sigma} \exp\left\{-\frac{a^2}{2(1+\sigma^2)}\right\} \int_{-\infty}^{\infty} \exp\{-cx^2\} dx$$

$$= C \exp\left\{-\frac{a^2}{2(1+\sigma^2)}\right\}$$

where C does not depend on a. But this implies that $X + Y$ is normal with mean 0 and variance $1 + \sigma^2$.

Now, suppose that X_1 and X_2 are independent normal random variables with X_i having mean μ_i and variance $\sigma_i^2, i = 1, 2$. Then

$$X_1 + X_2 = \sigma_2\left(\frac{X_1 - \mu_1}{\sigma_2} + \frac{X_2 - \mu_2}{\sigma_2}\right) + \mu_1 + \mu_2$$

But since $(X_1 - \mu_1)/\sigma_2$ is normal with mean 0 and variance σ_1^2/σ_2^2, and $(X_2 - \mu_2)/\sigma_2$ is normal with mean 0 and variance 1, it follows from our previous result that $(X_1 - \mu_1)/\sigma_2 + (X_2 - \mu_2)/\sigma_2$ is normal with mean 0 and variance $1 + \sigma_1^2/\sigma_2^2$, implying that $X_1 + X_2$ is normal with mean $\mu_1 + \mu_2$ and variance $\sigma_2^2(1 + \sigma_1^2/\sigma_2^2) = \sigma_1^2 + \sigma_2^2$.

Thus, Proposition 3.2 is established when $n = 2$. The general case now follows by induction. That is, assume that Proposition 3.2 is true when there are $n - 1$ random variables. Now consider the case of n, and write

$$\sum_{i=1}^{n} X_i = \sum_{i=1}^{n-1} X_i + X_n$$

By the induction hypothesis, $\sum_{i=1}^{n-1} X_i$ is normal with mean $\sum_{i=1}^{n-1} \mu_i$ and variance $\sum_{i=1}^{n-1} \sigma_i^2$. Therefore, by the result for $n = 2$, $\sum_{i=1}^{n} X_i$ is normal with mean $\sum_{i=1}^{n} \mu_i$ and variance $\sum_{i=1}^{n} \sigma_i^2$.

Example 3c

A basketball team will play a 44-game season. Twenty-six of these games are against class A teams and 18 are against class B teams. Suppose that the team will win each game against a class A team with probability .4 and will win each game against a class B team with probability .7. Suppose also that the results of the different games are independent. Approximate the probability that

(a) the team wins 25 games or more;

(b) the team wins more games against class A teams than it does against class B teams.

Solution (a) Let X_A and X_B respectively denote the number of games the team wins against class A and against class B teams. Note that X_A and X_B are independent binomial random variables and

$$E[X_A] = 26(.4) = 10.4 \quad \text{Var}(X_A) = 26(.4)(.6) = 6.24$$
$$E[X_B] = 18(.7) = 12.6 \quad \text{Var}(X_B) = 18(.7)(.3) = 3.78$$

By the normal approximation to the binomial, X_A and X_B will have approximately the same distribution as would independent normal random variables with the preceding expected values and variances. Hence, by Proposition 3.2, $X_A + X_B$ will have approximately a normal distribution with mean 23 and variance 10.02. Therefore, letting Z denote a standard normal random variable, we have

$$
\begin{aligned}
P\{X_A + X_B \geq 25\} &= P\{X_A + X_B \geq 24.5\} \\
&= P\left\{ \frac{X_A + X_B - 23}{\sqrt{10.02}} \geq \frac{24.5 - 23}{\sqrt{10.02}} \right\} \\
&\approx P\left\{ Z \geq \frac{1.5}{\sqrt{10.02}} \right\} \\
&\approx 1 - P\{Z < .4739\} \\
&\approx .3178
\end{aligned}
$$

(b) We note that $X_A - X_B$ will have approximately a normal distribution with mean -2.2 and variance 10.02. Hence,

$$
\begin{aligned}
P\{X_A - X_B \geq 1\} &= P\{X_A - X_B \geq .5\} \\
&= P\left\{ \frac{X_A - X_B + 2.2}{\sqrt{10.02}} \geq \frac{.5 + 2.2}{\sqrt{10.02}} \right\} \\
&\approx P\left\{ Z \geq \frac{2.7}{\sqrt{10.02}} \right\} \\
&\approx 1 - P\{Z < .8530\} \\
&\approx .1968
\end{aligned}
$$

Therefore, there is approximately a 31.78 percent chance that the team will win at least 25 games and approximately a 19.68 percent chance that it will win more games against class A teams than against class B teams. ∎

The random variable Y is said to be a *lognormal* random variable with parameters μ and σ if log (Y) is a normal random variable with mean μ and variance σ^2. That is, Y is lognormal if it can be expressed as

$$ Y = e^X $$

where X is a normal random variable.

Example 3d

Starting at some fixed time, let $S(n)$ denote the price of a certain security at the end of n additional weeks, $n \geq 1$. A popular model for the evolution of these prices assumes that the price ratios $S(n)/S(n - 1), n \geq 1$, are independent and identically distributed lognormal random variables. Assuming this model, with parameters $\mu = .0165, \sigma = .0730$, what is the probability that

(a) the price of the security increases over each of the next two weeks?

(b) the price at the end of two weeks is higher than it is today?

Solution Let Z be a standard normal random variable. To solve part (a), we use the fact that log(x) increases in x to conclude that $x > 1$ if and only if log$(x) > $ log$(1) = 0$.

As a result, we have

$$P\left\{\frac{S(1)}{S(0)} > 1\right\} = P\left\{\log\left(\frac{S(1)}{S(0)}\right) > 0\right\}$$

$$= P\left\{Z > \frac{-.0165}{.0730}\right\}$$

$$= P\{Z < .2260\}$$

$$= .5894$$

In other words, the probability that the price is up after one week is .5894. Since the successive price ratios are independent, the probability that the price increases over each of the next two weeks is $(.5894)^2 = .3474$.

To solve part (b), we reason as follows:

$$P\left\{\frac{S(2)}{S(0)} > 1\right\} = P\left\{\frac{S(2)}{S(1)}\frac{S(1)}{S(0)} > 1\right\}$$

$$= P\left\{\log\left(\frac{S(2)}{S(1)}\right) + \log\left(\frac{S(1)}{S(0)}\right) > 0\right\}$$

However, $\log\left(\frac{S(2)}{S(1)}\right) + \log\left(\frac{S(1)}{S(0)}\right)$, being the sum of two independent normal random variables with a common mean .0165 and a common standard deviation .0730, is a normal random variable with mean .0330 and variance $2(.0730)^2$. Consequently,

$$P\left\{\frac{S(2)}{S(0)} > 1\right\} = P\left\{Z > \frac{-.0330}{.0730\sqrt{2}}\right\}$$

$$= P\{Z < .31965\}$$

$$= .6254 \qquad \blacksquare$$

6.3.4 Poisson and Binomial Random Variables

Rather than attempt to derive a general expression for the distribution of $X + Y$ in the discrete case, we shall consider some examples.

Example 3e

Sums of independent Poisson random variables

If X and Y are independent Poisson random variables with respective parameters λ_1 and λ_2, compute the distribution of $X + Y$.

Solution Because the event $\{X + Y = n\}$ may be written as the union of the disjoint events $\{X = k, Y = n - k\}, 0 \le k \le n$, we have

$$P\{X + Y = n\} = \sum_{k=0}^{n} P\{X = k, Y = n - k\}$$

$$= \sum_{k=0}^{n} P\{X = k\}P\{Y = n - k\}$$

$$= \sum_{k=0}^{n} e^{-\lambda_1}\frac{\lambda_1^k}{k!}e^{-\lambda_2}\frac{\lambda_2^{n-k}}{(n-k)!}$$

$$= e^{-(\lambda_1 + \lambda_2)} \sum_{k=0}^{n} \frac{\lambda_1^k \lambda_2^{n-k}}{k!(n-k)!}$$

$$= \frac{e^{-(\lambda_1 + \lambda_2)}}{n!} \sum_{k=0}^{n} \frac{n!}{k!(n-k)!} \lambda_1^k \lambda_2^{n-k}$$

$$= \frac{e^{-(\lambda_1 + \lambda_2)}}{n!} (\lambda_1 + \lambda_2)^n$$

Thus, $X + Y$ has a Poisson distribution with parameter $\lambda_1 + \lambda_2$. ∎

Example 3f

Sums of independent binomial random variables

Let X and Y be independent binomial random variables with respective parameters (n, p) and (m, p). Calculate the distribution of $X + Y$.

Solution Recalling the interpretation of a binomial random variable, and without any computation at all, we can immediately conclude that $X + Y$ is binomial with parameters $(n + m, p)$. This follows because X represents the number of successes in n independent trials, each of which results in a success with probability p; similarly, Y represents the number of successes in m independent trials, each of which results in a success with probability p. Hence, given that X and Y are assumed independent, it follows that $X + Y$ represents the number of successes in $n + m$ independent trials when each trial has a probability p of resulting in a success. Therefore, $X + Y$ is a binomial random variable with parameters $(n + m, p)$. To check this conclusion analytically, note that

$$P\{X + Y = k\} = \sum_{i=0}^{n} P\{X = i, Y = k - i\}$$

$$= \sum_{i=0}^{n} P\{X = i\} P\{Y = k - i\}$$

$$= \sum_{i=0}^{n} \binom{n}{i} p^i q^{n-i} \binom{m}{k-i} p^{k-i} q^{m-k+i}$$

where $q = 1 - p$ and where $\binom{r}{j} = 0$ when $j < 0$. Thus,

$$P\{X + Y = k\} = p^k q^{n+m-k} \sum_{i=0}^{n} \binom{n}{i} \binom{m}{k-i}$$

and the conclusion follows upon application of the combinatorial identity

$$\binom{n+m}{k} = \sum_{i=0}^{n} \binom{n}{i} \binom{m}{k-i}$$

∎

6.4 Conditional Distributions: Discrete Case

Recall that for any two events E and F, the conditional probability of E given F is defined, provided that $P(F) > 0$, by

$$P(E|F) = \frac{P(EF)}{P(F)}$$

Hence, if X and Y are discrete random variables, it is natural to define the conditional probability mass function of X given that $Y = y$, by

$$p_{X|Y}(x|y) = P\{X = x|Y = y\}$$
$$= \frac{P\{X = x, Y = y\}}{P\{Y = y\}}$$
$$= \frac{p(x, y)}{p_Y(y)}$$

for all values of y such that $p_Y(y) > 0$. Similarly, the conditional probability distribution function of X given that $Y = y$ is defined, for all y such that $p_Y(y) > 0$, by

$$F_{X|Y}(x|y) = P\{X \le x|Y = y\}$$
$$= \sum_{a \le x} p_{X|Y}(a|y)$$

In other words, the definitions are exactly the same as in the unconditional case, except that everything is now conditional on the event that $Y = y$. If X is independent of Y, then the conditional mass function and the distribution function are the same as the respective unconditional ones. This follows because if X is independent of Y, then

$$p_{X|Y}(x|y) = P\{X = x|Y = y\}$$
$$= \frac{P\{X = x, Y = y\}}{P\{Y = y\}}$$
$$= \frac{P\{X = x\}P\{Y = y\}}{P\{Y = y\}}$$
$$= P\{X = x\}$$

Example 4a

Suppose that $p(x, y)$, the joint probability mass function of X and Y, is given by

$$p(0, 0) = .4 \quad p(0, 1) = .2 \quad p(1, 0) = .1 \quad p(1, 1) = .3$$

Calculate the conditional probability mass function of X given that $Y = 1$.

Solution We first note that

$$p_Y(1) = \sum_x p(x, 1) = p(0, 1) + p(1, 1) = .5$$

Hence,

$$p_{X|Y}(0|1) = \frac{p(0, 1)}{p_Y(1)} = \frac{2}{5}$$

and

$$p_{X|Y}(1|1) = \frac{p(1, 1)}{p_Y(1)} = \frac{3}{5}$$ ∎

Example 4b

If X and Y are independent Poisson random variables with respective parameters λ_1 and λ_2, calculate the conditional distribution of X given that $X + Y = n$.

Solution We calculate the conditional probability mass function of X given that $X + Y = n$ as follows:

$$
\begin{aligned}
P\{X = k | X + Y = n\} &= \frac{P\{X = k, X + Y = n\}}{P\{X + Y = n\}} \\
&= \frac{P\{X = k, Y = n - k\}}{P\{X + Y = n\}} \\
&= \frac{P\{X = k\}P\{Y = n - k\}}{P\{X + Y = n\}}
\end{aligned}
$$

where the last equality follows from the assumed independence of X and Y. Recalling (Example 3e) that $X + Y$ has a Poisson distribution with parameter $\lambda_1 + \lambda_2$, we see that the preceding equals

$$
\begin{aligned}
P\{X = k | X + Y = n\} &= \frac{e^{-\lambda_1}\lambda_1^k}{k!}\frac{e^{-\lambda_2}\lambda_2^{n-k}}{(n-k)!}\left[\frac{e^{-(\lambda_1+\lambda_2)}(\lambda_1 + \lambda_2)^n}{n!}\right]^{-1} \\
&= \frac{n!}{(n-k)!\,k!}\frac{\lambda_1^k \lambda_2^{n-k}}{(\lambda_1 + \lambda_2)^n} \\
&= \binom{n}{k}\left(\frac{\lambda_1}{\lambda_1 + \lambda_2}\right)^k \left(\frac{\lambda_2}{\lambda_1 + \lambda_2}\right)^{n-k}
\end{aligned}
$$

In other words, the conditional distribution of X given that $X + Y = n$ is the binomial distribution with parameters n and $\lambda_1/(\lambda_1 + \lambda_2)$. ∎

We can also talk about joint conditional distributions, as is indicated in the next two examples.

Example 4c

Consider the multinomial distribution with joint probability mass function

$$
P\{X_i = n_i, i = 1, \ldots, k\} = \frac{n!}{n_1! \cdots n_k!}p_1^{n_1} \cdots p_k^{n_k}, \quad n_i \geq 0, \ \sum_{i=1}^{k} n_i = n
$$

Such a mass function results when n independent trials are performed, with each trial resulting in outcome i with probability p_i, $\sum_{i=1}^{k} p_i = 1$. The random variables $X_i, i = 1, \ldots, k$, represent, respectively, the number of trials that result in outcome i, $i = 1, \ldots, k$. Suppose we are given that n_j of the trials resulted in outcome j, for $j = r + 1, \ldots, k$, where $\sum_{j=r+1}^{k} n_j = m \leq n$. Then, because each of the other $n - m$ trials must have resulted in one of the outcomes $1, \ldots, r$, it would seem that the conditional distribution of $X_1, \ldots, X_r$ is the multinomial distribution on $n - m$ trials with respective trial outcome probabilities

$$
P\{\text{outcome } i | \text{outcome is not any of } r + 1, \ldots, k\} = \frac{p_i}{F_r}, \ i = 1, \ldots, r
$$

where $F_r = \sum_{i=1}^{r} p_i$ is the probability that a trial results in one of the outcomes $1, \ldots, r$.

Solution To verify this intuition, let $n_1, \ldots, n_r$, be such that $\sum_{i=1}^{r} n_i = n - m$. Then

$$P\{X_1 = n_1, \ldots, X_r = n_r | X_{r+1} = n_{r+1}, \ldots X_k = n_k\}$$

$$= \frac{P\{X_1 = n_1, \ldots, X_k = n_k\}}{P\{X_{r+1} = n_{r+1}, \ldots X_k = n_k\}}$$

$$= \frac{\frac{n!}{n_1! \cdots n_k!} p_1^{n_1} \cdots p_r^{n_r} p_{r+1}^{n_{r+1}} \cdots p_k^{n_k}}{\frac{n!}{(n-m)! n_{r+1}! \cdots n_k!} F_r^{n-m} p_{r+1}^{n_{r+1}} \cdots p_k^{n_k}}$$

where the probability in the denominator was obtained by regarding outcomes $1, \ldots, r$ as a single outcome having probability F_r, thus showing that the probability is a multinomial probability on n trials with outcome probabilities $F_r, p_{r+1}, \ldots, p_k$. Because $\sum_{i=1}^{r} n_i = n - m$, the preceding can be written as

$$P\{X_1 = n_1, \ldots, X_r = n_r | X_{r+1} = n_{r+1}, \ldots X_k = n_k\}$$

$$= \frac{(n-m)!}{n_1! \cdots n_r!} \left(\frac{p_1}{F_r}\right)^{n_1} \cdots \left(\frac{p_r}{F_r}\right)^{n_r}$$

and our intuition is upheld. ∎

Example 4d

Consider n independent trials, with each trial being a success with probability p. Given a total of k successes, show that all possible orderings of the k successes and $n - k$ failures are equally likely.

Solution We want to show that given a total of k successes, each of the $\binom{n}{k}$ possible orderings of k successes and $n - k$ failures is equally likely. Let X denote the number of successes, and consider any ordering of k successes and $n - k$ failures, say, $\mathbf{o} = (s, \ldots, s, f, \ldots, f)$. Then

$$P(\mathbf{o}|X = k) = \frac{P(\mathbf{o}, X = k)}{P(X = k)}$$

$$= \frac{P(\mathbf{o})}{P(X = k)}$$

$$= \frac{p^k (1-p)^{n-k}}{\binom{n}{k} p^k (1-p)^{n-k}}$$

$$= \frac{1}{\binom{n}{k}}$$

∎

6.5 Conditional Distributions: Continuous Case

If X and Y have a joint probability density function $f(x, y)$, then the conditional probability density function of X given that $Y = y$ is defined, for all values of y such that $f_Y(y) > 0$, by

$$f_{X|Y}(x|y) = \frac{f(x, y)}{f_Y(y)}$$

To motivate this definition, multiply the left-hand side by dx and the right-hand side by $(dx\, dy)/dy$ to obtain

$$f_{X|Y}(x|y)\,dx = \frac{f(x,y)\,dx\,dy}{f_Y(y)\,dy}$$

$$\approx \frac{P\{x \le X \le x + dx, y \le Y \le y + dy\}}{P\{y \le Y \le y + dy\}}$$

$$= P\{x \le X \le x + dx | y \le Y \le y + dy\}$$

In other words, for small values of dx and dy, $f_{X|Y}(x|y)\,dx$ represents the conditional probability that X is between x and $x + dx$ given that Y is between y and $y + dy$.

The use of conditional densities allows us to define conditional probabilities of events associated with one random variable when we are given the value of a second random variable. That is, if X and Y are jointly continuous, then, for any set A,

$$P\{X \in A | Y = y\} = \int_A f_{X|Y}(x|y)\,dx$$

In particular, by letting $A = (-\infty, a)$ we can define the conditional cumulative distribution function of X given that $Y = y$ by

$$F_{X|Y}(a|y) \equiv P\{X \le a | Y = y\} = \int_{-\infty}^{a} f_{X|Y}(x|y)\,dx$$

The reader should note that by using the ideas presented in the preceding discussion, we have been able to give workable expressions for conditional probabilities, even though the event on which we are conditioning (namely, the event $\{Y = y\}$) has probability 0.

If X and Y are independent continuous random variables, the conditional density of X given that $Y = y$ is just the unconditional density of X. This is so because, in the independent case,

$$f_{X|Y}(x|y) = \frac{f(x,y)}{f_Y(y)} = \frac{f_X(x)f_Y(y)}{f_Y(y)} = f_X(x)$$

Example 5a

The joint density of X and Y is given by

$$f(x,y) = \begin{cases} \frac{12}{5}x(2 - x - y) & 0 < x < 1, 0 < y < 1 \\ 0 & \text{otherwise} \end{cases}$$

Compute the conditional density of X given that $Y = y$, where $0 < y < 1$.

Solution For $0 < x < 1, 0 < y < 1$, we have

$$f_{X|Y}(x|y) = \frac{f(x,y)}{f_Y(y)}$$

$$= \frac{f(x,y)}{\int_{-\infty}^{\infty} f(x,y)\,dx}$$

$$= \frac{x(2 - x - y)}{\int_0^1 x(2 - x - y)\,dx}$$

$$= \frac{x(2 - x - y)}{\frac{2}{3} - y/2}$$

$$= \frac{6x(2 - x - y)}{4 - 3y}$$

Example 5b

Suppose that the joint density of X and Y is given by

$$f(x, y) = \begin{cases} \dfrac{e^{-x/y}e^{-y}}{y} & 0 < x < \infty, 0 < y < \infty \\ 0 & \text{otherwise} \end{cases}$$

Find $P\{X > 1 | Y = y\}$.

Solution We first obtain the conditional density of X given that $Y = y$.

$$\begin{aligned} f_{X|Y}(x|y) &= \frac{f(x, y)}{f_Y(y)} \\ &= \frac{e^{-x/y}e^{-y}/y}{e^{-y} \int_0^\infty (1/y)e^{-x/y}\, dx} \\ &= \frac{1}{y}e^{-x/y} \end{aligned}$$

Hence,

$$\begin{aligned} P\{X > 1 | Y = y\} &= \int_1^\infty \frac{1}{y}e^{-x/y}\, dx \\ &= -e^{-x/y}\Big|_1^\infty \\ &= e^{-1/y} \end{aligned}$$ ∎

Example 5c

The t-distribution

If Z and Y are independent, with Z having a standard normal distribution and Y having a chi-squared distribution with n degrees of freedom, then the random variable T defined by

$$T = \frac{Z}{\sqrt{Y/n}} = \sqrt{n}\, \frac{Z}{\sqrt{Y}}$$

is said to have a *t-distribution* with n degrees of freedom. As will be seen in Section 7.8, the t-distribution has important applications in statistical inference. At present, we will content ourselves with computing its density function. This will be accomplished by using the conditional density of T given Y to obtain the joint density function of T and Y, from which we will then obtain the marginal density of T. To begin, note that because of the independence of Z and Y, it follows that the conditional distribution of T given that $Y = y$ is the distribution of $\sqrt{n/y}\, Z$, which is normal with mean 0 and variance n/y. Hence, the conditional density of T given that $Y = y$ is

$$f_{T|Y}(t|y) = \frac{1}{\sqrt{2\pi n/y}}\, e^{-t^2 y/2n}, \quad -\infty < t < \infty$$

Using the preceding, along with the following formula for the chi-squared density given in Example 3b of this chapter,

$$f_Y(y) = \frac{e^{-y/2}y^{n/2-1}}{2^{n/2}\, \Gamma(n/2)}, \quad y > 0$$

we obtain that the joint density of T, Y is

$$f_{T,Y}(t, y) = \frac{1}{\sqrt{2\pi n} \, 2^{n/2} \, \Gamma(n/2)} e^{-t^2 y/2n} e^{-y/2} y^{(n-1)/2}$$

$$= \frac{1}{\sqrt{\pi n} \, 2^{(n+1)/2} \, \Gamma(n/2)} e^{-\frac{t^2+n}{2n} y} y^{(n-1)/2}, \quad y > 0, \; -\infty < t < \infty$$

Letting $c = \frac{t^2+n}{2n}$, and integrating the preceding over all y, gives

$$f_T(t) = \int_0^\infty f_{T,Y}(t, y) \, dy$$

$$= \frac{1}{\sqrt{\pi n} \, 2^{(n+1)/2} \, \Gamma(n/2)} \int_0^\infty e^{-cy} y^{(n-1)/2} \, dy$$

$$= \frac{c^{-(n+1)/2}}{\sqrt{\pi n} \, 2^{(n+1)/2} \, \Gamma(n/2)} \int_0^\infty e^{-x} x^{(n-1)/2} \, dx \qquad \text{(by letting } x = cy)$$

$$= \frac{n^{(n+1)/2} \, \Gamma\left(\frac{n+1}{2}\right)}{\sqrt{\pi n} \, (t^2 + n)^{(n+1)/2} \, \Gamma\left(\frac{n}{2}\right)} \qquad \left(\text{because } \frac{1}{c} = \frac{2n}{t^2 + n}\right)$$

$$= \frac{\Gamma\left(\frac{n+1}{2}\right)}{\sqrt{\pi n} \, \Gamma\left(\frac{n}{2}\right)} \left(1 + \frac{t^2}{n}\right)^{-(n+1)/2}, \quad -\infty < t < \infty \qquad \blacksquare$$

Example 5d

The bivariate normal distribution

One of the most important joint distributions is the bivariate normal distribution. We say that the random variables X, Y have a bivariate normal distribution if, for constants $\mu_x, \mu_y, \sigma_x > 0, \sigma_y > 0, -1 < \rho < 1$, their joint density function is given, for all $-\infty < x, y < \infty$, by

$$f(x, y) = \frac{1}{2\pi \sigma_x \sigma_y \sqrt{1 - \rho^2}} \exp \left\{ -\frac{1}{2(1 - \rho^2)} \left[\left(\frac{x - \mu_x}{\sigma_x}\right)^2 \right. \right.$$

$$\left. \left. + \left(\frac{y - \mu_y}{\sigma_y}\right)^2 - 2\rho \frac{(x - \mu_x)(y - \mu_y)}{\sigma_x \sigma_y} \right] \right\}$$

We now determine the conditional density of X given that $Y = y$. In doing so, we will continually collect all factors that do not depend on x and represent them by the constants C_i. The final constant will then be found by using that $\int_{-\infty}^\infty f_{X|Y}(x|y) \, dx = 1$. We have

$$f_{X|Y}(x|y) = \frac{f(x, y)}{f_Y(y)}$$

$$= C_1 f(x, y)$$

$$= C_2 \exp \left\{ -\frac{1}{2(1 - \rho^2)} \left[\left(\frac{x - \mu_x}{\sigma_x}\right)^2 - 2\rho \frac{x(y - \mu_y)}{\sigma_x \sigma_y} \right] \right\}$$

$$= C_3 \exp\left\{-\frac{1}{2\sigma_x^2(1-\rho^2)}\left[x^2 - 2x\left(\mu_x + \rho\frac{\sigma_x}{\sigma_y}(y-\mu_y)\right)\right]\right\}$$

$$= C_4 \exp\left\{-\frac{1}{2\sigma_x^2(1-\rho^2)}\left[x - \left(\mu_x + \rho\frac{\sigma_x}{\sigma_y}(y-\mu_y)\right)\right]^2\right\}$$

Recognizing the preceding equation as a normal density, we can conclude that given $Y = y$, the random variable X is normally distributed with mean $\mu_x + \rho\frac{\sigma_x}{\sigma_y}(y-\mu_y)$ and variance $\sigma_x^2(1-\rho^2)$. Also, because the joint density of Y, X is exactly the same as that of X, Y, except that μ_x, σ_x are interchanged with μ_y, σ_y, it similarly follows that the conditional distribution of Y given $X = x$ is the normal distribution with mean $\mu_y + \rho\frac{\sigma_y}{\sigma_x}(x-\mu_x)$ and variance $\sigma_y^2(1-\rho^2)$. It follows from these results that the necessary and sufficient condition for the bivariate normal random variables X and Y to be independent is that $\rho = 0$ (a result that also follows directly from their joint density, because it is only when $\rho = 0$ that the joint density factors into two terms, one depending only on x and the other only on y).

With $C = \frac{1}{2\pi\sigma_x\sigma_y\sqrt{1-\rho^2}}$, the marginal density of X can be obtained from

$$f_X(x) = \int_{-\infty}^{\infty} f(x, y)\, dy$$

$$= C \int_{-\infty}^{\infty} \exp\left\{-\frac{1}{2(1-\rho^2)}\left[\left(\frac{x-\mu_x}{\sigma_x}\right)^2 + \left(\frac{y-\mu_y}{\sigma_y}\right)^2\right.\right.$$

$$\left.\left. -2\rho\frac{(x-\mu_x)(y-\mu_y)}{\sigma_x\sigma_y}\right]\right\}\, dy$$

Making the change of variables $w = \frac{y-\mu_y}{\sigma_y}$ gives

$$f_X(x) = C\sigma_y \exp\left\{-\frac{1}{2(1-\rho^2)}\left(\frac{x-\mu_x}{\sigma_x}\right)^2\right\}$$

$$\times \int_{-\infty}^{\infty} \exp\left\{-\frac{1}{2(1-\rho^2)}\left[w^2 - 2\rho\frac{x-\mu_x}{\sigma_x}w\right]\right\}\, dw$$

$$= C\sigma_y \exp\left\{-\frac{1}{2(1-\rho^2)}\left(\frac{x-\mu_x}{\sigma_x}\right)^2 (1-\rho^2)\right\}$$

$$\times \int_{-\infty}^{\infty} \exp\left\{-\frac{1}{2(1-\rho^2)}\left[w - \rho\frac{x-\mu_x}{\sigma_x}\right]^2\right\}\, dw$$

Because

$$\frac{1}{\sqrt{2\pi(1-\rho^2)}}\int_{-\infty}^{\infty}\exp\left\{-\frac{1}{2(1-\rho^2)}\left[w - \frac{\rho}{\sigma_x}(x-\mu_x)\right]^2\right\}\, dw = 1$$

we see that

$$f_X(x) = C\sigma_y\sqrt{2\pi(1 - \rho^2)}\ e^{-(x-\mu_x)^2/2\sigma_x^2}$$

$$= \frac{1}{\sqrt{2\pi}\,\sigma_x}\ e^{-(x-\mu_x)^2/2\sigma_x^2}$$

That is, X is normal with mean μ_x and variance σ_x^2. Similarly, Y is normal with mean μ_y and variance σ_y^2. ∎

We can also talk about conditional distributions when the random variables are neither jointly continuous nor jointly discrete. For example, suppose that X is a continuous random variable having probability density function f and N is a discrete random variable, and consider the conditional distribution of X given that $N = n$. Then

$$\frac{P\{x < X < x + dx|N = n\}}{dx}$$

$$= \frac{P\{N = n|x < X < x + dx\}\,P\{x < X < x + dx\}}{P\{N = n\}} \frac{P\{x < X < x + dx\}}{dx}$$

and letting dx approach 0 gives

$$\lim_{dx \to 0} \frac{P\{x < X < x + dx|N = n\}}{dx} = \frac{P\{N = n|X = x\}}{P\{N = n\}}f(x)$$

thus showing that the conditional density of X given that $N = n$ is given by

$$f_{X|N}(x|n) = \frac{P\{N = n|X = x\}}{P\{N = n\}}f(x)$$

Example 5e

Consider $n + m$ trials having a common probability of success. Suppose, however, that this success probability is not fixed in advance but is chosen from a uniform $(0, 1)$ population. What is the conditional distribution of the success probability given that the $n + m$ trials result in n successes?

Solution If we let X denote the probability that a given trial is a success, then X is a uniform $(0, 1)$ random variable. Also, given that $X = x$, the $n + m$ trials are independent with common probability of success x, so N, the number of successes, is a binomial random variable with parameters $(n + m, x)$. Hence, the conditional density of X given that $N = n$ is

$$f_{X|N}(x|n) = \frac{P\{N = n|X = x\}f_X(x)}{P\{N = n\}}$$

$$= \frac{\dbinom{n + m}{n}x^n(1 - x)^m}{P\{N = n\}} \qquad 0 < x < 1$$

$$= cx^n(1 - x)^m$$

where c does not depend on x. Thus, the conditional density is that of a beta random variable with parameters $n + 1, m + 1$.

The preceding result is quite interesting, for it states that if the original or *prior* (to the collection of data) distribution of a trial success probability is uniformly distributed over $(0, 1)$ [or, equivalently, is beta with parameters $(1, 1)$], then the posterior (or conditional) distribution given a total of n successes in $n + m$ trials is beta with parameters $(1 + n, 1 + m)$. This is valuable, for it enhances our intuition as to what it means to assume that a random variable has a beta distribution. ∎

*6.6 Order Statistics

Let $X_1, X_2, \ldots, X_n$ be n independent and identically distributed continuous random variables having a common density f and distribution function F. Define

$$X_{(1)} = \text{smallest of } X_1, X_2, \ldots, X_n$$
$$X_{(2)} = \text{second smallest of } X_1, X_2, \ldots, X_n$$

.
.
.

$$X_{(j)} = j\text{th smallest of } X_1, X_2, \ldots, X_n$$

.
.
.

$$X_{(n)} = \text{largest of } X_1, X_2, \ldots, X_n$$

The ordered values $X_{(1)} \leq X_{(2)} \leq \cdots \leq X_{(n)}$ are known as the *order statistics* corresponding to the random variables $X_1, X_2, \ldots, X_n$. In other words, $X_{(1)}, \ldots, X_{(n)}$ are the ordered values of $X_1, \ldots, X_n$.

The joint density function of the order statistics is obtained by noting that the order statistics $X_{(1)}, \ldots, X_{(n)}$ will take on the values $x_1 \leq x_2 \leq \cdots \leq x_n$ if and only if, for some permutation $(i_1, i_2, \ldots, i_n)$ of $(1, 2, \ldots, n)$,

$$X_1 = x_{i_1}, X_2 = x_{i_2}, \ldots, X_n = x_{i_n}$$

Since, for any permutation $(i_1, \ldots, i_n)$ of $(1, 2, \ldots, n)$,

$$P\left\{x_{i_1} - \frac{\varepsilon}{2} < X_1 < x_{i_1} + \frac{\varepsilon}{2}, \ldots, x_{i_n} - \frac{\varepsilon}{2} < X_n < x_{i_n} + \frac{\varepsilon}{2}\right\}$$
$$\approx \varepsilon^n f_{X_1, \cdots, X_n}(x_{i_1}, \ldots, x_{i_n})$$
$$= \varepsilon^n f(x_{i_1}) \cdots f(x_{i_n})$$
$$= \varepsilon^n f(x_1) \cdots f(x_n)$$

it follows that, for $x_1 < x_2 < \cdots < x_n$,

$$P\left\{x_1 - \frac{\varepsilon}{2} < X_{(1)} < x_1 + \frac{\varepsilon}{2}, \ldots, x_n - \frac{\varepsilon}{2} < X_{(n)} < x_n + \frac{\varepsilon}{2}\right\}$$
$$\approx n! \, \varepsilon^n f(x_1) \cdots f(x_n)$$

Dividing by ε^n and letting $\varepsilon \to 0$ yields

$$f_{X_{(1)}, \ldots, X_{(n)}}(x_1, x_2, \ldots, x_n) = n! f(x_1) \cdots f(x_n) \quad x_1 < x_2 < \cdots < x_n \tag{6.1}$$

Equation (6.1) is most simply explained by arguing that, in order for the vector $\langle X_{(1)}, \ldots, X_{(n)} \rangle$ to equal $\langle x_1, \ldots, x_n \rangle$, it is necessary and sufficient for $\langle X_1, \ldots, X_n \rangle$

to equal one of the $n!$ permutations of $\langle x_1, \ldots, x_n \rangle$. Since the probability (density) that $\langle X_1, \ldots, X_n \rangle$ equals any given permutation of $\langle x_1, \ldots, x_n \rangle$ is just $f(x_1) \cdots f(x_n)$, Equation (6.1) follows.

Example 6a

Along a road 1 mile long are 3 people "distributed at random." Find the probability that no 2 people are less than a distance of d miles apart when $d \leq \frac{1}{2}$.

Solution Let us assume that "distributed at random" means that the positions of the 3 people are independent and uniformly distributed over the road. If X_i denotes the position of the ith person, then the desired probability is $P\{X_{(i)} > X_{(i-1)} + d, i = 2, 3\}$. Because

$$f_{X_{(1)}, X_{(2)}, X_{(3)}}(x_1, x_2, x_3) = 3! \quad 0 < x_1 < x_2 < x_3 < 1$$

it follows that

$$P\{X_{(i)} > X_{(i-1)} + d, i = 2, 3\} = \int \int \int_{x_i > x_{j-1}+d} f_{X_{(1)}, X_{(2)}, X_{(3)}}(x_1, x_2, x_3) \, dx_1 \, dx_2 \, dx_3$$

$$= 3! \int_0^{1-2d} \int_{x_1+d}^{1-d} \int_{x_2+d}^{1} dx_3 \, dx_2 \, dx_1$$

$$= 6 \int_0^{1-2d} \int_{x_1+d}^{1-d} (1 - d - x_2) \, dx_2 \, dx_1$$

$$= 6 \int_0^{1-2d} \int_0^{1-2d-x_1} y_2 \, dy_2 \, dx_1$$

where we have made the change of variables $y_2 = 1 - d - x_2$. Continuing the string of equalities yields

$$= 3 \int_0^{1-2d} (1 - 2d - x_1)^2 \, dx_1$$

$$= 3 \int_0^{1-2d} y_1^2 \, dy_1$$

$$= (1 - 2d)^3$$

Hence, the desired probability that no 2 people are within a distance d of each other when 3 people are uniformly and independently distributed over an interval of size 1 is $(1 - 2d)^3$ when $d \leq \frac{1}{2}$. In fact, the same method can be used to prove that when n people are distributed at random over the unit interval, the desired probability is

$$[1 - (n - 1)d]^n \quad \text{when } d \leq \frac{1}{n - 1}$$

The proof is left as an exercise. ∎

The density function of the jth-order statistic $X_{(j)}$ can be obtained either by integrating the joint density function (6.1) or by direct reasoning as follows: In order for $X_{(j)}$ to equal x, it is necessary for $j - 1$ of the n values $X_1, \ldots, X_n$ to be less than x, $n - j$ of them to be greater than x, and 1 of them to equal x. Now, the probability density that any given set of $j - 1$ of the X_i's are less than x, another given set of $n - j$ are all greater than x, and the remaining value is equal to x equals

$$[F(x)]^{j-1}[1 - F(x)]^{n-j} f(x)$$

Hence, since there are

$$\binom{n}{j-1, n-j, 1} = \frac{n!}{(n-j)!(j-1)!}$$

different partitions of the n random variables $X_1, \ldots, X_n$ into the preceding three groups, it follows that the density function of $X_{(j)}$ is given by

$$f_{X_{(j)}}(x) = \frac{n!}{(n-j)!(j-1)!}[F(x)]^{j-1}[1 - F(x)]^{n-j}f(x) \qquad (6.2)$$

Example 6b

When a sample of $2n + 1$ random variables (that is, when $2n + 1$ independent and identically distributed random variables) is observed, the $(n + 1)$ smallest is called the *sample median*. If a sample of size 3 from a uniform distribution over $(0, 1)$ is observed, find the probability that the sample median is between $\frac{1}{4}$ and $\frac{3}{4}$.

Solution From Equation (6.2), the density of $X_{(2)}$ is given by

$$f_{X_{(2)}}(x) = \frac{3!}{1!1!}x(1 - x) \qquad 0 < x < 1$$

Hence,

$$P\left\{\frac{1}{4} < X_{(2)} < \frac{3}{4}\right\} = 6\int_{1/4}^{3/4} x(1 - x)\,dx$$

$$= 6\left\{\frac{x^2}{2} - \frac{x^3}{3}\right\}\Bigg|_{x=1/4}^{x=3/4} = \frac{11}{16} \qquad \blacksquare$$

The cumulative distribution function of $X_{(j)}$ can be found by integrating Equation (6.2). That is,

$$F_{X_{(j)}}(y) = \frac{n!}{(n-j)!(j-1)!}\int_{-\infty}^{y}[F(x)]^{j-1}[1 - F(x)]^{n-j}f(x)\,dx \qquad (6.3)$$

However, $F_{X_{(j)}}(y)$ could also have been derived directly by noting that the jth order statistic is less than or equal to y if and only if there are j or more of the X_i's that are less than or equal to y. Thus, because the number of X_i's that are less than or equal to y is a binomial random variable with parameters $n, p = F(y)$, it follows that

$$F_{X_{(j)}}(y) = P\{X_{(j)} \le y\} = P\{j \text{ or more of the } X_i\text{'s are } \le y\}$$

$$= \sum_{k=j}^{n}\binom{n}{k}[F(y)]^k[1 - F(y)]^{n-k} \qquad (6.4)$$

If, in Equations (6.3) and (6.4), we take F to be the uniform $(0, 1)$ distribution [that is, $f(x) = 1, 0 < x < 1$], then we obtain the interesting analytical identity

$$\sum_{k=j}^{n}\binom{n}{k}y^k(1 - y)^{n-k} = \frac{n!}{(n-j)!(j-1)!}\int_0^y x^{j-1}(1 - x)^{n-j}\,dx \quad 0 \le y \le 1 \quad (6.5)$$

By employing the same type of argument that we used in establishing Equation (6.2), we can show that the joint density function of the order statistics $X_{(i)}$ and $X_{(j)}$ when $i < j$ is

$$f_{X_{(i)}, X_{(j)}}(x_i, x_j) = \frac{n!}{(i-1)!(j-i-1)!(n-j)!}[F(x_i)]^{i-1} \tag{6.6}$$
$$\times [F(x_j) - F(x_i)]^{j-i-1}[1 - F(x_j)]^{n-j}f(x_i)f(x_j)$$

for all $x_i < x_j$.

Example 6c

Distribution of the range of a random sample

Suppose that n independent and identically distributed random variables $X_1, X_2, \ldots, X_n$ are observed. The random variable R defined by $R = X_{(n)} - X_{(1)}$ is called the *range* of the observed random variables. If the random variables X_i have distribution function F and density function f, then the distribution of R can be obtained from Equation (6.6) as follows: For $a \geq 0$,

$$P\{R \leq a\} = P\{X_{(n)} - X_{(1)} \leq a\}$$
$$= \iint\limits_{x_n - x_1 \leq a} f_{X_{(1)}, X_{(n)}}(x_1, x_n) \, dx_1 \, dx_n$$
$$= \int_{-\infty}^{\infty} \int_{x_1}^{x_1 + a} \frac{n!}{(n-2)!}[F(x_n) - F(x_1)]^{n-2}f(x_1)f(x_n) \, dx_n \, dx_1$$

Making the change of variable $y = F(x_n) - F(x_1), dy = f(x_n) \, dx_n$ yields

$$\int_{x_1}^{x_1 + a} [F(x_n) - F(x_1)]^{n-2}f(x_n) \, dx_n = \int_0^{F(x_1+a) - F(x_1)} y^{n-2} dy$$
$$= \frac{1}{n-1}[F(x_1 + a) - F(x_1)]^{n-1}$$

Thus,

$$P\{R \leq a\} = n \int_{-\infty}^{\infty} [F(x_1 + a) - F(x_1)]^{n-1}f(x_1) \, dx_1 \tag{6.7}$$

Equation (6.7) can be evaluated explicitly only in a few special cases. One such case is when the X_i's are all uniformly distributed on $(0, 1)$. In this case, we obtain, from Equation (6.7), that for $0 < a < 1$,

$$P\{R < a\} = n \int_0^1 [F(x_1 + a) - F(x_1)]^{n-1}f(x_1) \, dx_1$$
$$= n \int_0^{1-a} a^{n-1} \, dx_1 + n \int_{1-a}^1 (1 - x_1)^{n-1} \, dx_1$$
$$= n(1 - a)a^{n-1} + a^n$$

Differentiation yields the density function of the range: given in this case by

$$f_R(a) = \begin{cases} n(n-1)a^{n-2}(1-a) & 0 \leq a \leq 1 \\ 0 & \text{otherwise} \end{cases}$$

That is, the range of n independent uniform $(0, 1)$ random variables is a beta random variable with parameters $n - 1, 2$. ∎

6.7 Joint Probability Distribution of Functions of Random Variables

Let X_1 and X_2 be jointly continuous random variables with joint probability density function f_{X_1, X_2}. It is sometimes necessary to obtain the joint distribution of the random variables Y_1 and Y_2, which arise as functions of X_1 and X_2. Specifically, suppose that $Y_1 = g_1(X_1, X_2)$ and $Y_2 = g_2(X_1, X_2)$ for some functions g_1 and g_2.

Assume that the functions g_1 and g_2 satisfy the following conditions:

1. The equations $y_1 = g_1(x_1, x_2)$ and $y_2 = g_2(x_1, x_2)$ can be uniquely solved for x_1 and x_2 in terms of y_1 and y_2, with solutions given by, say, $x_1 = h_1(y_1, y_2), x_2 = h_2(y_1, y_2)$.

2. The functions g_1 and g_2 have continuous partial derivatives at all points (x_1, x_2) and are such that the 2×2 determinant

$$J(x_1, x_2) = \begin{vmatrix} \dfrac{\partial g_1}{\partial x_1} & \dfrac{\partial g_1}{\partial x_2} \\ \dfrac{\partial g_2}{\partial x_1} & \dfrac{\partial g_2}{\partial x_2} \end{vmatrix} \equiv \frac{\partial g_1}{\partial x_1}\frac{\partial g_2}{\partial x_2} - \frac{\partial g_1}{\partial x_2}\frac{\partial g_2}{\partial x_1} \neq 0$$

at all points (x_1, x_2).

Under these two conditions, it can be shown that the random variables Y_1 and Y_2 are jointly continuous with joint density function given by

$$f_{Y_1 Y_2}(y_1, y_2) = f_{X_1, X_2}(x_1, x_2)|J(x_1, x_2)|^{-1} \tag{7.1}$$

where $x_1 = h_1(y_1, y_2)$, $x_2 = h_2(y_1, y_2)$.

A proof of Equation (7.1) would proceed along the following lines:

$$P\{Y_1 \leq y_1, Y_2 \leq y_2\} = \iint\limits_{\substack{(x_1, x_2): \\ g_1(x_1, x_2) \leq y_1 \\ g_2(x_1, x_2) \leq y_2}} f_{X_1, X_2}(x_1, x_2)\, dx_1\, dx_2 \tag{7.2}$$

The joint density function can now be obtained by differentiating Equation (7.2) with respect to y_1 and y_2. That the result of this differentiation will be equal to the right-hand side of Equation (7.1) is an exercise in advanced calculus whose proof will not be presented in this book.

Example 7a

Let X_1 and X_2 be jointly continuous random variables with probability density function f_{X_1, X_2}. Let $Y_1 = X_1 + X_2, Y_2 = X_1 - X_2$. Find the joint density function of Y_1 and Y_2 in terms of f_{X_1, X_2}.

Solution Let $g_1(x_1, x_2) = x_1 + x_2$ and $g_2(x_1, x_2) = x_1 - x_2$. Then

$$J(x_1, x_2) = \begin{vmatrix} 1 & 1 \\ 1 & -1 \end{vmatrix} = -2$$

Also, since the equations $y_1 = x_1 + x_2$ and $y_2 = x_1 - x_2$ have $x_1 = (y_1 + y_2)/2$, $x_2 = (y_1 - y_2)/2$ as their solution, it follows from Equation (7.1) that the desired density is

$$f_{Y_1, Y_2}(y_1, y_2) = \frac{1}{2} f_{X_1, X_2}\left(\frac{y_1 + y_2}{2}, \frac{y_1 - y_2}{2}\right)$$

For instance, if X_1 and X_2 are independent uniform $(0, 1)$ random variables, then

$$f_{Y_1, Y_2}(y_1, y_2) = \begin{cases} \frac{1}{2} & 0 \le y_1 + y_2 \le 2,\ 0 \le y_1 - y_2 \le 2 \\ 0 & \text{otherwise} \end{cases}$$

or if X_1 and X_2 are independent exponential random variables with respective parameters λ_1 and λ_2, then

$$f_{Y_1, Y_2}(y_1, y_2)$$
$$= \begin{cases} \dfrac{\lambda_1 \lambda_2}{2} \exp\left\{ -\lambda_1\left(\dfrac{y_1 + y_2}{2}\right) - \lambda_2\left(\dfrac{y_1 - y_2}{2}\right) \right\} & y_1 + y_2 \ge 0,\ y_1 - y_2 \ge 0 \\ 0 & \text{otherwise} \end{cases}$$

Finally, if X_1 and X_2 are independent standard normal random variables, then

$$\begin{aligned} f_{Y_1, Y_2}(y_1, y_2) &= \frac{1}{4\pi} e^{-[(y_1+y_2)^2/8 + (y_1-y_2)^2/8]} \\ &= \frac{1}{4\pi} e^{-(y_1^2 + y_2^2)/4} \\ &= \frac{1}{\sqrt{4\pi}} e^{-y_1^2/4} \frac{1}{\sqrt{4\pi}} e^{-y_2^2/4} \end{aligned}$$

Thus, not only do we obtain (in agreement with Proposition 3.2) that both $X_1 + X_2$ and $X_1 - X_2$ are normal with mean 0 and variance 2, but we also conclude that these two random variables are independent. (In fact, it can be shown that if X_1 and X_2 are independent random variables having a common distribution function F, then $X_1 + X_2$ will be independent of $X_1 - X_2$ if and only if F is a normal distribution function.) ■

Example 7b

Let (X, Y) denote a random point in the plane, and assume that the rectangular coordinates X and Y are independent standard normal random variables. We are interested in the joint distribution of R, Θ, the polar coordinate representation of (x, y). (See Figure 6.4.)

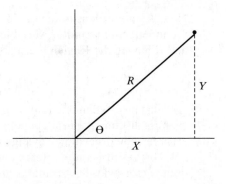

Figure 6.4 ● = Random point. $(X, Y) = (R, \Theta)$.

Suppose first that X and Y are both positive. For x and y positive, letting $r = g_1(x, y) = \sqrt{x^2 + y^2}$ and $\theta = g_2(x, y) = \tan^{-1} y/x$, we see that

$$\frac{\partial g_1}{\partial x} = \frac{x}{\sqrt{x^2 + y^2}}$$

$$\frac{\partial g_1}{\partial y} = \frac{y}{\sqrt{x^2 + y^2}}$$

$$\frac{\partial g_2}{\partial x} = \frac{1}{1 + (y/x)^2} \left(\frac{-y}{x^2}\right) = \frac{-y}{x^2 + y^2}$$

$$\frac{\partial g_2}{\partial y} = \frac{1}{x[1 + (y/x)^2]} = \frac{x}{x^2 + y^2}$$

Hence,

$$J(x, y) = \frac{x^2}{(x^2 + y^2)^{3/2}} + \frac{y^2}{(x^2 + y^2)^{3/2}} = \frac{1}{\sqrt{x^2 + y^2}} = \frac{1}{r}$$

Because the conditional joint density function of X, Y given that they are both positive is

$$f(x, y | X > 0, Y > 0) = \frac{f(x, y)}{P(X > 0, Y > 0)} = \frac{2}{\pi} e^{-(x^2 + y^2)/2}, \quad x > 0, y > 0$$

we see that the conditional joint density function of $R = \sqrt{X^2 + Y^2}$ and $\Theta = \tan^{-1}(Y/X)$, given that X and Y are both positive, is

$$f(r, \theta | X > 0, Y > 0) = \frac{2}{\pi} r e^{-r^2/2}, \quad 0 < \theta < \pi/2, \quad 0 < r < \infty$$

Similarly, we can show that

$$f(r, \theta | X < 0, Y > 0) = \frac{2}{\pi} r e^{-r^2/2}, \quad \pi/2 < \theta < \pi, \quad 0 < r < \infty$$

$$f(r, \theta | X < 0, Y < 0) = \frac{2}{\pi} r e^{-r^2/2}, \quad \pi < \theta < 3\pi/2, \quad 0 < r < \infty$$

$$f(r, \theta | X > 0, Y < 0) = \frac{2}{\pi} r e^{-r^2/2}, \quad 3\pi/2 < \theta < 2\pi, \quad 0 < r < \infty$$

As the joint density is an equally weighted average of these four conditional joint densities, we obtain that the joint density of R, Θ is given by

$$f(r, \theta) = \frac{1}{2\pi} r e^{-r^2/2} \quad 0 < \theta < 2\pi, \quad 0 < r < \infty$$

Now, this joint density factors into the marginal densities for R and Θ, so R and Θ are independent random variables, with Θ being uniformly distributed over $(0, 2\pi)$ and R having the Rayleigh distribution with density

$$f(r) = r e^{-r^2/2} \quad 0 < r < \infty$$

(For instance, when one is aiming at a target in the plane, if the horizontal and vertical miss distances are independent standard normals, then the absolute value of the error has the preceding Rayleigh distribution.)

This result is quite interesting, for it certainly is not evident a priori that a random vector whose coordinates are independent standard normal random variables will have an angle of orientation that not only is uniformly distributed, but also is independent of the vector's distance from the origin.

If we wanted the joint distribution of R^2 and Θ, then, since the transformation $d = g_1(x, y) = x^2 + y^2$ and $\theta = g_2(x, y) = \tan^{-1} y/x$ has the Jacobian

$$J = \begin{vmatrix} 2x & 2y \\ \dfrac{-y}{x^2 + y^2} & \dfrac{x}{x^2 + y^2} \end{vmatrix} = 2$$

it follows that

$$f(d, \theta) = \frac{1}{2} e^{-d/2} \frac{1}{2\pi} \qquad 0 < d < \infty, \qquad 0 < \theta < 2\pi$$

Therefore, R^2 and Θ are independent, with R^2 having an exponential distribution with parameter $\frac{1}{2}$. But because $R^2 = X^2 + Y^2$, it follows by definition that R^2 has a chi-squared distribution with 2 degrees of freedom. Hence, we have a verification of the result that the exponential distribution with parameter $\frac{1}{2}$ is the same as the chi-squared distribution with 2 degrees of freedom.

The preceding result can be used to simulate (or generate) normal random variables by making a suitable transformation on uniform random variables. Let U_1 and U_2 be independent random variables, each uniformly distributed over $(0, 1)$. We will transform U_1, U_2 into two independent unit normal random variables X_1 and X_2 by first considering the polar coordinate representation (R, Θ) of the random vector (X_1, X_2). From the preceding, R^2 and Θ will be independent, and, in addition, $R^2 = X_1^2 + X_2^2$ will have an exponential distribution with parameter $\lambda = \frac{1}{2}$. But $-2 \log U_1$ has such a distribution, since, for $x > 0$,

$$P\{-2 \log U_1 < x\} = P\left\{\log U_1 > -\frac{x}{2}\right\}$$

$$= P\{U_1 > e^{-x/2}\}$$

$$= 1 - e^{-x/2}$$

Also, because $2\pi U_2$ is a uniform $(0, 2\pi)$ random variable, we can use it to generate Θ. That is, if we let

$$R^2 = -2 \log U_1$$

$$\Theta = 2\pi U_2$$

then R^2 can be taken to be the square of the distance from the origin and θ can be taken to be the angle of orientation of (X_1, X_2). Now, since $X_1 = R \cos \Theta, X_2 = R \sin \Theta$, it follows that

$$X_1 = \sqrt{-2 \log U_1} \cos(2\pi U_2)$$

$$X_2 = \sqrt{-2 \log U_1} \sin(2\pi U_2)$$

are independent standard normal random variables. ∎

Example 7c

If X and Y are independent gamma random variables with parameters (α, λ) and (β, λ), respectively, compute the joint density of $U = X + Y$ and $V = X/(X + Y)$.

Solution The joint density of X and Y is given by

$$f_{X,Y}(x, y) = \frac{\lambda e^{-\lambda x}(\lambda x)^{\alpha-1}}{\Gamma(\alpha)} \frac{\lambda e^{-\lambda y}(\lambda y)^{\beta-1}}{\Gamma(\beta)}$$

$$= \frac{\lambda^{\alpha+\beta}}{\Gamma(\alpha)\Gamma(\beta)} e^{-\lambda(x+y)} x^{\alpha-1} y^{\beta-1}$$

Now, if $g_1(x, y) = x + y, g_2(x, y) = x/(x + y)$, then

$$\frac{\partial g_1}{\partial x} = \frac{\partial g_1}{\partial y} = 1 \quad \frac{\partial g_2}{\partial x} = \frac{y}{(x + y)^2} \quad \frac{\partial g_2}{\partial y} = -\frac{x}{(x + y)^2}$$

so

$$J(x, y) = \begin{vmatrix} 1 & 1 \\ \dfrac{y}{(x + y)^2} & \dfrac{-x}{(x + y)^2} \end{vmatrix} = -\frac{1}{x + y}$$

Finally, as the equations $u = x + y, v = x/(x + y)$ have as their solutions $x = uv$, $y = u(1 - v)$, we see that

$$f_{U,V}(u, v) = f_{X,Y}[uv, u(1 - v)]u$$
$$= \frac{\lambda e^{-\lambda u}(\lambda u)^{\alpha + \beta - 1}}{\Gamma(\alpha + \beta)} \frac{v^{\alpha - 1}(1 - v)^{\beta - 1}\Gamma(\alpha + \beta)}{\Gamma(\alpha)\Gamma(\beta)}$$

Hence, $X + Y$ and $X/(X + Y)$ are independent, with $X + Y$ having a gamma distribution with parameters $(\alpha + \beta, \lambda)$ and $X/(X + Y)$ having a beta distribution with parameters (α, β). The preceding reasoning also shows that $B(\alpha, \beta)$, the normalizing factor in the beta density, is such that

$$B(\alpha, \beta) \equiv \int_0^1 v^{\alpha - 1}(1 - v)^{\beta - 1}dv$$
$$= \frac{\Gamma(\alpha)\Gamma(\beta)}{\Gamma(\alpha + \beta)}$$

This entire result is quite interesting. For suppose there are $n + m$ jobs to be performed, each (independently) taking an exponential amount of time with rate λ to be completed and suppose that we have two workers to perform these jobs. Worker I will do jobs $1, 2, \ldots, n$, and worker II will do the remaining m jobs. If we let X and Y denote the total working times of workers I and II, respectively, then (either from the foregoing result or from Example 3b) X and Y will be independent gamma random variables having parameters (n, λ) and (m, λ), respectively. It then follows that independently of the working time needed to complete all $n + m$ jobs (that is, of $X + Y$), the proportion of this work that will be performed by worker I has a beta distribution with parameters (n, m). ∎

When the joint density function of the n random variables $X_1, X_2, \ldots, X_n$ is given and we want to compute the joint density function of $Y_1, Y_2, \ldots, Y_n$, where

$$Y_1 = g_1(X_1, \ldots, X_n) \quad Y_2 = g_2(X_1, \ldots, X_n), \ldots \quad Y_n = g_n(X_1, \ldots, X_n)$$

the approach is the same—namely, we assume that the functions g_i have continuous partial derivatives and that the Jacobian determinant

$$J(x_1, \ldots, x_n) = \begin{vmatrix} \dfrac{\partial g_1}{\partial x_1} & \dfrac{\partial g_1}{\partial x_2} & \cdots & \dfrac{\partial g_1}{\partial x_n} \\ \dfrac{\partial g_2}{\partial x_1} & \dfrac{\partial g_2}{\partial x_2} & \cdots & \dfrac{\partial g_2}{\partial x_n} \\ \dfrac{\partial g_n}{\partial x_1} & \dfrac{\partial g_n}{\partial x_2} & \cdots & \dfrac{\partial g_n}{\partial x_n} \end{vmatrix} \neq 0$$

at all points $(x_1, \ldots, x_n)$. Furthermore, we suppose that the equations $y_1 = g_1(x_1, \ldots, x_n), y_2 = g_2(x_1, \ldots, x_n), \ldots, y_n = g_n(x_1, \ldots, x_n)$ have a unique solution, say, $x_1 = h_1(y_1, \ldots, y_n), \ldots, x_n = h_n(y_1, \ldots, y_n)$. Under these assumptions, the joint density function of the random variables Y_i is given by

$$f_{Y_1, \ldots, Y_n}(y_1, \ldots, y_n) = f_{X_1, \ldots, X_n}(x_1, \ldots, x_n)|J(x_1, \ldots, x_n)|^{-1} \qquad (7.3)$$

where $x_i = h_i(y_1, \ldots, y_n), i = 1, 2, \ldots, n$.

Example 7d

Let X_1, X_2, and X_3 be independent standard normal random variables. If $Y_1 = X_1 + X_2 + X_3, Y_2 = X_1 - X_2$, and $Y_3 = X_1 - X_3$, compute the joint density function of Y_1, Y_2, Y_3.

Solution Letting $Y_1 = X_1 + X_2 + X_3, Y_2 = X_1 - X_2, Y_3 = X_1 - X_3$, the Jacobian of these transformations is given by

$$J = \begin{vmatrix} 1 & 1 & 1 \\ 1 & -1 & 0 \\ 1 & 0 & -1 \end{vmatrix} = 3$$

As the preceding transformations yield that

$$X_1 = \frac{Y_1 + Y_2 + Y_3}{3} \qquad X_2 = \frac{Y_1 - 2Y_2 + Y_3}{3} \qquad X_3 = \frac{Y_1 + Y_2 - 2Y_3}{3}$$

we see from Equation (7.3) that

$$f_{Y_1, Y_2, Y_3}(y_1, y_2, y_3)$$
$$= \frac{1}{3} f_{X_1, X_2, X_3}\left(\frac{y_1 + y_2 + y_3}{3}, \frac{y_1 - 2y_2 + y_3}{3}, \frac{y_1 + y_2 - 2y_3}{3}\right)$$

Hence, as

$$f_{X_1, X_2, X_3}(x_1, x_2, x_3) = \frac{1}{(2\pi)^{3/2}} e^{-\sum_{i=1}^{3} x_i^2/2}$$

we see that

$$f_{Y_1, Y_2, Y_3}(y_1, y_2, y_3) = \frac{1}{3(2\pi)^{3/2}} e^{-Q(y_1, y_2, y_3)/2}$$

where

$$Q(y_1, y_2, y_3)$$
$$= \left(\frac{y_1 + y_2 + y_3}{3}\right)^2 + \left(\frac{y_1 - 2y_2 + y_3}{3}\right)^2 + \left(\frac{y_1 + y_2 - 2y_3}{3}\right)^2$$
$$= \frac{y_1^2}{3} + \frac{2}{3}y_2^2 + \frac{2}{3}y_3^2 - \frac{2}{3}y_2 y_3 \qquad \blacksquare$$

Example 7e

Let $X_1, X_2, \ldots, X_n$ be independent and identically distributed exponential random variables with rate λ. Let

$$Y_i = X_1 + \cdots + X_i \quad i = 1, \ldots, n$$

(a) Find the joint density function of $Y_1, \ldots, Y_n$.

(b) Use the result of part (a) to find the density of Y_n.

Solution (a) The Jacobian of the transformations $Y_1 = X_1$, $Y_2 = X_1 + X_2, \ldots,$ $Y_n = X_1 + \cdots + X_n$ is

$$J = \begin{vmatrix} 1 & 0 & 0 & 0 & \cdots & 0 \\ 1 & 1 & 0 & 0 & \cdots & 0 \\ 1 & 1 & 1 & 0 & \cdots & 0 \\ \cdots & & & \cdots & & \\ \cdots & & & \cdots & & \\ 1 & 1 & 1 & 1 & \cdots & 1 \end{vmatrix}$$

Since only the first term of the determinant will be nonzero, we have $J = 1$. Now, the joint density function of $X_1, \ldots, X_n$ is given by

$$f_{X_1,\ldots,X_n}(x_1,\ldots,x_n) = \prod_{i=1}^{n} \lambda e^{-\lambda x_i} \quad 0 < x_i < \infty, \; i = 1, \ldots, n$$

Hence, because the preceding transformations yield

$$X_1 = Y_1, X_2 = Y_2 - Y_1, \ldots, X_i = Y_i - Y_{i-1}, \ldots, X_n = Y_n - Y_{n-1}$$

it follows from Equation (7.3) that the joint density function of $Y_1, \ldots, Y_n$ is $f_{Y_1,\ldots,Y_n}(y_1, y_2, \ldots, y_n)$

$$= f_{X_1,\ldots,X_n}(y_1, y_2 - y_1, \ldots, y_i - y_{i-1}, \ldots, y_n - y_{n-1})$$

$$= \lambda^n \exp\left\{ -\lambda \left[y_1 + \sum_{i=2}^{n} (y_i - y_{i-1}) \right] \right\}$$

$$= \lambda^n e^{-\lambda y_n} \quad 0 < y_1, 0 < y_i - y_{i-1}, i = 2, \ldots, n$$

$$= \lambda^n e^{-\lambda y_n} \quad 0 < y_1 < y_2 < \cdots < y_n$$

(b) To obtain the marginal density of Y_n, let us integrate out the other variables one at a time. Doing this gives

$$f_{Y_2,\ldots,Y_n}(y_2, \ldots, y_n) = \int_0^{y_2} \lambda^n e^{-\lambda y_n} dy_1$$

$$= \lambda^n y_2 e^{-\lambda y_n} \quad 0 < y_2 < y_3 < \cdots < y_n$$

Continuing, we obtain

$$f_{Y_3,\ldots,Y_n}(y_3, \ldots, y_n) = \int_0^{y_3} \lambda^n y_2 e^{-\lambda y_n} dy_2$$

$$= \lambda^n \frac{y_3^2}{2} e^{-\lambda y_n} \quad 0 < y_3 < y_4 < \cdots < y_n$$

The next integration yields

$$f_{Y_4,\ldots,Y_n}(y_4, \ldots, y_n) = \lambda^n \frac{y_4^3}{3!} e^{-\lambda y_n} \quad 0 < y_4 < \cdots < y_n$$

Continuing in this fashion gives

$$f_{Y_n}(y_n) = \lambda^n \frac{y_n^{n-1}}{(n-1)!} e^{-\lambda y_n} \quad 0 < y_n$$

which, in agreement with the result obtained in Example 3b, shows that $X_1 + \cdots + X_n$ is a gamma random variable with parameters n and λ. ∎

*6.8 Exchangeable Random Variables

The random variables $X_1, X_2, \ldots, X_n$ are said to be *exchangeable* if, for every permutation $i_1, \ldots, i_n$ of the integers $1, \ldots, n$,

$$P\{X_{i_1} \le x_1, X_{i_2} \le x_2, \ldots, X_{i_n} \le x_n\} = P\{X_1 \le x_1, X_2 \le x_2, \ldots, X_n \le x_n\}$$

for all $x_1, \ldots, x_n$. That is, the n random variables are exchangeable if their joint distribution is the same no matter in which order the variables are observed.

Discrete random variables will be exchangeable if

$$P\{X_{i_1} = x_1, X_{i_2} = x_2, \ldots, X_{i_n} = x_n\} = P\{X_1 = x_1, X_2 = x_2, \ldots, X_n = x_n\}$$

for all permutations $i_1, \ldots, i_n$, and all values $x_1, \ldots, x_n$. This is equivalent to stating that $p(x_1, x_2, \ldots, x_n) = P\{X_1 = x_1, \ldots, X_n = x_n\}$ is a symmetric function of the vector $(x_1, \ldots, x_n)$, which means that its value does not change when the values of the vector are permuted.

Example 8a

Suppose that balls are withdrawn one at a time and without replacement from an urn that initially contains n balls, of which k are considered special, in such a manner that each withdrawal is equally likely to be any of the balls that remains in the urn at the time. Let $X_i = 1$ if the ith ball withdrawn is special and let $X_i = 0$ otherwise. We will show that the random variables $X_1, \ldots, X_n$ are exchangeable. To do so, let $(x_1, \ldots, x_n)$ be a vector consisting of k ones and $n - k$ zeros. However, before considering the joint mass function evaluated at $(x_1, \ldots, x_n)$, let us try to gain some insight by considering a fixed such vector—for instance, consider the vector $(1, 1, 0, 1, 0, \ldots, 0, 1)$, which is assumed to have k ones and $n - k$ zeros. Then

$$p(1, 1, 0, 1, 0, \ldots, 0, 1) = \frac{k}{n} \frac{k-1}{n-1} \frac{n-k}{n-2} \frac{k-2}{n-3} \frac{n-k-1}{n-4} \cdots \frac{1}{2} \frac{1}{1}$$

which follows because the probability that the first ball is special is k/n, the conditional probability that the next one is special is $(k-1)/(n-1)$, the conditional probability that the next one is not special is $(n-k)/(n-2)$, and so on. By the same argument, it follows that $p(x_1, \ldots, x_n)$ can be expressed as the product of n fractions. The successive denominator terms of these fractions will go from n down to 1. The numerator term at the location where the vector $(x_1, \ldots, x_n)$ is 1 for the ith time is $k - (i - 1)$, and where it is 0 for the ith time it is $n - k - (i - 1)$. Hence, since the vector $(x_1, \ldots, x_n)$ consists of k ones and $n - k$ zeros, we obtain

$$p(x_1, \ldots, x_n) = \frac{k!(n-k)!}{n!} \quad x_i = 0, 1, \sum_{i=1}^{n} x_i = k$$

Since this is a symmetric function of $(x_1, \ldots, x_n)$, it follows that the random variables are exchangeable. ∎

Remark Another way to obtain the preceding formula for the joint probability mass function is to regard all the n balls as distinguishable from one another. Then, since the outcome of the experiment is an ordering of these balls, it follows that there are $n!$ equally likely outcomes. Finally, because the number of outcomes having special and nonspecial balls in specified places is equal to the number of ways of permuting the special and the nonspecial balls among themselves, namely $k!(n - k)!$, we obtain the preceding mass function. ∎

It is easily seen that if $X_1, X_2, \ldots, X_n$ are exchangeable, then each X_i has the same probability distribution. For instance, if X and Y are exchangeable discrete random variables, then

$$P\{X = x\} = \sum_y P\{X = x, Y = y\} = \sum_y P\{X = y, Y = x\} = P\{Y = x\}$$

For example, it follows from Example 8a that the ith ball withdrawn will be special with probability k/n, which is intuitively clear, since each of the n balls is equally likely to be the ith one selected.

Example 8b

In Example 8a, let Y_1 denote the selection number of the first special ball withdrawn, let Y_2 denote the additional number of balls that are then withdrawn until the second special ball appears, and, in general, let Y_i denote the additional number of balls withdrawn after the $(i-1)$ special ball is selected until the ith is selected, $i = 1, \ldots, k$. For instance, if $n = 4, k = 2$ and $X_1 = 1, X_2 = 0, X_3 = 0, X_4 = 1$, then $Y_1 = 1, Y_2 = 3$. Now, $Y_1 = i_1, Y_2 = i_2, \ldots, Y_k = i_k \Leftrightarrow X_{i_1} = X_{i_1 + i_2} = \cdots = X_{i_1 + \cdots + i_k} = 1, X_j = 0$, otherwise; thus, from the joint mass function of the X_i, we obtain

$$P\{Y_1 = i_1, Y_2 = i_2, \ldots, Y_k = i_k\} = \frac{k!(n-k)!}{n!} \quad i_1 + \cdots + i_k \le n$$

Hence, the random variables $Y_1, \ldots, Y_k$ are exchangeable. Note that it follows from this result that the number of cards one must select from a well-shuffled deck until an ace appears has the same distribution as the number of additional cards one must select after the first ace appears until the next one does, and so on. ∎

Example 8c

The following is known as Polya's urn model: Suppose that an urn initially contains n red and m blue balls. At each stage, a ball is randomly chosen, its color is noted, and it is then replaced along with another ball of the same color. Let $X_i = 1$ if the ith ball selected is red and let it equal 0 if the ith ball is blue, $i \ge 1$. To obtain a feeling for the joint probabilities of these X_i, note the following special cases:

$$P\{X_1 = 1, X_2 = 1, X_3 = 0, X_4 = 1, X_5 = 0\}$$
$$= \frac{n}{n+m} \frac{n+1}{n+m+1} \frac{m}{n+m+2} \frac{n+2}{n+m+3} \frac{m+1}{n+m+4}$$
$$= \frac{n(n+1)(n+2)m(m+1)}{(n+m)(n+m+1)(n+m+2)(n+m+3)(n+m+4)}$$

and

$$P\{X_1 = 0, X_2 = 1, X_3 = 0, X_4 = 1, X_5 = 1\}$$
$$= \frac{m}{n+m} \frac{n}{n+m+1} \frac{m+1}{n+m+2} \frac{n+1}{n+m+3} \frac{n+2}{n+m+4}$$
$$= \frac{n(n+1)(n+2)m(m+1)}{(n+m)(n+m+1)(n+m+2)(n+m+3)(n+m+4)}$$

By the same reasoning, for any sequence $x_1, \ldots, x_k$ that contains r ones and $k - r$ zeros, we have

$$P\{X_1 = x_1, \ldots, X_k = x_k\}$$
$$= \frac{n(n+1)\cdots(n+r-1)m(m+1)\cdots(m+k-r-1)}{(n+m)\cdots(n+m+k-1)}$$

Therefore, for any value of k, the random variables $X_1, \ldots, X_k$ are exchangeable.

An interesting corollary of the exchangeability in this model is that the probability that the ith ball selected is red is the same as the probability that the first ball selected is red, namely, $\frac{n}{n+m}$. (For an intuitive argument for this initially nonintuitive result, imagine that all the $n + m$ balls initially in the urn are of different types. That is, one is a red ball of type 1, one is a red ball of type 2, ..., one is a red ball type of n, one is a blue ball of type 1, and so on, down to the blue ball of type m. Suppose that when a ball is selected it is replaced along with another of its type. Then, by symmetry, the ith ball selected is equally likely to be of any of the $n + m$ distinct types. Because n of these $n + m$ types are red, the probability is $\frac{n}{n+m}$.) ∎

Our final example deals with continuous random variables that are exchangeable.

Example 8d

Let $X_1, X_2, \ldots, X_n$ be independent uniform $(0, 1)$ random variables, and denote their order statistics by $X_{(1)}, \ldots, X_{(n)}$. That is, $X_{(j)}$ is the jth smallest of $X_1, X_2, \ldots, X_n$. Also, let

$$Y_1 = X_{(1)},$$
$$Y_i = X_{(i)} - X_{(i-1)}, \quad i = 2, \ldots n$$

Show that $Y_1, \ldots, Y_n$ are exchangeable.

Solution The transformations

$$y_1 = x_1, \; y_i = x_i - x_{i-1}, \; i = 2, \ldots, n$$

yield

$$x_i = y_1 + \cdots + y_i \quad i = 1, \ldots, n$$

As it is easy to see that the Jacobian of the preceding transformations is equal to 1, so, from Equation (7.3), we obtain

$$f_{Y_1, \ldots, Y_n}(y_1, y_2, \ldots, y_n) = f(y_1, y_1 + y_2, \ldots, y_1 + \cdots + y_n)$$

where f is the joint density function of the order statistics. Hence, from Equation (6.1), we obtain that

$$f_{Y_1, \ldots, Y_n}(y_1, y_2, \ldots, y_n) = n! \quad 0 < y_1 < y_1 + y_2 < \cdots < y_1 + \cdots + y_n < 1$$

or, equivalently,

$$f_{Y_1, \ldots, Y_n}(y_1, y_2, \ldots, y_n) = n! \quad 0 < y_i < 1, i = 1, \ldots, n, \quad y_1 + \cdots + y_n < 1$$

Because the preceding joint density is a symmetric function of $y_1, \ldots, y_n$, we see that the random variables $Y_1, \ldots, Y_n$ are exchangeable. ∎

Summary

The *joint cumulative probability distribution function* of the pair of random variables X and Y is defined by

$$F(x,y) = P\{X \leq x, Y \leq y\} \qquad -\infty < x, y < \infty$$

All probabilities regarding the pair can be obtained from F. To find the individual probability distribution functions of X and Y, use

$$F_X(x) = \lim_{y \to \infty} F(x,y) \quad F_Y(y) = \lim_{x \to \infty} F(x,y)$$

If X and Y are both discrete random variables, then their *joint probability mass function* is defined by

$$p(i,j) = P\{X = i, Y = j\}$$

The individual mass functions are

$$P\{X = i\} = \sum_j p(i,j) \qquad P\{Y = j\} = \sum_i p(i,j)$$

The random variables X and Y are said to be *jointly continuous* if there is a function $f(x, y)$, called the *joint probability density function*, such that for any two-dimensional set C,

$$P\{(X,Y) \in C\} = \iint_C f(x,y)\, dx\, dy$$

It follows from the preceding formula that

$$P\{x < X < x + dx, y < Y < y + dy\} \approx f(x,y)\, dx\, dy$$

If X and Y are jointly continuous, then they are individually continuous with density functions

$$f_X(x) = \int_{-\infty}^{\infty} f(x,y) dy \qquad f_Y(y) = \int_{-\infty}^{\infty} f(x,y)\, dx$$

The random variables X and Y are *independent* if, for all sets A and B,

$$P\{X \in A, Y \in B\} = P\{X \in A\}P\{Y \in B\}$$

If the joint distribution function (or the joint probability mass function in the discrete case, or the joint density function in the continuous case) factors into a part depending only on x and a part depending only on y, then X and Y are independent.

In general, the random variables $X_1, \ldots, X_n$ are independent if, for all sets of real numbers $A_1, \ldots, A_n$,

$$P\{X_1 \in A_1, \ldots, X_n \in A_n\} = P\{X_1 \in A_1\} \cdots P\{X_n \in A_n\}$$

If X and Y are independent continuous random variables, then the distribution function of their sum can be obtained from the identity

$$F_{X+Y}(a) = \int_{-\infty}^{\infty} F_X(a - y)f_Y(y)dy$$

If $X_i, i = 1, \ldots, n$, are independent normal random variables with respective parameters μ_i and $\sigma_i^2, i = 1, \ldots, n$, then $\sum_{i=1}^{n} X_i$ is normal with parameters $\sum_{i=1}^{n} \mu_i$ and $\sum_{i=1}^{n} \sigma_i^2$.

If $X_i, i = 1, \ldots, n$, are independent Poisson random variables with respective parameters $\lambda_i, i = 1, \ldots, n$, then $\sum_{i=1}^{n} X_i$ is Poisson with parameter $\sum_{i=1}^{n} \lambda_i$.

If X and Y are discrete random variables, then the *conditional probability mass function* of X given that $Y = y$ is defined by

$$P\{X = x | Y = y\} = \frac{p(x,y)}{p_Y(y)}$$

where p is their joint probability mass function. Also, if X and Y are jointly continuous with joint density function f, then the *conditional probability density function* of X given that $Y = y$ is given by

$$f_{X|Y}(x|y) = \frac{f(x,y)}{f_Y(y)}$$

The ordered values $X_{(1)} \leq X_{(2)} \leq \cdots \leq X_{(n)}$ of a set of independent and identically distributed random variables are called the *order statistics* of that set. If the random variables are continuous and have density function f, then the joint density function of the order statistics is

$$f(x_1, \ldots, x_n) = n!f(x_1) \cdots f(x_n) \qquad x_1 \leq x_2 \leq \cdots \leq x_n$$

The random variables $X_1, \ldots, X_n$ are called *exchangeable* if the joint distribution of $X_{i_1}, \ldots, X_{i_n}$ is the same for every permutation $i_1, \ldots, i_n$ of $1, \ldots, n$.

Problems

6.1. Suppose that 2 pens are randomly selected without replacement from a box containing 3 red, 4 black and 5 blue pens. Find the joint probability mass function of X and Y when

(a) X denotes the number of red pens chosen and Y denotes the number of black pens chosen.

(b) X denotes the number of red pens and Y denotes the number of black or blue pens selected.

(c) X be equal to 1 if at least one red pen is selected and be equal to 0 otherwise and Y be equal to 1 if at least 1 blue pen is selected and 0 otherwise.

6.2. Suppose that 3 balls are chosen without replacement from an urn consisting of 5 white and 8 red balls. Let X_i equal 1 if the ith ball selected is white, and let it equal 0 otherwise. Give the joint probability mass function of

(a) X_1, X_2;

(b) X_1, X_2, X_3.

6.3. In Problem 6.2, suppose that the white balls are numbered, and let Y_i equal 1 if the ith white ball is selected and 0 otherwise. Find the joint probability mass function of

(a) Y_1, Y_2;

(b) Y_1, Y_2, Y_3.

6.4. Repeat Problem 6.2 when the ball selected is replaced in the urn before the next selection.

6.5. Repeat Problem 6.3a when the ball selected is replaced in the urn before the next selection.

6.6. A bin of 5 transistors is known to contain 2 that are defective. The transistors are to be tested, one at a time, until the defective ones are identified. Denote by N_1 the number of tests made until the first defective is identified and by N_2 the number of additional tests until the second defective is identified. Find the joint probability mass function of N_1 and N_2.

6.7. Consider a sequence of independent Bernoulli trials, each of which is a success with probability p. Let X_1 be the number of failures preceding the first success, and let X_2 be the number of failures between the first two successes. Find the joint mass function of X_1 and X_2.

6.8. The joint probability density function of X and Y is given by

$$f(x,y) = c(y^2 - x^2)e^{-y} \quad -y \le x \le y, 0 < y < \infty$$

(a) Find c.

(b) Find the marginal densities of X and Y.

(c) Find $E[X]$.

6.9. The joint density function of X and Y is given by

$$f(x,y) = \frac{6}{5}(x + y^2) \quad 0 < x < 1, 0 < y < 1$$

(a) Verify that $f(x, y)$ is a valid pdf.

(b) Find the marginal distribution of X.

(c) Find the marginal distribution of Y.

(d) Find $P(0 < X < 1/2/0 < Y < 1/2)$

(e) Find $E[X]$.

(f) Find $E[Y]$.

6.10. Let $f(x,y,z) = kxyz^2, 0 < x < 1, 0 < y < 1, 0 < z < 2$. be the joint density function of three random variables X, Y, and Z. Find $P(Z > X + Y)$.

6.11. Suppose you randomly pick an lot numbered from 1 to 4, with all possibilities being equally likely. Call this number N. You then randomly pick a lot numbered from N to 4, with all possibilities being equally likely. Call this second number M. What is the probability that M will be 2?

6.12. The number of people who enter a drugstore in a given hour is a Poisson random variable with parameter $\lambda = 10$. Compute the conditional probability that at most 3 men entered the drugstore, given that 10 women entered in that hour. What assumptions have you made?

6.13. Two persons A and B wait together at a certain bus stop at the same time (say time 0). Let the time taken for arrival of their busses be given by the random variables X and Y respectively.

$$f_1(x) = 1/10, \quad 0 \le x \le 10$$
$$f_2(x) = 1/15, \quad 0 \le x \le 15$$

What is the probability that bus of A will arrive before bus of B?

6.14. An ambulance travels back and forth at a constant speed along a road of length L. At a certain moment of time, an accident occurs at a point uniformly distributed on the road. [That is, the distance of the point from one of the fixed ends of the road is uniformly distributed over $(0, L)$.] Assuming that the ambulance's location at the moment of the accident is also uniformly distributed, and assuming independence of the variables, compute the distribution of the distance of the ambulance from the accident.

6.15. The random vector (X, Y) is said to be uniformly distributed over a region R in the plane if, for some constant c, its joint density is

$$f(x,y) = \begin{cases} c & \text{if}(x, y) \in R \\ 0 & \text{otherwise} \end{cases}$$

(a) Show that $1/c$ = area of region R.

Suppose that (X, Y) is uniformly distributed over the square centered at $(0, 0)$ and with sides of length 2.

(b) Show that X and Y are independent, with each being distributed uniformly over $(-1, 1)$.

(c) What is the probability that (X, Y) lies in the circle of radius 1 centered at the origin? That is, find $P\{X^2 + Y^2 \leq 1\}$.

6.16. Suppose that n points are independently chosen at random on the circumference of a circle, and we want the probability that they all lie in some semicircle. That is, we want the probability that there is a line passing through the center of the circle such that all the points are on one side of that line, as shown in the following diagram:

Let $P_1, \ldots, P_n$ denote the n points. Let A denote the event that all the points are contained in some semicircle, and let A_i be the event that all the points lie in the semicircle beginning at the point P_i and going clockwise for $180°, i = 1, \ldots, n$.

(a) Express A in terms of the A_i.

(b) Are the A_i mutually exclusive?

(c) Find $P(A)$.

6.17. Three points X_1, X_2, X_3 are selected at random on a line L. What is the probability that X_2 lies between X_1 and X_3?

6.18. Two points are selected randomly on a line of length L so as to be on opposite sides of the midpoint of the line. [In other words, the two points X and Y are independent random variables such that X is uniformly distributed over $(0, L/2)$ and Y is uniformly distributed over $(L/2, L)$.] Find the probability that the distance between the two points is greater than $L/3$.

6.19. Show that $f(x, y) = 1/x, 0 < y < x < 1$, is a joint density function. Assuming that f is the joint density function of X, Y, find

(a) the marginal density of Y;

(b) the marginal density of X;

(c) $E[X]$;

(d) $E[Y]$.

6.20. The joint density of X and Y are given by:
$f(x, y) = xe^{-(x+y)} x > 0, y > 0$

(a) Are X and Y independent?

(b) What are $f_X(x)$ and $f_Y(y)$?

(c) What is $P(X + Y > 2)$?

6.21. Random variables X and Y have joint density function $f(x, y) = 4xy \ 0 \leq x \leq 1, 0 \leq y \leq 1$

(a) Find $E[X]$.

(b) Find $E[Y]$.

(c) Find $E[X + Y]$.

6.22. The random variables X and Y have joint density function, $f(x, y) = k(2x + y) \ 2 < x < 6, 0 < y < 5$

(a) Obtain the constant k.

(b) Find the marginal densities of X and Y.

(c) Find $P(X + Y < 4)$.

6.23. The random variables X and Y have joint density function, $f(x, y) = \dfrac{1 + xy}{4} \ -1 \leq x \leq 1, -1 \leq y \leq 1$

(a) Are X and Y independent?

(b) Find $E[X]$.

(c) Find $E[Y]$.

(d) Find $Var(X)$.

(e) Find $Var(Y)$.

6.24. Consider independent trials, each of which results in outcome $i, i = 0, 1, \ldots, k$, with probability $p_i, \sum_{i=0}^{k} p_i = 1$. Let N denote the number of trials needed to obtain an outcome that is not equal to 0, and let X be that outcome.

(a) Find $P\{N = n\}, n \geq 1$.

(b) Find $P\{X = j\}, j = 1, \ldots, k$.

(c) Show that $P\{N = n, X = j\} = P\{N = n\}P\{X = j\}$.

(d) Is it intuitive to you that N is independent of X?

(e) Is it intuitive to you that X is independent of N?

6.25. Suppose that 10^6 people arrive at a service station at times that are independent random variables, each of which is uniformly distributed over $(0, 10^6)$. Let N denote the number that arrive in the first hour. Find an approximation for $P\{N = i\}$.

6.26. Suppose that A, B, C, are independent random variables, each being uniformly distributed over $(0, 1)$.

(a) What is the joint cumulative distribution function of A, B, C?

(b) What is the probability that all of the roots of the equation $Ax^2 + Bx + C = 0$ are real?

6.27. Let X and Y be independent exponential variables with means 1 and $(1/2)$ respectively. Then Find the value of $P(X > 2Y \mid X > Y)$.

6.28. The time that it takes to service a car is an exponential random variable with rate 1.

(a) If A. J. brings his car in at time 0 and M. J. brings her car in at time t, what is the probability that M. J.'s car is ready before A. J.'s car? (Assume that service times are independent and service begins upon arrival of the car.)

(b) If both cars are brought in at time 0, with work starting on M. J.'s car only when A. J.'s car has been completely serviced, what is the probability that M. J.'s car is ready before time 2?

6.29. The distance traveled my a sea farer in a day is normally distributed with mean 200 nautical miles and variance 64 nautical miles. What is the probability that,
(a) he travels 600 nautical miles in 3 days?
(b) he travels more than 200 nautical miles in at least one of the next 3 days?
Also state the independence assumptions made.

6.30. Runs scored by Virat Kohli and M.S.Dhoni in a one-day cricket match are approximately normally distributed with means 55 and 42 respectively and standard deviations 4 and 3 respectively. For an upcoming cricket match, assuming that the runs scored by these players are independent, what is the probability that
(a) Dhoni scores more runs than Virat?
(b) both of them score half-centuries? (more than 50 runs each)

6.31. According to the U.S. National Center for Health Statistics, 25.2 percent of males and 23.6 percent of females never eat breakfast. Suppose that random samples of 200 men and 200 women are chosen. Approximate the probability that
(a) at least 110 of these 400 people never eat breakfast;
(b) the number of the women who never eat breakfast is at least as large as the number of the men who never eat breakfast.

6.32. Monthly sales are independent normal random variables with mean 100 and standard deviation 5.
(a) Find the probability that exactly 3 of the next 6 months have sales greater than 100.
(b) Find the probability that the total of the sales in the next 4 months is greater than 420.

6.33. The expected number of typographical errors on a page of a certain magazine is .2. What is the probability that an article of 10 pages contains (a) 0 and (b) 2 or more typographical errors? Explain your reasoning!

6.34. You flip a fair coin. If the coin lands heads, you roll a fair die 10 times. If the coin lands tails, you roll the die 11 times. Let X be the number of heads and let Y be the total number of times that you roll a 6. Find $P(X = 1 | Y = 3)$

6.35. In Problem 6.4, calculate the conditional probability mass function of X_1 given that
(a) $X_2 = 1$;
(b) $X_2 = 0$.

6.36. In Problem 6.3, calculate the conditional probability mass function of Y_1 given that
(a) $Y_2 = 1$;
(b) $Y_2 = 0$.

6.37. In Problem 6.5, calculate the conditional probability mass function of Y_1 given that
(a) $Y_2 = 1$;
(b) $Y_2 = 0$.

6.38. Suppose Ram and Shyam roll two fair six-sided dice. Let the random variable X be the number shown on the Ram's die and Y be another random variable which takes the value 1, if Ram's die has a higher value than Shyam's die and takes the value 0, otherwise.
(a) Obtain the joint Probability mass function of X and Y.
(b) Find the conditional distribution function of X given $Y = 0$.

6.39. A fair die is rolled, and then a coin, with probability of heads p, is flipped as many times as the die roll says, i.e., if the result of the die roll is a 4, then the coin is flipped 4 times. Let X be the result of the die roll and Y be the number of times the coin lands heads. Find the joint probability mass function of X and Y. Are they independent?

6.40. The joint probability mass function of X and Y is given by

$$p(1,1) = \frac{1}{8} \qquad p(1,2) = \frac{1}{4}$$
$$p(2,1) = \frac{1}{8} \qquad p(2,2) = \frac{1}{2}$$

(a) Compute the conditional mass function of X given $Y = i, i = 1, 2$.
(b) Are X and Y independent?
(c) Compute $P\{XY \leq 3\}, P\{X + Y > 2\}, P\{X/Y > 1\}$.

6.41. The joint density function of X and Y is given by

$$f(x,y) = xe^{-x(y+1)} \quad x > 0, y > 0$$

(a) Find the conditional density of X, given $Y = y$, and that of Y, given $X = x$.
(b) Find the density function of $Z = XY$.

6.42. The joint density of X and Y is

$$f(x,y) = c(x^2 - y^2)e^{-x} \quad 0 \leq x < \infty, -x \leq y \leq x$$

Find the conditional distribution of Y, given $X = x$.

6.43. An insurance company supposes that each person has an accident parameter and that the yearly number of accidents of someone whose accident parameter is λ is Poisson distributed with mean λ. They also suppose that the parameter value of a newly insured person can be assumed to be the value of a gamma random variable with parameters s and α. If a newly insured person has n accidents in her first year, find the conditional density of her accident parameter. Also, determine the expected number of accidents that she will have in the following year.

6.44. Let A denote the area and L the length of the perimeter, of a rectangle with length X and height Y, such that X and Y are independent, and uniformly distributed on the interval $(0, 1)$.
(a) Obtain $E(A)$ and $E(L)$.
(b) Find the density function of A and L and verify the expectations obtained above.

6.45. A complex machine is able to operate effectively as long as at least 3 of its 5 motors are functioning. If each motor independently functions for a random amount of time with density function $f(x) = xe^{-x}, x > 0$, compute the density function of the length of time that the machine functions.

6.46. Two points are to be chosen at random on a line segment whose length is $a > 0$. Find the probability that the three line segments thus formed will be the sides of a triangle.

6.47. Two line segments, AB and CD, have lengths 8 and 6 units, respectively. Two points P and Q are to be chosen at random on AB and CD, respectively. Find that the probability that the area of a triangle will have height AP and that the base CQ will be greater than 12 square units.

6.48. If X_1, X_2, X_3, X_4, X_5 are independent and identically distributed exponential random variables with the parameter λ, compute
(a) $P\{\min(X_1, \ldots, X_5) \leq a\}$;
(b) $P\{\max(X_1, \ldots, X_5) \leq a\}$.

6.49. Let $X_{(1)}, X_{(2)}, \ldots, X_{(n)}$ be the order statistics of a set of n independent uniform $(0, 1)$ random variables. Find the conditional distribution of $X_{(n)}$ given that $X_{(1)} = s_1, X_{(2)} = s_2, \ldots, X_{(n-1)} = s_{n-1}$.

6.50. Let Z_1 and Z_2 be independent standard normal random variables. Show that X, Y has a bivariate normal distribution when $X = Z_1$, $Y = Z_1 + Z_2$.

6.51. Derive the distribution of the range of a sample of size 2 from a distribution having density function $f(x) = 2x, 0 < x < 1$.

6.52. Let X and Y denote the coordinates of a point uniformly chosen in the circle of radius 1 centered at the origin. That is, their joint density is

$$f(x, y) = \frac{1}{\pi} \quad x^2 + y^2 \leq 1$$

Find the joint density function of the polar coordinates $R = (X^2 + Y^2)^{1/2}$ and $\Theta = \tan^{-1} Y/X$.

6.53. If X and Y are independent random variables both uniformly distributed over $(0, 1)$, find the joint density function of $R = \sqrt{X^2 + Y^2}, \Theta = \tan^{-1} Y/X$.

6.54. If U is uniform on $(0, 2\pi)$ and Z, independent of U, is exponential with rate 1, show directly (without using the results of Example 7b) that X and Y defined by

$$X = \sqrt{2Z} \cos U$$
$$Y = \sqrt{2Z} \sin U$$

are independent standard normal random variables.

6.55. Let X and Y be independent random variables with uniform distribution on $(0, 1)$. Find
(a) $E(\min(X, Y))$
(b) $E(|X - Y|)$
(c) $E((X + Y)^2)$

6.56. If X and Y are independent and identically distributed uniform random variables on $(0, 1)$, compute the joint density of
(a) $U = X + Y, V = X/Y$;
(b) $U = X, V = X/Y$;
(c) $U = X + Y, V = X/(X + Y)$.

6.57. Repeat Problem 6.56 when X and Y are independent exponential random variables, each with parameter $\lambda = 1$.

6.58. If X_1 and X_2 are independent exponential random variables, each having parameter λ, find the joint density function of $Y_1 = X_1 + X_2$ and $Y_2 = e^{X_1}$.

6.59. Four tigers in a tiger reserve forest are monitored using geo-tags. If the waiting times for responses from 4 tigers in the reserve follow an iid exponential distribution with mean 3 minutes.
(a) What is the probability that all four responses will arrive within 8 minutes?
(b) If the system has to locate all four tigers within 5 minutes, it has to reduce the expected response time of each geo-tag. What is the maximum expected response time that will produce a location for all four vehicles within 5 minutes or less with at least 90% probability?

6.60. In Example 8b, let $Y_{k+1} = n + 1 - \sum_{i=1}^{k} Y_i$. Show that $Y_1, \ldots, Y_k, Y_{k+1}$ are exchangeable. Note that Y_{k+1} is the number of balls one must observe to obtain a special ball if one considers the balls in their reverse order of withdrawal.

6.61. Consider an urn containing n balls numbered $1, \ldots, n$, and suppose that k of them are randomly withdrawn. Let X_i equal 1 if ball number i is removed and let X_i be 0 otherwise. Show that $X_1, \ldots, X_n$ are exchangeable.

Theoretical Exercises

6.1. Verify Equation (1.2).

6.2. Suppose that the number of events occurring in a given time period is a Poisson random variable with parameter λ. If each event is classified as a type i event with probability p_i, $i = 1, \ldots, n, \sum p_i = 1$, independently of other events, show that the numbers of type i events that occur, $i = 1, \ldots, n$, are independent Poisson random variables with respective parameters λp_i, $i = 1, \ldots, n$.

6.3. Suggest a procedure for using Buffon's needle problem to estimate π. Surprisingly enough, this was once a common method of evaluating π.

6.4. Solve Buffon's needle problem when $L > D$.

ANSWER: $\dfrac{2L}{\pi D}(1 - \sin\theta) + 2\theta/\pi$, where $\cos\theta = D/L$.

6.5. In the Buffon's needle problem, for a needle of given length, what should be the side of a square so that the probability of intersection is maximum? Explain.

6.6. If X and Y are jointly continuous with joint density function $f_{X,Y}(x, y)$, show that $X + Y$ is continuous with density function

$$f_{X+Y}(t) = \int_{-\infty}^{\infty} f_{X,Y}(x, t - x)\, dx$$

6.7. (a) If X has a gamma distribution with parameters (t, λ), what is the distribution of $cX, c > 0$?

(b) Show that

$$\frac{1}{2\lambda}\chi^2_{2n}$$

has a gamma distribution with parameters n, λ when n is a positive integer and χ^2_{2n} is a chi-squared random variable with $2n$ degrees of freedom.

6.8. Let X and Y be independent continuous random variables with respective hazard rate functions $\lambda_X(t)$ and $\lambda_Y(t)$, and set $W = \min(X, Y)$.

(a) Determine the distribution function of W in terms of those of X and Y.

(b) Show that $\lambda_W(t)$, the hazard rate function of W, is given by

$$\lambda_W(t) = \lambda_X(t) + \lambda_Y(t)$$

6.9. Let $X_1, \ldots, X_n$ be independent exponential random variables having a common parameter λ. Determine the distribution of $\min(X_1, \ldots, X_n)$.

6.10. The lifetimes of batteries are independent exponential random variables, each having parameter λ. A flashlight needs 2 batteries to work. If one has a flashlight and a stockpile of n batteries, what is the distribution of time that the flashlight can operate?

6.11. Let $X_{(1)}, X_{(2)} \ldots X_{(n)}$ be the order statistics from a general continuous cdf F, $U_{(1)}, U_{(2)} \ldots U_{(n)}$ be the uniform order statistics. Then for $1 \le r_1 < r_2 < \ldots r_k \le n$,

$$P(X_{r_{(1)}} \le u_{(1)} \ldots X_{r_{(k)}} \le u_{(k)}) =$$
$$P(U_{r_{(1)}} \le F(u_{(1)}) \ldots U_{r_{(k)}} \le F(u_{(k)}))$$
$$\forall u_{(1)}, u_{(2)} \ldots u_{(k)}.$$

6.12. Show that the jointly continuous (discrete) random variables $X_1, \ldots, X_n$ are independent if and only if their joint probability density (mass) function $f(x_1, \ldots, x_n)$ can be written as

$$f(x_1, \ldots, x_n) = \prod_{i=1}^{n} g_i(x_i)$$

for nonnegative functions $g_i(x), i = 1, \ldots, n$.

6.13. Let $X_i's$ be independent random variables with some common distribution function F, and suppose they are independent of N, a geometric random variable with parameter p. If $M = max(X_1, X_2 \ldots X_N)$, obtain the distribution function of M while conditioning on N.

6.14. Suppose that X and Y are independent geometric random variables with the same parameter p.

(a) Without any computations, what do you think is the value of

$$P\{X = i | X + Y = n\}?$$

Hint: Imagine that you continually flip a coin having probability p of coming up heads. If the second head occurs on the nth flip, what is the probability mass function of the time of the first head?

(b) Verify your conjecture in part (a).

6.15. Consider a sequence of independent trials, with each trial being a success with probability p. Given that the kth success occurs on trial n, show that all possible outcomes of the first $n - 1$ trials that consist of $k - 1$ successes and $n - k$ failures are equally likely.

6.16. X and Y are independent poisson random variables with parameters λ_1 and λ_2. Given that $X + Y = n$, obtain the probability that X takes the value k ($k < n$)

6.17. If X and Y are independent geometric random variables. Show that $\min(X, Y)$ and $X - Y$ are independent.

6.18. Suppose X and Y are both integer-valued random variables. Let

$$p(i|j) = P(X = i|Y = j)$$

and

$$q(j|i) = P(Y = j|X = i)$$

Show that

$$P(X = i, Y = j) = \frac{p(i|j)}{\sum_i \frac{p(i|j)}{q(j|i)}}$$

6.19. Let X_1, X_2 and X_3 be independent exponential random variables with parameters α, β and γ. Then prove that

$$P(X < Y < Z) = \frac{\alpha}{\alpha + \beta + \gamma} \frac{\beta}{\beta + \gamma}$$

6.20. A stick of length L is to be broken into two parts. What is the probability that one part will have a length of more than double the other? State the assumptions made.

6.21. Suppose that W, the amount of moisture in the air on a given day, is a gamma random variable with parameters (t, β). That is, its density is $f(w) = \beta e^{-\beta w} (\beta w)^{t-1} / \Gamma(t)$, $w > 0$. Suppose also that given that $W = w$, the number of accidents during that day—call it N—has a Poisson distribution with mean w. Show that the conditional distribution of W given that $N = n$ is the gamma distribution with parameters $(t + n, \beta + 1)$.

6.22. Let W be a gamma random variable with parameters (t, β), and suppose that conditional on $W = w$, $X_1, X_2, \ldots, X_n$ are independent exponential random variables with rate w. Show that the conditional distribution of W given that $X_1 = x_1, X_2 = x_2, \ldots, X_n = x_n$ is gamma with parameters $\left(t + n, \beta + \sum_{i=1}^n x_i\right)$.

6.23. A rectangular array of mn numbers arranged in n rows, each consisting of m columns, is said to contain a *saddlepoint* if there is a number that is both the minimum of its row and the maximum of its column. For instance, in the array

$$\begin{array}{ccc} 1 & 3 & 2 \\ 0 & -2 & 6 \\ .5 & 12 & 3 \end{array}$$

the number 1 in the first row, first column is a saddlepoint. The existence of a saddlepoint is of significance in the theory of games. Consider a rectangular array of numbers as described previously and suppose that there are two individuals—A and B—who are playing the following game: A is to choose one of the numbers $1, 2, \ldots, n$ and B one of the numbers $1, 2, \ldots, m$. These choices are announced simultaneously, and if A chose i and B chose j, then A wins from B the amount specified by the number in the ith row, jth column of the array. Now suppose that the array contains a saddlepoint—say the number in the row r and column k—call this number x_{rk}. Now if player A chooses row r,

then that player can guarantee herself a win of at least x_{rk} (since x_{rk} is the minimum number in the row r). On the other hand, if player B chooses column k, then he can guarantee that he will lose no more than x_{rk} (since x_{rk} is the maximum number in the column k). Hence, as A has a way of playing that guarantees her a win of x_{rk} and as B has a way of playing that guarantees he will lose no more than x_{rk}, it seems reasonable to take these two strategies as being optimal and declare that the value of the game to player A is x_{rk}.

If the nm numbers in the rectangular array described are independently chosen from an arbitrary continuous distribution, what is the probability that the resulting array will contain a saddlepoint?

6.24. If X is exponential with rate λ, find $P\{[X] = n, X - [X] \le x\}$, where $[x]$ is defined as the largest integer less than or equal to x. Can you conclude that $[X]$ and $X - [X]$ are independent?

6.25. Let Y_r be the rth order statistics of X_i, $i = 1, \ldots, n$, uniformly distributed in $(0, 1)$. Show that Y_r has a beta distribution.

6.26. Show that if n people are distributed at random along a road L miles long, then the probability that no 2 people are less than a distance D miles apart is when $D \le L/(n-1)$, $[1 - (n-1)D/L]^n$. What if $D > L/(n-1)$?

6.27. Let X and Y be independent random variables, each distributed $N(0, 1)$. Define $R = \sqrt{X^2 + Y^2}$. Show that, for each $r > 0$, the conditional distribution of X given $R = r$ has density

$$h(x | R = r) = \frac{I(|x| > r)}{\pi\sqrt{r^2 - x^2}}$$

6.28. For Y_r defined as in Theoretical Problem 6.25, obtain $PY_r > p$ as the probability of an event associated with a sequence of n Bernoulli trials with probability of success p $(0 < p < 1)$ on a given trial.

6.29. At an archery competition, an arrow is shot at a rectangular target board. Let random variables X and Y denote the distance of the hit from the target point. If the probability of the hit being on any point of the xy plane depends only on the distance of the point from the target, show that (X, Y) is a bivariate normal random variable.

6.30. Let X and Y are non-degenerate positive random variables. Then show that if $A = X + Y$ and $B = X/Y$ are independent, X and Y are gamma distributed random variables with the same parameter.

6.31. Let $X_{(1)} \le X_{(2)} \le \cdots \le X_{(n)}$ be the ordered values of n independent uniform $(0, 1)$ random variables. Prove that for $1 \le k \le n + 1$,

$$P\{X_{(k)} - X_{(k-1)} > t\} = (1 - t)^n$$

where $X_{(0)} \equiv 0, X_{(n+1)} \equiv t$.

6.32. Let $X_1,\ldots,X_n$ be a set of independent and identically distributed continuous random variables having distribution function F, and let $X_{(i)}, i=1,\ldots,n$ denote their ordered values. If X, independent of the $X_i, i=1,\ldots,n$, also has distribution F, determine

(a) $P\{X > X_{(n)}\}$;
(b) $P\{X > X_{(1)}\}$;
(c) $P\{X_{(i)} < X < X_{(j)}\}, 1 \le i < j \le n$.

6.33. Let $X_1,\ldots,X_n$ be independent and identically distributed random variables having distribution function F and density f. The quantity $M \equiv [X_{(1)} + X_{(n)}]/2$, defined to be the average of the smallest and largest values in $X_1,\ldots,X_n$, is called the *midrange* of the sequence. Show that its distribution function is

$$F_M(m) = n \int_{-\infty}^{m} [F(2m - x) - F(x)]^{n-1} f(x)\, dx$$

6.34. Let $X_1,\ldots,X_n$ be independent uniform $(0, 1)$ random variables. Let $R = X_{(n)} - X_{(1)}$ denote the range and $M = [X_{(n)} + X_{(1)}]/2$ the midrange of $X_1,\ldots,X_n$. Compute the joint density function of R and M.

6.35. If X and Y are independent standard normal random variables, determine the joint density function of

$$U = X \quad V = \frac{X}{Y}$$

Then use your result to show that X/Y has a Cauchy distribution.

Self-Test Problems and Exercises

6.1. An unfair die roll results in number i with probability $i/k, i = 1, 2, 3\ldots n$.

(a) Find the constant value k.
(b) If the die is rolled 6 times, what is the probability that the face six will appear exactly once?
(c) Find the probability that three out of the 6 outcomes are even and three are odd.
(d) Find the probability that even numbered outcomes outnumber the odd numbered outcomes when die is rolled 6 times.

6.2. The joint probability mass function of the random variables X, Y, Z is
$$p(1,1,-1) = p(0,0,1) = p(-1,0,-1) = p(0,-1,-1) = 1/4$$
Find (a) $E(XYZ)$ (b) $E(XY + XZ + YZ)$

6.3. The joint density of X and Y is given by
$f(x,y) = kxy$, if $0 < 2y < x < 1$ and 0, elsewhere.

(a) Find the value of k.
(b) Find the density function of X.
(c) Find the density function of Y.
(d) Find $E[X]$.
(e) Find $E[Y]$.

6.4. Let $r = r_1 + \ldots + r_k$, where all r_i are positive integers. Argue that if $X_1,\ldots,X_r$ has a multinomial distribution, then so does $Y_1,\ldots,Y_k$ where, with $r_0 = 0$,

$$Y_i = \sum_{j=r_{i-1}+1}^{r_{i-1}+r_i} X_j, \quad i \le k$$

That is, Y_1 is the sum of the first r_1 of the X's, Y_2 is the sum of the next r_2, and so on.

6.5. Suppose that X, Y, and Z are independent random variables that are each equally likely to be either 1 or 2. Find the probability mass function of (a) XYZ, (b) $XY + XZ + YZ$, and (c) $X^2 + YZ$.

6.6. For the random variables X, Y with joint density function
$$f(x,y) = cx^2y(1- x)(y-1) \ \ 0 \le x \le 1, 0 \le y \le 1 \text{ and } 0,$$
otherwise
(a) For what value of c is this a joint density function?
(b) Are X and Y independent.
(c) Find $P(X+Y>1)$.

6.7. The joint density function of X and Y is

$$f(x,y) = \begin{cases} xy & 0 < x < 1, 0 < y < 2 \\ 0 & \text{otherwise} \end{cases}$$

(a) Are X and Y independent?
(b) Find the density function of X.
(c) Find the density function of Y.
(d) Find the joint distribution function.
(e) Find $E[Y]$.
(f) Find $P\{X + Y < 1\}$.

6.8. Consider two components and three types of shocks. A type 1 shock causes component 1 to fail, a type 2 shock causes component 2 to fail, and a type 3 shock causes both components 1 and 2 to fail. The times until shocks 1, 2, and 3 occur are independent exponential random variables with respective rates λ_1, λ_2, and λ_3. Let X_i denote the time at which component i fails, $i = 1, 2$. The random variables X_1, X_2 are said to have a joint bivariate exponential distribution. Find $P\{X_1 > s, X_2 > t\}$.

6.9. Consider a directory of classified advertisements that consists of m pages, where m is very large. Suppose that the number of advertisements per page varies and that your only method of finding out how many advertisements there are on a specified page is to count them. In addition, suppose that there are too many pages for it to be feasible to make a complete count of the total number of advertisements and that your objective is to choose a directory advertisement in such a way that each of them has an equal chance of being selected.

(a) If you randomly choose a page and then randomly choose an advertisement from that page, would that satisfy your objective? Why or why not?

Let $n(i)$ denote the number of advertisements on page $i, i = 1, \ldots, m$, and suppose that whereas these quantities are unknown, we can assume that they are all less than or equal to some specified value n. Consider the following algorithm for choosing an advertisement.

Step 1. Choose a page at random. Suppose it is page X. Determine $n(X)$ by counting the number of advertisements on page X.

Step 2. "Accept" page X with probability $n(X)/n$. If page X is accepted, go to step 3. Otherwise, return to step 1.

Step 3. Randomly choose one of the advertisements on page X.

Call each pass of the algorithm through step 1 an iteration. For instance, if the first randomly chosen page is rejected and the second accepted, then we would have needed 2 iterations of the algorithm to obtain an advertisement.

(b) What is the probability that a single iteration of the algorithm results in the acceptance of an advertisement on page i?

(c) What is the probability that a single iteration of the algorithm results in the acceptance of an advertisement?

(d) What is the probability that the algorithm goes through k iterations, accepting the jth advertisement on page i on the final iteration?

(e) What is the probability that the jth advertisement on page i is the advertisement obtained from the algorithm?

(f) What is the expected number of iterations taken by the algorithm?

6.10. The "random" parts of the algorithm in Self-Test Problem 6.8 can be written in terms of the generated values of a sequence of independent uniform $(0, 1)$ random variables, known as random numbers. With $[x]$ defined as the largest integer less than or equal to x, the first step can be written as follows:

Step 1. Generate a uniform $(0, 1)$ random variable U. Let $X = [mU] + 1$, and determine the value of $n(X)$.

(a) Explain why the above is equivalent to step 1 of Problem 6.8.

Hint: What is the probability mass function of X?

(b) Write the remaining steps of the algorithm in a similar style.

6.11. Let $X_1, X_2, \ldots$ be a sequence of independent uniform $(0, 1)$ random variables. For a fixed constant c, define the random variable N by

$$N = \min\{n : X_n > c\}$$

Is N independent of X_N? That is, does knowing the value of the first random variable that is greater than c affect the probability distribution of when this random variable occurs? Give an intuitive explanation for your answer.

6.12. The accompanying dartboard is a square whose sides are of length 6:

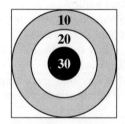

The three circles are all centered at the center of the board and are of radii 1, 2, and 3, respectively. Darts landing within the circle of radius 1 score 30 points, those landing outside this circle, but within the circle of radius 2, are worth 20 points, and those landing outside the circle of radius 2, but within the circle of radius 3, are worth 10 points. Darts that do not land within the circle of radius 3 do not score any points. Assuming that each dart that you throw will, independently of what occurred on your previous throws, land on a point uniformly distributed in the square, find the probabilities of the accompanying events:

(a) You score 20 on a throw of the dart.

(b) You score at least 20 on a throw of the dart.

(c) You score 0 on a throw of the dart.

(d) The expected value of your score on a throw of the dart.

(e) Both of your first two throws score at least 10.

(f) Your total score after two throws is 30.

6.13. A model proposed for NBA basketball supposes that when two teams with roughly the same record play each other, the number of points scored in a quarter by the home team minus the number scored by the visiting team is approximately a normal random variable with mean 1.5 and variance 6. In addition, the model supposes that the point differentials for the four quarters are independent. Assume that this model is correct.

(a) What is the probability that the home team wins?

(b) What is the conditional probability that the home team wins, given that it is behind by 5 points at halftime?

(c) What is the conditional probability that the home team wins, given that it is ahead by 5 points at the end of the first quarter?

6.14. Let $Y_1 < Y_2 < Y_3 < Y_4$ be the order statistics of X_1, X_2, X_3 and X_4, where the X_i are uniformly distributed in $(0, 1)$. Find the density of $R = Y_4 - Y_1$.

6.15. X and Y are independent exponentially distributed random variables, each with parameter λ. Then obtain the distribution for $Z = \dfrac{X-Y}{X+Y}$.

6.16. You and three other people are to place bids for an object, with the high bid winning. If you win, you plan to sell the object immediately for $10,000. How much should you bid to maximize your expected profit if you believe that the bids of the others can be regarded as being independent and uniformly distributed between $7,000 and $10,000 thousand dollars?

6.17. Find the probability that $X_1, X_2, \ldots, X_n$ is a permutation of $1, 2, \ldots, n$, when $X_1, X_2, \ldots, X_n$ are independent and

(a) each is equally likely to be any of the values $1, \ldots, n$;

(b) each has the probability mass function $P\{X_i = j\} = p_j, j = 1, \ldots, n$.

6.18. Let $X_1, \ldots, X_n$ and $Y_1, \ldots, Y_n$ be independent random vectors, with each vector being a random ordering of k ones and $n - k$ zeros. That is, their joint probability mass functions are

$$P\{X_1 = i_1, \ldots, X_n = i_n\} = P\{Y_1 = i_1, \ldots, Y_n = i_n\}$$

$$= \frac{1}{\dbinom{n}{k}}, \quad i_j = 0, 1, \sum_{j=1}^{n} i_j = k$$

Let

$$N = \sum_{i=1}^{n} |X_i - Y_i|$$

denote the number of coordinates at which the two vectors have different values. Also, let M denote the number of values of i for which $X_i = 1, Y_i = 0$.

(a) Relate N to M.

(b) What is the distribution of M?

(c) Find $E[N]$.

(d) Find $\text{Var}(N)$.

****6.19.** Let $Z_1, Z_2, \ldots, Z_n$ be independent standard normal random variables, and let

$$S_j = \sum_{i=1}^{j} Z_i$$

(a) What is the conditional distribution of S_n given that $S_k = y$, for $k = 1, \ldots, n$?

(b) Show that, for $1 \leq k \leq n$, the conditional distribution of S_k given that $S_n = x$ is normal with mean xk/n and variance $k(n - k)/n$.

6.20. Let $X_1, X_2, \ldots$ be a sequence of independent and identically distributed continuous random variables. Find

(a) $P\{X_6 > X_1 | X_1 = \max(X_1, \ldots, X_5)\}$

(b) $P\{X_6 > X_2 | X_1 = \max(X_1, \ldots, X_5)\}$

6.21. Prove the identity

$$P\{X \leq s, Y \leq t\} = P\{X \leq s\} + P\{Y \leq t\} + P\{X > s, Y > t\} - 1$$

Hint: Derive an expression for $P\{X > s, Y > t\}$ by taking the probability of the complementary event.

PROPERTIES OF EXPECTATION

Chapter 7

Contents

7.1 Introduction
7.2 Expectation of Sums of Random Variables
7.3 Moments of the Number of Events that Occur
7.4 Covariance, Variance of Sums, and Correlations

7.5 Conditional Expectation
7.6 Conditional Expectation and Prediction
7.7 Moment Generating Functions
7.8 Additional Properties of Normal Random Variables
7.9 General Definition of Expectation

7.1 Introduction

In this chapter, we develop and exploit additional properties of expected values. To begin, recall that the expected value of the random variable X is defined by

$$E[X] = \sum_x x p(x)$$

where X is a discrete random variable with probability mass function $p(x)$, and by

$$E[X] = \int_{-\infty}^{\infty} x f(x)\, dx$$

when X is a continuous random variable with probability density function $f(x)$.

Since $E[X]$ is a weighted average of the possible values of X, it follows that if X must lie between a and b, then so must its expected value. That is, if

$$P\{a \leq X \leq b\} = 1$$

then

$$a \leq E[X] \leq b$$

To verify the preceding statement, suppose that X is a discrete random variable for which $P\{a \leq X \leq b\} = 1$. Since this implies that $p(x) = 0$ for all x outside of the interval $[a, b]$, it follows that

$$E[X] = \sum_{x:p(x)>0} x p(x)$$

$$\geq \sum_{x:p(x)>0} a p(x)$$

$$= a \sum_{x:p(x)>0} p(x)$$

$$= a$$

In the same manner, it can be shown that $E[X] \leq b$, so the result follows for discrete random variables. As the proof in the continuous case is similar, the result follows.

7.2 Expectation of Sums of Random Variables

For a two-dimensional analog of Propositions 4.1 of Chapter 4 and 2.1 of Chapter 5, which give the computational formulas for the expected value of a function of a random variable, suppose that X and Y are random variables and g is a function of two variables. Then we have the following result.

Proposition 2.1 If X and Y have a joint probability mass function $p(x,y)$, then

$$E[g(X,Y)] = \sum_y \sum_x g(x,y)p(x,y)$$

If X and Y have a joint probability density function $f(x,y)$, then

$$E[g(X,Y)] = \int_{-\infty}^{\infty} \int_{-\infty}^{\infty} g(x,y)f(x,y)\,dx\,dy$$

Let us give a proof of Proposition 2.1 when the random variables X and Y are jointly continuous with joint density function $f(x,y)$ and when $g(X,Y)$ is a nonnegative random variable. Because $g(X,Y) \geq 0$, we have, by Lemma 2.1 of Chapter 5, that

$$E[g(X,Y)] = \int_0^{\infty} P\{g(X,Y) > t\}\,dt$$

Writing

$$P\{g(X,Y) > t\} = \int\int_{(x,y):g(x,y)>t} f(x,y)\,dy\,dx$$

shows that

$$E[g(X,Y)] = \int_0^{\infty} \int\int_{(x,y):g(x,y)>t} f(x,y)\,dy\,dx\,dt$$

Interchanging the order of integration gives

$$E[g(X,Y)] = \int_x \int_y \int_{t=0}^{g(x,y)} f(x,y)\,dt\,dy\,dx$$
$$= \int_x \int_y g(x,y)\,f(x,y)\,dy\,dx$$

Thus, the result is proven when $g(X,Y)$ is a nonnegative random variable. The general case then follows as in the one-dimensional case. (See Theoretical Exercises 2 and 3 of Chapter 5.)

Example 2a

An accident occurs at a point X that is uniformly distributed on a road of length L. At the time of the accident, an ambulance is at a location Y that is also uniformly distributed on the road. Assuming that X and Y are independent, find the expected distance between the ambulance and the point of the accident.

Solution We need to compute $E[|X - Y|]$. Since the joint density function of X and Y is

$$f(x,y) = \frac{1}{L^2}, \quad 0 < x < L, \quad 0 < y < L$$

it follows from Proposition 2.1 that

$$E[|X - Y|] = \frac{1}{L^2} \int_0^L \int_0^L |x - y| \, dy \, dx$$

Now,

$$\int_0^L |x - y| \, dy = \int_0^x (x - y) \, dy + \int_x^L (y - x) \, dy$$

$$= \frac{x^2}{2} + \frac{L^2}{2} - \frac{x^2}{2} - x(L - x)$$

$$= \frac{L^2}{2} + x^2 - xL$$

Therefore,

$$E[|X - Y|] = \frac{1}{L^2} \int_0^L \left(\frac{L^2}{2} + x^2 - xL \right) dx$$

$$= \frac{L}{3} \qquad \blacksquare$$

For an important application of Proposition 2.1, suppose that $E[X]$ and $E[Y]$ are both finite and let $g(X, Y) = X + Y$. Then, in the continuous case,

$$E[X + Y] = \int_{-\infty}^{\infty} \int_{-\infty}^{\infty} (x + y) f(x, y) \, dx \, dy$$

$$= \int_{-\infty}^{\infty} \int_{-\infty}^{\infty} x f(x, y) \, dy \, dx + \int_{-\infty}^{\infty} \int_{-\infty}^{\infty} y f(x, y) \, dx \, dy$$

$$= \int_{-\infty}^{\infty} x f_X(x) \, dx + \int_{-\infty}^{\infty} y f_Y(y) \, dy$$

$$= E[X] + E[Y]$$

The same result holds in general; thus, whenever $E[X]$ and $E[Y]$ are finite,

$$E[X + Y] = E[X] + E[Y] \tag{2.1}$$

Example 2b

Suppose that for random variables X and Y,

$$X \geq Y$$

That is, for any outcome of the probability experiment, the value of the random variable X is greater than or equal to the value of the random variable Y. Since $X \geq Y$ is equivalent to the inequality $X - Y \geq 0$, it follows that $E[X - Y] \geq 0$, or, equivalently,

$$E[X] \geq E[Y] \qquad \blacksquare$$

Using Equation (2.1), we may show by a simple induction proof that if $E[X_i]$ is finite for all $i = 1, \ldots, n$, then

$$E[X_1 + \cdots + X_n] = E[X_1] + \cdots + E[X_n] \tag{2.2}$$

Equation (2.2) is an extremely useful formula whose utility will now be illustrated by a series of examples.

Example 2c

The sample mean

Let $X_1, \ldots, X_n$ be independent and identically distributed random variables having distribution function F and expected value μ. Such a sequence of random variables is said to constitute a sample from the distribution F. The quantity

$$\overline{X} = \sum_{i=1}^{n} \frac{X_i}{n}$$

is called the *sample mean*. Compute $E[\overline{X}]$.

Solution

$$E[\overline{X}] = E\left[\sum_{i=1}^{n} \frac{X_i}{n}\right]$$

$$= \frac{1}{n} E\left[\sum_{i=1}^{n} X_i\right]$$

$$= \frac{1}{n} \sum_{i=1}^{n} E[X_i]$$

$$= \mu \quad \text{since } E[X_i] \equiv \mu$$

That is, the expected value of the sample mean is μ, the mean of the distribution. When the distribution mean μ is unknown, the sample mean is often used in statistics to estimate it. ∎

Example 2d

Boole's inequality

Let $A_1, \ldots, A_n$ denote events, and define the indicator variables $X_i, i = 1, \ldots, n$, by

$$X_i = \begin{cases} 1 & \text{if } A_i \text{ occurs} \\ 0 & \text{otherwise} \end{cases}$$

Let

$$X = \sum_{i=1}^{n} X_i$$

so X denotes the number of the events A_i that occur. Finally, let

$$Y = \begin{cases} 1 & \text{if } X \geq 1 \\ 0 & \text{otherwise} \end{cases}$$

so Y is equal to 1 if at least one of the A_i occurs and is 0 otherwise. Now, it is immediate that

$$X \geq Y$$

so

$$E[X] \geq E[Y]$$

But since

$$E[X] = \sum_{i=1}^{n} E[X_i] = \sum_{i=1}^{n} P(A_i)$$

and

$$E[Y] = P\{\text{at least one of the } A_i \text{ occur}\} = P\left(\bigcup_{i=1}^{n} A_i\right)$$

we obtain Boole's inequality, namely,

$$P\left(\bigcup_{i=1}^{n} A_i\right) \leq \sum_{i=1}^{n} P(A_i) \qquad \blacksquare$$

The next three examples show how Equation (2.2) can be used to calculate the expected value of binomial, negative binomial, and hypergeometric random variables. These derivations should be compared with those presented in Chapter 4.

Example 2e

Expectation of a binomial random variable

Let X be a binomial random variable with parameters n and p. Recalling that such a random variable represents the number of successes in n independent trials when each trial has probability p of being a success, we have that

$$X = X_1 + X_2 + \cdots + X_n$$

where

$$X_i = \begin{cases} 1 & \text{if the } i\text{th trial is a success} \\ 0 & \text{if the } i\text{th trial is a failure} \end{cases}$$

Hence, X_i is a Bernoulli random variable having expectation $E[X_i] = 1(p) + 0(1 - p)$. Thus,

$$E[X] = E[X_1] + E[X_2] + \cdots + E[X_n] = np \qquad \blacksquare$$

Example 2f

Mean of a negative binomial random variable

If independent trials having a constant probability p of being successes are performed, determine the expected number of trials required to amass a total of r successes.

Solution If X denotes the number of trials needed to amass a total of r successes, then X is a negative binomial random variable that can be represented by

$$X = X_1 + X_2 + \cdots + X_r$$

where X_1 is the number of trials required to obtain the first success, X_2 the number of additional trials until the second success is obtained, X_3 the number of additional trials until the third success is obtained, and so on. That is, X_i represents the number of additional trials required after the $(i - 1)$ success until a total of i successes is amassed. A little thought reveals that each of the random variables X_i is a geometric random variable with parameter p. Hence, from the results of Example 8b of Chapter 4, $E[X_i] = 1/p, i = 1, 2, \ldots, r$; thus,

$$E[X] = E[X_1] + \cdots + E[X_r] = \frac{r}{p} \qquad \blacksquare$$

Example 2g

Mean of a hypergeometric random variable

If n balls are randomly selected from an urn containing N balls of which m are white, find the expected number of white balls selected.

Solution Let X denote the number of white balls selected, and represent X as

$$X = X_1 + \cdots + X_m$$

where

$$X_i = \begin{cases} 1 & \text{if the } i\text{th white ball is selected} \\ 0 & \text{otherwise} \end{cases}$$

Now

$$E[X_i] = P\{X_i = 1\}$$
$$= P\{i\text{th white ball is selected}\}$$
$$= \frac{\dbinom{1}{1}\dbinom{N-1}{n-1}}{\dbinom{N}{n}}$$
$$= \frac{n}{N}$$

Hence,

$$E[X] = E[X_1] + \cdots + E[X_m] = \frac{mn}{N}$$

We could also have obtained the preceding result by using the alternative representation

$$X = Y_1 + \cdots + Y_n$$

where

$$Y_i = \begin{cases} 1 & \text{if the } i\text{th ball selected is white} \\ 0 & \text{otherwise} \end{cases}$$

Since the ith ball selected is equally likely to be any of the N balls, it follows that

$$E[Y_i] = \frac{m}{N}$$

so

$$E[X] = E[Y_1] + \cdots + E[Y_n] = \frac{nm}{N} \qquad \blacksquare$$

Example 2h

Expected number of matches

Suppose that N people throw their hats into the center of a room. The hats are mixed up, and each person randomly selects one. Find the expected number of people who select their own hat.

Solution Letting X denote the number of matches, we can compute $E[X]$ most easily by writing

$$X = X_1 + X_2 + \cdots + X_N$$

where

$$X_i = \begin{cases} 1 & \text{if the } i\text{th person selects his own hat} \\ 0 & \text{otherwise} \end{cases}$$

Since, for each i, the ith person is equally likely to select any of the N hats,

$$E[X_i] = P\{X_i = 1\} = \frac{1}{N}$$

Thus,

$$E[X] = E[X_1] + \cdots + E[X_N] = \left(\frac{1}{N}\right)N = 1$$

Hence, on the average, exactly one person selects his own hat. ∎

Example 2i

Coupon-collecting problems

Suppose that there are N types of coupons, and each time one obtains a coupon, it is equally likely to be any one of the N types. Find the expected number of coupons one needs to amass before obtaining a complete set of at least one of each type.

Solution Let X denote the number of coupons collected before a complete set is attained. We compute $E[X]$ by using the same technique we used in computing the mean of a negative binomial random variable (Example 2f). That is, we define $X_i, i = 0, 1, \ldots, N - 1$ to be the number of additional coupons that need be obtained after i distinct types have been collected in order to obtain another distinct type, and we note that

$$X = X_0 + X_1 + \cdots + X_{N-1}$$

When i distinct types of coupons have already been collected, a new coupon obtained will be of a distinct type with probability $(N - i)/N$. Therefore,

$$P\{X_i = k\} = \frac{N - i}{N}\left(\frac{i}{N}\right)^{k-1} \quad k \geq 1$$

or, in other words, X_i is a geometric random variable with parameter $(N - i)/N$. Hence,

$$E[X_i] = \frac{N}{N - i}$$

implying that

$$E[X] = 1 + \frac{N}{N - 1} + \frac{N}{N - 2} + \cdots + \frac{N}{1}$$

$$= N\left[1 + \cdots + \frac{1}{N - 1} + \frac{1}{N}\right]$$ ∎

Example 2j

Ten hunters are waiting for ducks to fly by. When a flock of ducks flies overhead, the hunters fire at the same time, but each chooses his target at random, independently of the others. If each hunter independently hits his target with probability p, compute the expected number of ducks that escape unhurt when a flock of size 10 flies overhead.

Solution Let X_i equal 1 if the ith duck escapes unhurt and 0 otherwise, for $i = 1,$ $2, \ldots, 10$. The expected number of ducks to escape can be expressed as

$$E[X_1 + \cdots + X_{10}] = E[X_1] + \cdots + E[X_{10}]$$

To compute $E[X_i] = P\{X_i = 1\}$, we note that each of the hunters will, independently, hit the ith duck with probability $p/10$, so

$$P\{X_i = 1\} = \left(1 - \frac{p}{10}\right)^{10}$$

Hence,

$$E[X] = 10\left(1 - \frac{p}{10}\right)^{10}$$ ∎

Example 2k

Expected number of runs

Suppose that a sequence of n 1's and m 0's is randomly permuted so that each of the $(n + m)!/(n!m!)$ possible arrangements is equally likely. Any consecutive string of 1's is said to constitute a run of 1's—for instance, if $n = 6, m = 4$, and the ordering is 1, 1, 1, 0, 1, 1, 0, 0, 1, 0, then there are 3 runs of 1's—and we are interested in computing the mean number of such runs. To compute this quantity, let

$$I_i = \begin{cases} 1 & \text{if a run of 1's starts at the } i\text{th position} \\ 0 & \text{otherwise} \end{cases}$$

Therefore, $R(1)$, the number of runs of 1, can be expressed as

$$R(1) = \sum_{i=1}^{n+m} I_i$$

and it follows that

$$E[R(1)] = \sum_{i=1}^{n+m} E[I_i]$$

Now,

$$E[I_1] = P\{\text{"1" in position 1}\}$$
$$= \frac{n}{n + m}$$

and for $1 < i \le n + m$,

$$E[I_i] = P\{\text{"0" in position } i - 1, \text{"1" in position } i\}$$
$$= \frac{m}{n + m}\frac{n}{n + m - 1}$$

Hence,

$$E[R(1)] = \frac{n}{n + m} + (n + m - 1)\frac{nm}{(n + m)(n + m - 1)}$$

Similarly, $E[R(0)]$, the expected number of runs of 0's, is

$$E[R(0)] = \frac{m}{n + m} + \frac{nm}{n + m}$$

and the expected number of runs of either type is

$$E[R(1) + R(0)] = 1 + \frac{2nm}{n + m}$$ ∎

Example
21

A random walk in the plane

Consider a particle initially located at a given point in the plane, and suppose that it undergoes a sequence of steps of fixed length, but in a completely random direction. Specifically, suppose that the new position after each step is one unit of distance from the previous position and at an angle of orientation from the previous position that is uniformly distributed over $(0, 2\pi)$. (See Figure 7.1.) Compute the expected square of the distance from the origin after n steps.

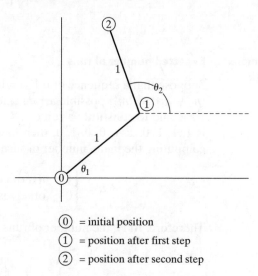

$\textcircled{0}$ = initial position
$\textcircled{1}$ = position after first step
$\textcircled{2}$ = position after second step

Figure 7.1

Solution Letting (X_i, Y_i) denote the change in position at the ith step, $i = 1, \ldots, n$, in rectangular coordinates, we have

$$X_i = \cos \theta_i$$
$$Y_i = \sin \theta_i$$

where $\theta_i, i = 1, \ldots, n$, are, by assumption, independent uniform $(0, 2\pi)$ random variables. Because the position after n steps has rectangular coordinates $\left(\sum_{i=1}^{n} X_i, \sum_{i=1}^{n} Y_i \right)$, it follows that D^2, the square of the distance from the origin, is given by

$$D^2 = \left(\sum_{i=1}^{n} X_i \right)^2 + \left(\sum_{i=1}^{n} Y_i \right)^2$$

$$= \sum_{i=1}^{n} (X_i^2 + Y_i^2) + \sum \sum_{i \neq j} (X_i X_j + Y_i Y_j)$$

$$= n + \sum \sum_{i \neq j} (\cos \theta_i \cos \theta_j + \sin \theta_i \sin \theta_j)$$

where $\cos^2 \theta_i + \sin^2 \theta_i = 1$. Taking expectations and using the independence of θ_i and θ_j when $i \neq j$ and the fact that

$$2\pi E[\cos \theta_i] = \int_0^{2\pi} \cos u \, du = \sin 2\pi - \sin 0 = 0$$

$$2\pi E[\sin \theta_i] = \int_0^{2\pi} \sin u \, du = \cos 0 - \cos 2\pi = 0$$

we arrive at

$$E[D^2] = n \qquad \blacksquare$$

Example 2m

Analyzing the quick-sort algorithm

Suppose that we are presented with a set of n distinct values $x_1, x_2, \ldots, x_n$ and that we desire to put them in increasing order, or as it is commonly stated, to *sort* them. An efficient procedure for accomplishing this task is the quick-sort algorithm, which is defined as follows: When $n = 2$, the algorithm compares the two values and then puts them in the appropriate order. When $n > 2$, one of the elements is randomly chosen—say it is x_i—and then all of the other values are compared with x_i. Those smaller than x_i are put in a bracket to the left of x_i and those larger than x_i are put in a bracket to the right of x_i. The algorithm then repeats itself on these brackets and continues until all values have been sorted. For instance, suppose that we desire to sort the following 10 distinct values:

$$5, 9, 3, 10, 11, 14, 8, 4, 17, 6$$

We start by choosing one of them at random (that is, each value has probability $\frac{1}{10}$ of being chosen). Suppose, for instance, that the value 10 is chosen. We then compare each of the others to this value, putting in a bracket to the left of 10 all those values smaller than 10 and to the right all those larger. This gives

$$\{5, 9, 3, 8, 4, 6\}, 10, \{11, 14, 17\}$$

We now focus on a bracketed set that contains more than a single value—say the one on the left of the preceding—and randomly choose one of its values—say that 6 is chosen. Comparing each of the values in the bracket with 6 and putting the smaller ones in a new bracket to the left of 6 and the larger ones in a bracket to the right of 6 gives

$$\{5, 3, 4\}, 6, \{9, 8\}, 10, \{11, 14, 17\}$$

If we now consider the leftmost bracket, and randomly choose the value 4 for comparison, then the next iteration yields

$$\{3\}, 4, \{5\}, 6, \{9, 8\}, 10, \{11, 14, 17\}$$

This continues until there is no bracketed set that contains more than a single value.

If we let X denote the number of comparisons that it takes the quick-sort algorithm to sort n distinct numbers, then $E[X]$ is a measure of the effectiveness of this algorithm. To compute $E[X]$, we will first express X as a sum of other random variables as follows. To begin, give the following names to the values that are to be sorted: Let 1 stand for the smallest, let 2 stand for the next smallest, and so on. Then, for $1 \leq i < j \leq n$, let $I(i, j)$ equal 1 if i and j are ever directly compared, and let it equal 0 otherwise. With this definition, it follows that

$$X = \sum_{i=1}^{n-1} \sum_{j=i+1}^{n} I(i,j)$$

implying that

$$E[X] = E\left[\sum_{i=1}^{n-1} \sum_{j=i+1}^{n} I(i,j)\right]$$

$$= \sum_{i=1}^{n-1} \sum_{j=i+1}^{n} E[I(i,j)]$$

$$= \sum_{i=1}^{n-1} \sum_{j=i+1}^{n} P\{i \text{ and } j \text{ are ever compared}\}$$

To determine the probability that i and j are ever compared, note that the values $i, i+1, \ldots, j-1, j$ will initially be in the same bracket (since all values are initially in the same bracket) and will remain in the same bracket if the number chosen for the first comparison is not between i and j. For instance, if the comparison number is larger than j, then all the values $i, i+1, \ldots, j-1, j$ will go in a bracket to the left of the comparison number, and if it is smaller than i, then they will all go in a bracket to the right. Thus all the values $i, i+1, \ldots, j-1, j$ will remain in the same bracket until the first time that one of them is chosen as a comparison value. At that point all the other values between i and j will be compared with this comparison value. Now, if this comparison value is neither i nor j, then upon comparison with it, i will go into a left bracket and j into a right bracket, and thus i and j will be in different brackets and so will never be compared. On the other hand, if the comparison value of the set $i, i+1, \ldots, j-1, j$ is either i or j, then there will be a direct comparison between i and j. Now, given that the comparison value is one of the values between i and j, it follows that it is equally likely to be any of these $j - i + 1$ values, and thus the probability that it is either i or j is $2/(j - i + 1)$. Therefore, we can conclude that

$$P\{i \text{ and } j \text{ are ever compared}\} = \frac{2}{j - i + 1}$$

and

$$E[X] = \sum_{i=1}^{n-1} \sum_{j=i+1}^{n} \frac{2}{j - i + 1}$$

To obtain a rough approximation of the magnitude of $E[X]$ when n is large, we can approximate the sums by integrals. Now

$$\sum_{j=i+1}^{n} \frac{2}{j - i + 1} \approx \int_{i+1}^{n} \frac{2}{x - i + 1} \, dx$$

$$= 2\log(x - i + 1)\big|_{i+1}^{n}$$

$$= 2\log(n - i + 1) - 2\log(2)$$

$$\approx 2\log(n - i + 1)$$

Thus

$$E[X] \approx \sum_{i=1}^{n-1} 2 \log(n - i + 1)$$

$$\approx 2 \int_1^{n-1} \log(n - x + 1)\, dx$$

$$= 2 \int_2^n \log(y)\, dy$$

$$= 2(y \log(y) - y)|_2^n$$

$$\approx 2n \log(n)$$

Thus we see that when n is large, the quick-sort algorithm requires, on average, approximately $2n \log(n)$ comparisons to sort n distinct values. ■

Example 2n

The probability of a union of events

Let $A_1, \ldots A_n$ denote events, and define the indicator variables $X_i, i = 1, \ldots, n$, by

$$X_i = \begin{cases} 1 & \text{if } A_i \text{ occurs} \\ 0 & \text{otherwise} \end{cases}$$

Now, note that

$$1 - \prod_{i=1}^{n}(1 - X_i) = \begin{cases} 1 & \text{if } \cup A_i \text{ occurs} \\ 0 & \text{otherwise} \end{cases}$$

Hence,

$$E\left[1 - \prod_{i=1}^{n}(1 - X_i)\right] = P\left(\bigcup_{i=1}^{n} A_i\right)$$

Expanding the left side of the preceding formula yields

$$P\left(\bigcup_{i=1}^{n} A_i\right) = E\left[\sum_{i=1}^{n} X_i - \sum\sum_{i<j} X_i X_j + \sum\sum\sum_{i<j<k} X_i X_j X_k\right.$$

$$\left. - \cdots + (-1)^{n+1} X_1 \cdots X_n\right] \qquad (2.3)$$

However,

$$X_{i_1} X_{i_2} \cdots X_{i_k} = \begin{cases} 1 & \text{if } A_{i_1} A_{i_2} \cdots A_{i_k} \text{ occurs} \\ 0 & \text{otherwise} \end{cases}$$

so

$$E[X_{i_1} \cdots X_{i_k}] = P(A_{i_1} \cdots A_{i_k})$$

Thus, Equation (2.3) is just a statement of the well-known formula for the union of events:

$$P(\cup A_i) = \sum_i P(A_i) - \sum\sum_{i<j} P(A_i A_j) + \sum\sum\sum_{i<j<k} P(A_i A_j A_k)$$

$$- \cdots + (-1)^{n+1} P(A_1 \cdots A_n)$$

■

When one is dealing with an infinite collection of random variables $X_i, i \geq 1$, each having a finite expectation, it is not necessarily true that

$$E\left[\sum_{i=1}^{\infty} X_i\right] = \sum_{i=1}^{\infty} E[X_i] \qquad (2.4)$$

To determine when (2.4) is valid, we note that $\sum_{i=1}^{\infty} X_i = \lim_{n \to \infty} \sum_{i=1}^{n} X_i$. Thus,

$$\begin{aligned}
E\left[\sum_{i=1}^{\infty} X_i\right] &= E\left[\lim_{n \to \infty} \sum_{i=1}^{n} X_i\right] \\
&\stackrel{?}{=} \lim_{n \to \infty} E\left[\sum_{i=1}^{n} X_i\right] \\
&= \lim_{n \to \infty} \sum_{i=1}^{n} E[X_i] \\
&= \sum_{i=1}^{\infty} E[X_i]
\end{aligned} \qquad (2.5)$$

Hence, Equation (2.4) is valid whenever we are justified in interchanging the expectation and limit operations in Equation (2.5). Although, in general, this interchange is *not* justified, it can be shown to be valid in two important special cases:

1. The X_i are all nonnegative random variables. (That is, $P\{X_i \geq 0\} = 1$ for all i.)
2. $\sum_{i=1}^{\infty} E[|X_i|] < \infty$.

Example 2o

Consider any nonnegative, integer-valued random variable X. If, for each $i \geq 1$, we define

$$X_i = \begin{cases} 1 & \text{if } X \geq i \\ 0 & \text{if } X < i \end{cases}$$

then

$$\begin{aligned}
\sum_{i=1}^{\infty} X_i &= \sum_{i=1}^{X} X_i + \sum_{i=X+1}^{\infty} X_i \\
&= \sum_{i=1}^{X} 1 + \sum_{i=X+1}^{\infty} 0 \\
&= X
\end{aligned}$$

Hence, since the X_i are all nonnegative, we obtain

$$\begin{aligned}
E[X] &= \sum_{i=1}^{\infty} E(X_i) \\
&= \sum_{i=1}^{\infty} P\{X \geq i\}
\end{aligned} \qquad (2.6)$$

a useful identity. ∎

Example 2p

Suppose that n elements—call them $1, 2, \ldots, n$—must be stored in a computer in the form of an ordered list. Each unit of time, a request will be made for one of these elements—i being requested, independently of the past, with probability $P(i), i \geq 1$, $\sum_i P(i) = 1$. Assuming that these probabilities are known, what ordering minimizes the average position in the line of the element requested?

Solution Suppose that the elements are numbered so that $P(1) \geq P(2) \geq \cdots \geq P(n)$. To show that $1, 2, \ldots, n$ is the optimal ordering, let X denote the position of the requested element. Now, under any ordering—say, $O = i_1, i_2, \ldots, i_n$,

$$P_O\{X \geq k\} = \sum_{j=k}^{n} P(i_j)$$

$$\geq \sum_{j=k}^{n} P(j)$$

$$= P_{1,2,\ldots,n}\{X \geq k\}$$

Summing over k and using Equation (2.6) yields

$$E_o[X] \geq E_{1,2,\ldots,n}[X]$$

thus showing that ordering the elements in decreasing order of the probability that they are requested minimizes the expected position of the element requested. ∎

*7.2.1 Obtaining Bounds from Expectations via the Probabilistic Method

The probabilistic method is a technique for analyzing the properties of the elements of a set by introducing probabilities on the set and then studying an element chosen according to those probabilities. The technique was previously seen in Example 4l of Chapter 3, where it was used to show that a set contained an element that satisfied a certain property. In this subsection, we show how it can sometimes be used to bound complicated functions.

Let f be a function on the elements of a finite set A, and suppose that we are interested in

$$m = \max_{s \in A} f(s)$$

A useful lower bound for m can often be obtained by letting S be a random element of A for which the expected value of $f(S)$ is computable and then noting that $m \geq f(S)$ implies that

$$m \geq E[f(S)]$$

with strict inequality if $f(S)$ is not a constant random variable. That is, $E[f(S)]$ is a lower bound on the maximum value.

Example 2q

The maximum number of Hamiltonian paths in a tournament

A round-robin tournament of $n > 2$ contestants is a tournament in which each of the $\binom{n}{2}$ pairs of contestants play each other exactly once. Suppose that the players are numbered $1, 2, 3, \ldots, n$. The permutation $i_1, i_2, \ldots i_n$ is said to be a *Hamiltonian path* if i_1 beats i_2, i_2 beats $i_3, \ldots$, and i_{n-1} beats i_n. A problem of some interest is to determine the largest possible number of Hamiltonian paths.

As an illustration, suppose that there are 3 players. On the one hand, one of them wins twice, then there is a single Hamiltonian path. (For instance, if 1 wins twice and 2 beats 3, then the only Hamiltonian path is $1, 2, 3$.) On the other hand, if each of the players wins once, then there are 3 Hamiltonian paths. (For instance, if 1 beats 2, 2 beats 3, and 3 beats 1, then $1, 2, 3$; $2, 3, 1$; and $3, 1, 2$, are all Hamiltonians.) Hence, when $n = 3$, there is a maximum of 3 Hamiltonian paths.

We now show that there is an outcome of the tournament that results in more than $n!/2^{n-1}$ Hamiltonian paths. To begin, let the outcome of the tournament specify the result of each of the $\binom{n}{2}$ games played, and let A denote the set of all $2^{\binom{n}{2}}$ possible tournament outcomes. Then, with $f(s)$ defined as the number of Hamiltonian paths that result when the outcome is $s \in A$, we are asked to show that

$$\max_s f(s) \geq \frac{n!}{2^{n-1}}$$

To show this, consider the randomly chosen outcome S that is obtained when the results of the $\binom{n}{2}$ games are independent, with each contestant being equally likely to win each encounter. To determine $E[f(S)]$, the expected number of Hamiltonian paths that result from the outcome S, number the $n!$ permutations, and, for $i = 1, \ldots, n!$, let

$$X_i = \begin{cases} 1, & \text{if permutation } i \text{ is a Hamiltonian} \\ 0, & \text{otherwise} \end{cases}$$

Since

$$f(S) = \sum_i X_i$$

it follows that

$$E[f(S)] = \sum_i E[X_i]$$

Because, by the assumed independence of the outcomes of the games, the probability that any specified permutation is a Hamiltonian is $(1/2)^{n-1}$, it follows that

$$E[X_i] = P\{X_i = 1\} = (1/2)^{n-1}$$

Therefore,

$$E[f(S)] = n!(1/2)^{n-1}$$

Since $f(S)$ is not a constant random variable, the preceding equation implies that there is an outcome of the tournament having more than $n!/2^{n-1}$ Hamiltonian paths. ∎

Example 2r

A grove of 52 trees is arranged in a circular fashion. If 15 chipmunks live in these trees, show that there is a group of 7 consecutive trees that together house at least 3 chipmunks.

Solution Let the neighborhood of a tree consist of that tree along with the next six trees visited by moving in the clockwise direction. We want to show that for any choice of living accommodations of the 15 chipmunks, there is a tree that has at least

3 chipmunks living in its neighborhood. To show this, choose a tree at random and let X denote the number of chipmunks that live in its neighborhood. To determine $E[X]$, arbitrarily number the 15 chipmunks and for $i = 1, \ldots, 15$, let

$$X_i = \begin{cases} 1, & \text{if chipmunk } i \text{ lives in the neighborhood of the randomly chosen tree} \\ 0, & \text{otherwise} \end{cases}$$

Because

$$X = \sum_{i=1}^{15} X_i$$

we obtain that

$$E[X] = \sum_{i=1}^{15} E[X_i]$$

However, because X_i will equal 1 if the randomly chosen tree is any of the 7 trees consisting of the tree in which chipmunk i lives along with its 6 neighboring trees when moving in the counterclockwise direction,

$$E[X_i] = P\{X_i = 1\} = \frac{7}{52}$$

Consequently,

$$E[X] = \frac{105}{52} > 2$$

showing that there exists a tree with more than 2 chipmunks living in its neighborhood. ∎

*7.2.2 The Maximum–Minimums Identity

We start with an identity relating the maximum of a set of numbers to the minimums of the subsets of these numbers.

Proposition 2.2 For arbitrary numbers $x_i, i = 1, \ldots, n,$

$$\max_i x_i = \sum_i x_i - \sum_{i<j} \min(x_i, x_j) + \sum_{i<j<k} \min(x_i, x_j, x_k)$$
$$+ \ldots + (-1)^{n+1} \min(x_1, \ldots, x_n)$$

Proof We will give a probabilistic proof of the proposition. To begin, assume that all the x_i are in the interval $[0, 1]$. Let U be a uniform $(0, 1)$ random variable, and define the events $A_i, i = 1, \ldots, n,$ by $A_i = \{U < x_i\}$. That is, A_i is the event that the uniform random variable is less than x_i. Because at least one of these events A_i will occur if U is less than at least one of the values x_i, we have that

$$\cup_i A_i = \left\{ U < \max_i x_i \right\}$$

Therefore,

$$P(\cup_i A_i) = P\left\{ U < \max_i x_i \right\} = \max_i x_i$$

Also,

$$P(A_i) = P\{U < x_i\} = x_i$$

In addition, because all of the events $A_{i_1}, \ldots, A_{i_r}$ will occur if U is less than all the values $x_{i_1}, \ldots, x_{i_r}$, we see that the intersection of these events is

$$A_{i_1} \ldots A_{i_r} = \left\{ U < \min_{j=1,\ldots r} x_{i_j} \right\}$$

implying that

$$P(A_{i_1} \ldots A_{i_r}) = P\left\{ U < \min_{j=1,\ldots r} x_{i_j} \right\} = \min_{j=1,\ldots r} x_{i_j}$$

Thus, the proposition follows from the inclusion–exclusion formula for the probability of the union of events:

$$P(\cup_i A_i) = \sum_i P(A_i) - \sum_{i<j} P(A_i A_j) + \sum_{i<j<k} P(A_i A_j A_k)$$
$$+ \cdots + (-1)^{n+1} P(A_1 \ldots A_n)$$

When the x_i are nonnegative, but not restricted to the unit interval, let c be such that all the x_i are less than c. Then the identity holds for the values $y_i = x_i/c$, and the desired result follows by multiplying through by c. When the x_i can be negative, let b be such that $x_i + b > 0$ for all i. Therefore, by the preceding,

$$\max_i(x_i + b) = \sum_i (x_i + b) - \sum_{i<j} \min(x_i + b, x_j + b)$$
$$+ \cdots + (-1)^{n+1} \min(x_1 + b, \ldots, x_n + b)$$

Letting

$$M = \sum_i x_i - \sum_{i<j} \min(x_i, x_j) + \cdots + (-1)^{n+1} \min(x_1, \ldots, x_n)$$

we can rewrite the foregoing identity as

$$\max_i x_i + b = M + b\left(n - \binom{n}{2} + \cdots + (-1)^{n+1} \binom{n}{n} \right)$$

But

$$0 = (1 - 1)^n = 1 - n + \binom{n}{2} + \cdots + (-1)^n \binom{n}{n}$$

The preceding two equations show that

$$\max_i x_i = M$$

and the proposition is proven. $\square$

It follows from Proposition 2.2 that for any random variables $X_1, \ldots, X_n$,

$$\max_i X_i = \sum_i X_i - \sum_{i<j} \min(X_i, X_j) + \cdots + (-1)^{n+1} \min(X_1, \ldots, X_n)$$

Taking expectations of both sides of this equality yields the following relationship between the expected value of the maximum and those of the partial minimums:

$$E\left[\max_i X_i\right] = \sum_i E[X_i] - \sum_{i<j} E[\min(X_i, X_j)]$$

$$+ \cdots + (-1)^{n+1} E[\min(X_1, \ldots, X_n)] \qquad (2.7)$$

Example 2s

Coupon collecting with unequal probabilities

Suppose there are n types of coupons and that each time one collects a coupon, it is, independently of previous coupons collected, a type i coupon with probability p_i, $\sum_{i=1}^{n} p_i = 1$. Find the expected number of coupons one needs to collect to obtain a complete set of at least one of each type.

Solution If we let X_i denote the number of coupons one needs to collect to obtain a type i, then we can express X as

$$X = \max_{i=1,\ldots,n} X_i$$

Because each new coupon obtained is a type i with probability p_i, X_i is a geometric random variable with parameter p_i. Also, because the minimum of X_i and X_j is the number of coupons needed to obtain either a type i or a type j, it follows that for $i \neq j$, $\min(X_i, X_j)$ is a geometric random variable with parameter $p_i + p_j$. Similarly, $\min(X_i, X_j, X_k)$, the number needed to obtain any of types i, j, and k, is a geometric random variable with parameter $p_i + p_j + p_k$, and so on. Therefore, the identity (2.7) yields

$$E[X] = \sum_i \frac{1}{p_i} - \sum_{i<j} \frac{1}{p_i + p_j} + \sum_{i<j<k} \frac{1}{p_i + p_j + p_k}$$

$$+ \cdots + (-1)^{n+1} \frac{1}{p_1 + \cdots + p_n}$$

Noting that

$$\int_0^\infty e^{-px}\, dx = \frac{1}{p}$$

and using the identity

$$1 - \prod_{i=1}^{n}(1 - e^{-p_i x}) = \sum_i e^{-p_i x} - \sum_{i<j} e^{-(p_i+p_j)x} + \cdots + (-1)^{n+1} e^{-(p_1+\cdots+p_n)x}$$

shows, upon integrating the identity, that

$$E[X] = \int_0^\infty \left(1 - \prod_{i=1}^{n}(1 - e^{-p_i x})\right) dx$$

is a more useful computational form. ∎

7.3 Moments of the Number of Events that Occur

Many of the examples solved in the previous section were of the following form: For given events $A_1, \ldots, A_n$, find $E[X]$, where X is the number of these events that occur. The solution then involved defining an indicator variable I_i for event A_i such that

$$
I_i = \begin{cases} 1, & \text{if } A_i \text{ occurs} \\ 0, & \text{otherwise} \end{cases}
$$

Because

$$
X = \sum_{i=1}^{n} I_i
$$

we obtained the result

$$
E[X] = E\left[\sum_{i=1}^{n} I_i\right] = \sum_{i=1}^{n} E[I_i] = \sum_{i=1}^{n} P(A_i) \tag{3.1}
$$

Now suppose we are interested in the number of *pairs* of events that occur. Because $I_i I_j$ will equal 1 if both A_i and A_j occur and will equal 0 otherwise, it follows that the number of pairs is equal to $\sum_{i<j} I_i I_j$. But because X is the number of events that occur, it also follows that the number of pairs of events that occur is $\binom{X}{2}$. Consequently,

$$
\binom{X}{2} = \sum_{i<j} I_i I_j
$$

where there are $\binom{n}{2}$ terms in the summation. Taking expectations yields

$$
E\left[\binom{X}{2}\right] = \sum_{i<j} E[I_i I_j] = \sum_{i<j} P(A_i A_j) \tag{3.2}
$$

or

$$
E\left[\frac{X(X-1)}{2}\right] = \sum_{i<j} P(A_i A_j)
$$

giving that

$$
E[X^2] - E[X] = 2\sum_{i<j} P(A_i A_j) \tag{3.3}
$$

which yields $E[X^2]$, and thus $\text{Var}(X) = E[X^2] - (E[X])^2$.

Moreover, by considering the number of distinct subsets of k events that all occur, we see that

$$
\binom{X}{k} = \sum_{i_1 < i_2 < \ldots < i_k} I_{i_1} I_{i_2} \cdots I_{i_k}
$$

Taking expectations gives the identity

$$
E\left[\binom{X}{k}\right] = \sum_{i_1 < i_2 < \ldots < i_k} E[I_{i_1} I_{i_2} \cdots I_{i_k}] = \sum_{i_1 < i_2 < \ldots < i_k} P(A_{i_1} A_{i_2} \cdots A_{i_k}) \tag{3.4}
$$

**Example
3a**

Moments of binomial random variables

Consider n independent trials, with each trial being a success with probability p. Let A_i be the event that trial i is a success. When $i \neq j$, $P(A_iA_j) = p^2$. Consequently, Equation (3.2) yields

$$E\left[\binom{X}{2}\right] = \sum_{i<j} p^2 = \binom{n}{2}p^2$$

or

$$E[X(X - 1)] = n(n - 1)p^2$$

or

$$E[X^2] - E[X] = n(n - 1)p^2$$

Now, $E[X] = \sum_{i=1}^{n} P(A_i) = np$, so, from the preceding equation

$$\text{Var}(X) = E[X^2] - (E[X])^2 = n(n - 1)p^2 + np - (np)^2 = np(1 - p)$$

which is in agreement with the result obtained in Section 4.6.1.

In general, because $P(A_{i_1}A_{i_2}\cdots A_{i_k}) = p^k$, we obtain from Equation (3.4) that

$$E\left[\binom{X}{k}\right] = \sum_{i_1 < i_2 < \ldots < i_k} p^k = \binom{n}{k}p^k$$

or, equivalently,

$$E[X(X - 1)\cdots(X - k + 1)] = n(n - 1)\cdots(n - k + 1)p^k$$

The successive values $E[X^k]$, $k \geq 3$, can be recursively obtained from this identity. For instance, with $k = 3$, it yields

$$E[X(X - 1)(X - 2)] = n(n - 1)(n - 2)p^3$$

or

$$E[X^3 - 3X^2 + 2X] = n(n - 1)(n - 2)p^3$$

or

$$E[X^3] = 3E[X^2] - 2E[X] + n(n - 1)(n - 2)p^3$$
$$= 3n(n - 1)p^2 + np + n(n - 1)(n - 2)p^3$$ ∎

**Example
3b**

Moments of hypergeometric random variables

Suppose n balls are randomly selected from an urn containing N balls, of which m are white. Let A_i be the event that the ith ball selected is white. Then X, the number of white balls selected, is equal to the number of the events $A_1, \ldots, A_n$ that occur. Because the ith ball selected is equally likely to be any of the N balls, of which m are white, $P(A_i) = m/N$. Consequently, Equation (3.1) gives that $E[X] = \sum_{i=1}^{n} P(A_i) = nm/N$. Also, since

$$P(A_iA_j) = P(A_i)P(A_j|A_i) = \frac{m}{N}\frac{m - 1}{N - 1}$$

we obtain, from Equation (3.2), that

$$E\left[\binom{X}{2}\right] = \sum_{i<j} \frac{m(m-1)}{N(N-1)} = \binom{n}{2} \frac{m(m-1)}{N(N-1)}$$

or

$$E[X(X-1)] = n(n-1)\frac{m(m-1)}{N(N-1)}$$

showing that

$$E[X^2] = n(n-1)\frac{m(m-1)}{N(N-1)} + E[X]$$

This formula yields the variance of the hypergeometric, namely,

$$\begin{aligned}
\text{Var}(X) &= E[X^2] - (E[X])^2 \\
&= n(n-1)\frac{m(m-1)}{N(N-1)} + \frac{nm}{N} - \frac{n^2 m^2}{N^2} \\
&= \frac{mn}{N}\left[\frac{(n-1)(m-1)}{N-1} + 1 - \frac{mn}{N}\right]
\end{aligned}$$

which agrees with the result obtained in Example 8j of Chapter 4.

Higher moments of X are obtained by using Equation (3.4). Because

$$P(A_{i_1} A_{i_2} \cdots A_{i_k}) = \frac{m(m-1)\cdots(m-k+1)}{N(N-1)\cdots(N-k+1)}$$

Equation (3.4) yields

$$E\left[\binom{X}{k}\right] = \binom{n}{k}\frac{m(m-1)\cdots(m-k+1)}{N(N-1)\cdots(N-k+1)}$$

or

$$E[X(X-1)\cdots(X-k+1)]$$
$$= n(n-1)\cdots(n-k+1)\frac{m(m-1)\cdots(m-k+1)}{N(N-1)\cdots(N-k+1)} \quad \blacksquare$$

Example 3c

Moments in the match problem

For $i = 1, \ldots, N$, let A_i be the event that person i selects his or her own hat in the match problem. Then

$$P(A_i A_j) = P(A_i)P(A_j|A_i) = \frac{1}{N}\frac{1}{N-1}$$

which follows because, conditional on person i selecting her own hat, the hat selected by person j is equally likely to be any of the other $N-1$ hats, of which one is his own. Consequently, with X equal to the number of people who select their own hat, it follows from Equation (3.2) that

$$E\left[\binom{X}{2}\right] = \sum_{i<j} \frac{1}{N(N-1)} = \binom{N}{2}\frac{1}{N(N-1)}$$

thus showing that

$$E[X(X-1)] = 1$$

Therefore, $E[X^2] = 1 + E[X]$. Because $E[X] = \sum_{i=1}^{N} P(A_i) = 1$, we obtain that

$$\text{Var}(X) = E[X^2] - (E[X])^2 = 1.$$

Hence, both the mean and variance of the number of matches is 1. For higher moments, we use Equation (3.4), along with the fact that $P(A_{i_1} A_{i_2} \cdots A_{i_k}) = \frac{1}{N(N-1)\cdots(N-k+1)}$, to obtain

$$E\left[\binom{X}{k}\right] = \binom{N}{k} \frac{1}{N(N-1)\cdots(N-k+1)}$$

or

$$E[X(X-1)\cdots(X-k+1)] = 1 \qquad \blacksquare$$

Example 3d

Another coupon-collecting problem

Suppose that there are N distinct types of coupons and that, independently of past types collected, each new one obtained is type j with probability p_j, $\sum_{j=1}^{N} p_j = 1$. Find the expected value and variance of the number of different types of coupons that appear among the first n collected.

Solution We will find it more convenient to work with the number of uncollected types. So, let Y equal the number of types of coupons collected, and let $X = N - Y$ denote the number of uncollected types. With A_i defined as the event that there are no type i coupons in the collection, X is equal to the number of the events $A_1, \ldots, A_N$ that occur. Because the types of the successive coupons collected are independent, and, with probability $1 - p_i$ each new coupon is not type i, we have

$$P(A_i) = (1 - p_i)^n$$

Hence, $E[X] = \sum_{i=1}^{N} (1 - p_i)^n$, from which it follows that

$$E[Y] = N - E[X] = N - \sum_{i=1}^{N} (1 - p_i)^n$$

Similarly, because each of the n coupons collected is neither a type i nor a type j coupon, with probability $1 - p_i - p_j$, we have

$$P(A_i A_j) = (1 - p_i - p_j)^n, \quad i \neq j$$

Thus,

$$E[X(X-1)] = 2 \sum_{i<j} P(A_i A_j) = 2 \sum_{i<j} (1 - p_i - p_j)^n$$

or

$$E[X^2] = 2 \sum_{i<j} (1 - p_i - p_j)^n + E[X]$$

Hence, we obtain

$$\text{Var}(Y) = \text{Var}(X)$$
$$= E[X^2] - (E[X])^2$$
$$= 2 \sum_{i<j} (1 - p_i - p_j)^n + \sum_{i=1}^{N} (1 - p_i)^n - \left(\sum_{i=1}^{N} (1 - p_i)^n \right)^2$$

In the special case where $p_i = 1/N$, $i = 1, \ldots, N$, the preceding formulas give

$$E[Y] = N\left[1 - \left(1 - \frac{1}{N}\right)^n\right]$$

and

$$\text{Var}(Y) = N(N - 1)\left(1 - \frac{2}{N}\right)^n + N\left(1 - \frac{1}{N}\right)^n - N^2\left(1 - \frac{1}{N}\right)^{2n} \quad \blacksquare$$

Example 3e

The negative hypergeometric random variables

Suppose an urn contains $n + m$ balls, of which n are special and m are ordinary. These items are removed one at a time, with each new removal being equally likely to be any of the balls that remain in the urn. The random variable Y, equal to the number of balls that need be withdrawn until a total of r special balls have been removed, is said to have a *negative hypergeometric distribution*. The negative hypergeometric distribution bears the same relationship to the hypergeometric distribution as the negative binomial does to the binomial. That is, in both cases, rather than considering a random variable equal to the number of successes in a fixed number of trials (as are the binomial and hypergeometric variables), they refer to the number of trials needed to obtain a fixed number of successes.

To obtain the probability mass function of a negative hypergeometric random variable Y, note that Y will equal k if both

1. the first $k - 1$ withdrawals consist of $r - 1$ special and $k - r$ ordinary balls and
2. the kth ball withdrawn is special.

Consequently,

$$P\{Y = k\} = \frac{\binom{n}{r-1}\binom{m}{k-r}}{\binom{n+m}{k-1}} \frac{n - r + 1}{n + m - k + 1}$$

We will not, however, utilize the preceding probability mass function to obtain the mean and variance of Y. Rather, let us number the m ordinary balls as $o_1, \ldots, o_m$, and then, for each $i = 1, \ldots, n$, let A_i be the event that o_i is withdrawn before r special balls have been removed. Then, if X is the number of the events $A_1, \ldots, A_m$ that occur, it follows that X is the number of ordinary balls that are withdrawn before a total of r special balls have been removed. Consequently,

$$Y = r + X$$

showing that

$$E[Y] = r + E[X] = r + \sum_{i=1}^{m} P(A_i)$$

To determine $P(A_i)$, consider the $n + 1$ balls consisting of o_i along with the n special balls. Of these $n + 1$ balls, o_i is equally likely to be the first one withdrawn, or the second one withdrawn, $\ldots$, or the final one withdrawn. Hence, the probability that it is among the first r of these to be selected (and so is removed before a total or r special balls have been withdrawn) is $\frac{r}{n+1}$. Consequently,

$$P(A_i) = \frac{r}{n + 1}$$

and

$$E[Y] = r + m\frac{r}{n+1} = \frac{r(n+m+1)}{n+1}$$

Thus, for instance, the expected number of cards of a well-shuffled deck that would need to be turned over until a spade appears is $1 + \frac{39}{14} = 3.786$, and the expected number of cards that would need to be turned over until an ace appears is $1 + \frac{48}{5} = 10.6$.

To determine $\text{Var}(Y) = \text{Var}(X)$, we use the identity

$$E[X(X-1)] = 2\sum_{i<j} P(A_iA_j)$$

Now, $P(A_iA_j)$ is the probability that both o_i and o_j are removed before there have been a total of r special balls removed. So consider the $n + 2$ balls consisting of o_i, o_j, and the n special balls. Because all withdrawal orderings of these balls are equally likely, the probability that o_i and o_j are both among the first $r + 1$ of them to be removed (and so are both removed before r special balls have been withdrawn) is

$$P(A_iA_j) = \frac{\binom{2}{2}\binom{n}{r-1}}{\binom{n+2}{r+1}} = \frac{r(r+1)}{(n+1)(n+2)}$$

Consequently,

$$E[X(X-1)] = 2\binom{m}{2}\frac{r(r+1)}{(n+1)(n+2)}$$

so

$$E[X^2] = m(m-1)\frac{r(r+1)}{(n+1)(n+2)} + E[X]$$

Because $E[X] = m\frac{r}{n+1}$, this yields

$$\text{Var}(Y) = \text{Var}(X) = m(m-1)\frac{r(r+1)}{(n+1)(n+2)} + m\frac{r}{n+1} - \left(m\frac{r}{n+1}\right)^2$$

A little algebra now shows that

$$\text{Var}(Y) = \frac{mr(n+1-r)(n+m+1)}{(n+1)^2(n+2)} \qquad \blacksquare$$

Example 3f

Singletons in the coupon collector's problem

Suppose that there are n distinct types of coupons and that, independently of past types collected, each new one obtained is equally likely to be any of the n types. Suppose also that one continues to collect coupons until a complete set of at least one of each type has been obtained. Find the expected value and variance of the number of types for which exactly one coupon of that type is collected.

Solution Let X equal the number of types for which exactly one of that type is collected. Also, let T_i denote the ith type of coupon to be collected, and let A_i be the event that there is only a single type T_i coupon in the complete set. Because X is equal to the number of the events $A_1, \ldots, A_n$ that occur, we have

$$E[X] = \sum_{i=1}^{n} P(A_i)$$

Now, at the moment when the first type T_i coupon is collected, there remain $n - i$ types that need to be collected to have a complete set. Because, starting at this moment, each of these $n - i + 1$ types (the $n - i$ not yet collected and type T_i) is equally likely to be the last of these types to be collected, it follows that the type T_i will be the last of these types (and so will be a singleton) with probability $\frac{1}{n-i+1}$. Consequently, $P(A_i) = \frac{1}{n-i+1}$, yielding

$$E[X] = \sum_{i=1}^{n} \frac{1}{n - i + 1} = \sum_{i=1}^{n} \frac{1}{i}$$

To determine the variance of the number of singletons, let $S_{i,j}$, for $i < j$, be the event that the first type T_i coupon to be collected is still the only one of its type to have been collected at the moment that the first type T_j coupon has been collected. Then

$$P(A_i A_j) = P(A_i A_j | S_{i,j}) P(S_{i,j})$$

Now, $P(S_{i,j})$ is the probability that when a type T_i has just been collected, of the $n - i + 1$ types consisting of type T_i and the $n - i$ as yet uncollected types, a type T_i is not among the first $j - i$ of these types to be collected. Because type T_i is equally likely to be the first, or second, or $\ldots, n - i + 1$ of these types to be collected, we have

$$P(S_{i,j}) = 1 - \frac{j - i}{n - i + 1} = \frac{n + 1 - j}{n + 1 - i}$$

Now, conditional on the event $S_{i,j}$, both A_i and A_j will occur if, at the time the first type T_j coupon is collected, of the $n - j + 2$ types consisting of types T_i, T_j, and the $n - j$ as yet uncollected types, T_i and T_j are both collected after the other $n - j$. But this implies that

$$P(A_i A_j | S_{i,j}) = 2 \frac{1}{n - j + 2} \frac{1}{n - j + 1}$$

Therefore,

$$P(A_i A_j) = \frac{2}{(n + 1 - i)(n + 2 - j)}, \quad i < j$$

yielding

$$E[X(X - 1)] = 4 \sum_{i<j} \frac{1}{(n + 1 - i)(n + 2 - j)}$$

Consequently, using the previous result for $E[X]$, we obtain

$$\text{Var}(X) = 4 \sum_{i<j} \frac{1}{(n + 1 - i)(n + 2 - j)} + \sum_{i=1}^{n} \frac{1}{i} - \left(\sum_{i=1}^{n} \frac{1}{i} \right)^2 \qquad \blacksquare$$

7.4 Covariance, Variance of Sums, and Correlations

The following proposition shows that the expectation of a product of independent random variables is equal to the product of their expectations.

Proposition 4.1 If X and Y are independent, then, for any functions h and g,

$$E[g(X)h(Y)] = E[g(X)]E[h(Y)]$$

Proof Suppose that X and Y are jointly continuous with joint density $f(x,y)$. Then

$$E[g(X)h(Y)] = \int_{-\infty}^{\infty} \int_{-\infty}^{\infty} g(x)h(y)f(x,y)\,dx\,dy$$
$$= \int_{-\infty}^{\infty} \int_{-\infty}^{\infty} g(x)h(y)f_X(x)f_Y(y)\,dx\,dy$$
$$= \int_{-\infty}^{\infty} h(y)f_Y(y)dy \int_{-\infty}^{\infty} g(x)f_X(x)\,dx$$
$$= E[h(Y)]E[g(X)]$$

The proof in the discrete case is similar. □

Just as the expected value and the variance of a single random variable give us information about that random variable, so does the covariance between two random variables give us information about the relationship between the random variables.

Definition

The covariance between X and Y, denoted by Cov (X,Y), is defined by

$$\text{Cov}(X,Y) = E[(X - E[X])(Y - E[Y])]$$

Upon expanding the right side of the preceding definition, we see that

$$\text{Cov}(X,Y) = E[XY - E[X]Y - XE[Y] + E[Y]E[X]]$$
$$= E[XY] - E[X]E[Y] - E[X]E[Y] + E[X]E[Y]$$
$$= E[XY] - E[X]E[Y]$$

Note that if X and Y are independent, then, by Proposition 4.1, $\text{Cov}(X,Y) = 0$. However, the converse is not true. A simple example of two dependent random variables X and Y having zero covariance is obtained by letting X be a random variable such that

$$P\{X = 0\} = P\{X = 1\} = P\{X = -1\} = \frac{1}{3}$$

and defining

$$Y = \begin{cases} 0 & \text{if } X \neq 0 \\ 1 & \text{if } X = 0 \end{cases}$$

Now, $XY = 0$, so $E[XY] = 0$. Also, $E[X] = 0$. Thus,

$$\text{Cov}(X,Y) = E[XY] - E[X]E[Y] = 0$$

However, X and Y are clearly not independent.

The following proposition lists some of the properties of covariance.

Proposition 4.2
(i) $\text{Cov}(X,Y) = \text{Cov}(Y,X)$
(ii) $\text{Cov}(X,X) = \text{Var}(X)$
(iii) $\text{Cov}(aX,Y) = a\,\text{Cov}(X,Y)$

(iv) $\mathrm{Cov}\left(\sum_{i=1}^{n} X_i, \sum_{j=1}^{m} Y_j\right) = \sum_{i=1}^{n}\sum_{j=1}^{m}\mathrm{Cov}(X_i, Y_j)$

Proof of Proposition 4.2 Parts (i) and (ii) follow immediately from the definition of covariance, and part (iii) is left as an exercise for the reader. To prove part (iv), which states that the covariance operation is additive (as is the operation of taking expectations), let $\mu_i = E[X_i]$ and $v_j = E[Y_j]$. Then

$$E\left[\sum_{i=1}^{n} X_i\right] = \sum_{i=1}^{n}\mu_i, \quad E\left[\sum_{j=1}^{m} Y_j\right] = \sum_{j=1}^{m}v_j$$

and

$$\mathrm{Cov}\left(\sum_{i=1}^{n} X_i, \sum_{j=1}^{m} Y_j\right) = E\left[\left(\sum_{i=1}^{n} X_i - \sum_{i=1}^{n}\mu_i\right)\left(\sum_{j=1}^{m} Y_j - \sum_{j=1}^{m}v_j\right)\right]$$

$$= E\left[\sum_{i=1}^{n}(X_i - \mu_i)\sum_{j=1}^{m}(Y_j - v_j)\right]$$

$$= E\left[\sum_{i=1}^{n}\sum_{j=1}^{m}(X_i - \mu_i)(Y_j - v_j)\right]$$

$$= \sum_{i=1}^{n}\sum_{j=1}^{m}E[(X_i - \mu_i)(Y_j - v_j)]$$

where the last equality follows because the expected value of a sum of random variables is equal to the sum of the expected values. □

It follows from parts (ii) and (iv) of Proposition 4.2, upon taking $Y_j = X_j, j = 1, \ldots, n$, that

$$\mathrm{Var}\left(\sum_{i=1}^{n} X_i\right) = \mathrm{Cov}\left(\sum_{i=1}^{n} X_i, \sum_{j=1}^{n} X_j\right)$$

$$= \sum_{i=1}^{n}\sum_{j=1}^{n}\mathrm{Cov}(X_i, X_j)$$

$$= \sum_{i=1}^{n}\mathrm{Var}(X_i) + \sum\sum_{i\neq j}\mathrm{Cov}(X_i, X_j)$$

Since each pair of indices $i, j, i \neq j$, appears twice in the double summation, the preceding formula is equivalent to

$$\boxed{\mathrm{Var}\left(\sum_{i=1}^{n} X_i\right) = \sum_{i=1}^{n}\mathrm{Var}(X_i) + 2\sum\sum_{i<j}\mathrm{Cov}(X_i, X_j)} \qquad (4.1)$$

If $X_1, \ldots, X_n$ are pairwise independent, in that X_i and X_j are independent for $i \neq j$, then Equation (4.1) reduces to

$$\text{Var}\left(\sum_{i=1}^{n} X_i\right) = \sum_{i=1}^{n} \text{Var}(X_i)$$

The following examples illustrate the use of Equation (4.1).

Example 4a

Let $X_1, \ldots, X_n$ be independent and identically distributed random variables having expected value μ and variance σ^2, and as in Example 2c, let $\overline{X} = \sum_{i=1}^{n} X_i/n$ be the sample mean. The quantities $X_i - \overline{X}, i = 1, \ldots, n$, are called *deviations*, as they equal the differences between the individual data and the sample mean. The random variable

$$S^2 = \sum_{i=1}^{n} \frac{(X_i - \overline{X})^2}{n - 1}$$

is called the *sample variance*. Find (a) $\text{Var}(\overline{X})$ and (b) $E[S^2]$.

Solution

$$\text{(a)} \quad \text{Var}(\overline{X}) = \left(\frac{1}{n}\right)^2 \text{Var}\left(\sum_{i=1}^{n} X_i\right)$$

$$= \left(\frac{1}{n}\right)^2 \sum_{i=1}^{n} \text{Var}(X_i) \quad \text{by independence}$$

$$= \frac{\sigma^2}{n}$$

(b) We start with the following algebraic identity:

$$(n - 1)S^2 = \sum_{i=1}^{n}(X_i - \mu + \mu - \overline{X})^2$$

$$= \sum_{i=1}^{n}(X_i - \mu)^2 + \sum_{i=1}^{n}(\overline{X} - \mu)^2 - 2(\overline{X} - \mu)\sum_{i=1}^{n}(X_i - \mu)$$

$$= \sum_{i=1}^{n}(X_i - \mu)^2 + n(\overline{X} - \mu)^2 - 2(\overline{X} - \mu)n(\overline{X} - \mu)$$

$$= \sum_{i=1}^{n}(X_i - \mu)^2 - n(\overline{X} - \mu)^2$$

Taking expectations of the preceding yields

$$(n - 1)E[S^2] = \sum_{i=1}^{n} E[(X_i - \mu)^2] - nE[(\overline{X} - \mu)^2]$$

$$= n\sigma^2 - n\text{Var}(\overline{X})$$

$$= (n - 1)\sigma^2$$

where the final equality made use of part (a) of this example and the one preceding it made use of the result of Example 2c, namely, that $E[\overline{X}] = \mu$. Dividing through by $n - 1$ shows that the expected value of the sample variance is the distribution variance σ^2. ∎

Our next example presents another method for obtaining the variance of a binomial random variable.

Example 4b

Variance of a binomial random variable

Compute the variance of a binomial random variable X with parameters n and p.

Solution Since such a random variable represents the number of successes in n independent trials when each trial has the common probability p of being a success, we may write

$$X = X_1 + \cdots + X_n$$

where the X_i are independent Bernoulli random variables such that

$$X_i = \begin{cases} 1 & \text{if the } i\text{th trial is a success} \\ 0 & \text{otherwise} \end{cases}$$

Hence, from Equation (4.1), we obtain

$$\mathrm{Var}(X) = \mathrm{Var}(X_1) + \cdots + \mathrm{Var}(X_n)$$

But

$$\begin{aligned} \mathrm{Var}(X_i) &= E[X_i^2] - (E[X_i])^2 \\ &= E[X_i] - (E[X_i])^2 \quad \text{since } X_i^2 = X_i \\ &= p - p^2 \end{aligned}$$

Thus,

$$\mathrm{Var}(X) = np(1 - p)$$ ∎

Example 4c

Sampling from a finite population

Consider a set of N people, each of whom has an opinion about a certain subject that is measured by a real number v that represents the person's "strength of feeling" about the subject. Let v_i represent the strength of feeling of person i, $i = 1, \ldots N$.

Suppose that the quantities $v_i, i = 1, \ldots, N$, are unknown and, to gather information, a group of n of the N people is "randomly chosen" in the sense that all of the $\binom{N}{n}$ subsets of size n are equally likely to be chosen. These n people are then questioned and their feelings determined. If S denotes the sum of the n sampled values, determine its mean and variance.

An important application of the preceding problem is to a forthcoming election in which each person in the population is either for or against a certain candidate or proposition. If we take v_i to equal 1 if person i is in favor and 0 if he or she is against, then $\overline{v} = \sum_{i=1}^{N} v_i/N$ represents the proportion of the population that is in favor. To estimate $\overline{v}$, a random sample of n people is chosen, and these people are polled.

The proportion of those polled who are in favor—that is, S/n—is often used as an estimate of $\bar{v}$.

Solution For each person $i, i = 1, \ldots, N$, define an indicator variable I_i to indicate whether or not that person is included in the sample. That is,

$$I_i = \begin{cases} 1 & \text{if person } i \text{ is in the random sample} \\ 0 & \text{otherwise} \end{cases}$$

Now, S can be expressed by

$$S = \sum_{i=1}^{N} v_i I_i$$

so

$$E[S] = \sum_{i=1}^{N} v_i E[I_i]$$

$$\text{Var}(S) = \sum_{i=1}^{N} \text{Var}(v_i I_i) + 2 \sum\sum_{i<j} \text{Cov}(v_i I_i, v_j I_j)$$

$$= \sum_{i=1}^{N} v_i^2 \text{Var}(I_i) + 2 \sum\sum_{i<j} v_i v_j \text{Cov}(I_i, I_j)$$

Because

$$E[I_i] = \frac{n}{N}$$

$$E[I_i I_j] = \frac{n}{N} \frac{n-1}{N-1}$$

it follows that

$$\text{Var}(I_i) = \frac{n}{N}\left(1 - \frac{n}{N}\right)$$

$$\text{Cov}(I_i, I_j) = \frac{n(n-1)}{N(N-1)} - \left(\frac{n}{N}\right)^2$$

$$= \frac{-n(N-n)}{N^2(N-1)}$$

Hence,

$$E[S] = n \sum_{i=1}^{N} \frac{v_i}{N} = n\bar{v}$$

$$\text{Var}(S) = \frac{n}{N}\left(\frac{N-n}{N}\right) \sum_{i=1}^{N} v_i^2 - \frac{2n(N-n)}{N^2(N-1)} \sum\sum_{i<j} v_i v_j$$

The expression for Var(S) can be simplified somewhat by using the identity $(v_1 + \cdots + v_N)^2 = \sum_{i=1}^{N} v_i^2 + 2\sum\sum_{i<j} v_i v_j$. After some simplification, we obtain

$$\text{Var}(S) = \frac{n(N-n)}{N-1} \left(\frac{\sum_{i=1}^{N} v_i^2}{N} - \bar{v}^2 \right)$$

Consider now the special case in which Np of the v's are equal to 1 and the remainder equal to 0. Then, in this case, S is a hypergeometric random variable and has mean and variance given, respectively, by

$$E[S] = n\bar{v} = np \qquad \text{since } \bar{v} = \frac{Np}{N} = p$$

and

$$\text{Var}(S) = \frac{n(N-n)}{N-1} \left(\frac{Np}{N} - p^2 \right)$$
$$= \frac{n(N-n)}{N-1} p(1-p)$$

The quantity S/n, equal to the proportion of those sampled that have values equal to 1, is such that

$$E\left[\frac{S}{n} \right] = p$$
$$\text{Var}\left(\frac{S}{n} \right) = \frac{N-n}{n(N-1)} p(1-p) \qquad\blacksquare$$

The correlation of two random variables X and Y, denoted by $\rho(X, Y)$, is defined, as long as Var(X) Var(Y) is positive, by

$$\rho(X, Y) = \frac{\text{Cov}(X, Y)}{\sqrt{\text{Var}(X)\text{Var}(Y)}}$$

It can be shown that

$$-1 \le \rho(X, Y) \le 1 \qquad (4.2)$$

To prove Equation (4.2), suppose that X and Y have variances given by σ_x^2 and σ_y^2, respectively. Then, on the one hand,

$$0 \le \text{Var}\left(\frac{X}{\sigma_x} + \frac{Y}{\sigma_y} \right)$$
$$= \frac{\text{Var}(X)}{\sigma_x^2} + \frac{\text{Var}(Y)}{\sigma_y^2} + \frac{2\text{Cov}(X, Y)}{\sigma_x \sigma_y}$$
$$= 2[1 + \rho(X, Y)]$$

implying that

$$-1 \le \rho(X, Y)$$

On the other hand,

$$0 \le \text{Var}\left(\frac{X}{\sigma_x} - \frac{Y}{\sigma_y}\right)$$

$$= \frac{\text{Var}(X)}{\sigma_x^2} + \frac{\text{Var}(Y)}{(-\sigma_y)^2} - \frac{2\text{Cov}(X,Y)}{\sigma_x \sigma_y}$$

$$= 2[1 - \rho(X,Y)]$$

implying that

$$\rho(X,Y) \le 1$$

which completes the proof of Equation (4.2).

In fact, since $\text{Var}(Z) = 0$ implies that Z is constant with probability 1 (this intuitive relationship will be rigorously proven in Chapter 8), it follows from the proof of Equation (4.2) that $\rho(X,Y) = 1$ implies that $Y = a + bX$, where $b = \sigma_y/\sigma_x > 0$ and $\rho(X,Y) = -1$ implies that $Y = a + bX$, where $b = -\sigma_y/\sigma_x < 0$. We leave it as an exercise for the reader to show that the reverse is also true: that if $Y = a + bX$, then $\rho(X,Y)$ is either $+1$ or -1, depending on the sign of b.

The correlation coefficient is a measure of the degree of linearity between X and Y. A value of $\rho(X,Y)$ near $+1$ or -1 indicates a high degree of linearity between X and Y, whereas a value near 0 indicates that such linearity is absent. A positive value of $\rho(X,Y)$ indicates that Y tends to increase when X does, whereas a negative value indicates that Y tends to decrease when X increases. If $\rho(X,Y) = 0$, then X and Y are said to be *uncorrelated*.

Example 4d

Let I_A and I_B be indicator variables for the events A and B. That is,

$$I_A = \begin{cases} 1 & \text{if } A \text{ occurs} \\ 0 & \text{otherwise} \end{cases}$$

$$I_B = \begin{cases} 1 & \text{if } B \text{ occurs} \\ 0 & \text{otherwise} \end{cases}$$

Then

$$E[I_A] = P(A)$$
$$E[I_B] = P(B)$$
$$E[I_A I_B] = P(AB)$$

so

$$\text{Cov}(I_A, I_B) = P(AB) - P(A)P(B)$$
$$= P(B)[P(A|B) - P(A)]$$

Thus, we obtain the quite intuitive result that the indicator variables for A and B are either positively correlated, uncorrelated, or negatively correlated, depending on whether $P(A|B)$ is, respectively, greater than, equal to, or less than $P(A)$. ■

Our next example shows that the sample mean and a deviation from the sample mean are uncorrelated.

Example 4e

Let $X_1, \ldots, X_n$ be independent and identically distributed random variables having variance σ^2. Show that

$$\text{Cov}(X_i - \overline{X}, \overline{X}) = 0$$

Solution We have

$$\text{Cov}(X_i - \overline{X}, \overline{X}) = \text{Cov}(X_i, \overline{X}) - \text{Cov}(\overline{X}, \overline{X})$$

$$= \text{Cov}\left(X_i, \frac{1}{n}\sum_{j=1}^{n} X_j\right) - \text{Var}(\overline{X})$$

$$= \frac{1}{n}\sum_{j=1}^{n}\text{Cov}(X_i, X_j) - \frac{\sigma^2}{n}$$

$$= \frac{\sigma^2}{n} - \frac{\sigma^2}{n} = 0$$

where the next-to-last equality uses the result of Example 4a and the final equality follows because

$$\text{Cov}(X_i, X_j) = \begin{cases} 0 & \text{if } j \neq i \text{ by independence} \\ \sigma^2 & \text{if } j = i \text{ since } \text{Var}(X_i) = \sigma^2 \end{cases}$$

Although $\overline{X}$ and the deviation $X_i - \overline{X}$ are uncorrelated, they are not, in general, independent. However, in the special case where the X_i are normal random variables, it turns out that not only is $\overline{X}$ independent of a single deviation, but it is independent of the entire sequence of deviations $X_j - \overline{X}, j = 1, \ldots, n$. This result will be established in Section 7.8, where we will also show that, in this case, the sample mean $\overline{X}$ and the sample variance S^2 are independent, with $(n - 1)S^2/\sigma^2$ having a chi-squared distribution with $n - 1$ degrees of freedom. (See Example 4a for the definition of S^2.) ∎

Example 4f

Consider m independent trials, each of which results in any of r possible outcomes with probabilities $p_1, \ldots, p_r, \sum_{i=1}^{r} p_i = 1$. If we let $N_i, i = 1, \ldots, r$, denote the number of the m trials that result in outcome i, then $N_1, N_2, \ldots, N_r$ have the multinomial distribution

$$P\{N_1 = n_1, \ldots, N_r = n_r\} = \frac{m!}{n_1! \ldots n_r!}p_1^{n_1} \cdots p_r^{n_r}, \quad \sum_{i=1}^{r} n_i = m$$

For $i \neq j$, it seems likely that when N_i is large, N_j would tend to be small; hence, it is intuitive that they should be negatively correlated. Let us compute their covariance by using Proposition 4.2(iv) and the representation

$$N_i = \sum_{k=1}^{m} I_i(k) \quad \text{and} \quad N_j = \sum_{k=1}^{m} I_j(k)$$

where

$$I_i(k) = \begin{cases} 1 & \text{if trial } k \text{ results in outcome } i \\ 0 & \text{otherwise} \end{cases}$$

$$I_j(k) = \begin{cases} 1 & \text{if trial } k \text{ results in outcome } j \\ 0 & \text{otherwise} \end{cases}$$

From Proposition 4.2(iv), we have

$$\text{Cov}(N_i, N_j) = \sum_{\ell=1}^{m} \sum_{k=1}^{m} \text{Cov}(I_i(k), I_j(\ell))$$

Now, on the one hand, when $k \neq \ell$,

$$\text{Cov}(I_i(k), I_j(\ell)) = 0$$

since the outcome of trial k is independent of the outcome of trial ℓ. On the other hand,

$$\text{Cov}(I_i(\ell), I_j(\ell)) = E[I_i(\ell)I_j(\ell)] - E[I_i(\ell)]E[I_j(\ell)]$$
$$= 0 - p_i p_j = -p_i p_j$$

where the equation uses the fact that $I_i(\ell)I_j(\ell) = 0$, since trial ℓ cannot result in both outcome i and outcome j. Hence, we obtain

$$\text{Cov}(N_i, N_j) = -m p_i p_j$$

which is in accord with our intuition that N_i and N_j are negatively correlated. ∎

7.5 Conditional Expectation

7.5.1 Definitions

Recall that if X and Y are jointly discrete random variables, then the conditional probability mass function of X, given that $Y = y$, is defined for all y such that $P\{Y = y\} > 0$, by

$$p_{X|Y}(x|y) = P\{X = x|Y = y\} = \frac{p(x, y)}{p_Y(y)}$$

It is therefore natural to define, in this case, the conditional expectation of X given that $Y = y$, for all values of y such that $p_Y(y) > 0$, by

$$E[X|Y = y] = \sum_x x P\{X = x|Y = y\}$$
$$= \sum_x x p_{X|Y}(x|y)$$

Example 5a

If X and Y are independent binomial random variables with identical parameters n and p, calculate the conditional expected value of X given that $X + Y = m$.

Solution Let us first calculate the conditional probability mass function of X given that $X + Y = m$. For $k \leq \min(n, m)$,

$$P\{X = k|X + Y = m\} = \frac{P\{X = k, X + Y = m\}}{P\{X + Y = m\}}$$
$$= \frac{P\{X = k, Y = m - k\}}{P\{X + Y = m\}}$$
$$= \frac{P\{X = k\}P\{Y = m - k\}}{P\{X + Y = m\}}$$

$$= \frac{\binom{n}{k} p^k (1-p)^{n-k} \binom{n}{m-k} p^{m-k} (1-p)^{n-m+k}}{\binom{2n}{m} p^m (1-p)^{2n-m}}$$

$$= \frac{\binom{n}{k} \binom{n}{m-k}}{\binom{2n}{m}}$$

where we have used the fact (see Example 3f of Chapter 6) that $X + Y$ is a binomial random variable with parameters $2n$ and p. Hence, the conditional distribution of X, given that $X + Y = m$, is the hypergeometric distribution, and from Example 2g, we obtain

$$E[X|X + Y = m] = \frac{m}{2} \qquad \blacksquare$$

Similarly, let us recall that if X and Y are jointly continuous with a joint probability density function $f(x, y)$, then the conditional probability density of X, given that $Y = y$, is defined for all values of y such that $f_Y(y) > 0$ by

$$f_{X|Y}(x|y) = \frac{f(x, y)}{f_Y(y)}$$

It is natural, in this case, to define the conditional expectation of X, given that $Y = y$, by

$$E[X|Y = y] = \int_{-\infty}^{\infty} x f_{X|Y}(x|y) \, dx$$

provided that $f_Y(y) > 0$.

Example 5b

Suppose that the joint density of X and Y is given by

$$f(x, y) = \frac{e^{-x/y} e^{-y}}{y} \qquad 0 < x < \infty, \ 0 < y < \infty$$

Compute $E[X|Y = y]$.

Solution We start by computing the conditional density

$$f_{X|Y}(x|y) = \frac{f(x, y)}{f_Y(y)}$$

$$= \frac{f(x, y)}{\int_{-\infty}^{\infty} f(x, y) \, dx}$$

$$= \frac{(1/y) e^{-x/y} e^{-y}}{\int_{0}^{\infty} (1/y) e^{-x/y} e^{-y} \, dx}$$

$$= \frac{(1/y) e^{-x/y}}{\int_{0}^{\infty} (1/y) e^{-x/y} \, dx}$$

$$= \frac{1}{y} e^{-x/y}$$

Hence, the conditional distribution of X, given that $Y = y$, is just the exponential distribution with mean y. Thus,

$$E[X|Y = y] = \int_0^\infty \frac{x}{y} e^{-x/y} \, dx = y \qquad \blacksquare$$

Remark Just as conditional probabilities satisfy all of the properties of ordinary probabilities, so do conditional expectations satisfy the properties of ordinary expectations. For instance, such formulas as

$$E[g(X)|Y = y] = \begin{cases} \displaystyle\sum_x g(x) p_{X|Y}(x|y) & \text{in the discrete case} \\[2ex] \displaystyle\int_{-\infty}^\infty g(x) f_{X|Y}(x|y) \, dx & \text{in the continuous case} \end{cases}$$

and

$$E\left[\sum_{i=1}^n X_i \middle| Y = y\right] = \sum_{i=1}^n E[X_i|Y = y]$$

remain valid. As a matter of fact, conditional expectation given that $Y = y$ can be thought of as being an ordinary expectation on a reduced sample space consisting only of outcomes for which $Y = y$. $\blacksquare$

7.5.2 Computing Expectations by Conditioning

Let us denote by $E[X|Y]$ that function of the random variable Y whose value at $Y = y$ is $E[X|Y = y]$. Note that $E[X|Y]$ is itself a random variable. An extremely important property of conditional expectations is given by the following proposition.

Proposition 5.1

$$E[X] = E[E[X|Y]] \tag{5.1}$$

If Y is a discrete random variable, then Equation (5.1) states that

$$E[X] = \sum_y E[X|Y = y] P\{Y = y\} \tag{5.1a}$$

whereas if Y is continuous with density $f_Y(y)$, then Equation (5.1) states

$$E[X] = \int_{-\infty}^\infty E[X|Y = y] f_Y(y) \, dy \tag{5.1b}$$

We now give a proof of Equation (5.1) in the case where X and Y are both discrete random variables.

Proof of Equation (5.1) When X and Y Are Discrete: We must show that

$$E[X] = \sum_y E[X|Y = y] P\{Y = y\} \tag{5.2}$$

Now, the right-hand side of Equation (5.2) can be written as

$$\sum_y E[X|Y=y]P\{Y=y\} = \sum_y \sum_x xP\{X=x|Y=y\}P\{Y=y\}$$

$$= \sum_y \sum_x x \frac{P\{X=x, Y=y\}}{P\{Y=y\}} P\{Y=y\}$$

$$= \sum_y \sum_x xP\{X=x, Y=y\}$$

$$= \sum_x x \sum_y P\{X=x, Y=y\}$$

$$= \sum_x xP\{X=x\}$$

$$= E[X]$$

and the result is proved. □

One way to understand Equation (5.2) is to interpret it as follows: To calculate $E[X]$, we may take a weighted average of the conditional expected value of X given that $Y=y$, each of the terms $E[X|Y=y]$ being weighted by the probability of the event on which it is conditioned. (Of what does this remind you?) This is an extremely useful result that often enables us to compute expectations easily by first conditioning on some appropriate random variable. The following examples illustrate its use.

Example 5c

A miner is trapped in a mine containing 3 doors. The first door leads to a tunnel that will take him to safety after 3 hours of travel. The second door leads to a tunnel that will return him to the mine after 5 hours of travel. The third door leads to a tunnel that will return him to the mine after 7 hours. If we assume that the miner is at all times equally likely to choose any one of the doors, what is the expected length of time until he reaches safety?

Solution Let X denote the amount of time (in hours) until the miner reaches safety, and let Y denote the door he initially chooses. Now,

$$E[X] = E[X|Y=1]P\{Y=1\} + E[X|Y=2]P\{Y=2\}$$
$$+ E[X|Y=3]P\{Y=3\}$$
$$= \frac{1}{3}(E[X|Y=1] + E[X|Y=2] + E[X|Y=3])$$

However,

$$E[X|Y=1] = 3$$
$$E[X|Y=2] = 5 + E[X] \qquad (5.3)$$
$$E[X|Y=3] = 7 + E[X]$$

To understand why Equation (5.3) is correct, consider, for instance, $E[X|Y=2]$ and reason as follows: If the miner chooses the second door, he spends 5 hours in the tunnel and then returns to his cell. But once he returns to his cell, the problem is as before; thus, his expected additional time until safety is just $E[X]$. Hence, $E[X|Y=2] = 5 + E[X]$. The argument behind the other equalities in Equation (5.3) is similar. Hence,

$$E[X] = \frac{1}{3}(3 + 5 + E[X] + 7 + E[X])$$

or

$$E[X] = 15 \qquad \blacksquare$$

Example 5d

Expectation of a sum of a random number of random variables

Suppose that the number of people entering a department store on a given day is a random variable with mean 50. Suppose further that the amounts of money spent by these customers are independent random variables having a common mean of $8. Finally, suppose also that the amount of money spent by a customer is also independent of the total number of customers who enter the store. What is the expected amount of money spent in the store on a given day?

Solution If we let N denote the number of customers who enter the store and X_i the amount spent by the ith such customer, then the total amount of money spent can be expressed as $\sum_{i=1}^{N} X_i$. Now,

$$E\left[\sum_{1}^{N} X_i\right] = E\left[E\left[\sum_{1}^{N} X_i | N\right]\right]$$

But

$$E\left[\sum_{1}^{N} X_i | N = n\right] = E\left[\sum_{1}^{n} X_i | N = n\right]$$

$$= E\left[\sum_{1}^{n} X_i\right] \quad \text{by the independence of the } X_i \text{ and } N$$

$$= nE[X] \quad \text{where } E[X] = E[X_i]$$

which implies that

$$E\left[\sum_{1}^{N} X_i | N\right] = NE[X]$$

Thus,

$$E\left[\sum_{i=1}^{N} X_i\right] = E[NE[X]] = E[N]E[X]$$

Hence, in our example, the expected amount of money spent in the store is $50 \times \$8$, or $400. \qquad \blacksquare$

Example 5e

The game of craps is begun by rolling an ordinary pair of dice. If the sum of the dice is 2, 3, or 12, the player loses. If it is 7 or 11, the player wins. If it is any other number i, the player continues to roll the dice until the sum is either 7 or i. If it is 7, the player loses; if it is i, the player wins. Let R denote the number of rolls of the dice in a game of craps. Find

(a) $E[R]$;

(b) $E[R|\text{player wins}]$;

(c) $E[R|\text{player loses}]$.

Solution If we let P_i denote the probability that the sum of the dice is i, then

$$P_i = P_{14-i} = \frac{i-1}{36}, \quad i = 2, \ldots, 7$$

To compute $E[R]$, we condition on S, the initial sum, giving

$$E[R] = \sum_{i=2}^{12} E[R|S=i]P_i$$

However,

$$E[R|S=i] = \begin{cases} 1, & \text{if } i = 2,3,7,11,12 \\ 1 + \dfrac{1}{P_i + P_7}, & \text{otherwise} \end{cases}$$

The preceding equation follows because if the sum is a value i that does not end the game, then the dice will continue to be rolled until the sum is either i or 7, and the number of rolls until this occurs is a geometric random variable with parameter $P_i + P_7$. Therefore,

$$E[R] = 1 + \sum_{i=4}^{6} \frac{P_i}{P_i + P_7} + \sum_{i=8}^{10} \frac{P_i}{P_i + P_7}$$

$$= 1 + 2(3/9 + 4/10 + 5/11) = 3.376$$

To determine $E[R|\text{win}]$, let us start by determining p, the probability that the player wins. Conditioning on S yields

$$p = \sum_{i=2}^{12} P\{\text{win}|S=i\}P_i$$

$$= P_7 + P_{11} + \sum_{i=4}^{6} \frac{P_i}{P_i + P_7}P_i + \sum_{i=8}^{10} \frac{P_i}{P_i + P_7}P_i$$

$$= 0.493$$

where the preceding uses the fact that the probability of obtaining a sum of i before one of 7 is $P_i/(P_i + P_7)$. Now, let us determine the conditional probability mass function of S, given that the player wins. Letting $Q_i = P\{S=i|\text{win}\}$, we have

$$Q_2 = Q_3 = Q_{12} = 0, \quad Q_7 = P_7/p, \quad Q_{11} = P_{11}/p$$

and, for $i = 4, 5, 6, 8, 9, 10$,

$$Q_i = \frac{P\{S=i, \text{win}\}}{P\{\text{win}\}}$$

$$= \frac{P_i P\{\text{win}|S=i\}}{p}$$

$$= \frac{P_i^2}{p(P_i + P_7)}$$

Now, conditioning on the initial sum gives

$$E[R|\text{win}] = \sum_i E[R|\text{win}, S = i]Q_i$$

However, as was noted in Example 2j of Chapter 6, given that the initial sum is i, the number of additional rolls needed and the outcome (whether a win or a loss) are independent. (This is easily seen by first noting that conditional on an initial sum of i, the outcome is independent of the number of additional dice rolls needed and then using the symmetry property of independence, which states that if event A is independent of event B, then event B is independent of event A.) Therefore,

$$E[R|\text{win}] = \sum_i E[R|S = i]Q_i$$

$$= 1 + \sum_{i=4}^{6} \frac{Q_i}{P_i + P_7} + \sum_{i=8}^{10} \frac{Q_i}{P_i + P_7}$$

$$= 2.938$$

Although we could determine $E[R|\text{player loses}]$ exactly as we did $E[R|\text{player wins}]$, it is easier to use

$$E[R] = E[R|\text{win}]p + E[R|\text{lose}](1 - p)$$

implying that

$$E[R|\text{lose}] = \frac{E[R] - E[R|\text{win}]p}{1 - p} = 3.801 \qquad \blacksquare$$

Example 5f

As defined in Example 5d of Chapter 6, the bivariate normal joint density function of the random variables X and Y is

$$f(x, y) = \frac{1}{2\pi\sigma_x\sigma_y\sqrt{1 - \rho^2}} \exp\left\{-\frac{1}{2(1 - \rho^2)}\left[\left(\frac{x - \mu_x}{\sigma_x}\right)^2 + \left(\frac{y - \mu_y}{\sigma_y}\right)^2\right.\right.$$

$$\left.\left. - 2\rho\frac{(x - \mu_x)(y - \mu_y)}{\sigma_x\sigma_y}\right]\right\}$$

We will now show that ρ is the correlation between X and Y. As shown in Example 5c, $\mu_x = E[X]$, $\sigma_x^2 = \text{Var}(X)$, and $\mu_y = E[Y]$, $\sigma_y^2 = \text{Var}(Y)$. Consequently,

$$\text{Corr}(X, Y) = \frac{\text{Cov}(X, Y)}{\sigma_x\sigma_y}$$

$$= \frac{E[XY] - \mu_x\mu_y}{\sigma_x\sigma_y}$$

To determine $E[XY]$, we condition on Y. That is, we use the identity

$$E[XY] = E\big[E[XY|Y]\big]$$

Recalling from Example 5d that the conditional distribution of X given that $Y = y$ is normal with mean $\mu_x + \rho\frac{\sigma_x}{\sigma_y}(y - \mu_y)$, we see that

$$E[XY|Y = y] = E[Xy|Y = y]$$
$$= yE[X|Y = y]$$
$$= y\left[\mu_x + \rho\frac{\sigma_x}{\sigma_y}(y - \mu_y)\right]$$
$$= y\mu_x + \rho\frac{\sigma_x}{\sigma_y}(y^2 - \mu_y y)$$

Consequently,

$$E[XY|Y] = Y\mu_x + \rho\frac{\sigma_x}{\sigma_y}(Y^2 - \mu_y Y)$$

implying that

$$E[XY] = E\left[Y\mu_x + \rho\frac{\sigma_x}{\sigma_y}(Y^2 - \mu_y Y)\right]$$
$$= \mu_x E[Y] + \rho\frac{\sigma_x}{\sigma_y}E[Y^2 - \mu_y Y]$$
$$= \mu_x\mu_y + \rho\frac{\sigma_x}{\sigma_y}\left(E[Y^2] - \mu_y^2\right)$$
$$= \mu_x\mu_y + \rho\frac{\sigma_x}{\sigma_y}\text{Var}(Y)$$
$$= \mu_x\mu_y + \rho\sigma_x\sigma_y$$

Therefore,

$$\text{Corr}(X, Y) = \frac{\rho\sigma_x\sigma_y}{\sigma_x\sigma_y} = \rho \qquad \blacksquare$$

Sometimes $E[X]$ is easy to compute, and we use the conditioning identity to compute a conditional expected value. This approach is illustrated by our next example.

Example 5g

Consider n independent trials, each of which results in one of the outcomes $1, \ldots, k$, with respective probabilities $p_1, \ldots, p_k$, $\sum_{i=1}^{k} p_i = 1$. Let N_i denote the number of trials that result in outcome i, $i = 1, \ldots, k$. For $i \neq j$, find

(a) $E[N_j|N_i > 0]$ and (b) $E[N_j|N_i > 1]$

Solution To solve (a), let

$$I = \begin{cases} 0, & \text{if } N_i = 0 \\ 1, & \text{if } N_i > 0 \end{cases}$$

Then

$$E[N_j] = E[N_j|I = 0]P\{I = 0\} + E[N_j|I = 1]P\{I = 1\}$$

or, equivalently,

$$E[N_j] = E[N_j|N_i = 0]P\{N_i = 0\} + E[N_j|N_i > 0]P\{N_i > 0\}$$

Now, the unconditional distribution of N_j is binomial with parameters n, p_j. Also, given that $N_i = r$, each of the $n - r$ trials that does not result in outcome i will, independently, result in outcome j with probability $P(j|\text{not } i) = \frac{p_j}{1-p_i}$. Consequently, the conditional distribution of N_j, given that $N_i = r$, is binomial with parameters $n - r, \frac{p_j}{1 - p_i}$. (For a more detailed argument for this conclusion, see Example 4c of Chapter 6.) Because $P\{N_i = 0\} = (1 - p_i)^n$, the preceding equation yields

$$np_j = n\frac{p_j}{1 - p_i}(1 - p_i)^n + E[N_j|N_i > 0](1 - (1 - p_i)^n)$$

giving the result

$$E[N_j|N_i > 0] = np_j \frac{1 - (1 - p_i)^{n-1}}{1 - (1 - p_i)^n}$$

We can solve part (b) in a similar manner. Let

$$J = \begin{cases} 0, & \text{if } N_i = 0 \\ 1, & \text{if } N_i = 1 \\ 2, & \text{if } N_i > 1 \end{cases}$$

Then

$$E[N_j] = E[N_j|J = 0]P\{J = 0\} + E[N_j|J = 1]P\{J = 1\}$$
$$+ E[N_j|J = 2]P\{J = 2\}$$

or, equivalently,

$$E[N_j] = E[N_j|N_i = 0]P\{N_i = 0\} + E[N_j|N_i = 1]P\{N_i = 1\}$$
$$+ E[N_j|N_i > 1]P\{N_i > 1\}$$

This equation yields

$$np_j = n\frac{p_j}{1 - p_i}(1 - p_i)^n + (n - 1)\frac{p_j}{1 - p_i}np_i(1 - p_i)^{n-1}$$
$$+ E[N_j|N_i > 1](1 - (1 - p_i)^n - np_i(1 - p_i)^{n-1})$$

giving the result

$$E[N_j|N_i > 1] = \frac{np_j[1 - (1 - p_i)^{n-1} - (n - 1)p_i(1 - p_i)^{n-2}]}{1 - (1 - p_i)^n - np_i(1 - p_i)^{n-1}} \qquad \blacksquare$$

It is also possible to obtain the variance of a random variable by conditioning. We illustrate this approach by the following example.

Example 5h

Variance of the geometric distribution

Independent trials, each resulting in a success with probability p, are successively performed. Let N be the time of the first success. Find Var(N).

Solution Let $Y = 1$ if the first trial results in a success and $Y = 0$ otherwise. Now,

$$\text{Var}(N) = E[N^2] - (E[N])^2$$

To calculate $E[N^2]$, we condition on Y as follows:

$$E[N^2] = E[E[N^2|Y]]$$

However,

$$E[N^2|Y = 1] = 1$$
$$E[N^2|Y = 0] = E[(1 + N)^2]$$

These two equations follow because, on the one hand, if the first trial results in a success, then, clearly, $N = 1$; thus, $N^2 = 1$. On the other hand, if the first trial results in a failure, then the total number of trials necessary for the first success will have the same distribution as 1 (the first trial that results in failure) plus the necessary number of additional trials. Since the latter quantity has the same distribution as N, we obtain $E[N^2|Y = 0] = E[(1 + N)^2]$. Hence,

$$E[N^2] = E[N^2|Y = 1]P\{Y = 1\} + E[N^2|Y = 0]P\{Y = 0\}$$
$$= p + (1 - p)E[(1 + N)^2]$$
$$= 1 + (1 - p)E[2N + N^2]$$

However, as was shown in Example 8b of Chapter 4, $E[N] = 1/p$; therefore,

$$E[N^2] = 1 + \frac{2(1 - p)}{p} + (1 - p)E[N^2]$$

or

$$E[N^2] = \frac{2 - p}{p^2}$$

Consequently,

$$\text{Var}(N) = E[N^2] - (E[N])^2$$
$$= \frac{2 - p}{p^2} - \left(\frac{1}{p}\right)^2$$
$$= \frac{1 - p}{p^2} \qquad \blacksquare$$

Example 5i

Consider a gambling situation in which there are r players, with player i initially having n_i units, $n_i > 0$, $i = 1,\ldots,r$. At each stage, two of the players are chosen to play a game, with the winner of the game receiving 1 unit from the loser. Any player whose fortune drops to 0 is eliminated, and this continues until a single player has all $n \equiv \sum_{i=1}^{r} n_i$ units, with that player designated as the victor. Assuming that the results of successive games are independent and that each game is equally likely to be won by either of its two players, find the average number of stages until one of the players has all n units.

Solution To find the expected number of stages played, suppose first that there are only 2 players, with players 1 and 2 initially having j and $n - j$ units, respectively. Let X_j denote the number of stages that will be played, and let $m_j = E[X_j]$. Then, for $j = 1,\ldots,n - 1$,

$$X_j = 1 + A_j$$

where A_j is the additional number of stages needed beyond the first stage. Taking expectations gives

$$m_j = 1 + E[A_j]$$

Conditioning on the result of the first stage then yields

$$m_j = 1 + E[A_j|1 \text{ wins first stage}]1/2 + E[A_j|2 \text{ wins first stage}]1/2$$

Now, if player 1 wins at the first stage, then the situation from that point on is exactly the same as in a problem that supposes that player 1 starts with $j + 1$ and player 2 with $n - (j + 1)$ units. Consequently,

$$E[A_j|1 \text{ wins first stage}] = m_{j+1}$$

and, analogously,

$$E[A_j|2 \text{ wins first stage}] = m_{j-1}$$

Thus,

$$m_j = 1 + \frac{1}{2}m_{j+1} + \frac{1}{2}m_{j-1}$$

or, equivalently,

$$m_{j+1} = 2m_j - m_{j-1} - 2, \quad j = 1, \dots, n-1 \qquad (5.4)$$

Using that $m_0 = 0$, the preceding equation yields

$$m_2 = 2m_1 - 2$$
$$m_3 = 2m_2 - m_1 - 2 = 3m_1 - 6 = 3(m_1 - 2)$$
$$m_4 = 2m_3 - m_2 - 2 = 4m_1 - 12 = 4(m_1 - 3)$$

suggesting that

$$m_i = i(m_1 - i + 1), \qquad i = 1, \dots, n \qquad (5.5)$$

To prove the preceding equality, we use mathematical induction. Since we've already shown the equation to be true for $i = 1, 2$, we take as the induction hypothesis that it is true whenever $i \le j < n$. Now we must prove that it is true for $j + 1$. Using Equation (5.4) yields

$$
\begin{aligned}
m_{j+1} &= 2m_j - m_{j-1} - 2 \\
&= 2j(m_1 - j + 1) - (j-1)(m_1 - j + 2) - 2 \quad \text{(by the induction hypothesis)} \\
&= (j+1)m_1 - 2j^2 + 2j + j^2 - 3j + 2 - 2 \\
&= (j+1)m_1 - j^2 - j \\
&= (j+1)(m_1 - j)
\end{aligned}
$$

which completes the induction proof of (5.5). Letting $i = n$ in (5.5), and using that $m_n = 0$, now yields that

$$m_1 = n - 1$$

which, again using (5.5), gives the result

$$m_i = i(n - i)$$

Thus, the mean number of games played when there are only 2 players with initial amounts i and $n - i$ is the product of their initial amounts. Because both players play all stages, this is also the mean number of stages involving player 1.

Now let us return to the problem involving r players with initial amounts $n_i, i = 1, \dots, r$, $\sum_{i=1}^{r} n_i = n$. Let X denote the number of stages needed to obtain a victor, and let X_i denote the number of stages involving player i. Now, from the point of view of player i, starting with n_i, he will continue to play stages, independently being equally likely to win or lose each one, until his fortune is either n or 0. Thus, the number of stages he plays is exactly the same as when he has a single opponent with an initial fortune of $n - n_i$. Consequently, by the preceding result, it follows that

$$E[X_i] = n_i(n - n_i)$$

so

$$E\left[\sum_{i=1}^{r} X_i\right] = \sum_{i=1}^{r} n_i(n - n_i) = n^2 - \sum_{i=1}^{r} n_i^2$$

But because each stage involves two players,

$$X = \frac{1}{2}\sum_{i=1}^{r} X_i$$

Taking expectations now yields

$$E[X] = \frac{1}{2}\left(n^2 - \sum_{i=1}^{r} n_i^2\right)$$

It is interesting to note that while our argument shows that the mean number of stages does not depend on the manner in which the teams are selected at each stage, the same is not true for the distribution of the number of stages. To see this, suppose $r = 3$, $n_1 = n_2 = 1$, and $n_3 = 2$. If players *1* and *2* are chosen in the first stage, then it will take at least three stages to determine a winner, whereas if player 3 is in the first stage, then it is possible for there to be only two stages. ∎

In our next example, we use conditioning to verify a result previously noted in Section 6.3.1: that the expected number of uniform $(0, 1)$ random variables that need to be added for their sum to exceed 1 is equal to e.

Example 5j Let $U_1, U_2, \ldots$ be a sequence of independent uniform $(0, 1)$ random variables. Find $E[N]$ when

$$N = \min\left\{n: \sum_{i=1}^{n} U_i > 1\right\}$$

Solution We will find E[N] by obtaining a more general result. For $x \in [0, 1]$, let

$$N(x) = \min\left\{n: \sum_{i=1}^{n} U_i > x\right\}$$

and set

$$m(x) = E[N(x)]$$

That is, $N(x)$ is the number of uniform $(0, 1)$ random variables we must add until their sum exceeds x, and $m(x)$ is its expected value. We will now derive an equation for $m(x)$ by conditioning on U_1. This gives, from Equation (5.1b),

$$m(x) = \int_0^1 E[N(x)|U_1 = y]\, dy \tag{5.6}$$

Now,

$$E[N(x)|U_1 = y] = \begin{cases} 1 & \text{if } y > x \\ 1 + m(x - y) & \text{if } y \le x \end{cases} \tag{5.7}$$

The preceding formula is obviously true when $y > x$. It is also true when $y \le x$, since, if the first uniform value is y, then, at that point, the remaining number of uniform random variables needed is the same as if we were just starting and were going to add uniform random variables until their sum exceeded $x - y$. Substituting Equation (5.7) into Equation (5.6) gives

$$m(x) = 1 + \int_0^x m(x - y)\,dy$$

$$= 1 + \int_0^x m(u)\,du \qquad \text{by letting} \atop u = x - y$$

Differentiating the preceding equation yields

$$m'(x) = m(x)$$

or, equivalently,

$$\frac{m'(x)}{m(x)} = 1$$

Integrating this equation gives

$$\log[m(x)] = x + c$$

or

$$m(x) = ke^x$$

Since $m(0) = 1$, it follows that $k = 1$, so we obtain

$$m(x) = e^x$$

Therefore, $m(1)$, the expected number of uniform $(0, 1)$ random variables that need to be added until their sum exceeds 1, is equal to e. ∎

7.5.3   Computing Probabilities by Conditioning

Not only can we obtain expectations by first conditioning on an appropriate random variable, but we can also use this approach to compute probabilities. To see this, let E denote an arbitrary event, and define the indicator random variable X by

$$X = \begin{cases} 1 & \text{if } E \text{ occurs} \\ 0 & \text{if } E \text{ does not occur} \end{cases}$$

It follows from the definition of X that

$$E[X] = P(E)$$
$$E[X|Y = y] = P(E|Y = y) \quad \text{for any random variable } Y$$

Therefore, from Equations (5.1a) and (5.1b), we obtain

$$P(E) = \sum_y P(E|Y = y)P(Y = y) \quad \text{if } Y \text{ is discrete}$$

$$= \int_{-\infty}^{\infty} P(E|Y = y)f_Y(y)\,dy \quad \text{if } Y \text{ is continuous}$$

(5.8)

Note that if Y is a discrete random variable taking on one of the values $y_1, \ldots, y_n$, then by defining the events $F_i, i = 1, \ldots, n$, by $F_i = \{Y = y_i\}$, Equation (5.8) reduces to the familiar equation

$$P(E) = \sum_{i=1}^n P(E|F_i)P(F_i)$$

where $F_1, \ldots, F_n$ are mutually exclusive events whose union is the sample space.

Example
5k

The best-prize problem

Suppose that we are to be presented with n distinct prizes, in sequence. After being presented with a prize, we must immediately decide whether to accept it or to reject it and consider the next prize. The only information we are given when deciding whether to accept a prize is the relative rank of that prize compared to ones already seen. That is, for instance, when the fifth prize is presented, we learn how it compares with the four prizes we've already seen. Suppose that once a prize is rejected, it is lost, and that our objective is to maximize the probability of obtaining the best prize. Assuming that all $n!$ orderings of the prizes are equally likely, how well can we do?

Solution Rather surprisingly, we can do quite well. To see this, fix a value k, $0 \le k < n$, and consider the strategy that rejects the first k prizes and then accepts the first one that is better than all of those first k. Let $P_k(\text{best})$ denote the probability that the best prize is selected when this strategy is employed. To compute this probability, condition on X, the position of the best prize. This gives

$$P_k(\text{best}) = \sum_{i=1}^{n} P_k(\text{best}|X=i)P(X=i)$$

$$= \frac{1}{n} \sum_{i=1}^{n} P_k(\text{best}|X=i)$$

Now, on the one hand, if the overall best prize is among the first k, then no prize is ever selected under the strategy considered. That is,

$$P_k(\text{best}|X=i) = 0 \quad \text{if } i \le k$$

On the other hand, if the best prize is in position i, where $i > k$, then the best prize will be selected if the best of the first $i - 1$ prizes is among the first k (for then none of the prizes in positions $k + 1, k + 2, \ldots, i - 1$ would be selected). But, conditional on the best prize being in position i, it is easy to verify that all possible orderings of the other prizes remain equally likely, which implies that each of the first $i - 1$ prizes is equally likely to be the best of that batch. Hence, we have

$$P_k(\text{best}|X=i) = P\{\text{best of first } i - 1 \text{ is among the first } k|X=i\}$$

$$= \frac{k}{i - 1} \quad \text{if } i > k$$

From the preceding, we obtain

$$P_k(\text{best}) = \frac{k}{n} \sum_{i=k+1}^{n} \frac{1}{i - 1}$$

$$\approx \frac{k}{n} \int_{k+1}^{n} \frac{1}{x - 1} \, dx$$

$$= \frac{k}{n} \log\left(\frac{n - 1}{k}\right)$$

$$\approx \frac{k}{n} \log\left(\frac{n}{k}\right)$$

Now, if we consider the function

$$g(x) = \frac{x}{n} \log\left(\frac{n}{x}\right)$$

then

$$g'(x) = \frac{1}{n} \log\left(\frac{n}{x}\right) - \frac{1}{n}$$

so

$$g'(x) = 0 \Rightarrow \log\left(\frac{n}{x}\right) = 1 \Rightarrow x = \frac{n}{e}$$

Thus, since $P_k(\text{best}) \approx g(k)$, we see that the best strategy of the type considered is to let the first n/e prizes go by and then accept the first one to appear that is better than all of those. In addition, since $g(n/e) = 1/e$, the probability that this strategy selects the best prize is approximately $1/e \approx .36788$.

Remark Most people are quite surprised by the size of the probability of obtaining the best prize, thinking that this probability would be close to 0 when n is large. However, even without going through the calculations, a little thought reveals that the probability of obtaining the best prize can be made reasonably large. Consider the strategy of letting half of the prizes go by and then selecting the first one to appear that is better than all of those. The probability that a prize is actually selected is the probability that the overall best is among the second half, and this is $\frac{1}{2}$. In addition, given that a prize is selected, at the time of selection that prize would have been the best of more than $n/2$ prizes to have appeared and would thus have probability of at least $\frac{1}{2}$ of being the overall best. Hence, the strategy of letting the first half of all prizes go by and then accepting the first one that is better than all of those prizes has a probability greater than $\frac{1}{4}$ of obtaining the best prize. ∎

Example 5l

Let U be a uniform random variable on $(0, 1)$, and suppose that the conditional distribution of X, given that $U = p$, is binomial with parameters n and p. Find the probability mass function of X.

Solution Conditioning on the value of U gives

$$P\{X = i\} = \int_0^1 P\{X = i | U = p\} f_U(p)\, dp$$

$$= \int_0^1 P\{X = i | U = p\}\, dp$$

$$= \frac{n!}{i!(n-i)!} \int_0^1 p^i(1-p)^{n-i}\, dp$$

Now, it can be shown (a probabilistic proof is given in Section 6.6) that

$$\int_0^1 p^i(1-p)^{n-i} dp = \frac{i!(n-i)!}{(n+1)!}$$

Hence, we obtain

$$P\{X = i\} = \frac{1}{n+1} \quad i = 0,\ldots,n$$

That is, we obtain the surprising result that if a coin whose probability of coming up heads is uniformly distributed over $(0, 1)$ is flipped n times, then the number of heads occurring is equally likely to be any of the values $0,\ldots,n$.

Because the preceding conditional distribution has such a nice form, it is worth trying to find another argument to enhance our intuition as to why such a result is true. To do so, let $U, U_1, \ldots, U_n$ be $n + 1$ independent uniform $(0, 1)$ random variables, and let X denote the number of the random variables $U_1, \ldots, U_n$ that are smaller than U. Since all the random variables $U, U_1, \ldots, U_n$ have the same distribution, it follows that U is equally likely to be the smallest, or second smallest, or largest of them; so X is equally likely to be any of the values $0, 1, \ldots, n$. However, given that $U = p$, the number of the U_i that are less than U is a binomial random variable with parameters n and p, thus establishing our previous result. ∎

Example 5m

Suppose that X and Y are independent continuous random variables having densities f_X and f_Y, respectively. Compute $P\{X < Y\}$.

Solution Conditioning on the value of Y yields

$$
\begin{aligned}
P\{X < Y\} &= \int_{-\infty}^{\infty} P\{X < Y | Y = y\} f_Y(y)\, dy \\
&= \int_{-\infty}^{\infty} P\{X < y | Y = y\} f_Y(y)\, dy \\
&= \int_{-\infty}^{\infty} P\{X < y\} f_Y(y)\, dy \quad \text{by independence} \\
&= \int_{-\infty}^{\infty} F_X(y) f_Y(y)\, dy
\end{aligned}
$$

where

$$
F_X(y) = \int_{-\infty}^{y} f_X(x)\, dx \qquad ∎
$$

Example 5n

Suppose that X and Y are independent continuous random variables. Find the distribution of $X + Y$.

Solution By conditioning on the value of Y, we obtain

$$
\begin{aligned}
P\{X + Y < a\} &= \int_{-\infty}^{\infty} P\{X + Y < a | Y = y\} f_Y(y)\, dy \\
&= \int_{-\infty}^{\infty} P\{X + y < a | Y = y\} f_Y(y)\, dy \\
&= \int_{-\infty}^{\infty} P\{X < a - y\} f_Y(y)\, dy \\
&= \int_{-\infty}^{\infty} F_X(a - y) f_Y(y)\, dy \qquad ∎
\end{aligned}
$$

7.5.4 Conditional Variance

Just as we have defined the conditional expectation of X given the value of Y, we can also define the conditional variance of X given that $Y = y$:

$$
\mathrm{Var}(X|Y) \equiv E[(X - E[X|Y])^2 | Y]
$$

That is, $\mathrm{Var}(X|Y)$ is equal to the (conditional) expected square of the difference between X and its (conditional) mean when the value of Y is given. In other words, $\mathrm{Var}(X|Y)$ is exactly analogous to the usual definition of variance, but now all expectations are conditional on the fact that Y is known.

There is a very useful relationship between $\mathrm{Var}(X)$, the unconditional variance of X, and $\mathrm{Var}(X|Y)$, the conditional variance of X given Y, that can often be applied to compute $\mathrm{Var}(X)$. To obtain this relationship, note first that by the same reasoning that yields $\mathrm{Var}(X) = E[X^2] - (E[X])^2$, we have

$$\mathrm{Var}(X|Y) = E[X^2|Y] - (E[X|Y])^2$$

so

$$
\begin{aligned}
E[\mathrm{Var}(X|Y)] &= E[E[X^2|Y]] - E[(E[X|Y])^2] \\
&= E[X^2] - E[(E[X|Y])^2]
\end{aligned}
\tag{5.9}
$$

Also, since $E[E[X|Y]] = E[X]$, we have

$$\mathrm{Var}(E[X|Y]) = E[(E[X|Y])^2] - (E[X])^2 \tag{5.10}$$

Hence, by adding Equations (5.9) and (5.10), we arrive at the following proposition.

Proposition 5.2
The conditional variance formula

$$\mathrm{Var}(X) = E[\mathrm{Var}(X|Y)] + \mathrm{Var}(E[X|Y])$$

Example 5o
Suppose that by any time t the number of people who have arrived at a train depot is a Poisson random variable with mean λt. If the initial train arrives at the depot at a time (independent of when the passengers arrive) that is uniformly distributed over $(0, T)$, what are the mean and variance of the number of passengers who enter the train?

Solution For each $t \geq 0$, let $N(t)$ denote the number of arrivals by t, and let Y denote the time at which the train arrives. The random variable of interest is then $N(Y)$. Conditioning on Y gives

$$
\begin{aligned}
E[N(Y)|Y = t] &= E[N(t)|Y = t] \\
&= E[N(t)] \quad \text{by the independence of } Y \text{ and } N(t) \\
&= \lambda t \qquad \text{since } N(t) \text{ is Poisson with mean } \lambda t
\end{aligned}
$$

Hence,

$$E[N(Y)|Y] = \lambda Y$$

so taking expectations gives

$$E[N(Y)] = \lambda E[Y] = \frac{\lambda T}{2}$$

To obtain $\mathrm{Var}(N(Y))$, we use the conditional variance formula:

$$
\begin{aligned}
\mathrm{Var}(N(Y)|Y = t) &= \mathrm{Var}(N(t)|Y = t) \\
&= \mathrm{Var}(N(t)) \quad \text{by independence} \\
&= \lambda t
\end{aligned}
$$

Thus,

$$
\begin{aligned}
\mathrm{Var}(N(Y)|Y) &= \lambda Y \\
E[N(Y)|Y] &= \lambda Y
\end{aligned}
$$

Hence, from the conditional variance formula,

$$\text{Var}(N(Y)) = E[\lambda Y] + \text{Var}(\lambda Y)$$

$$= \lambda \frac{T}{2} + \lambda^2 \frac{T^2}{12}$$

where we have used the fact that $\text{Var}(Y) = T^2/12$. ∎

Example 5p

Variance of a sum of a random number of random variables

Let $X_1, X_2, \ldots$ be a sequence of independent and identically distributed random variables, and let N be a nonnegative integer-valued random variable that is independent of the sequence $X_i, i \geq 1$. To compute $\text{Var}\left(\sum_{i=1}^{N} X_i\right)$, we condition on N:

$$E\left[\sum_{i=1}^{N} X_i | N\right] = NE[X]$$

$$\text{Var}\left(\sum_{i=1}^{N} X_i | N\right) = N\text{Var}(X)$$

The preceding result follows because, given N, $\sum_{i=1}^{N} X_i$ is just the sum of a fixed number of independent random variables, so its expectation and variance are just the sums of the individual means and variances, respectively. Hence, from the conditional variance formula,

$$\text{Var}\left(\sum_{i=1}^{N} X_i\right) = E[N]\text{Var}(X) + (E[X])^2\text{Var}(N)$$ ∎

7.6   Conditional Expectation and Prediction

Sometimes a situation arises in which the value of a random variable X is observed and then, on the basis of the observed value, an attempt is made to predict the value of a second random variable Y. Let $g(X)$ denote the predictor; that is, if X is observed to equal x, then $g(x)$ is our prediction for the value of Y. Clearly, we would like to choose g so that $g(X)$ tends to be close to Y. One possible criterion for closeness is to choose g so as to minimize $E[(Y - g(X))^2]$. We now show that, under this criterion, the best possible predictor of Y is $g(X) = E[Y|X]$.

Proposition 6.1

$$E[(Y - g(X))^2] \geq E[(Y - E[Y|X])^2]$$

Proof

$$E[(Y - g(X))^2|X] = E[(Y - E[Y|X] + E[Y|X] - g(X))^2|X]$$
$$= E[(Y - E[Y|X])^2|X]$$
$$\quad + E[(E[Y|X] - g(X))^2|X]$$
$$\quad + 2E[(Y - E[Y|X])(E[Y|X] - g(X))|X] \quad (6.1)$$

However, given $X, E[Y|X] - g(X)$, being a function of X, can be treated as a constant. Thus,

$$E[(Y - E[Y|X])(E[Y|X] - g(X))|X]$$
$$= (E[Y|X] - g(X))E[Y - E[Y|X]|X]$$
$$= (E[Y|X] - g(X))(E[Y|X] - E[Y|X])$$
$$= 0 \qquad (6.2)$$

Hence, from Equations (6.1) and (6.2), we obtain

$$E[(Y - g(X))^2|X] \geq E[(Y - E[Y|X])^2|X]$$

and the desired result follows by taking expectations of both sides of the preceding expression. □

Remark A second, more intuitive, although less rigorous, argument verifying Proposition 6.1 is as follows: It is straightforward to verify that $E[(Y - c)^2]$ is minimized at $c = E[Y]$. (See Theoretical Exercise 1.) Thus, if we want to predict the value of Y when there are no data available to use, the best possible prediction, in the sense of minimizing the mean square error, is to predict that Y will equal its mean. However, if the value of the random variable X is observed to be x, then the prediction problem remains exactly as in the previous (no-data) case, with the exception that all probabilities and expectations are now conditional on the event that $X = x$. Hence, the best prediction in this situation is to predict that Y will equal its conditional expected value given that $X = x$, thus establishing Proposition 6.1. ∎

Example 6a

Suppose that the son of a man of height x (in inches) attains a height that is normally distributed with mean $x + 1$ and variance 4. What is the best prediction of the height at full growth of the son of a man who is 6 feet tall?

Solution Formally, this model can be written as

$$Y = X + 1 + e$$

where e is a normal random variable, independent of X, having mean 0 and variance 4. The X and Y, of course, represent the heights of the man and his son, respectively. The best prediction $E[Y|X = 72]$ is thus equal to

$$E[Y|X = 72] = E[X + 1 + e|X = 72]$$
$$= 73 + E[e|X = 72]$$
$$= 73 + E(e) \quad \text{by independence}$$
$$= 73$$

∎

Example 6b

Suppose that if a signal value s is sent from location A, then the signal value received at location B is normally distributed with parameters $(s, 1)$. If S, the value of the signal sent at A, is normally distributed with parameters (μ, σ^2), what is the best estimate of the signal sent if R, the value received at B, is equal to r?

Solution Let us start by computing the conditional density of S given R. We have

$$f_{S|R}(s|r) = \frac{f_{S,R}(s,r)}{f_R(r)}$$

$$= \frac{f_S(s)f_{R|S}(r|s)}{f_R(r)}$$

$$= Ke^{-(s-\mu)^2/2\sigma^2}e^{-(r-s)^2/2}$$

where K does not depend on s. Now,

$$\frac{(s-\mu)^2}{2\sigma^2} + \frac{(r-s)^2}{2} = s^2\left(\frac{1}{2\sigma^2} + \frac{1}{2}\right) - \left(\frac{\mu}{\sigma^2} + r\right)s + C_1$$

$$= \frac{1+\sigma^2}{2\sigma^2}\left[s^2 - 2\left(\frac{\mu + r\sigma^2}{1+\sigma^2}\right)s\right] + C_1$$

$$= \frac{1+\sigma^2}{2\sigma^2}\left(s - \frac{(\mu + r\sigma^2)}{1+\sigma^2}\right)^2 + C_2$$

where C_1 and C_2 do not depend on s. Hence,

$$f_{S|R}(s|r) = C \exp\left\{\frac{-\left[s - \frac{(\mu + r\sigma^2)}{1+\sigma^2}\right]^2}{2\left(\frac{\sigma^2}{1+\sigma^2}\right)}\right\}$$

where C does not depend on s. Thus, we may conclude that the conditional distribution of S, the signal sent, given that r is received, is normal with mean and variance now given by

$$E[S|R = r] = \frac{\mu + r\sigma^2}{1+\sigma^2}$$

$$\text{Var}(S|R = r) = \frac{\sigma^2}{1+\sigma^2}$$

Consequently, from Proposition 6.1, given that the value received is r, the best estimate, in the sense of minimizing the mean square error, for the signal sent is

$$E[S|R = r] = \frac{1}{1+\sigma^2}\mu + \frac{\sigma^2}{1+\sigma^2}r$$

Writing the conditional mean as we did previously is informative, for it shows that it equals a weighted average of μ, the a priori expected value of the signal, and r, the value received. The relative weights given to μ and r are in the same proportion to each other as 1 (the conditional variance of the received signal when s is sent) is to σ^2 (the variance of the signal to be sent). ∎

Example 6c

In digital signal processing, raw continuous analog data X must be quantized, or discretized, in order to obtain a digital representation. In order to quantize the raw data X, an increasing set of numbers $a_i, i = 0, \pm1, \pm2, \ldots$, such that $\lim_{i \to +\infty} a_i = \infty$ and $\lim_{i \to -\infty} a_i = -\infty$ is fixed, and the raw data are then quantized according to the interval $(a_i, a_{i+1}]$ in which X lies. Let us denote by y_i the discretized value when $X \in (a_i, a_{i+1}]$, and let Y denote the observed discretized value–that is,

$$Y = y_i \quad \text{if } a_i < X \le a_{i+1}$$

The distribution of Y is given by

$$P\{Y = y_i\} = F_X(a_{i+1}) - F_X(a_i)$$

Suppose now that we want to choose the values $y_i, i = 0, \pm 1, \pm 2, \ldots$ so as to minimize $E[(X - Y)^2]$, the expected mean square difference between the raw data and their quantized version.

(a) Find the optimal values $y_i, i = 0, \pm 1, \ldots$.
  For the optimal quantizer Y, show that
(b) $E[Y] = E[X]$, so the mean square error quantizer preserves the input mean;
(c) $\text{Var}(Y) = \text{Var}(X) - E[(X - Y)^2]$.

Solution (a) For any quantizer Y, upon conditioning on the value of Y, we obtain

$$E[(X - Y)^2] = \sum_i E[(X - y_i)^2 | a_i < X \le a_{i+1}] P\{a_i < X \le a_{i+1}\}$$

Now, if we let

$$I = i \quad \text{if } a_i < X \le a_{i+1}$$

then

$$E[(X - y_i)^2 | a_i < X \le a_{i+1}] = E[(X - y_i)^2 | I = i]$$

and by Proposition 6.1, this quantity is minimized when

$$\begin{aligned}
y_i &= E[X | I = i] \\
&= E[X | a_i < X \le a_{i+1}] \\
&= \int_{a_i}^{a_{i+1}} \frac{x f_X(x)\, dx}{F_X(a_{i+1}) - F_X(a_i)}
\end{aligned}$$

Now, since the optimal quantizer is given by $Y = E[X | I]$, it follows that

(b) $E[Y] = E[X]$
(c)
$$\begin{aligned}
\text{Var}(X) &= E[\text{Var}(X|I)] + \text{Var}(E[X|I]) \\
&= E[E[(X - Y)^2 | I]] + \text{Var}(Y) \\
&= E[(X - Y)^2] + \text{Var}(Y)
\end{aligned}$$ ∎

It sometimes happens that the joint probability distribution of X and Y is not completely known; or if it is known, it is such that the calculation of $E[Y | X = x]$ is mathematically intractable. If, however, the means and variances of X and Y and the correlation of X and Y are known, then we can at least determine the best *linear* predictor of Y with respect to X.

To obtain the best linear predictor of Y with respect to X, we need to choose a and b so as to minimize $E[(Y - (a + bX))^2]$. Now,

$$\begin{aligned}
E[(Y - (a + bX))^2] &= E[Y^2 - 2aY - 2bXY + a^2 + 2abX + b^2 X^2] \\
&= E[Y^2] - 2aE[Y] - 2bE[XY] + a^2 \\
&\quad + 2abE[X] + b^2 E[X^2]
\end{aligned}$$

Taking partial derivatives, we obtain

$$\frac{\partial}{\partial a} E[(Y - a - bX)^2] = -2E[Y] + 2a + 2bE[X]$$

$$\frac{\partial}{\partial b} E[(Y - a - bX)^2] = -2E[XY] + 2aE[X] + 2bE[X^2] \tag{6.3}$$

Setting Equations (6.3) to 0 and solving for a and b yields the solutions

$$b = \frac{E[XY] - E[X]E[Y]}{E[X^2] - (E[X])^2} = \frac{\text{Cov}(X, Y)}{\sigma_x^2} = \rho \frac{\sigma_y}{\sigma_x}$$

$$a = E[Y] - bE[X] = E[Y] - \frac{\rho \sigma_y E[X]}{\sigma_x} \tag{6.4}$$

where $\rho = \text{Correlation}(X, Y), \sigma_y^2 = \text{Var}(Y)$, and $\sigma_x^2 = \text{Var}(X)$. It is easy to verify that the values of a and b from Equation (6.4) minimize $E[(Y - a - bX)^2]$; thus, the best (in the sense of mean square error) linear predictor Y with respect to X is

$$\mu_y + \frac{\rho \sigma_y}{\sigma_x}(X - \mu_x)$$

where $\mu_y = E[Y]$ and $\mu_x = E[X]$.

The mean square error of this predictor is given by

$$E\left[\left(Y - \mu_y - \rho \frac{\sigma_y}{\sigma_x}(X - \mu_x)\right)^2\right]$$

$$= E\left[(Y - \mu_y)^2\right] + \rho^2 \frac{\sigma_y^2}{\sigma_x^2} E\left[(X - \mu_x)^2\right] - 2\rho \frac{\sigma_y}{\sigma_x} E\left[(Y - \mu_y)(X - \mu_x)\right]$$

$$= \sigma_y^2 + \rho^2 \sigma_y^2 - 2\rho^2 \sigma_y^2$$

$$= \sigma_y^2(1 - \rho^2) \tag{6.5}$$

We note from Equation (6.5) that if ρ is near $+1$ or -1, then the mean square error of the best linear predictor is near zero. ∎

Example 6d

An example in which the conditional expectation of Y given X is linear in X, and hence in which the best linear predictor of Y with respect to X is the best overall predictor, is when X and Y have a bivariate normal distribution. For, as shown in Example 5d of Chapter 6, in that case,

$$E[Y|X = x] = \mu_y + \rho \frac{\sigma_y}{\sigma_x}(x - \mu_x)$$

∎

7.7 Moment Generating Functions

The moment generating function $M(t)$ of the random variable X is defined for all real values of t by

$$M(t) = E[e^{tX}]$$

$$= \begin{cases} \displaystyle\sum_x e^{tx} p(x) & \text{if } X \text{ is discrete with mass function } p(x) \\[2ex] \displaystyle\int_{-\infty}^{\infty} e^{tx} f(x)\, dx & \text{if } X \text{ is continuous with density } f(x) \end{cases}$$

We call $M(t)$ the moment generating function because all of the moments of X can be obtained by successively differentiating $M(t)$ and then evaluating the result at $t = 0$. For example,

$$\begin{aligned} M'(t) &= \frac{d}{dt} E[e^{tX}] \\ &= E\left[\frac{d}{dt}(e^{tX})\right] \\ &= E[Xe^{tX}] \end{aligned} \quad (7.1)$$

where we have assumed that the interchange of the differentiation and expectation operators is legitimate. That is, we have assumed that

$$\frac{d}{dt}\left[\sum_x e^{tx} p(x)\right] = \sum_x \frac{d}{dt}[e^{tx} p(x)]$$

in the discrete case and

$$\frac{d}{dt}\left[\int e^{tx} f(x)\, dx\right] = \int \frac{d}{dt}[e^{tx} f(x)]\, dx$$

in the continuous case. This assumption can almost always be justified and, indeed, is valid for all of the distributions considered in this book. Hence, from Equation (7.1), evaluated at $t = 0$, we obtain

$$M'(0) = E[X]$$

Similarly,

$$\begin{aligned} M''(t) &= \frac{d}{dt} M'(t) \\ &= \frac{d}{dt} E[Xe^{tX}] \\ &= E\left[\frac{d}{dt}(Xe^{tX})\right] \\ &= E[X^2 e^{tX}] \end{aligned}$$

Thus,

$$M''(0) = E[X^2]$$

In general, the nth derivative of $M(t)$ is given by

$$M^n(t) = E[X^n e^{tX}] \quad n \geq 1$$

implying that

$$M^n(0) = E[X^n] \quad n \geq 1$$

We now compute $M(t)$ for some common distributions.

Example 7a

Binomial distribution with parameters n and p

If X is a binomial random variable with parameters n and p, then

$$M(t) = E[e^{tX}]$$

$$= \sum_{k=0}^{n} e^{tk} \binom{n}{k} p^k (1 - p)^{n-k}$$

$$= \sum_{k=0}^{n} \binom{n}{k} (pe^t)^k (1 - p)^{n-k}$$

$$= (pe^t + 1 - p)^n$$

where the last equality follows from the binomial theorem. Differentiation yields

$$M'(t) = n(pe^t + 1 - p)^{n-1} pe^t$$

Thus,

$$E[X] = M'(0) = np$$

Differentiating a second time yields

$$M''(t) = n(n - 1)(pe^t + 1 - p)^{n-2}(pe^t)^2 + n(pe^t + 1 - p)^{n-1} pe^t$$

so

$$E[X^2] = M''(0) = n(n - 1)p^2 + np$$

The variance of X is given by

$$\mathrm{Var}(X) = E[X^2] - (E[X])^2$$

$$= n(n - 1)p^2 + np - n^2 p^2$$

$$= np(1 - p)$$

verifying the result obtained previously. ∎

Example 7b

Poisson distribution with mean λ

If X is a Poisson random variable with parameter λ, then

$$M(t) = E[e^{tX}]$$

$$= \sum_{n=0}^{\infty} \frac{e^{tn} e^{-\lambda} \lambda^n}{n!}$$

$$= e^{-\lambda} \sum_{n=0}^{\infty} \frac{(\lambda e^t)^n}{n!}$$

$$= e^{-\lambda} e^{\lambda e^t}$$

$$= \exp\{\lambda(e^t - 1)\}$$

Differentiation yields

$$M'(t) = \lambda e^t \exp\{\lambda(e^t - 1)\}$$

$$M''(t) = (\lambda e^t)^2 \exp\{\lambda(e^t - 1)\} + \lambda e^t \exp\{\lambda(e^t - 1)\}$$

Thus,

$$E[X] = M'(0) = \lambda$$
$$E[X^2] = M''(0) = \lambda^2 + \lambda$$
$$\mathrm{Var}(X) = E[X^2] - (E[X])^2$$
$$= \lambda$$

Hence, both the mean and the variance of the Poisson random variable equal λ. ■

Example 7c

Exponential distribution with parameter λ

$$M(t) = E[e^{tX}]$$
$$= \int_0^\infty e^{tx} \lambda e^{-\lambda x}\, dx$$
$$= \lambda \int_0^\infty e^{-(\lambda - t)x}\, dx$$
$$= \frac{\lambda}{\lambda - t} \qquad \text{for } t < \lambda$$

We note from this derivation that for the exponential distribution, $M(t)$ is defined only for values of t less than λ. Differentiation of $M(t)$ yields

$$M'(t) = \frac{\lambda}{(\lambda - t)^2}, \quad M''(t) = \frac{2\lambda}{(\lambda - t)^3}$$

Hence,

$$E[X] = M'(0) = \frac{1}{\lambda}, \quad E[X^2] = M''(0) = \frac{2}{\lambda^2}$$

The variance of X is given by

$$\mathrm{Var}(X) = E[X^2] - (E[X])^2$$
$$= \frac{1}{\lambda^2}$$

■

Example 7d

Normal distribution

We first compute the moment generating function of a unit normal random variable with parameters 0 and 1. Letting Z be such a random variable, we have

$$M_Z(t) = E[e^{tZ}]$$
$$= \frac{1}{\sqrt{2\pi}} \int_{-\infty}^\infty e^{tx} e^{-x^2/2}\, dx$$
$$= \frac{1}{\sqrt{2\pi}} \int_{-\infty}^\infty \exp\left\{ -\frac{(x^2 - 2tx)}{2} \right\} dx$$
$$= \frac{1}{\sqrt{2\pi}} \int_{-\infty}^\infty \exp\left\{ -\frac{(x - t)^2}{2} + \frac{t^2}{2} \right\} dx$$
$$= e^{t^2/2} \frac{1}{\sqrt{2\pi}} \int_{-\infty}^\infty e^{-(x-t)^2/2}\, dx$$
$$= e^{t^2/2}$$

Hence, the moment generating function of the unit normal random variable Z is given by $M_Z(t) = e^{t^2/2}$. To obtain the moment generating function of an arbitrary normal random variable, we recall (see Section 5.4) that $X = \mu + \sigma Z$ will have a normal distribution with parameters μ and σ^2 whenever Z is a unit normal random variable. Hence, the moment generating function of such a random variable is given by

$$
\begin{aligned}
M_X(t) &= E[e^{tX}] \\
&= E[e^{t(\mu + \sigma Z)}] \\
&= E[e^{t\mu} e^{t\sigma Z}] \\
&= e^{t\mu} E[e^{t\sigma Z}] \\
&= e^{t\mu} M_Z(t\sigma) \\
&= e^{t\mu} e^{(t\sigma)^2/2} \\
&= \exp\left\{ \frac{\sigma^2 t^2}{2} + \mu t \right\}
\end{aligned}
$$

By differentiating, we obtain

$$
M'_X(t) = (\mu + t\sigma^2) \exp\left\{ \frac{\sigma^2 t^2}{2} + \mu t \right\}
$$

$$
M''_X(t) = (\mu + t\sigma^2)^2 \exp\left\{ \frac{\sigma^2 t^2}{2} + \mu t \right\} + \sigma^2 \exp\left\{ \frac{\sigma^2 t^2}{2} + \mu t \right\}
$$

Thus,

$$
E[X] = M'(0) = \mu
$$
$$
E[X^2] = M''(0) = \mu^2 + \sigma^2
$$

implying that

$$
\begin{aligned}
\mathrm{Var}(X) &= E[X^2] - E([X])^2 \\
&= \sigma^2
\end{aligned}
$$

∎

Tables 7.1 and 7.2 (on page 340) give the moment generating functions for some common discrete and continuous distributions.

An important property of moment generating functions is that the moment generating function of the sum of independent random variables equals the product of the individual moment generating functions. To prove this, suppose that X and Y are independent and have moment generating functions $M_X(t)$ and $M_Y(t)$, respectively. Then $M_{X+Y}(t)$, the moment generating function of $X + Y$, is given by

$$
\begin{aligned}
M_{X+Y}(t) &= E[e^{t(X+Y)}] \\
&= E[e^{tX} e^{tY}] \\
&= E[e^{tX}] E[e^{tY}] \\
&= M_X(t) M_Y(t)
\end{aligned}
$$

where the next-to-last equality follows from Proposition 4.1, since X and Y are independent.

Table 7.1 Discrete Probability Distribution.

	Probability mass function, $p(x)$	Moment generating function, $M(t)$	Mean	Variance
Binomial with parameters n, p; $0 \le p \le 1$	$\binom{n}{x} p^x (1-p)^{n-x}$ $x = 0, 1, \ldots, n$	$(pe^t + 1 - p)^n$	np	$np(1-p)$
Poisson with parameter $\lambda > 0$	$e^{-\lambda} \dfrac{\lambda^x}{x!}$ $x = 0, 1, 2, \ldots$	$\exp\{\lambda(e^t - 1)\}$	λ	λ
Geometric with parameter $0 \le p \le 1$	$p(1-p)^{x-1}$ $x = 1, 2, \ldots$	$\dfrac{pe^t}{1 - (1-p)e^t}$	$\dfrac{1}{p}$	$\dfrac{1-p}{p^2}$
Negative binomial with parameters r, p; $0 \le p \le 1$	$\binom{n-1}{r-1} p^r (1-p)^{n-r}$ $n = r, r+1, \ldots$	$\left[\dfrac{pe^t}{1 - (1-p)e^t} \right]^r$	$\dfrac{r}{p}$	$\dfrac{r(1-p)}{p^2}$

Another important result is that the moment generating function uniquely determines the distribution. That is, if $M_X(t)$ exists and is finite in some region about $t = 0$, then the distribution of X is uniquely determined. For instance, if

$$M_X(t) = \left(\frac{1}{2}\right)^{10} (e^t + 1)^{10},$$

then it follows from Table 7.1 that X is a binomial random variable with parameters 10 and $\frac{1}{2}$.

Example 7e

Suppose that the moment generating function of a random variable X is given by $M(t) = e^{3(e^t - 1)}$. What is $P\{X = 0\}$?

Solution We see from Table 7.1 that $M(t) = e^{3(e^t - 1)}$ is the moment generating function of a Poisson random variable with mean 3. Hence, by the one-to-one correspondence between moment generating functions and distribution functions, it follows that X must be a Poisson random variable with mean 3. Thus, $P\{X = 0\} = e^{-3}$. ■

Example 7f

Sums of independent binomial random variables

If X and Y are independent binomial random variables with parameters (n, p) and (m, p), respectively, what is the distribution of $X + Y$?

Solution The moment generating function of $X + Y$ is given by

$$M_{X+Y}(t) = M_X(t) M_Y(t) = (pe^t + 1 - p)^n (pe^t + 1 - p)^m$$
$$= (pe^t + 1 - p)^{m+n}$$

However, $(pe^t + 1 - p)^{m+n}$ is the moment generating function of a binomial random variable having parameters $m + n$ and p. Thus, this must be the distribution of $X + Y$. ■

Table 7.2 Continuous Probability Distribution.

	Probability density function, $f(x)$	Moment generating function, $M(t)$	Mean	Variance
Uniform over (a, b)	$f(x) = \begin{cases} \dfrac{1}{b-a} & a < x < b \\ 0 & \text{otherwise} \end{cases}$	$\dfrac{e^{tb} - e^{ta}}{t(b-a)}$	$\dfrac{a+b}{2}$	$\dfrac{(b-a)^2}{12}$
Exponential with parameter $\lambda > 0$	$f(x) = \begin{cases} \lambda e^{-\lambda x} & x \geq 0 \\ 0 & x < 0 \end{cases}$	$\dfrac{\lambda}{\lambda - t}$	$\dfrac{1}{\lambda}$	$\dfrac{1}{\lambda^2}$
Gamma with parameters $(s, \lambda), \lambda > 0$	$f(x) = \begin{cases} \dfrac{\lambda e^{-\lambda x}(\lambda x)^{s-1}}{\Gamma(s)} & x \geq 0 \\ 0 & x < 0 \end{cases}$	$\left(\dfrac{\lambda}{\lambda - t} \right)^s$	$\dfrac{s}{\lambda}$	$\dfrac{s}{\lambda^2}$
Normal with parameters (μ, σ^2)	$f(x) = \dfrac{1}{\sqrt{2\pi}\sigma} e^{-(x-\mu)^2/2\sigma^2} \quad -\infty < x < \infty$	$\exp\left\{ \mu t + \dfrac{\sigma^2 t^2}{2} \right\}$	μ	σ^2

Example 7g

Sums of independent Poisson random variables

Calculate the distribution of $X + Y$ when X and Y are independent Poisson random variables with means respectively λ_1 and λ_2.

Solution

$$
\begin{aligned}
M_{X+Y}(t) &= M_X(t)M_Y(t) \\
&= \exp\{\lambda_1(e^t - 1)\}\exp\{\lambda_2(e^t - 1)\} \\
&= \exp\{(\lambda_1 + \lambda_2)(e^t - 1)\}
\end{aligned}
$$

Hence, $X + Y$ is Poisson distributed with mean $\lambda_1 + \lambda_2$, verifying the result given in Example 3e of Chapter 6. ∎

Example 7h

Sums of independent normal random variables

Show that if X and Y are independent normal random variables with respective parameters (μ_1, σ_1^2) and (μ_2, σ_2^2), then $X + Y$ is normal with mean $\mu_1 + \mu_2$ and variance $\sigma_1^2 + \sigma_2^2$.

Solution

$$
\begin{aligned}
M_{X+Y}(t) &= M_X(t)M_Y(t) \\
&= \exp\left\{\frac{\sigma_1^2 t^2}{2} + \mu_1 t\right\}\exp\left\{\frac{\sigma_2^2 t^2}{2} + \mu_2 t\right\} \\
&= \exp\left\{\frac{(\sigma_1^2 + \sigma_2^2)t^2}{2} + (\mu_1 + \mu_2)t\right\}
\end{aligned}
$$

which is the moment generating function of a normal random variable with mean $\mu_1 + \mu_2$ and variance $\sigma_1^2 + \sigma_2^2$. The desired result then follows because the moment generating function uniquely determines the distribution. ∎

Example 7i

Compute the moment generating function of a chi-squared random variable with n degrees of freedom.

Solution We can represent such a random variable as

$$
Z_1^2 + \cdots + Z_n^2
$$

where $Z_1, \ldots, Z_n$ are independent standard normal random variables. Let $M(t)$ be its moment generating function. Then, by the preceding,

$$
M(t) = (E[e^{tZ^2}])^n
$$

where Z is a standard normal random variable. Now,

$$
\begin{aligned}
E[e^{tZ^2}] &= \frac{1}{\sqrt{2\pi}}\int_{-\infty}^{\infty} e^{tx^2}e^{-x^2/2}\,dx \\
&= \frac{1}{\sqrt{2\pi}}\int_{-\infty}^{\infty} e^{-x^2/2\sigma^2}\,dx \quad \text{where } \sigma^2 = (1 - 2t)^{-1} \\
&= \sigma \\
&= (1 - 2t)^{-1/2}
\end{aligned}
$$

where the next-to-last equality uses the fact that the normal density with mean 0 and variance σ^2 integrates to 1. Therefore,

$$M(t) = (1 - 2t)^{-n/2} \qquad \blacksquare$$

Example 7j

Moment generating function of the sum of a random number of random variables

Let $X_1, X_2, \ldots$ be a sequence of independent and identically distributed random variables, and let N be a nonnegative, integer-valued random variable that is independent of the sequence $X, i \geq 1$. We want to compute the moment generating function of

$$Y = \sum_{i=1}^{N} X_i$$

(In Example 5d, Y was interpreted as the amount of money spent in a store on a given day when both the amount spent by a customer and the number of customers are random variables.)

To compute the moment generating function of Y, we first condition on N as follows:

$$E\left[\exp\left\{ t\sum_1^N X_i \right\} \,\middle|\, N = n \right] = E\left[\exp\left\{ t\sum_1^n X_i \right\} \,\middle|\, N = n \right]$$

$$= E\left[\exp\left\{ t\sum_1^n X_i \right\} \right]$$

$$= [M_X(t)]^n$$

where

$$M_X(t) = E[e^{tX_i}]$$

Hence,

$$E[e^{tY} | N] = (M_X(t))^N$$

Thus,

$$M_Y(t) = E[(M_X(t))^N]$$

The moments of Y can now be obtained upon differentiation, as follows:

$$M_Y'(t) = E[N(M_X(t))^{N-1}M_X'(t)]$$

So

$$
\begin{aligned}
E[Y] &= M_Y'(0) \\
&= E[N(M_X(0))^{N-1}M_X'(0)] \\
&= E[NE[X]] \\
&= E[N]E[X]
\end{aligned}
\qquad (7.2)
$$

verifying the result of Example 5d. (In this last set of equalities, we have used the fact that $M_X(0) = E[e^{0X}] = 1$.)

Also,

$$M_Y''(t) = E[N(N - 1)(M_X(t))^{N-2}(M_X'(t))^2 + N(M_X(t))^{N-1}M_X''(t)]$$

so

$$
\begin{aligned}
E[Y^2] &= M_Y''(0) \\
&= E[N(N - 1)(E[X])^2 + NE[X^2]] \\
&= (E[X])^2(E[N^2] - E[N]) + E[N]E[X^2] \\
&= E[N](E[X^2] - (E[X])^2) + (E[X])^2E[N^2] \\
&= E[N]\mathrm{Var}(X) + (E[X])^2E[N^2]
\end{aligned}
\tag{7.3}
$$

Hence, from Equations (7.2) and (7.3), we have

$$
\begin{aligned}
\mathrm{Var}(Y) &= E[N]\mathrm{Var}(X) + (E[X])^2(E[N^2] - (E[N])^2) \\
&= E[N]\mathrm{Var}(X) + (E[X])^2\mathrm{Var}(N)
\end{aligned}
$$
∎

Example 7k

Let Y denote a uniform random variable on $(0, 1)$, and suppose that conditional on $Y = p$, the random variable X has a binomial distribution with parameters n and p. In Example 5k, we showed that X is equally likely to take on any of the values $0, 1, \ldots, n$. Establish this result by using moment generating functions.

Solution To compute the moment generating function of X, start by conditioning on the value of Y. Using the formula for the binomial moment generating function gives

$$E[e^{tX}|Y = p] = (pe^t + 1 - p)^n$$

Now, Y is uniform on $(0, 1)$, so, upon taking expectations, we obtain

$$
\begin{aligned}
E[e^{tX}] &= \int_0^1 (pe^t + 1 - p)^n \, dp \\
&= \frac{1}{e^t - 1}\int_1^{e^t} y^n dy \quad \text{(by the substitution } y = pe^t + 1 - p) \\
&= \frac{1}{n + 1}\frac{e^{t(n+1)} - 1}{e^t - 1} \\
&= \frac{1}{n + 1}(1 + e^t + e^{2t} + \cdots + e^{nt})
\end{aligned}
$$

Because the preceding is the moment generating function of a random variable that is equally likely to be any of the values $0, 1, \ldots, n$, the desired result follows from the fact that the moment generating function of a random variable uniquely determines its distribution. ∎

7.7.1 Joint Moment Generating Functions

It is also possible to define the joint moment generating function of two or more random variables. This is done as follows: For any n random variables $X_1, \ldots, X_n$, the joint moment generating function, $M(t_1, \ldots, t_n)$, is defined, for all real values of $t_1, \ldots, t_n$, by

$$M(t_1, \ldots, t_n) = E[e^{t_1X_1 + \cdots + t_nX_n}]$$

The individual moment generating functions can be obtained from $M(t_1, \ldots, t_n)$ by letting all but one of the t_j's be 0. That is,

$$M_{X_i}(t) = E[e^{tX_i}] = M(0, \ldots, 0, t, 0, \ldots, 0)$$

where the t is in the ith place.

It can be proven (although the proof is too advanced for this text) that the joint moment generating function $M(t_1, \ldots, t_n)$ uniquely determines the joint distribution of $X_1, \ldots, X_n$. This result can then be used to prove that the n random variables $X_1, \ldots, X_n$ are independent if and only if

$$M(t_1, \ldots, t_n) = M_{X_1}(t_1) \cdots M_{X_n}(t_n) \tag{7.4}$$

For the proof in one direction, if the n random variables are independent, then

$$
\begin{aligned}
M(t_1, \ldots, t_n) &= E[e^{(t_1 X_1 + \cdots + t_n X_n)}] \\
&= E[e^{t_1 X_1} \cdots e^{t_n X_n}] \\
&= E[e^{t_1 X_1}] \cdots E[e^{t_n X_n}] \quad \text{by independence} \\
&= M_{X_1}(t_1) \cdots M_{X_n}(t_n)
\end{aligned}
$$

For the proof in the other direction, if Equation (7.4) is satisfied, then the joint moment generating function $M(t_1, \ldots, t_n)$ is the same as the joint moment generating function of n independent random variables, the ith of which has the same distribution as X_i. As the joint moment generating function uniquely determines the joint distribution, this must be the joint distribution; hence, the random variables are independent.

Example 7l

Let X and Y be independent normal random variables, each with mean μ and variance σ^2. In Example 7a of Chapter 6, we showed that $X + Y$ and $X - Y$ are independent. Let us now establish that $X + Y$ and $X - Y$ are independent by computing their joint moment generating function:

$$
\begin{aligned}
E[e^{t(X+Y)+s(X-Y)}] &= E[e^{(t+s)X+(t-s)Y}] \\
&= E[e^{(t+s)X}]E[e^{(t-s)Y}] \\
&= e^{\mu(t+s)+\sigma^2(t+s)^2/2} e^{\mu(t-s)+\sigma^2(t-s)^2/2} \\
&= e^{2\mu t + \sigma^2 t^2} e^{\sigma^2 s^2}
\end{aligned}
$$

But we recognize the preceding as the joint moment generating function of the sum of a normal random variable with mean 2μ and variance $2\sigma^2$ and an independent normal random variable with mean 0 and variance $2\sigma^2$. Because the joint moment generating function uniquely determines the joint distribution, it follows that $X + Y$ and $X - Y$ are independent normal random variables. ∎

In the next example, we use the joint moment generating function to verify a result that was established in Example 2b of Chapter 6.

Example 7m

Suppose that the number of events that occur is a Poisson random variable with mean λ and that each event is independently counted with probability p. Show that the number of counted events and the number of uncounted events are independent Poisson random variables with respective means λp and $\lambda(1 - p)$.

Solution Let X denote the total number of events, and let X_c denote the number of them that are counted. To compute the joint moment generating function of X_c, the number of events that are counted, and $X - X_c$, the number that are uncounted, start by conditioning on X to obtain

$$E[e^{sX_c+t(X-X_c)}|X = n] = e^{tn}E[e^{(s-t)X_c}|X = n]$$
$$= e^{tn}(pe^{s-t} + 1 - p)^n$$
$$= (pe^s + (1 - p)e^t)^n$$

which follows because, conditional on $X = n$, X_c is a binomial random variable with parameters n and p. Hence,

$$E[e^{sX_c+t(X-X_c)}|X] = (pe^s + (1 - p)e^t)^X$$

Taking expectations of both sides of this equation yields

$$E[e^{sX_c+t(X-X_c)}] = E[(pe^s + (1 - p)e^t)^X]$$

Now, since X is Poisson with mean λ, it follows that $E[e^{tX}] = e^{\lambda(e^t-1)}$. Therefore, for any positive value a we see (by letting $a = e^t$) that $E[a^X] = e^{\lambda(a-1)}$. Thus,

$$E[e^{sX_c+t(X-X_c)}] = e^{\lambda(pe^s+(1-p)e^t-1)}$$
$$= e^{\lambda p(e^s-1)}e^{\lambda(1-p)(e^t-1)}$$

As the preceding is the joint moment generating function of independent Poisson random variables with respective means λp and $\lambda(1 - p)$, the result is proven. ■

7.8 Additional Properties of Normal Random Variables

7.8.1 The Multivariate Normal Distribution

Let $Z_1, \ldots, Z_n$ be a set of n independent unit normal random variables. If, for some constants $a_{ij}, 1 \le i \le m, 1 \le j \le n$, and $\mu_i, 1 \le i \le m$,

$$X_1 = a_{11}Z_1 + \cdots + a_{1n}Z_n + \mu_1$$
$$X_2 = a_{21}Z_1 + \cdots + a_{2n}Z_n + \mu_2$$
$$\vdots$$
$$X_i = a_{i1}Z_1 + \cdots + a_{in}Z_n + \mu_i$$
$$\vdots$$
$$X_m = a_{m1}Z_1 + \cdots + a_{mn}Z_n + \mu_m$$

then the random variables $X_1, \ldots, X_m$ are said to have a multivariate normal distribution.

From the fact that the sum of independent normal random variables is itself a normal random variable, it follows that each X_i is a normal random variable with mean and variance given, respectively, by

$$E[X_i] = \mu_i$$

$$\mathrm{Var}(X_i) = \sum_{j=1}^{n} a_{ij}^2$$

Let us now consider

$$M(t_1, \ldots, t_m) = E[\exp\{t_1 X_1 + \cdots + t_m X_m\}]$$

the joint moment generating function of $X_1, \ldots, X_m$. The first thing to note is that since $\sum_{i=1}^{m} t_i X_i$ is itself a linear combination of the independent normal random variables $Z_1, \ldots, Z_n$, it is also normally distributed. Its mean and variance are

$$E\left[\sum_{i=1}^{m} t_i X_i\right] = \sum_{i=1}^{m} t_i \mu_i$$

and

$$\mathrm{Var}\left(\sum_{i=1}^{m} t_i X_i\right) = \mathrm{Cov}\left(\sum_{i=1}^{m} t_i X_i, \sum_{j=1}^{m} t_j X_j\right)$$

$$= \sum_{i=1}^{m} \sum_{j=1}^{m} t_i t_j \mathrm{Cov}(X_i, X_j)$$

Now, if Y is a normal random variable with mean μ and variance σ^2, then

$$E[e^Y] = M_Y(t)|_{t=1} = e^{\mu + \sigma^2/2}$$

Thus,

$$M(t_1, \ldots, t_m) = \exp\left\{\sum_{i=1}^{m} t_i \mu_i + \frac{1}{2} \sum_{i=1}^{m} \sum_{j=1}^{m} t_i t_j \mathrm{Cov}(X_i, X_j)\right\}$$

which shows that the joint distribution of $X_1, \ldots, X_m$ is completely determined from a knowledge of the values of $E[X_i]$ and $\mathrm{Cov}(X_i, X_j), i, j = 1, \ldots, m$.

It can be shown that when $m = 2$, the multivariate normal distribution reduces to the bivariate normal.

Example 8a

Find $P(X < Y)$ for bivariate normal random variables X and Y having parameters

$$\mu_x = E[X], \ \mu_y = E[Y], \ \sigma_x^2 = \mathrm{Var}(X), \ \sigma_y^2 = \mathrm{Var}(Y), \ \rho = \mathrm{Corr}(X, Y)$$

Solution Because $X - Y$ is normal with mean

$$E[X - Y] = \mu_x - \mu_y$$

and variance

$$\mathrm{Var}(X - Y) = \mathrm{Var}(X) + \mathrm{Var}(-Y) + 2\mathrm{Cov}(X, -Y)$$
$$= \sigma_x^2 + \sigma_y^2 - 2\rho\sigma_x\sigma_y$$

we obtain

$$P\{X < Y\} = P\{X - Y < 0\}$$

$$= P\left\{\frac{X - Y - (\mu_x - \mu_y)}{\sqrt{\sigma_x^2 + \sigma_y^2 - 2\rho\sigma_x\sigma_y}} < \frac{-(\mu_x - \mu_y)}{\sqrt{\sigma_x^2 + \sigma_y^2 - 2\rho\sigma_x\sigma_y}}\right\}$$

$$= \Phi\left(\frac{\mu_y - \mu_x}{\sqrt{\sigma_x^2 + \sigma_y^2 - 2\rho\sigma_x\sigma_y}}\right) \qquad \blacksquare$$

Example 8b

Suppose that the conditional distribution of X, given that $\Theta = \theta$, is normal with mean θ and variance 1. Moreover, suppose that Θ itself is a normal random variable with mean μ and variance σ^2. Find the conditional distribution of Θ given that $X = x$.

Solution Rather than using and then simplifying Bayes's formula, we will solve this problem by first showing that X, Θ has a bivariate normal distribution. To do so, note that the joint density function of X, Θ can be written as

$$f_{X,\Theta}(x, \theta) = f_{X|\Theta}(x|\theta)f_{\Theta}(\theta)$$

where $f_{X|\Theta}(x|\theta)$ is a normal density with mean θ and variance 1. However, if we let Z be a standard normal random variable that is independent of Θ, then the conditional distribution of $Z + \Theta$, given that $\Theta = \theta$, is also normal with mean θ and variance 1. Consequently, the joint density of $Z + \Theta, \Theta$ is the same as that of X, Θ. Because the former joint density is clearly bivariate normal (since $Z + \Theta$ and Θ are both linear combinations of the independent normal random variables Z and Θ), it follows that X, Θ has a bivariate normal distribution. Now,

$$E[X] = E[Z + \Theta] = \mu$$
$$\mathrm{Var}(X) = \mathrm{Var}(Z + \Theta) = 1 + \sigma^2$$

and

$$\rho = \mathrm{Corr}(X, \Theta)$$
$$= \mathrm{Corr}(Z + \Theta, \Theta)$$
$$= \frac{\mathrm{Cov}(Z + \Theta, \Theta)}{\sqrt{\mathrm{Var}(Z + \Theta)\mathrm{Var}(\Theta)}}$$
$$= \frac{\sigma}{\sqrt{1 + \sigma^2}}$$

Because X, Θ has a bivariate normal distribution, the conditional distribution of Θ, given that $X = x$, is normal with mean

$$E[\Theta|X = x] = E[\Theta] + \rho\sqrt{\frac{\mathrm{Var}(\Theta)}{\mathrm{Var}(X)}}(x - E[X])$$

$$= \mu + \frac{\sigma^2}{1 + \sigma^2}(x - \mu)$$

and variance

$$\mathrm{Var}(\Theta|X = x) = \mathrm{Var}(\Theta)(1 - \rho^2)$$
$$= \frac{\sigma^2}{1 + \sigma^2} \qquad \blacksquare$$

7.8.2 The Joint Distribution of the Sample Mean and Sample Variance

Let $X_1, \ldots, X_n$ be independent normal random variables, each with mean μ and variance σ^2. Let $\overline{X} = \sum_{i=1}^{n} X_i/n$ denote their sample mean. Since the sum of independent normal random variables is also a normal random variable, it follows that $\overline{X}$ is a normal random variable with (from Examples 2c and 4a) expected value μ and variance σ^2/n.

Now, recall from Example 4e that

$$\text{Cov}(\overline{X}, X_i - \overline{X}) = 0, \quad i = 1, \ldots, n \tag{8.1}$$

Also, note that since $\overline{X}, X_1 - \overline{X}, X_2 - \overline{X}, \ldots, X_n - \overline{X}$ are all linear combinations of the independent standard normals $(X_i - \mu)/\sigma, i = 1, \ldots, n$, it follows that $\overline{X}, X_i - \overline{X}, i = 1, \ldots, n$ has a joint distribution that is multivariate normal. If we let Y be a normal random variable, with mean μ and variance σ^2/n, that is independent of the $X_i, i = 1, \ldots, n$, then $Y, X_i - \overline{X}, i = 1, \ldots, n$ also has a multivariate normal distribution and, indeed, because of Equation (8.1), has the same expected values and covariances as the random variables $\overline{X}, X_i - \overline{X}, i = 1, \ldots, n$. But since a multivariate normal distribution is determined completely by its expected values and covariances, it follows that $Y, X_i - \overline{X}, i = 1, \ldots, n$ and $\overline{X}, X_i - \overline{X}, i = 1, \ldots, n$ have the same joint distribution, thus showing that $\overline{X}$ is independent of the sequence of deviations $X_i - \overline{X}, i = 1, \ldots, n$.

Since $\overline{X}$ is independent of the sequence of deviations $X_i - \overline{X}, i = 1, \ldots, n$, it is also independent of the sample variance $S^2 \equiv \sum_{i=1}^{n}(X_i - \overline{X})^2/(n-1)$.

Since we already know that $\overline{X}$ is normal with mean μ and variance σ^2/n, it remains only to determine the distribution of S^2. To accomplish this, recall, from Example 4a, the algebraic identity

$$(n-1)S^2 = \sum_{i=1}^{n}(X_i - \overline{X})^2$$

$$= \sum_{i=1}^{n}(X_i - \mu)^2 - n(\overline{X} - \mu)^2$$

Upon dividing the preceding equation by σ^2, we obtain

$$\frac{(n-1)S^2}{\sigma^2} + \left(\frac{\overline{X} - \mu}{\sigma/\sqrt{n}}\right)^2 = \sum_{i=1}^{n}\left(\frac{X_i - \mu}{\sigma}\right)^2 \tag{8.2}$$

Now,

$$\sum_{i=1}^{n}\left(\frac{X_i - \mu}{\sigma}\right)^2$$

is the sum of the squares of n independent standard normal random variables and so is a chi-squared random variable with n degrees of freedom. Hence, from Example 7i, its moment generating function is $(1 - 2t)^{-n/2}$. Also, because

$$\left(\frac{\overline{X} - \mu}{\sigma/\sqrt{n}}\right)^2$$

is the square of a standard normal variable, it is a chi-squared random variable with 1 degree of freedom, and so has moment generating function $(1 - 2t)^{-1/2}$. Now, we have seen previously that the two random variables on the left side of Equation (8.2) are independent. Hence, as the moment generating function of the sum of independent random variables is equal to the product of their individual moment generating functions, we have

$$E[e^{t(n-1)S^2/\sigma^2}](1 - 2t)^{-1/2} = (1 - 2t)^{-n/2}$$

or

$$E[e^{t(n-1)S^2/\sigma^2}] = (1 - 2t)^{-(n-1)/2}$$

But as $(1 - 2t)^{-(n-1)/2}$ is the moment generating function of a chi-squared random variable with $n - 1$ degrees of freedom, we can conclude, since the moment generating function uniquely determines the distribution of the random variable, that that is the distribution of $(n - 1)S^2/\sigma^2$.

Summing up, we have shown the following.

Proposition 8.1 If $X_1, \ldots, X_n$ are independent and identically distributed normal random variables with mean μ and variance σ^2, then the sample mean $\overline{X}$ and the sample variance S^2 are independent. $\overline{X}$ is a normal random variable with mean μ and variance σ^2/n; $(n - 1)S^2/\sigma^2$ is a chi-squared random variable with $n - 1$ degrees of freedom.

7.9 General Definition of Expectation

Up to this point, we have defined expectations only for discrete and continuous random variables. However, there also exist random variables that are neither discrete nor continuous, and they, too, may possess an expectation. As an example of such a random variable, let X be a Bernoulli random variable with parameter $p = \frac{1}{2}$, and let Y be a uniformly distributed random variable over the interval $[0, 1]$. Furthermore, suppose that X and Y are independent, and define the new random variable W by

$$W = \begin{cases} X & \text{if } X = 1 \\ Y & \text{if } X \neq 1 \end{cases}$$

Clearly, W is neither a discrete (since its set of possible values, $[0, 1]$, is uncountable) nor a continuous (since $P\{W = 1\} = \frac{1}{2}$) random variable.

In order to define the expectation of an arbitrary random variable, we require the notion of a Stieltjes integral. Before defining this integral, let us recall that for any function g, $\int_a^b g(x)\,dx$ is defined by

$$\int_a^b g(x)\,dx = \lim \sum_{i=1}^n g(x_i)(x_i - x_{i-1})$$

where the limit is taken over all $a = x_0 < x_1 < x_2 \cdots < x_n = b$ as $n \to \infty$ and where $\max_{i=1,\ldots,n}(x_i - x_{i-1}) \to 0$.

For any distribution function F, we define the Stieltjes integral of the nonnegative function g over the interval $[a, b]$ by

$$\int_a^b g(x)\,dF(x) = \lim \sum_{i=1}^n g(x_i)[F(x_i) - F(x_{i-1})]$$

where, as before, the limit is taken over all $a = x_0 < x_1 < \cdots < x_n = b$ as $n \to \infty$ and where $\max_{i=1,\ldots,n} (x_i - x_{i-1}) \to 0$. Further, we define the Stieltjes integral over the whole real line by

$$\int_{-\infty}^{\infty} g(x)\, dF(x) = \lim_{\substack{a \to -\infty \\ b \to +\infty}} \int_{a}^{b} g(x)\, dF(x)$$

Finally, if g is not a nonnegative function, we define g^+ and g^- by

$$g^+(x) = \begin{cases} g(x) & \text{if } g(x) \geq 0 \\ 0 & \text{if } g(x) < 0 \end{cases}$$

$$g^-(x) = \begin{cases} 0 & \text{if } g(x) \geq 0 \\ -g(x) & \text{if } g(x) < 0 \end{cases}$$

Because $g(x) = g^+(x) - g^-(x)$ and g^+ and g^- are both nonnegative functions, it is natural to define

$$\int_{-\infty}^{\infty} g(x)\, dF(x) = \int_{-\infty}^{\infty} g^+(x)\, dF(x) - \int_{-\infty}^{\infty} g^-(x)\, dF(x)$$

and we say that $\int_{-\infty}^{\infty} g(x)\, dF(x)$ exists as long as $\int_{-\infty}^{\infty} g^+(x)\, dF(x)$ and $\int_{-\infty}^{\infty} g^-(x)\, dF(x)$ are not both equal to $+\infty$.

If X is an arbitrary random variable having cumulative distribution F, we define the expected value of X by

$$E[X] = \int_{-\infty}^{\infty} x\, dF(x) \tag{9.1}$$

It can be shown that if X is a discrete random variable with mass function $p(x)$, then

$$\int_{-\infty}^{\infty} x\, dF(x) = \sum_{x: p(x) > 0} x p(x)$$

whereas if X is a continuous random variable with density function $f(x)$, then

$$\int_{-\infty}^{\infty} x\, dF(x) = \int_{-\infty}^{\infty} x f(x)\, dx$$

The reader should note that Equation (9.1) yields an intuitive definition of $E[X]$; consider the approximating sum

$$\sum_{i=1}^{n} x_i [F(x_i) - F(x_{i-1})]$$

of $E[X]$. Because $F(x_i) - F(x_{i-1})$ is just the probability that X will be in the interval $(x_{i-1}, x_i]$, the approximating sum multiplies the approximate value of X when it is in the interval $(x_{i-1}, x_i]$ by the probability that it will be in that interval and then sums over all the intervals. Clearly, as these intervals get smaller and smaller in length, we obtain the "expected value" of X.

Stieltjes integrals are mainly of theoretical interest because they yield a compact way of defining and dealing with the properties of expectation. For instance, the use of Stieltjes integrals avoids the necessity of having to give separate statements and proofs of theorems for the continuous and the discrete cases. However, their properties are very much the same as those of ordinary integrals, and all of the proofs presented in this chapter can easily be translated into proofs in the general case.

Summary

If X and Y have a joint probability mass function $p(x, y)$, then

$$E[g(X, Y)] = \sum_y \sum_x g(x, y)p(x, y)$$

whereas if they have a joint density function $f(x, y)$, then

$$E[g(X, Y)] = \int_{-\infty}^{\infty} \int_{-\infty}^{\infty} g(x, y)f(x, y)\, dx\, dy$$

A consequence of the preceding equations is that

$$E[X + Y] = E[X] + E[Y]$$

which generalizes to

$$E\left[\sum_{i=1}^n X_i\right] = \sum_{i=1}^n E[X_i]$$

The *covariance* between random variables X and Y is given by

$$\text{Cov}(X, Y) = E[(X - E[X])(Y - E[Y])]$$
$$= E[XY] - E[X]E[Y]$$

A useful identity is

$$\text{Cov}\left(\sum_{i=1}^n X_i, \sum_{j=1}^m Y_j\right) = \sum_{i=1}^n \sum_{j=1}^m \text{Cov}(X_i, Y_j)$$

When $n = m$ and $Y_i = X_i, i = 1, \ldots, n$, the preceding formula gives

$$\text{Var}\left(\sum_{i=1}^n X_i\right) = \sum_{i=1}^n \text{Var}(X_i) + 2\sum \sum_{i<j} \text{Cov}(X_i, Y_j)$$

The correlation between X and Y, denoted by $\rho(X, Y)$, is defined by

$$\rho(X, Y) = \frac{\text{Cov}(X, Y)}{\sqrt{\text{Var}(X)\text{Var}(Y)}}$$

If X and Y are jointly discrete random variables, then the conditional expected value of X, given that $Y = y$, is defined by

$$E[X|Y = y] = \sum_x xP\{X = x|Y = y\}$$

If X and Y are jointly continuous random variables, then

$$E[X|Y = y] = \int_{-\infty}^{\infty} xf_{X|Y}(x|y)\, dx$$

where

$$f_{X|Y}(x|y) = \frac{f(x, y)}{f_Y(y)}$$

is the conditional probability density of X given that $Y = y$. Conditional expectations, which are similar to ordinary expectations except that all probabilities are now computed conditional on the event that $Y = y$, satisfy all the properties of ordinary expectations.

Let $E[X|Y]$ denote that function of Y whose value at $Y = y$ is $E[X|Y = y]$. A very useful identity is

$$E[X] = E[E[X|Y]]$$

In the case of discrete random variables, this equation reduces to the identity

$$E[X] = \sum_y E[X|Y = y]P\{Y = y\}$$

and, in the continuous case, to

$$E[X] = \int_{-\infty}^{\infty} E[X|Y = y]f_Y(y)dy$$

The preceding equations can often be applied to obtain $E[X]$ by first "conditioning" on the value of some other random variable Y. In addition, since, for any event A, $P(A) = E[I_A]$, where I_A is 1 if A occurs and is 0 otherwise, we can use the same equations to compute probabilities.

The conditional variance of X, given that $Y = y$, is defined by

$$\text{Var}(X|Y = y) = E[(X - E[X|Y = y])^2|Y = y]$$

Let $\text{Var}(X|Y)$ be that function of Y whose value at $Y = y$ is $\text{Var}(X|Y = y)$. The following is known as the *conditional variance formula*:

$$\text{Var}(X) = E[\text{Var}(X|Y)] + \text{Var}(E[X|Y])$$

Suppose that the random variable X is to be observed and, on the basis of its value, one must then predict the value of the random variable Y. In such a situation, it turns out that among all predictors, $E[Y|X]$ has the smallest expectation of the square of the difference between it and Y.

The *moment generating function* of the random variable X is defined by

$$M(t) = E[e^{tX}]$$

The moments of X can be obtained by successively differentiating $M(t)$ and then evaluating the resulting quantity at $t = 0$. Specifically, we have

$$E[X^n] = \left.\frac{d^n}{dt^n}M(t)\right|_{t=0} \qquad n = 1, 2, \ldots$$

Two useful results concerning moment generating functions are, first, that the moment generating function uniquely determines the distribution function of the random variable and, second, that the moment generating function of the sum of independent random variables is equal to the product of their moment generating functions. These results lead to simple proofs that the sum of independent normal (Poisson, gamma) random variables remains a normal (Poisson, gamma) random variable.

If $X_1, \ldots, X_m$ are all linear combinations of a finite set of independent standard normal random variables, then they are said to have a *multivariate normal distribution*. Their joint distribution is specified by the values of $E[X_i], \mathrm{Cov}(X_i, X_j), i, j = 1, \ldots, m$.

If $X_1, \ldots, X_n$ are independent and identically distributed normal random variables, then their *sample mean*

$$\overline{X} = \sum_{i=1}^{n} \frac{X_i}{n}$$

and their *sample variance*

$$S^2 = \sum_{i=1}^{n} \frac{(X_i - \overline{X})^2}{n - 1}$$

are independent. The sample mean $\overline{X}$ is a normal random variable with mean μ and variance σ^2/n; the random variable $(n - 1)S^2/\sigma^2$ is a chi-squared random variable with $n - 1$ degrees of freedom.

Problems

7.1. A player throws a fair die and simultaneously flips a fair coin. If the coin lands heads, then she wins twice, and if tails, then she wins one-half of the value that appears on the die. Determine her expected winnings.

7.2. The game of Clue involves 6 suspects, 6 weapons, and 9 rooms. One of each is randomly chosen and the object of the game is to guess the chosen three.

(a) How many solutions are possible?
In one version of the game, the selection is made and then each of the players is randomly given three of the remaining cards. Let S, W, and R be, respectively, the numbers of suspects, weapons, and rooms in the set of three cards given to a specified player. Also, let X denote the number of solutions that are possible after that player observes his or her three cards.
(b) Express X in terms of S, W, and R.
(c) Find $E[X]$.

7.3. Gambles are independent, and each one results in the player being equally likely to win or lose 1 unit. Let W denote the net winnings of a gambler whose strategy is to stop gambling immediately after his first win. Find
(a) $P\{W > 0\}$
(b) $P\{W < 0\}$
(c) $E[W]$

7.4. If X and Y have joint density function
$$f(x, y) = 8xy, 0 < x < 1, 0 < y < x$$
Find
(a) $E(XY)$
(b) $E(X)$
(c) $E(Y)$

7.5. The county hospital is located at the center of a square whose sides are 3 miles wide. If an accident occurs within this square, then the hospital sends out an ambulance. The road network is rectangular, so the travel distance from the hospital, whose coordinates are (0, 0), to the point (x, y) is $|x| + |y|$. If an accident occurs at a point that is uniformly distributed in the square, find the expected travel distance of the ambulance.

7.6. A fair die is rolled 10 times. Calculate the expected sum of the 10 rolls.

7.7. Suppose that A and B each randomly and independently choose 4 of 12 objects. Find the expected number of objects
(a) chosen by both A and B,
(b) not chosen by either A or B
(c) chosen by exactly one of A and B.

7.8. N people arrive separately to a professional dinner. Upon arrival, each person looks to see if he or she has any friends among those present. That person then sits either at the table of a friend or at an unoccupied table if none of those present is a friend. Assuming that each of the $\binom{N}{2}$ pairs of people is, independently, a pair of friends with probability p, find the expected number of occupied tables.
Hint: Let X_i equal 1 or 0, depending on whether the ith arrival sits at a previously unoccupied table.

7.9. A total of n balls, numbered 1 through n, are put into n urns, also numbered 1 through n in such a way that ball i is equally likely to go into any of the urns $1, 2, \ldots, i$. Find
(a) the expected number of urns that are empty;
(b) the probability that none of the urns is empty.

7.10. Consider 4 trials, each having the same probability of success. Let X denote the total number of successes in these trials. If $E[X] = 2$, what is
(a) the largest possible value of $P(X = 4)$
(b) the smallest possible value of $P(X = 4)$

In both cases, construct a probability scenario that results in $P(X = 2)$ having the stated value.

7.11. Consider n independent flips of a coin having probability p of landing on heads. Say that a changeover occurs whenever an outcome differs from the one preceding it. For instance, if $n = 5$ and the outcome is $HHTHT$, then there are 3 changeovers. Find the expected number of changeovers.

Hint: Express the number of changeovers as the sum of $n - 1$ Bernoulli random variables.

7.12. A group of n men and m women is lined up at random.
(a) Find the expected number of men who have a woman next to them.
(b) Repeat part (a), but now assuming that the group is randomly seated at a round table.

7.13. A set of 1000 cards numbered 1 through 1000 is randomly distributed among 1000 people with each receiving one card. Compute the expected number of cards that are given to people whose age matches the number on the card.

7.14. An urn has m black balls. At each stage, a black ball is removed and a new ball that is black with probability p and white with probability $1 - p$ is put in its place. Find the expected number of stages needed until there are no more black balls in the urn.

NOTE: The preceding has possible applications to understanding the AIDS disease. Part of the body's immune system consists of a certain class of cells known as T-cells. There are 2 types of T-cells, called CD4 and CD8. Now, while the total number of T-cells in AIDS sufferers is (at least in the early stages of the disease) the same as that in healthy individuals, it has recently been discovered that the mix of CD4 and CD8 T-cells is different. Roughly 60 percent of the T-cells of a healthy person are of the CD4 type, whereas the percentage of the T-cells that are of CD4 type appears to decrease continually in AIDS sufferers. A recent model proposes that the HIV virus (the virus that causes AIDS) attacks CD4 cells and that the body's mechanism for replacing killed T-cells does not differentiate between whether the killed T-cell was CD4 or CD8. Instead, it just produces a new T-cell that is CD4 with probability .6 and CD8 with probability .4. However, although this would seem to be a very efficient way of replacing killed T-cells when each one killed is equally likely to be any of the body's T-cells (and thus has probability .6 of being CD4), it has dangerous consequences when facing a virus that targets only the CD4 T-cells.

7.15. In Example 2h, say that i and j, $i \neq j$, form a matched pair if i chooses the hat belonging to j and j chooses the hat belonging to i. Find the expected number of matched pairs.

7.16. Let Z be a standard normal random variable, and, for a fixed x, set

$$X = \begin{cases} Z & \text{if } Z > x \\ 0 & \text{otherwise} \end{cases}$$

Show that $E[X] = \dfrac{1}{\sqrt{2\pi}} e^{-x^2/2}$.

7.17. A deck of n cards numbered 1 through n is thoroughly shuffled so that all possible $n!$ orderings can be assumed to be equally likely. Suppose you are to make n guesses sequentially, where the ith one is a guess of the card in position i. Let N denote the number of correct guesses.

(a) If you are not given any information about your earlier guesses, show that for any strategy, $E[N] = 1$.

(b) Suppose that after each guess you are shown the card that was in the position in question. What do you think is the best strategy? Show that under this strategy,

$$E[N] = \frac{1}{n} + \frac{1}{n-1} + \cdots + 1$$
$$\approx \int_1^n \frac{1}{x} \, dx = \log n$$

(c) Suppose that you are told after each guess whether you are right or wrong. In this case, it can be shown that the strategy that maximizes $E[N]$ is one that keeps on guessing the same card until you are told you are correct and then changes to a new card. For this strategy, show that

$$E[N] = 1 + \frac{1}{2!} + \frac{1}{3!} + \cdots + \frac{1}{n!}$$
$$\approx e - 1$$

Hint: For all parts, express N as the sum of indicator (that is, Bernoulli) random variables.

7.18. Cards from an ordinary deck of 52 playing cards are turned face up one at a time. If the 1st card is an ace, or the 2nd a deuce, or the 3rd a three, or ..., or the 13th a king, or the 14 an ace, and so on, we say that a match occurs. Note that we do not require that the $(13n + 1)$ card be any particular ace for a match to occur but only that it be an ace. Compute the expected number of matches that occur.

7.19. A certain region is inhabited by r distinct types of a certain species of insect. Each insect caught will, independently of the types of the previous catches, be of type i with probability

$$P_i, i = 1, \ldots, r \quad \sum_1^r P_i = 1$$

(a) Compute the mean number of insects that are caught before the first type 1 catch.

(b) Compute the mean number of types of insects that are caught before the first type 1 catch.

7.20. In an urn containing n balls, the ith ball has weight $W(i), i = 1, \ldots, n$. The balls are removed without replacement, one at a time, according to the following rule: At each selection, the probability that a given ball in the urn is chosen is equal to its weight divided by the sum of the weights remaining in the urn. For instance, if at some time $i_1, \ldots, i_r$ is the set of balls remaining in the urn, then the next selection will be i_j with probability $W(i_j) / \sum_{k=1}^{r} W(i_k)$, $j = 1, \ldots, r$. Compute the expected number of balls that are withdrawn before ball number 1 is removed.

7.21. For a group of 100 people, compute

(a) the expected number of days of the year that are birthdays of exactly 3 people;

(b) the expected number of distinct birthdays.

7.22. How many times would you expect to roll a fair die before all 6 sides appeared at least once

7.23. Urn 1 contains 5 white and 6 black balls, while urn 2 contains 8 white and 10 black balls. Two balls are randomly selected from urn 1 and are put into urn 2. If 3 balls are then randomly selected from urn 2, compute the expected number of white balls in the trio.
Hint: Let $X_i = 1$ if the ith white ball initially in urn 1 is one of the three selected, and let $X_i = 0$ otherwise. Similarly, let $Y_i = 1$ if the ith white ball from urn 2 is one of the three selected, and let $Y_i = 0$ otherwise. The number of white balls in the trio can now be written as $\sum_{1}^{5} X_i + \sum_{1}^{8} Y_i$.

7.24. A bottle initially contains m large pills and n small pills. Each day, a patient randomly chooses one of the pills. If a small pill is chosen, then that pill is eaten. If a large pill is chosen, then the pill is broken in two; one part is returned to the bottle (and is now considered a small pill) and the other part is then eaten.

(a) Let X denote the number of small pills in the bottle after the last large pill has been chosen and its smaller half returned. Find $E[X]$.
Hint: Define $n + m$ indicator variables, one for each of the small pills initially present and one for each of the m small pills created when a large one is split in two. Now use the argument of Example 2m.

(b) Let Y denote the day on which the last large pill is chosen. Find $E[Y]$.
Hint: What is the relationship between X and Y?

7.25. Let $X_1, X_2, \ldots$ be a sequence of independent and identically distributed continuous random variables. Let $N \geq 2$ be such that

$$X_1 \geq X_2 \geq \cdots \geq X_{N-1} < X_N$$

That is, N is the point at which the sequence stops decreasing. Show that $E[N] = e$.
Hint: First find $P\{N \geq n\}$.

7.26. If X_1, X_2 are independent and identically distributed random variables having exponential distribution with mean $= 2$, find

(a) $E(\min(X_1, X_2))$;

(b) $E(\max(X_1, X_2))$

*7.27. If 101 items are distributed among 10 boxes, then at least one of the boxes must contain more than 10 items. Use the probabilistic method to prove this result.

*7.28. The k-of-r-out-of-n circular reliability system, $k \leq r \leq n$, consists of n components that are arranged in a circular fashion. Each component is either functional or failed, and the system functions if there is no block of r consecutive components of which at least k are failed. Show that there is no way to arrange 47 components, 8 of which are failed, to make a functional 3-of-12-out-of-47 circular system.

*7.29. There are 4 different types of coupons, the first 2 of which comprise one group and the second 2 another group. Each new coupon obtained is type i with probability p_i, where $p_1 = p_2 = 1/8, p_3 = p_4 = 3/8$. Find the expected number of coupons that one must obtain to have at least one of

(a) all 4 types;

(b) all the types of the first group;

(c) all the types of the second group;

(d) all the types of either group.

7.30. If X and Y are independent and identically distributed with mean μ and variance σ^2, find,

$$E[(X - Y)(Y - X)]$$

7.31. Let X and Y be two independent poisson variable with $P(X = 1) = P(X = 2)$ and $P(Y = 2) = P(Y = 3)$. Obtain the variance of $(Y - 3X)$.

7.32. Lot X and Y be independent random variables, each having the uniform distribution on $[-1, 1]$. Then find $\text{Var}(X + Y)$.

7.33. If $E(X) = 2$ and $E(X^2) = 5$, find

(a) $E((X - 3)^2)$.

(b) $\text{Var}[(2/3) - 4X]$

7.34. If 8 married couples are randomly seated at a round table, compute
(a) the expected number and
(b) the variance of the number of wives who are seated next to their husbands.

7.35. Cards from an ordinary deck are turned face up one at a time. Compute the expected number of cards that need to be turned face up in order to obtain

(a) 2 aces;

(b) 5 spades;

(c) all 13 hearts.

7.36. Let X be the number of odd faces and Y the number of even faces that occur in n rolls of a fair die. Compute $\text{Cov}(X,Y)$.

7.37. A die is rolled twice. Let X equal the sum of the outcomes, and let Y equal the second outcome minus the first. Compute $\text{Cov}(X, Y)$.

7.38. The joint density of X and Y is given by
$$f(x,y) = \begin{cases} 1 & \text{if } 0 < y < 1,\ y-1 < x < 1-y \\ 0 & \text{otherwise} \end{cases}$$
Compute $\text{Cov}(X,Y)$.

7.39. Let $X_1, \ldots$ be independent with common mean μ and common variance σ^2, and set $Y_n = X_n + X_{n+1} + X_{n+2}$. For $j \geq 0$, find $\text{Cov}(Y_n, Y_{n+j})$.

7.40. The joint density function of X and Y is given by
$$f(x,y) = \frac{1}{y}e^{-(y+x/y)}, \quad x > 0, y > 0$$
Find $E[X]$, $E[Y]$, and show that $\text{Cov}(X, Y) = 1$.

7.41. Out of Deepa's 50 friends, 30 are vegan. Deepa hosted a party for 10 of these friends (chosen randomly), what is the mean and variance of number of vegan among the selected friends?

7.42. In a company sponsored dinner, 20 tables are arranged with each table having the capacity to accommodate two people. A manager and a junior executive from each of their 20 outlets are invited for the dinner. If the seating arrangement is done randomly,
(a) compute the expectation and variance of the number of pairs that consist of a manager and an executive.
(b) Also compute the expectation and variance of the number of pairs that consist of a manager and an executive from the same outlet woman **(b)**
(a) $E[X] = 1/19 \text{Var}[X] = 0.5279$

7.43. Let $X_1, X_2, \ldots, X_n$ be independent random variables having an unknown continuous distribution function F, and let $Y_1, Y_2, \ldots, Y_m$ be independent random variables having an unknown continuous distribution function G. Now order those $n + m$ variables, and let
$$I_i = \begin{cases} 1 & \text{if the } i\text{th smallest of the } n + m \\ & \text{variables is from the } X \text{ sample} \\ 0 & \text{otherwise} \end{cases}$$

The random variable $R = \sum_{i=1}^{n+m} iI_i$ is the sum of the ranks of the X sample and is the basis of a standard statistical procedure (called the Wilcoxon sum-of-ranks test) for testing whether F and G are identical distributions. This test accepts the hypothesis that $F = G$ when R is neither too large nor too small. Assuming that the hypothesis of

equality is in fact correct, compute the mean and variance of R.
Hint: Use the results of Example 3e.

7.44. Between two distinct methods for manufacturing certain goods, the quality of goods produced by method i is a continuous random variable having distribution $F_i, i = 1, 2$. Suppose that n goods are produced by method 1 and m by method 2. Rank the $n + m$ goods according to quality, and let
$$X_j = \begin{cases} 1 & \text{if the } j\text{th best was produced from} \\ & \text{method 1} \\ 2 & \text{otherwise} \end{cases}$$
For the vector $X_1, X_2, \ldots, X_{n+m}$, which consists of n 1's and m 2's, let R denote the number of runs of 1. For instance, if $n = 5, m = 2$, and $X = 1, 2, 1, 1, 1, 1, 2$, then $R = 2$. If $F_1 = F_2$ (that is, if the two methods produce identically distributed goods), what are the mean and variance of R?

7.45. If X_1, X_2 and X_3 are (pairwise) uncorrelated random variables, each having mean 0 and variance 1, compute the correlations of
(a) $X_1 - X_2$ and $X_2 - X_3$
(b) $X_1 - X_2$ and $X_3 - X_4$

7.46. Consider the following dice game, as played at a certain gambling casino: Players 1 and 2 roll a pair of dice in turn. The bank then rolls the dice to determine the outcome according to the following rule: Player $i, i = 1, 2$, wins if his roll is strictly greater than the bank's. For $i = 1, 2$, let
$$I_i = \begin{cases} 1 & \text{if } i \text{ wins} \\ 0 & \text{otherwise} \end{cases}$$
and show that I_1 and I_2 are positively correlated. Explain why this result was to be expected.

7.47. Consider a graph having n vertices labeled $1, 2, \ldots, n$, and suppose that, between each of the $\binom{n}{2}$ pairs of distinct vertices, an edge is independently present with probability p. The degree of vertex i, designated as D_i, is the number of edges that have vertex i as one of their vertices.
(a) What is the distribution of D_i?
(b) Find $\rho(D_i, D_j)$, the correlation between D_i and D_j.

7.48. A fair die is successively rolled. Let X and Y denote, respectively, the number of rolls necessary to obtain an even number and a 3. Find
(a) $E(X)$
(b) $E(X | Y = 2)$
(c) $E(Y | X = 1)$

7.49. Two fair dice are thrown simultaneously. Find the expectation of the sum of the faces showed up if we known that different sides came up.

7.50. The joint density of X and Y is given by

$$f(x,y) = \begin{cases} 6xy^2 & \text{if } 0 < x < 1,\ 0 < y < 1 \\ 0 & \text{otherwise} \end{cases}$$

Compute $E(X^3 \mid Y = y)$.

7.51. The joint density of X and Y is given by

$$f(x,y) = \begin{cases} e^{-y} & \text{if } 0 < x < y < \infty, \\ 0 & \text{otherwise} \end{cases}$$

Compute $E(X^2 \mid Y = y)$.

7.52. A unbiased coin tossed three times and let X denotes the number of heads appear. Also let Y be an indicator variable taking values 1 if the first toss resulted in head and zero other wise. Find $E(X \mid Y = 1)$.

7.53. A prisoner is trapped in a cell containing 3 doors. The first door leads to a tunnel that returns him to his cell after 2 days' travel. The second leads to a tunnel that returns him to his cell after 4 days' travel. The third door leads to freedom after 1 day of travel. If it is assumed that the prisoner will always select doors 1, 2, and 3 with respective probabilities .5, .3, and .2, what is the expected number of days until the prisoner reaches freedom?

7.54. Consider the following dice game: A pair of dice is rolled. If the sum is 7, then the game ends and you win 0. If the sum is not 7, then you have the option of either stopping the game and receiving an amount equal to that sum or starting over again. For each value of $i, i = 2, \ldots, 12$, find your expected return if you employ the strategy of stopping the first time that a value at least as large as i appears. What value of i leads to the largest expected return?
Hint: Let X_i denote the return when you use the critical value i. To compute $E[X_i]$, condition on the initial sum.

7.55. Ten hunters are waiting for ducks to fly by. When a flock of ducks flies overhead, the hunters fire at the same time, but each chooses his target at random, independently of the others. If each hunter independently hits his target with probability .6, compute the expected number of ducks that are hit. Assume that the number of ducks in a flock is a Poisson random variable with mean 6.

7.56. The number of people who enter an elevator on the ground floor is a Poisson random variable with mean 10. If there are N floors above the ground floor, and if each person is equally likely to get off at any one of the N floors, independently of where the others get off, compute the expected number of stops that the elevator will make before discharging all of its passengers.

7.57. Suppose that the expected number of accidents per week at an industrial plant is 5. Suppose also that the numbers of workers injured in each accident are independent

random variables with a common mean of 2.5. If the number of workers injured in each accident is independent of the number of accidents that occur, compute the expected number of workers injured in a week.

7.58. A fair die is continually rolled until the both odd and even numbers have appeared. Find
(a) the expected number of rolls;
(b) the probability that the last roll shows an odd number.

7.59. There are $n + 1$ participants in a game. Each person independently is a winner with probability p. The winners share a total prize of 1 unit. (For instance, if 4 people win, then each of them receives $\frac{1}{4}$, whereas if there are no winners, then none of the participants receives anything.) Let A denote a specified one of the players, and let X denote the amount that is received by A.

(a) Compute the expected total prize shared by the players.

(b) Argue that $E[X] = \dfrac{1 - (1 - p)^{n+1}}{n + 1}$.

(c) Compute $E[X]$ by conditioning on whether A is a winner, and conclude that

$$E[(1 + B)^{-1}] = \frac{1 - (1 - p)^{n+1}}{(n + 1)p}$$

when B is a binomial random variable with parameters n and p.

7.60. Each of $m + 2$ players pays 1 unit to a kitty in order to play the following game: A fair coin is to be flipped successively n times, where n is an odd number, and the successive outcomes are noted. Before the n flips, each player writes down a prediction of the outcomes. For instance, if $n = 3$, then a player might write down (H, H, T), which means that he or she predicts that the first flip will land on heads, the second on heads, and the third on tails. After the coins are flipped, the players count their total number of correct predictions. Thus, if the actual outcomes are all heads, then the player who wrote (H, H, T) would have 2 correct predictions. The total kitty of $m + 2$ is then evenly split up among those players having the largest number of correct predictions.

Since each of the coin flips is equally likely to land on either heads or tails, m of the players have decided to make their predictions in a totally random fashion. Specifically, they will each flip one of their own fair coins n times and then use the result as their prediction. However, the final 2 of the players have formed a syndicate and will use the following strategy: One of them will make predictions in the same random fashion as the other m players, but the other one will then predict exactly the opposite of the first. That is, when the randomizing member of the syndicate predicts an H, the other member predicts a T. For instance, if the randomizing member of the syndicate predicts (H, H, T), then the other one predicts (T, T, H).

(a) Argue that exactly one of the syndicate members will have more than $n/2$ correct predictions. (Remember, n is odd.)

(b) Let X denote the number of the m nonsyndicate players who have more than $n/2$ correct predictions. What is the distribution of X?

(c) With X as defined in part (b), argue that

$$E[\text{payoff to the syndicate}] = (m + 2)$$
$$\times E\left[\frac{1}{X + 1}\right]$$

(d) Use part (c) of Problem 7.59 to conclude that

$$E[\text{payoff to the syndicate}] = \frac{2(m + 2)}{m + 1}$$
$$\times \left[1 - \left(\frac{1}{2}\right)^{m+1}\right]$$

and explicitly compute this number when $m = 1, 2$, and 3. Because it can be shown that

$$\frac{2(m + 2)}{m + 1}\left[1 - \left(\frac{1}{2}\right)^{m+1}\right] > 2$$

it follows that the syndicate's strategy always gives it a positive expected profit.

7.61. Let $X_1, \ldots$ be independent random variables with the common distribution function F, and suppose they are independent of N, a geometric random variable with parameter p. Let $M = \max(X_1, \ldots, X_N)$.

(a) Find $P\{M \le x\}$ by conditioning on N.

(b) Find $P\{M \le x | N = 1\}$.

(c) Find $P\{M \le x | N > 1\}$.

(d) Use (b) and (c) to rederive the probability you found in (a).

7.62. Let $U_1, U_2, \ldots$ be a sequence of independent uniform $(0, 1)$ random variables. In Example 5i, we showed that for $0 \le x \le 1, E[N(x)] = e^x$, where

$$N(x) = \min\left\{n : \sum_{i=1}^{n} U_i > x\right\}$$

This problem gives another approach to establishing that result.

(a) Show by induction on n that for $0 < x \le 1$ and all $n \ge 0$,

$$P\{N(x) \ge n + 1\} = \frac{x^n}{n!}$$

Hint: First condition on U_1 and then use the induction hypothesis.

Use part (a) to conclude that

$$E[N(x)] = e^x$$

7.63. An urn contains 30 balls, of which 10 are red and 8 are blue. From this urn, 12 balls are randomly withdrawn. Let X denote the number of red and Y the number of blue balls that are withdrawn. Find $\text{Cov}(X, Y)$

(a) by defining appropriate indicator (that is, Bernoulli) random variables

$$X_i, Y_j \text{ such that } X = \sum_{i=1}^{10} X_i, Y = \sum_{j=1}^{8} Y_j$$

(b) by conditioning (on either X or Y) to determine $E[XY]$.

7.64. Two types of ball point pens, Cello and Reynolds, writes for a random amount of time having mean μ_i and standard deviation σ_i, $i = 1, 2$. Tintin randomly choose a Cello pen or a Reynolds pen from his desk which have m Cello and n Reynolds pens. Let X denote the lifetime of the pen so chosen. Find

(a) $E[X]$;

(b) $\text{Var}(X)$.

7.65. The number of bore-wells drilled in a locality the year after a drought is poisson with mean 6. After a year without a drought, the number of bore-wells drilled is poison with mean 2. Find the expectation and variance of bore-wells drilled in any year if drought occurrence has a probability 0.3 each year.

7.66. In Example 5c, compute the variance of the length of time until the miner reaches safety.

7.67. Consider a gambler who, at each gamble, either wins or loses her bet with respective probabilities p and $1 - p$. A popular gambling system known as the Kelley strategy is to always bet the fraction $2p - 1$ of your current fortune when $p > \frac{1}{2}$. Compute the expected fortune after n gambles of a gambler who starts with x units and employs the Kelley strategy.

7.68. The number of accidents that a person has in a given year is a Poisson random variable with mean λ. However, suppose that the value of λ changes from person to person, being equal to 2 for 60 percent of the population and 3 for the other 40 percent. If a person is chosen at random, what is the probability that he will have (a) 0 accidents and (b) exactly 3 accidents in a certain year? What is the conditional probability that he will have 3 accidents in a given year, given that he had no accidents the preceding year?

7.69. Repeat Problem 7.68 when the proportion of the population having a value of λ less than x is equal to $1 - e^{-x}$.

7.70. Consider an urn containing a large number of coins, and suppose that each of the coins has some probability p of turning up heads when it is flipped. However, this value of p varies from coin to coin. Suppose that the composition of the urn is such that if a coin is selected at random from it, then the p-value of the coin can be regarded as being the value of a random variable that is uniformly distributed over $[0, 1]$. If a coin is selected at random from the urn and flipped twice, compute the probability that

(a) the first flip results in a head;

(b) both flips result in heads.

7.71. In Problem 7.70, suppose that the coin is tossed n times. Let X denote the number of heads that occur. Show that

$$P\{X = i\} = \frac{1}{n + 1} \qquad i = 0, 1, \dots, n$$

Hint: Make use of the fact that

$$\int_0^1 x^{a-1}(1 - x)^{b-1} \, dx = \frac{(a - 1)!(b - 1)!}{(a + b - 1)!}$$

when a and b are positive integers.

7.72. Suppose that in Problem 7.70, we continue to flip the coin until a head appears. Let N denote the number of flips needed. Find

(a) $P\{N \geq i\}, i \geq 1$;

(b) $P\{N = i\}$;

(c) $E[N]$.

7.73. In Example 6b, let S denote the signal sent and R the signal received.

(a) Compute $E[R]$.

(b) Compute $\text{Var}(R)$.

(c) Is R normally distributed?

(d) Compute $\text{Cov}(R, S)$.

7.74. In Example 6c, suppose that X is uniformly distributed over $(0, 1)$. If the discretized regions are determined by $a_0 = 0, a_1 = \frac{1}{2}$, and $a_2 = 1$, calculate the optimal quantizer Y and compute $E[(X - Y)^2]$.

7.75. The moment generating function of X is given by $M_X(t) = (1/3) + (2/3)e^t$ and Y is given by $M_Y(t) = e^{(1/2)(e^t - 1)}$. If X and Y are independent, what are

(a) $P(X + Y = 1)$?

(b) $P(XY = 0)$?

(c) $E(XY)$?

7.76. Let X be the value of the first die and Y the absolute difference of the values when two dice are rolled. Compute the joint moment generating function of X and Y.

7.77. The joint density of X and Y is given by

$$f(x,y) = \begin{cases} e^{-x-y} & \text{if } 0 < y < \infty, \ 0 < x < \infty \\ 0 & \text{otherwise} \end{cases}$$

(a) Compute the joint moment generating function of X and Y.

(b) Compute the individual moment generating functions.

7.78. Two envelopes, each containing a check, are placed in front of you. You are to choose one of the envelopes, open it, and see the amount of the check. At this point, either you can accept that amount or you can exchange it for the check in the unopened envelope. What should you do? Is it possible to devise a strategy that does better than just accepting the first envelope?

Let A and $B, A < B$, denote the (unknown) amounts of the checks, and note that the strategy that randomly selects an envelope and always accepts its check has an expected return of $(A + B)/2$. Consider the following strategy: Let $F(\cdot)$ be any strictly increasing (that is, continuous) distribution function. Choose an envelope randomly and open it. If the discovered check has the value x, then accept it with probability $F(x)$ and exchange it with probability $1 - F(x)$.

(a) Show that if you employ the latter strategy, then your expected return is greater than $(A + B)/2$.

Hint: Condition on whether the first envelope has the value A or B.

Now consider the strategy that fixes a value x and then accepts the first check if its value is greater than x and exchanges it otherwise.

(b) Show that for any x, the expected return under the x-strategy is always at least $(A + B)/2$ and that it is strictly larger than $(A + B)/2$ if x lies between A and B.

(c) Let X be a continuous random variable on the whole line, and consider the following strategy: Generate the value of X, and if $X = x$, then employ the x-strategy of part (b). Show that the expected return under this strategy is greater than $(A + B)/2$.

7.79. Successive weekly sales, in units of $\$1,000$, have a bivariate normal distribution with common mean 40, common standard deviation 6, and correlation .6.

(a) Find the probability that the total of the next 2 weeks' sales exceeds 90.

(b) If the correlation were .2 rather than .6, do you think that this would increase or decrease the answer to (a)? Explain your reasoning.

(c) Repeat (a) when the correlation is .2.

Theoretical Exercises

7.1. Show that $E[(X - a)^2]$ is minimized at $a = E[X]$.

7.2. Suppose that X is a continuous random variable with density function f. Show that $E[|X - a|]$ is minimized when a is equal to the median of F.
Hint: Write

$$E[|X - a|] = \int |x - a| f(x)\, dx$$

Now break up the integral into the regions where $x < a$ and where $x > a$, and differentiate.

7.3. Prove Proposition 2.1 when

(a) X and Y have a joint probability mass function;

(b) X and Y have a joint probability density function and $g(x, y) \geq 0$ for all x, y.

7.4. Let X be a random variable having finite expectation μ and variance σ^2, and let $g(\cdot)$ be a twice differentiable function. Show that

$$E[g(X)] \approx g(\mu) + \frac{g''(\mu)}{2}\sigma^2$$

Hint: Expand $g(\cdot)$ in a Taylor series about μ. Use the first three terms and ignore the remainder.

7.5. Let $A_1, A_2, \ldots, A_n$ be arbitrary events, and define $C_k = \{$at least k of the A_i occur$\}$. Show that

$$\sum_{k=1}^{n} P(C_k) = \sum_{k=1}^{n} P(A_k)$$

Hint: Let X denote the number of the A_i that occur. Show that both sides of the preceding equation are equal to $E[X]$.

7.6. In the text, we noted that

$$E\left[\sum_{i=1}^{\infty} X_i\right] = \sum_{i=1}^{\infty} E[X_i]$$

when the X_i are all nonnegative random variables. Since an integral is a limit of sums, one might expect that

$$E\left[\int_0^{\infty} X(t)dt\right] = \int_0^{\infty} E[X(t)]\, dt$$

whenever $X(t), 0 \leq t < \infty$, are all nonnegative random variables; this result is indeed true. Use it to give another proof of the result that for a nonnegative random variable X,

$$E[X] = \int_0^{\infty} P\{X > t\}\, dt$$

Hint: Define, for each nonnegative t, the random variable $X(t)$ by

$$X(t) = \begin{cases} 1 & \text{if } t < X \\ 0 & \text{if } t \geq X \end{cases}$$

Now relate $\int_0^{\infty} X(t)dt$ to X.

7.7. We say that X is *stochastically larger* than Y, written $X \geq_{st} Y$, if, for all t,

$$P\{X > t\} \geq P\{Y > t\}$$

Show that if $X \geq_{st} Y$, then $E[X] \geq E[Y]$ when

(a) X and Y are nonnegative random variables;

(b) X and Y are arbitrary random variables.
Hint: Write X as

$$X = X^+ - X^-$$

where

$$X^+ = \begin{cases} X & \text{if } X \geq 0 \\ 0 & \text{if } X < 0 \end{cases}, \quad X^- = \begin{cases} 0 & \text{if } X \geq 0 \\ -X & \text{if } X < 0 \end{cases}$$

Similarly, represent Y as $Y^+ - Y^-$. Then make use of part (a).

7.8. Let X be positive random variable with distribution function F. Define the hazard rate $h(x) = f(x)/(1 - F(x))$. Show that

$$E(h(X)) \geq \frac{1}{E(X)}.$$

7.9. Let X be positive random variable with distribution function F. Mean residual life of X at x is defined as $r(x) = E(X - x \mid X > x)$. Show that $r(x)$ can be expressed as

$$r(x) = \frac{1}{(1 - F(x))}\int_x^{\infty}(1 - F(x))dx.$$

What can you say about discrete case.

7.10. Let $X_1, X_2, \ldots, X_n$ be independent and identically distributed exponential random variables with mean one. Find $E\left(1 / \sum_{k=1}^{n} X_k\right)$.

7.11. Consider n independent trials, each resulting in any one of r possible outcomes with probabilities $P_1, P_2, \ldots, P_r$. Let X denote the number of outcomes that never occur in any of the trials. Find $E[X]$ and show that among all probability vectors $P_1, \ldots, P_r, E[X]$ is minimized when $P_i = 1/r, i = 1, \ldots, r$.

7.12. Let $X_1, X_2, \ldots$ be a sequence of independent random variables having the probability mass function

$$P\{X_n = 0\} = P\{X_n = 2\} = 1/2, \quad n \geq 1$$

The random variable $X = \sum_{n=1}^{\infty} X_n/3^n$ is said to have the *Cantor distribution*. Find $E[X]$ and $\text{Var}(X)$.

7.13. Let $X_1, \ldots, X_n$ be independent and identically distributed continuous random variables. We say that a record value occurs at time $j, j \leq n$, if $X_j \geq X_i$ for all $1 \leq i \leq j$. Show that

(a) $E[\text{number of record values}] = \sum_{j=1}^{n} 1/j$;

(b) $\text{Var}(\text{number of record values}) = \sum_{j=1}^{n} (j-1)/j^2$.

7.14. For Example 2i, show that the variance of the number of coupons needed to amass a full set is equal to

$$\sum_{i=1}^{N-1} \frac{iN}{(N-i)^2}$$

When N is large, this can be shown to be approximately equal (in the sense that their ratio approaches 1 as $N \to \infty$) to $N^2 \pi^2/6$.

7.15. Consider n independent trials, the ith of which results in a success with probability P_i.

(a) Compute the expected number of successes in the n trials—call it μ.

(b) For a fixed value of μ, what choice of $P_1, \ldots, P_n$ maximizes the variance of the number of successes?

(c) What choice minimizes the variance?

*7.16. Suppose that each of the elements of $S = \{1, 2, \ldots, n\}$ is to be colored either red or blue. Show that if $A_1, \ldots, A_r$ are subsets of S, there is a way of doing the coloring so that at most $\sum_{i=1}^{r} (1/2)^{|A_i|-1}$ of these subsets have all their elements the same color (where $|A|$ denotes the number of elements in the set A).

7.17. Suppose that X_1 and X_2 are independent random variables having a common mean μ. Suppose also that $\text{Var}(X_1) = \sigma_1^2$ and $\text{Var}(X_2) = \sigma_2^2$. The value of μ is unknown, and it is proposed that μ be estimated by a weighted average of X_1 and X_2. That is, $\lambda X_1 + (1 - \lambda)X_2$ will be used as an estimate of μ for some appropriate value of λ. Which value of λ yields the estimate having the lowest possible variance? Explain why it is desirable to use this value of λ.

7.18. In Example 4f, we showed that the covariance of the multinomial random variables N_i and N_j is equal to $-mP_iP_j$ by expressing N_i and N_j as the sum of indicator variables. We could also have obtained that result by using the formula

$$\text{Var}(N_i + N_j) = \text{Var}(N_i) + \text{Var}(N_j) + 2\,\text{Cov}(N_i, N_j)$$

(a) What is the distribution of $N_i + N_j$?

(b) Use the preceding identity to show that $\text{Cov}(N_i, N_j) = -mP_iP_j$.

7.19. Let $X_1, X_2, \ldots, X_n$ be independent and identically distributed random variables. Denote $\bar{X} = \frac{1}{n} \sum_{k=1}^{n} X_k$ and $S^2 = \frac{1}{n} \sum_{k=1}^{n} (X_k - \bar{X})^2$. Show that $n \cdot \text{Cov}(\bar{X}, S^2) = E((X - \mu)^3)$.

7.20. *The Conditional Covariance Formula.* The conditional covariance of X and Y, given Z, is defined by

$$\text{Cov}(X, Y|Z) \equiv E[(X - E[X|Z])(Y - E[Y|Z])|Z]$$

(a) Show that

$$\text{Cov}(X, Y|Z) = E[XY|Z] - E[X|Z]E[Y|Z]$$

(b) Prove the conditional covariance formula

$$\text{Cov}(X, Y) = E[\text{Cov}(X, Y|Z)] + \text{Cov}(E[X|Z], E[Y|Z])$$

(c) Set $X = Y$ in part (b) and obtain the conditional variance formula.

7.21. Let $X_{(i)}, i = 1, \ldots, n$, denote the order statistics from a set of n uniform $(0, 1)$ random variables, and note that the density function of $X_{(i)}$ is given by

$$f(x) = \frac{n!}{(i-1)!(n-i)!} x^{i-1}(1-x)^{n-i} \quad 0 < x < 1$$

(a) Compute $\text{Var}(X_{(i)}), i = 1, \ldots, n$.

(b) Which value of i minimizes, and which value maximizes, $\text{Var}(X_{(i)})$?

7.22. Let $Y = a + bX$. Show that

$$(\text{Cov}(X, Y))^2 = \text{Var}(X)\text{Var}(Y).$$

7.23. Let X be symmetric random variable with mean zero and variance σ^2. If Y is defined by $Y = a + bZ + cZ^2, c \neq 0$, then

(a) Show that

$$\rho(Y, X) = \frac{b}{\sqrt{b^2 + c^2\sigma^2\left(\frac{E(X^4)}{\sigma^2} - 1\right)}}.$$

(b) Also show that the above formula reduces to

$$\rho(Y, X) \quad \frac{b}{\sqrt{b^2 + 2c^2}},$$

when X is standard normal random variable.

(c) Find an example where $E(X^4) = \sigma^2$ so that $\rho(Y, X) = 1$ and analyse the result.

7.24. Let discrete random vector (X, Y) has joint uniform distribution on the 4 points $(-k, -a-\varepsilon)$, $(-k, -a+\varepsilon)$, $(k, a-\varepsilon)$ and $(k, a+\varepsilon)$. Show that

$$\rho(Y, X) = \frac{a}{\sqrt{a^2 + \varepsilon^2}}$$

Hint: Unless $Y = -tX$ for some constant, in which case the inequality holds with equality, it follows that for all t,

$$0 < E[(tX + Y)^2] = E[X^2]t^2 + 2E[XY]t + E[Y^2]$$

Hence, the roots of the quadratic equation

$$E[X^2]t^2 + 2E[XY]t + E[Y^2] = 0$$

must be imaginary, which implies that the discriminant of this quadratic equation must be negative.

7.25. Show that if X and Y are independent, then

$$E[X|Y = y] = E[X] \quad \text{for all } y$$

(a) in the discrete case;

(b) in the continuous case.

7.26. Prove that $E[g(X)Y|X] = g(X)E[Y|X]$.

7.27. Prove that if $E[Y|X = x] = E[Y]$ for all x, then X and Y are uncorrelated; give a counterexample to show that the converse is not true.
Hint: Prove and use the fact that $E[XY] = E[XE[Y|X]]$.

7.28. Let X_1 and X_2 be independent and identically distributed random variables. Find

$$E(X_1 + X_2 | X_1 = x_1, X_2 = x_2).$$

7.29. Let $X_1, \dots, X_n$ be independent and identically distributed random variables. Find

$$E[X_1 | X_1 + \cdots + X_n = x]$$

7.30. Let X and Y be independent random variables and g be a nonnegative convex function. Show that

$$E[g(X + Y)] \geq E[g(X + EY)],$$

provided expectation exist.

7.31. An urn initially contains b black and w white balls. At each stage, we add r black balls and then withdraw, at random, r balls from the $b + w + r$ balls in the urn. Show that

$E[\text{number of white balls after stage } t]$

$$= \left(\frac{b + w}{b + w + r} \right)^t w$$

7.32. For an event A, let I_A equal 1 if A occurs and let it equal 0 if A does not occur. For a random variable X, show that

$$E[X|A] = \frac{E[XI_A]}{P(A)}$$

7.33. A coin that lands on heads with probability p is continually flipped. Compute the expected number of flips that are made until a string of r heads in a row is obtained.
Hint: Condition on the time of the first occurrence of tails to obtain the equation

$$E[X] = (1 - p) \sum_{i=1}^{r} p^{i-1}(i + E[X])$$

$$+ (1 - p) \sum_{i=r+1}^{\infty} p^{i-1} r$$

Simplify and solve for $E[X]$.

7.34. For another approach to Theoretical Exercise 7.33, let T_r denote the number of flips required to obtain a run of r consecutive heads.

(a) Determine $E[T_r | T_{r-1}]$.
(b) Determine $E[T_r]$ in terms of $E[T_{r-1}]$.
(c) What is $E[T_1]$?
(d) What is $E[T_r]$?

7.35. The probability generating function of the discrete nonnegative integer valued random variable X having probability mass function $p_j, j \geq 0$, is defined by

$$\phi(s) = E[s^X] = \sum_{j=0}^{\infty} p_j s^j$$

Let Y be a geometric random variable with parameter $p = 1 - s$, where $0 < s < 1$. Suppose that Y is independent of X, and show that

$$\phi(s) = P\{X < Y\}$$

7.36. A pencil box contains m pencils sharpened at both ends and n pencils sharpened at one end initially. Each day a student chooses a pencil at random; if a pencil with one sharpened end is selected, he uses it; otherwise, he breaks the selected pencil into two and uses one half, replacing the other half, which thenceforth is considered to be a pencil with one sharpened end. What is the expected number of pencils sharpened at one end remaining when the last pencil sharpened at both ends is selected?

7.37. An urn contains a white and b black balls. After a ball is drawn, it is returned to the urn if it is white; but if it is black, it is replaced by a white ball from another urn. Let M_n denote the expected number of white balls in the urn after the foregoing operation has been repeated n times.

(a) Derive the recursive equation

$$M_{n+1} = \left(1 - \frac{1}{a+b}\right)M_n + 1$$

(b) Use part (a) to prove that

$$M_n = a + b - b\left(1 - \frac{1}{a+b}\right)^n$$

(c) What is the probability that the $(n+1)$ ball drawn is white?

7.38. Show that, for a random variable X, $E[(X - \psi(X)^2]$ is minimum when $F(X) = E[X\,|\,Y]$.

7.39. The best quadratic predictor of Y with respect to X is $a + bX + cX^2$, where a, b, and c are chosen to minimize $E[(Y - (a + bX + cX^2))^2]$. Determine a, b, and c.

7.40. Let $X_1, X_2, \ldots, X_n$ be a positive random variables and N is a geometric random variable with parameter p. Define $S_N = \sum_{k=1}^{N} X_k$. Find $E(S_N)$.

7.41. Let X be a normal random variable with parameters $\mu = 0$ and $\sigma^2 = 1$, and let I, independent of X, be such that $P\{I = 1\} = \frac{1}{2} = P\{I = 0\}$. Now define Y by

$$Y = \begin{cases} X & \text{if } I = 1 \\ -X & \text{if } I = 0 \end{cases}$$

In words, Y is equally likely to equal either X or $-X$.

(a) Are X and Y independent?
(b) Are I and Y independent?
(c) Show that Y is normal with mean 0 and variance 1.
(d) Show that $\text{Cov}(X, Y) = 0$.

7.42. Let X be a normal random variables with parameters $\mu = 0$ and $\sigma^2 = 1$. Define $Y = \max(0, X)$.

(a) Are X and Y independent?
(b) Find $E(Y)$.

7.43. Let X, Y and Z be random variables. Find

(a) $E[E[X\,|\,Y, Z]\,|\,Y] = E[X\,|\,Y]$
(b) $E[X\,|\,Y, g(Y)] = E[X\,|\,Y]$, where g is a function defined on R.

7.44. Consider a population consisting of individuals able to produce offspring of the same kind. Suppose that by the end of its lifetime, each individual will have produced j new offspring with probability P_j, $j \geq 0$, independently of the number produced by any other individual. The number of individuals initially present, denoted by X_0, is called the size of the zeroth generation. All offspring of the zeroth generation constitute the first generation, and their number is denoted by X_1. In general, let X_n denote the size of the nth generation. Let $\mu = \sum_{j=0}^{\infty} jP_j$ and $\sigma^2 = \sum_{j=0}^{\infty} (j - \mu)^2 P_j$ denote, respectively, the mean and the variance of the number of offspring produced by a single individual. Suppose that $X_0 = 1$—that is, initially there is a single individual in the population.

(a) Show that

$$E[X_n] = \mu E[X_{n-1}]$$

(b) Use part (a) to conclude that

$$E[X_n] = \mu^n$$

(c) Show that

$$\text{Var}(X_n) = \sigma^2 \mu^{n-1} + \mu^2 \text{Var}(X_{n-1})$$

(d) Use part (c) to conclude that

$$\text{Var}(X_n) = \begin{cases} \sigma^2 \mu^{n-1}\left(\dfrac{\mu^n - 1}{\mu - 1}\right) & \text{if } \mu \neq 1 \\ n\sigma^2 & \text{if } \mu = 1 \end{cases}$$

The model just described is known as a *branching process*, and an important question for a population that evolves along such lines is the probability that the population will eventually die out. Let π denote this probability when the population starts with a single individual. That is,

$$\pi = P\{\text{population eventually dies out}\,|\,X_0 = 1)$$

(e) Argue that π satisfies

$$\pi = \sum_{j=0}^{\infty} P_j \pi^j$$

Hint: Condition on the number of offspring of the initial member of the population.

7.45. Verify the formula for the moment generating function of a uniform random variable that is given in Table 7.2. Also, differentiate to verify the formulas for the mean and variance.

7.46. For a standard normal random variable Z, let $\mu_n = E[Z^n]$. Show that

$$\mu_n = \begin{cases} 0 & \text{when } n \text{ is odd} \\ \dfrac{(2j)!}{2^j j!} & \text{when } n = 2j \end{cases}$$

Hint: Start by expanding the moment generating function of Z into a Taylor series about 0 to obtain

$$E[e^{tZ}] = e^{t^2/2}$$

$$= \sum_{j=0}^{\infty} \frac{(t^2/2)^j}{j!}$$

7.47. Let X be a normal random variable with mean μ and variance σ^2. Use the results of Theoretical Exercise 7.46 to show that

$$E[X^n] = \sum_{j=0}^{[n/2]} \frac{\binom{n}{2j} \mu^{n-2j} \sigma^{2j}(2j)!}{2^j j!}$$

In the preceding equation, $[n/2]$ is the largest integer less than or equal to $n/2$. Check your answer by letting $n = 1$ and $n = 2$.

7.48. Let X and Y be two discrete random variables. Also let $Y = aX + b$, where a and b are constants. Express the probability generating function of Y in terms of the probability generating function of X. *Hint*: Refer question number 35.

7.49. The positive random variable X is said to be a *lognormal* random variable with parameters μ and σ^2 if $\log(X)$ is a normal random variable with mean μ and variance σ^2. Use the normal moment generating function to find the mean and variance of a lognormal random variable.

7.50. Let X have moment generating function $M(t)$, and define $\Psi(t) = \log M(t)$. Show that

$$\Psi''(t)|_{t=0} = \text{Var}(X)$$

7.51. Let X be a discrete random variable with probability generating function $\psi(t)$. Obtain expression for finding $E(X)$ and $\text{Var}(X)$ using $\psi(t)$.

7.52. Define Gini correlation as

$$\rho_G = \frac{\text{Cov}(Y, F_X(X))}{\text{Cov}(Y, F_Y(Y))}.$$

Show that ρ_G reduces to correlation coefficient when (X,Y) is distributed as bivariate normal.

7.53. Suppose that $X_1, \ldots, X_n$ have a multivariate normal distribution. Show that $X_1, \ldots, X_n$ are independent random variables if and only if

$$\text{Cov}(X_i, X_j) = 0 \quad \text{when } i \neq j$$

7.54. Let X be a symmetric random variable with mean zero, what is $\text{Cov}(X, X^{2k})$? where k is a positive integer.

7.55. Suppose that Y is a normal random variable with mean μ and variance σ^2, and suppose also that the conditional distribution of X, given that $Y = y$, is normal with mean y and variance 1.

(a) Argue that the joint distribution of X, Y is the same as that of $Y + Z, Y$ when Z is a standard normal random variable that is independent of Y.

(b) Use the result of part (a) to argue that X, Y has a bivariate normal distribution.

(c) Find $E[X]$, $\text{Var}(X)$, and $\text{Corr}(X, Y)$.

(d) Find $E[Y|X = x]$.

(e) What is the conditional distribution of Y given that $X = x$?

Self-Test Problems and Exercises

7.1. Consider a list of m names, where the same name may appear more than once on the list. Let $n(i), i = 1, \ldots, m$, denote the number of times that the name in position i appears on the list, and let d denote the number of distinct names on the list.

(a) Express d in terms of the variables $m, n(i), i = 1, \ldots, m$. Let U be a uniform $(0, 1)$ random variable, and let $X = [mU] + 1$.

(b) What is the probability mass function of X?

(c) Argue that $E[m/n(X)] = d$.

7.2. An urn has n white and m black balls that are removed one at a time in a randomly chosen order. Find the expected number of instances in which a white ball is immediately followed by the same color.

7.3. Twenty individuals consisting of 10 married couples are to be seated at 5 different tables, with 4 people at each table.

(a) If the seating is done "at random," what is the expected number of married couples that are seated at the same table?

(b) If 2 men and 2 women are randomly chosen to be seated at each table, what is the expected number of married couples that are seated at the same table?

7.4. If a die is to be rolled until all sides have appeared at least once, find the expected number of times that outcome 6 appears. If a die is to be rolled until all sides have appeared at least two times, find the expected number of times that outcome 6 appears twice.

Hint: For the second part use the approximation of the formula due to A.N.Kolmogrov which states that, with an n-faced die with uniform probability, if you wait for all dices to appear m times, the expected number of tries is given by

$$E_m(n) = n \int_0^\infty \left[1 - \left(1 - e^{-t} \sum_{k=0}^{m-1} \frac{t^k}{k!} \right)^n \right] dt$$

7.5. A deck of $2n$ cards consists of n red and n black cards. The cards are shuffled and then turned over one at a time. Suppose that each time a red card is turned over, we win 1 unit if more red cards than black cards have been turned over by that time. (For instance, if $n = 2$ and the result is $r\,b\,r\,b$, then we would win a total of 2 units.) Find the expected amount that we win.

7.6. Let $A_1, A_2, \ldots, A_n$ be events, and let N denote the number of them that occur. Also, let $I = 1$ if all of these events occur, and let it be 0 otherwise. Prove Bonferroni's inequality, namely,

$$P(A_1 \cdots A_n) \geq \sum_{i=1}^n P(A_i) - (n - 1)$$

Hint: Argue first that $N \leq n - 1 + I$.

7.7. Let X_1 and X_2 be two iid observations from F. Denote $E(X_{(2)}) = E(\max\{X_1, X_2\})$, $E(X_{(1)}) = E(\min\{X_1, X_2\})$. The Gini mean difference is defined as $G = E|X_1 - X_2|$. Express G in terms of $E(X_{(1)})$ and $E(X_{(2)})$.

7.8. An arriving plane carries r families. A total of n_j of these families have checked in a total of j pieces of luggage, $\sum_j n_j = r$. Suppose that when the plane lands, the $N = \sum_j j n_j$ pieces of luggage come out of the plane in a random order. As soon as a family collects all of its luggage, it immediately departs the airport. If the Sanchez family checked in j pieces of luggage, find the expected number of families that depart after they do.

*7.9. Nineteen items on the rim of a circle of radius 1 are to be chosen. Show that for any choice of these points, there will be an arc of (arc) length 1 that contains at least 4 of them.

7.10. Let X be a Poisson random variable with mean λ. Show that if λ is not too small, then

$$\text{Var}(\sqrt{X}) \approx .25$$

Hint: Use the result of Theoretical Exercise 7.4 to approximate $E[\sqrt{X}]$.

7.11. Suppose in Self-Test Problem 7.3 that the 20 people are to be seated at seven tables, three of which have 4 seats and four of which have 2 seats. If the people are randomly seated, find the expected value of the number of married couples that are seated at the same table.

7.12. Individuals 1 through $n, n > 1$, are to be recruited into a firm in the following manner: Individual 1 starts the firm and recruits individual 2. Individuals 1 and 2 will then compete to recruit individual 3. Once individual 3 is recruited, individuals 1, 2, and 3 will compete to recruit individual 4, and so on. Suppose that when individuals $1, 2, \ldots, i$ compete to recruit individual $i + 1$, each of them is equally likely to be the successful recruiter.

(a) Find the expected number of the individuals $1, \ldots, n$ who did not recruit anyone else.

(b) Derive an expression for the variance of the number of individuals who did not recruit anyone else, and evaluate it for $n = 5$.

7.13. The nine players on a basketball team consist of 2 centers, 3 forwards, and 4 backcourt players. If the players are paired up at random into three groups of size 3 each, find (a) the expected value and (b) the variance of the number of triplets consisting of one of each type of player.

7.14. A deck of 52 cards is shuffled and a bridge hand of 13 cards is dealt out. Let X and Y denote, respectively, the number of aces and the number of spades in the hand.

(a) Show that X and Y are uncorrelated.

(b) Are they independent?

7.15. Each coin in a bin has a value attached to it. Each time that a coin with value p is flipped, it lands on heads with probability p. When a coin is randomly chosen from the bin, its value is uniformly distributed on (0, 1). Suppose that after the coin is chosen but before it is flipped, you must predict whether it will land on heads or on tails. You will win 1 if you are correct and will lose 1 otherwise.

(a) What is your expected gain if you are not told the value of the coin?

(b) Suppose now that you are allowed to inspect the coin before it is flipped, with the result of your inspection being that you learn the value of the coin. As a function of p, the value of the coin, what prediction should you make?

(c) Under the conditions of part (b), what is your expected gain?

7.16. In Self-Test Problem 7.1, we showed how to use the value of a uniform (0, 1) random variable (commonly called a *random number*) to obtain the value of a random variable whose mean is equal to the expected number of distinct names on a list. However, its use required that one choose a random position and then determine the number of times that the name in that position appears on the list. Another approach, which can be more efficient when there is a large amount of replication of names, is as follows: As before, start by choosing the random variable X as in Problem 7.1. Now identify the name in position X, and then go through the list, starting at the beginning,

until that name appears. Let I equal 0 if you encounter that name before getting to position X, and let I equal 1 if your first encounter with the name is at position X. Show that $E[mI] = d$.
Hint: Compute $E[I]$ by using conditional expectation.

7.17. A total of m items are to be sequentially distributed among n cells, with each item independently being put in cell j with probability $p_j, j = 1, \ldots, n$. Find the expected number of collisions that occur, where a collision occurs whenever an item is put into a nonempty cell.

7.18. Let X be the length of the initial run in a random ordering of n ones and m zeros. That is, if the first k values are the same (either all ones or all zeros), then $X \geq k$. Find $E[X]$.

7.19. There are n items in a box labeled H and m in a box labeled T. A coin that comes up heads with probability p and tails with probability $1 - p$ is flipped. Each time it comes up heads, an item is removed from the H box, and each time it comes up tails, an item is removed from the T box. (If a box is empty and its outcome occurs, then no items are removed.) Find the expected number of coin flips needed for both boxes to become empty.
Hint: Condition on the number of heads in the first $n + m$ flips.

7.20. Let X be a nonnegative random variable having distribution function F. Show that if $\bar{F}(x) = 1 - F(x)$, then

(a) $E(X^n) = n \int_0^\infty x^{n-1} \bar{F}(x) dx.$

(b) The result is true for a random variable having non-negative support.

*7.21. Let $a_1, \ldots, a_n$, not all equal to 0, be such that $\sum_{i=1}^n a_i = 0$. Show that there is a permutation $i_1, \ldots, i_n$ such that $\sum_{j=1}^n a_{i_j} a_{i_{j+1}} < 0$.
Hint: Use the probabilistic method. (It is interesting that there need not be a permutation whose sum of products of successive pairs is positive. For instance, if $n = 3$, $a_1 = a_2 = -1$, and $a_3 = 2$, there is no such permutation.)

7.22. Suppose that $X_i, i = 1, 2, 3$, are independent Poisson random variables with respective means $\lambda_i, i = 1, 2, 3$. Let $X = X_1 + X_2$ and $Y = X_2 + X_3$. The random vector X, Y is said to have a bivariate Poisson distribution.

(a) Find $E[X]$ and $E[Y]$.

(b) Find $\text{Cov}(X, Y)$.

(c) Find the joint probability mass function $P\{X = i, Y = j\}$.

7.23. Let $(X_i, Y_i), i = 1, \ldots$, be a sequence of independent and identically distributed random vectors. That is, X_1, Y_1 is independent of, and has the same distribution as, X_2, Y_2, and so on. Although X_i and Y_i can be dependent, X_i and Y_j are independent when $i \neq j$. Let

$$\mu_x = E[X_i], \quad \mu_y = E[Y_i], \quad \sigma_x^2 = \text{Var}(X_i),$$
$$\sigma_y^2 = \text{Var}(Y_i), \quad \rho = \text{Corr}(X_i, Y_i)$$

Find $\text{Corr}(\sum_{i=1}^n X_i, \sum_{j=1}^n Y_j)$.

7.24. Four cards are randomly chosen without replacement from an ordinary deck of 52 cards. Let X denote the number of King chosen.

(a) Find $E[X \mid$ the King of spades is chosen$]$.

(b) Find $E[X \mid$ at least one King is chosen$]$.

(c) Find $E[X \mid$ at least two King is chosen$]$.

7.25. Let Φ be the standard normal distribution function, and let X be a normal random variable with mean μ and variance 1. We want to find $E[\Phi(X)]$. To do so, let Z be a standard normal random variable that is independent of X, and let

$$I = \begin{cases} 1, & \text{if } Z < X \\ 0, & \text{if } Z \geq X \end{cases}$$

(a) Show that $E[I|X = x] = \Phi(x)$.

(b) Show that $E[\Phi(X)] = P\{Z < X\}$.

(c) Show that $E[\Phi(X)] = \Phi\left(\frac{\mu}{\sqrt{2}}\right)$.

Hint: What is the distribution of $X - Z$?

The preceding comes up in statistics. Suppose you are about to observe the value of a random variable X that is normally distributed with an unknown mean μ and variance 1, and suppose that you want to test the hypothesis that the mean μ is greater than or equal to 0. Clearly you would want to reject this hypothesis if X is sufficiently small. If it results that $X = x$, then the *p-value* of the hypothesis that the mean is greater than or equal to 0 is defined to be the probability that X would be as small as x if μ were equal to 0 (its smallest possible value if the hypothesis were true). (A small *p*-value is taken as an indication that the hypothesis is probably false.) Because X has a standard normal distribution when $\mu = 0$, the *p*-value that results when $X = x$ is $\Phi(x)$. Therefore, the preceding shows that the expected *p*-value that results when the true mean is μ is $\Phi\left(\frac{\mu}{\sqrt{2}}\right)$.

7.26. A coin that comes up heads with probability p is flipped until either a total of n heads or of m tails is amassed. Find the expected number of flips.
Hint: Imagine that one continues to flip even after the goal is attained. Let X denote the number of flips needed to obtain n heads, and let Y denote the number of flips needed to obtain m tails. Note that $\max(X, Y) + \min(X, Y) = X + Y$. Compute $E[\max(X, Y)]$ by conditioning on the number of heads in the first $n + m - 1$ flips.

7.27. A deck of n cards numbered 1 through n, initially in any arbitrary order, is shuffled in the following manner: At each stage, we randomly choose one of the cards and move it to the front of the deck, leaving the relative positions of the other cards unchanged. This procedure is continued until all but one of the cards has been chosen. At this point, it follows by symmetry that all $n!$ possible orderings are equally likely. Find the expected number of stages that are required.

7.28. Let X be a non-negative integer valued random variable, then show that

$$E(X) = \sum_{k=1}^{\infty} P(X \geq k).$$

7.29. Let X_1 and X_2 be a sample of two independent observations drawn from a population having a Bernoulli distribution with success probability p, $0 < p < 1$. Define $\bar{X} = \dfrac{X_1 + X_2}{2}$ and $S^2 = \dfrac{(X_1 - X_2)^2}{2}$. Show that $\mathrm{Cov}(\bar{X}, S^2) = 0$ does not imply $\bar{X}$ and S^2 independent.

7.30. Consider a sequence of independent trials in which each trial is a success with probability p is performed until either a success occurs or until the nth trial. Find the mean number of trials that are performed.

7.31. Show that $\mathrm{Cov}(X, Y) = 0$ does not implies that $\rho = 0$.

7.32. Starting with

$$e^{tX} = 1 + tX + \frac{t^2 X^2}{2!} + \frac{t^3 X^3}{3!} + \dots + \frac{t^n X^n}{n!} + \dots$$

show that

(a)

$$M(t) = E[e^{tX}] = 1 + tE[X] + \frac{t^2 E[X^2]}{2!} + \dots + \frac{t^n E[X^n]}{n!} + \dots$$

(b) Use (a) to show that $\dfrac{d^n}{dt^n} M(t)|_{t=0} = E[X^n]$

LIMIT THEOREMS

Contents

8.1 Introduction
8.2 Chebyshev's Inequality and the Weak
Law of Large Numbers
8.3 The Central Limit Theorem
8.4 The Strong Law of Large Numbers

8.5 Other Inequalities
8.6 Bounding the Error Probability When
Approximating a Sum of Independent
Bernoulli Random Variables by a Poisson
Random Variable

8.1 Introduction

The most important theoretical results in probability theory are limit theorems. Of these, the most important are those classified either under the heading *laws of large numbers* or under the heading *central limit theorems*. Usually, theorems are considered to be laws of large numbers if they are concerned with stating conditions under which the average of a sequence of random variables converges (in some sense) to the expected average. By contrast, central limit theorems are concerned with determining conditions under which the sum of a large number of random variables has a probability distribution that is approximately normal.

8.2 Chebyshev's Inequality and the Weak Law of Large Numbers

We start this section by proving a result known as Markov's inequality.

Proposition 2.1

Markov's inequality

If X is a random variable that takes only nonnegative values, then for any value $a > 0$,

$$P\{X \geq a\} \leq \frac{E[X]}{a}$$

Proof For $a > 0$, let

$$I = \begin{cases} 1 & \text{if } X \geq a \\ 0 & \text{otherwise} \end{cases}$$

and note that, since $X \geq 0$,

$$I \leq \frac{X}{a}$$

Taking expectations of the preceding inequality yields

$$E[I] \leq \frac{E[X]}{a}$$

which, because $E[I] = P\{X \geq a\}$, proves the result. □

As a corollary, we obtain Proposition 2.2.

Proposition 2.2

Chebyshev's inequality

If X is a random variable with finite mean μ and variance σ^2, then for any value $k > 0$,

$$P\{|X - \mu| \geq k\} \leq \frac{\sigma^2}{k^2}$$

Proof Since $(X - \mu)^2$ is a nonnegative random variable, we can apply Markov's inequality (with $a = k^2$) to obtain

$$P\{(X - \mu)^2 \geq k^2\} \leq \frac{E[(X - \mu)^2]}{k^2} \tag{2.1}$$

But since $(X - \mu)^2 \geq k^2$ if and only if $|X - \mu| \geq k$, Equation (2.1) is equivalent to

$$P\{|X - \mu| \geq k\} \leq \frac{E[(X - \mu)^2]}{k^2} = \frac{\sigma^2}{k^2}$$

and the proof is complete. □

The importance of Markov's and Chebyshev's inequalities is that they enable us to derive bounds on probabilities when only the mean or both the mean and the variance of the probability distribution are known. Of course, if the actual distribution were known, then the desired probabilities could be computed exactly and we would not need to resort to bounds.

Example 2a

Suppose that it is known that the number of items produced in a factory during a week is a random variable with mean 50.

(a) What can be said about the probability that this week's production will exceed 75?

(b) If the variance of a week's production is known to equal 25, then what can be said about the probability that this week's production will be between 40 and 60?

Solution Let X be the number of items that will be produced in a week.

(a) By Markov's inequality,

$$P\{X > 75\} \leq \frac{E[X]}{75} = \frac{50}{75} = \frac{2}{3}$$

(b) By Chebyshev's inequality,

$$P\{|X - 50| \geq 10\} \leq \frac{\sigma^2}{10^2} = \frac{1}{4}$$

Hence,

$$P\{|X - 50| < 10\} \geq 1 - \frac{1}{4} = \frac{3}{4}$$

so the probability that this week's production will be between 40 and 60 is at least .75. ∎

As Chebyshev's inequality is valid for all distributions of the random variable X, we cannot expect the bound on the probability to be very close to the actual probability in most cases. For instance, consider Example 2b.

Example
2b

If X is uniformly distributed over the interval $(0, 10)$, then, since $E[X] = 5$ and $\text{Var}(X) = \frac{25}{3}$, it follows from Chebyshev's inequality that

$$P\{|X - 5| > 4\} \le \frac{25}{3(16)} \approx .52$$

whereas the exact result is

$$P\{|X - 5| > 4\} = .20$$

Thus, although Chebyshev's inequality is correct, the upper bound that it provides is not particularly close to the actual probability.

Similarly, if X is a normal random variable with mean μ and variance σ^2, Chebyshev's inequality states that

$$P\{|X - \mu| > 2\sigma\} \le \frac{1}{4}$$

whereas the actual probability is given by

$$P\{|X - \mu| > 2\sigma\} = P\left\{\left|\frac{X - \mu}{\sigma}\right| > 2\right\} = 2[1 - \Phi(2)] \approx .0456 \qquad \blacksquare$$

Chebyshev's inequality is often used as a theoretical tool in proving results. This use is illustrated first by Proposition 2.3 and then, most importantly, by the weak law of large numbers.

Proposition
2.3

If $\text{Var}(X) = 0$, then
$$P\{X = E[X]\} = 1$$

In other words, the only random variables having variances equal to 0 are those that are constant with probability 1.

Proof By Chebyshev's inequality, we have, for any $n \ge 1$,

$$P\left\{|X - \mu| > \frac{1}{n}\right\} = 0$$

Letting $n \to \infty$ and using the continuity property of probability yields

$$0 = \lim_{n \to \infty} P\left\{|X - \mu| > \frac{1}{n}\right\} = P\left\{\lim_{n \to \infty}\left\{|X - \mu| > \frac{1}{n}\right\}\right\}$$
$$= P\{X \ne \mu\}$$

and the result is established. $\qquad\square$

Theorem
2.1

The weak law of large numbers

Let $X_1, X_2, \ldots$ be a sequence of independent and identically distributed random variables, each having finite mean $E[X_i] = \mu$. Then, for any $\varepsilon > 0$,

$$P\left\{\left|\frac{X_1 + \cdots + X_n}{n} - \mu\right| \ge \varepsilon\right\} \to 0 \quad \text{as} \quad n \to \infty$$

Proof We shall prove the theorem only under the additional assumption that the random variables have a finite variance σ^2. Now, since

$$E\left[\frac{X_1 + \cdots + X_n}{n}\right] = \mu \quad \text{and} \quad \text{Var}\left(\frac{X_1 + \cdots + X_n}{n}\right) = \frac{\sigma^2}{n}$$

it follows from Chebyshev's inequality that

$$P\left\{\left|\frac{X_1 + \cdots + X_n}{n} - \mu\right| \geq \varepsilon\right\} \leq \frac{\sigma^2}{n\varepsilon^2}$$

and the result is proven. $\square$

The weak law of large numbers was originally proven by James Bernoulli for the special case where the X_i are 0, 1 (that is, Bernoulli) random variables. His statement and proof of this theorem were presented in his book *Ars Conjectandi*, which was published in 1713, eight years after his death, by his nephew Nicholas Bernoulli. Note that because Chebyshev's inequality was not known in Bernoulli's time, Bernoulli had to resort to a quite ingenious proof to establish the result. The general form of the weak law of large numbers presented in Theorem 2.1 was proved by the Russian mathematician Khintchine.

8.3 The Central Limit Theorem

The central limit theorem is one of the most remarkable results in probability theory. Loosely put, it states that the sum of a large number of independent random variables has a distribution that is approximately normal. Hence, it not only provides a simple method for computing approximate probabilities for sums of independent random variables, but also helps explain the remarkable fact that the empirical frequencies of so many natural populations exhibit bell-shaped (that is, normal) curves.

In its simplest form, the central limit theorem is as follows.

Theorem 3.1

The central limit theorem

Let $X_1, X_2, \ldots$ be a sequence of independent and identically distributed random variables, each having mean μ and variance σ^2. Then the distribution of

$$\frac{X_1 + \cdots + X_n - n\mu}{\sigma\sqrt{n}}$$

tends to the standard normal as $n \to \infty$. That is, for $-\infty < a < \infty$,

$$P\left\{\frac{X_1 + \cdots + X_n - n\mu}{\sigma\sqrt{n}} \leq a\right\} \to \frac{1}{\sqrt{2\pi}} \int_{-\infty}^{a} e^{-x^2/2}\, dx \quad \text{as} \quad n \to \infty$$

The key to the proof of the central limit theorem is the following lemma, which we state without proof.

Lemma 3.1

Let $Z_1, Z_2, \ldots$ be a sequence of random variables having distribution functions F_{Z_n} and moment generating functions $M_{Z_n}, n \geq 1$, and let Z be a random variable having distribution function F_Z and moment generating function M_Z. If $M_{Z_n}(t) \to M_Z(t)$ for all t, then $F_{Z_n}(t) \to F_Z(t)$ for all t at which $F_Z(t)$ is continuous.

If we let Z be a standard normal random variable, then, since $M_Z(t) = e^{t^2/2}$, it follows from Lemma 3.1 that if $M_{Z_n}(t) \to e^{t^2/2}$ as $n \to \infty$, then $F_{Z_n}(t) \to \Phi(t)$ as $n \to \infty$.

We are now ready to prove the central limit theorem.

Proof of the Central Limit Theorem: Let us assume at first that $\mu = 0$ and $\sigma^2 = 1$. We shall prove the theorem under the assumption that the moment generating function of the $X_i, M(t)$, exists and is finite. Now, the moment generating function of $X_i/\sqrt{n}$ is given by

$$E\left[\exp\left\{\frac{tX_i}{\sqrt{n}}\right\}\right] = M\left(\frac{t}{\sqrt{n}}\right)$$

Thus, the moment generating function of $\sum_{i=1}^{n} X_i/\sqrt{n}$ is given by $\left[M\left(\frac{t}{\sqrt{n}}\right)\right]^n$. Let

$$L(t) = \log M(t)$$

and note that

$$L(0) = 0$$

$$L'(0) = \frac{M'(0)}{M(0)}$$

$$= \mu$$

$$= 0$$

$$L''(0) = \frac{M(0)M''(0) - [M'(0)]^2}{[M(0)]^2}$$

$$= E[X^2]$$

$$= 1$$

Now, to prove the theorem, we must show that $[M(t/\sqrt{n})]^n \to e^{t^2/2}$ as $n \to \infty$, or, equivalently, that $nL(t/\sqrt{n}) \to t^2/2$ as $n \to \infty$. To show this, note that

$$\lim_{n\to\infty} \frac{L(t/\sqrt{n})}{n^{-1}} = \lim_{n\to\infty} \frac{-L'(t/\sqrt{n})n^{-3/2}t}{-2n^{-2}} \quad \text{by L'Hôpital's rule}$$

$$= \lim_{n\to\infty}\left[\frac{L'(t/\sqrt{n})t}{2n^{-1/2}}\right]$$

$$= \lim_{n\to\infty}\left[\frac{-L''(t/\sqrt{n})n^{-3/2}t^2}{-2n^{-3/2}}\right] \quad \text{again by L'Hôpital's rule}$$

$$= \lim_{n\to\infty}\left[L''\left(\frac{t}{\sqrt{n}}\right)\frac{t^2}{2}\right]$$

$$= \frac{t^2}{2}$$

Thus, the central limit theorem is proven when $\mu = 0$ and $\sigma^2 = 1$. The result now follows in the general case by considering the standardized random variables $X_i^* = (X_i - \mu)/\sigma$ and applying the preceding result, since $E[X_i^*] = 0, \text{Var}(X_i^*) = 1$.

Remark Although Theorem 3.1 states only that, for each a,

$$P\left\{\frac{X_1 + \cdots + X_n - n\mu}{\sigma\sqrt{n}} \le a\right\} \to \Phi(a)$$

it can, in fact, be shown that the convergence is uniform in a. [We say that $f_n(a) \to f(a)$ uniformly in a if, for each $\varepsilon > 0$, there exists an N such that $|f_n(a) - f(a)| < \varepsilon$ for all a whenever $n \ge N$.] ∎

The first version of the central limit theorem was proven by DeMoivre around 1733 for the special case where the X_i are Bernoulli random variables with $p = \frac{1}{2}$. The theorem was subsequently extended by Laplace to the case of arbitrary p. (Since a binomial random variable may be regarded as the sum of n independent and identically distributed Bernoulli random variables, this justifies the normal approximation to the binomial that was presented in Section 5.4.1.) Laplace also discovered the more general form of the central limit theorem given in Theorem 3.1. His proof, however, was not completely rigorous and, in fact, cannot easily be made rigorous. A truly rigorous proof of the central limit theorem was first presented by the Russian mathematician Liapounoff in the period 1901–1902.

Figure 8.1 illustrates the central limit theorem by plotting the probability mass functions of n independent random variables having a specified mass function when (a) $n = 5$, (b) $n = 10$, (c) $n = 25$, and (d) $n = 100$.

Example 3a

An astronomer is interested in measuring the distance, in light-years, from his observatory to a distant star. Although the astronomer has a measuring technique, he knows that because of changing atmospheric conditions and normal error, each time a measurement is made, it will not yield the exact distance, but merely an estimate. As a result, the astronomer plans to make a series of measurements and then use the average value of these measurements as his estimated value of the actual distance. If the astronomer believes that the values of the measurements are independent and identically distributed random variables having a common mean d (the actual

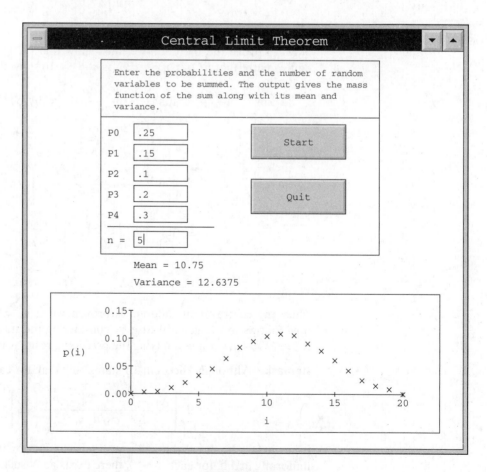

Figure 8.1(a)

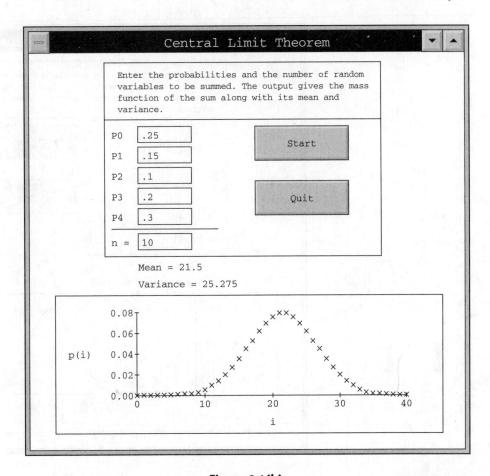

Figure 8.1(b)

distance) and a common variance of 4 (light-years), how many measurements need he make to be reasonably sure that his estimated distance is accurate to within $\pm.5$ light-year?

Solution Suppose that the astronomer decides to make n observations. If X_1, $X_2, \ldots, X_n$ are the n measurements, then, from the central limit theorem, it follows that

$$Z_n = \frac{\displaystyle\sum_{i=1}^{n} X_i - nd}{2\sqrt{n}}$$

has approximately a standard normal distribution. Hence,

$$P\left\{ -.5 \le \frac{\displaystyle\sum_{i=1}^{n} X_i}{n} - d \le .5 \right\} = P\left\{ -.5\frac{\sqrt{n}}{2} \le Z_n \le .5\frac{\sqrt{n}}{2} \right\}$$

$$\approx \Phi\left(\frac{\sqrt{n}}{4}\right) - \phi\left(-\frac{\sqrt{n}}{4}\right) = 2\Phi\left(\frac{\sqrt{n}}{4}\right) - 1$$

Therefore, if the astronomer wants, for instance, to be 95 percent certain that his estimated value is accurate to within .5 light-year, he should make n^* measurements, where n^* is such that

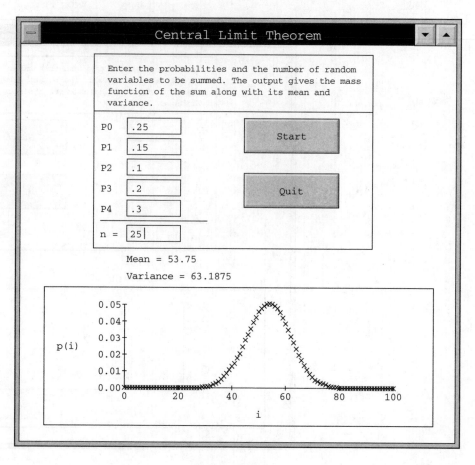

Figure 8.1(c)

$$2\Phi\left(\frac{\sqrt{n^*}}{4}\right) - 1 = .95 \quad \text{or} \quad \Phi\left(\frac{\sqrt{n^*}}{4}\right) = .975$$

Thus, from Table 5.1 of Chapter 5,

$$\frac{\sqrt{n^*}}{4} = 1.96 \quad \text{or} \quad n^* = (7.84)^2 \approx 61.47$$

As n^* is not integral valued, he should make 62 observations.

Note, however, that the preceding analysis has been done under the assumption that the normal approximation will be a good approximation when $n = 62$. Although this will usually be the case, in general the question of how large n need be before the approximation is "good" depends on the distribution of the X_i. If the astronomer is concerned about this point and wants to take no chances, he can still solve his problem by using Chebyshev's inequality. Since

$$E\left[\sum_{i=1}^{n} \frac{X_i}{n}\right] = d \quad \text{Var}\left(\sum_{i=1}^{n} \frac{X_i}{n}\right) = \frac{4}{n}$$

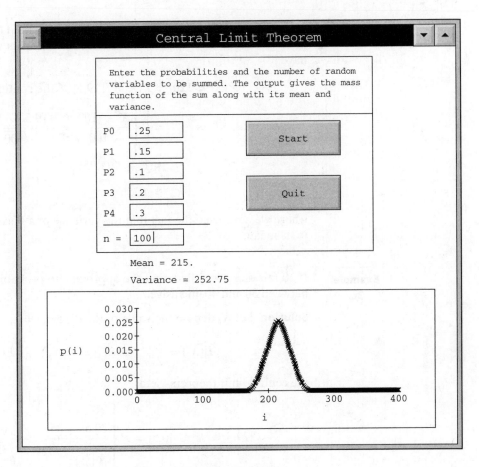

Figure 8.1(d)

Chebyshev's inequality yields

$$P\left\{ \left| \sum_{i=1}^{n} \frac{X_i}{n} - d \right| > .5 \right\} \le \frac{4}{n(.5)^2} = \frac{16}{n}$$

Hence, if he makes $n = 16/.05 = 320$ observations, he can be 95 percent certain that his estimate will be accurate to within .5 light-year. ∎

Example 3b

The number of students who enroll in a psychology course is a Poisson random variable with mean 100. The professor in charge of the course has decided that if the number enrolling is 120 or more, he will teach the course in two separate sections, whereas if fewer than 120 students enroll, he will teach all of the students together in a single section. What is the probability that the professor will have to teach two sections?

Solution The exact solution

$$e^{-100} \sum_{i=120}^{\infty} \frac{(100)^i}{i!}$$

does not readily yield a numerical answer. However, by recalling that a Poisson random variable with mean 100 is the sum of 100 independent Poisson random variables, each with mean 1, we can make use of the central limit theorem to obtain an approximate solution. If X denotes the number of students who enroll in the course, we have

$$P\{X \geq 120\} = P\{X \geq 119.5\} \quad \text{(the continuity correction)}$$

$$= P\left\{\frac{X - 100}{\sqrt{100}} \geq \frac{119.5 - 100}{\sqrt{100}}\right\}$$

$$\approx 1 - \Phi(1.95)$$

$$\approx .0256$$

where we have used the fact that the variance of a Poisson random variable is equal to its mean. ∎

Example 3c

If 10 fair dice are rolled, find the approximate probability that the sum obtained is between 30 and 40, inclusive.

Solution Let X_i denote the value of the ith die, $i = 1, 2, \ldots, 10$. Since

$$E(X_i) = \frac{7}{2}, \quad \text{Var}(X_i) = E[X_i^2] - (E[X_i])^2 = \frac{35}{12},$$

the central limit theorem yields

$$P\{29.5 \leq X \leq 40.5\} = P\left\{\frac{29.5 - 35}{\sqrt{\frac{350}{12}}} \leq \frac{X - 35}{\sqrt{\frac{350}{12}}} \leq \frac{40.5 - 35}{\sqrt{\frac{350}{12}}}\right\}$$

$$\approx 2\Phi(1.0184) - 1$$

$$\approx .692$$ ∎

Example 3d

Let $X_i, i = 1, \ldots, 10$, be independent random variables, each uniformly distributed over $(0, 1)$. Calculate an approximation to $P\left\{\sum_{i=1}^{10} X_i > 6\right\}$.

Solution Since $E[X_i] = \frac{1}{2}$ and $\text{Var}(X_i) = \frac{1}{12}$, we have, by the central limit theorem,

$$P\left\{\sum_{1}^{10} X_i > 6\right\} = P\left\{\frac{\sum_{1}^{10} X_i - 5}{\sqrt{10\left(\frac{1}{12}\right)}} > \frac{6 - 5}{\sqrt{10\left(\frac{1}{12}\right)}}\right\}$$

$$\approx 1 - \Phi(\sqrt{1.2})$$

$$\approx .1367$$

Hence, $\sum_{i=1}^{10} X_i$ will be greater than 6 only 14 percent of the time. ∎

Example 3e

An instructor has 50 exams that will be graded in sequence. The times required to grade the 50 exams are independent, with a common distribution that has mean 20 minutes and standard deviation 4 minutes. Approximate the probability that the instructor will grade at least 25 of the exams in the first 450 minutes of work.

Solution If we let X_i be the time that it takes to grade exam i, then

$$X = \sum_{i=1}^{25} X_i$$

is the time it takes to grade the first 25 exams. Because the instructor will grade at least 25 exams in the first 450 minutes of work if the time it takes to grade the first 25 exams is less than or equal to 450, we see that the desired probability is $P\{X \leq 450\}$. To approximate this probability, we use the central limit theorem. Now,

$$E[X] = \sum_{i=1}^{25} E[X_i] = 25(20) = 500$$

and

$$\text{Var}(X) = \sum_{i=1}^{25} \text{Var}(X_i) = 25(16) = 400$$

Consequently, with Z being a standard normal random variable, we have

$$P\{X \leq 450\} = P\left\{ \frac{X - 500}{\sqrt{400}} \leq \frac{450 - 500}{\sqrt{400}} \right\}$$

$$\approx P\{Z \leq -2.5\}$$

$$= P\{Z \geq 2.5\}$$

$$= 1 - \Phi(2.5) \approx .006 \qquad \blacksquare$$

Central limit theorems also exist when the X_i are independent, but not necessarily identically distributed random variables. One version, by no means the most general, is as follows.

Theorem 3.2

Central limit theorem for independent random variables

Let $X_1, X_2, \ldots$ be a sequence of independent random variables having respective means and variances $\mu_i = E[X_i], \sigma_i^2 = \text{Var}(X_i)$. If (a) the X_i are uniformly bounded—that is, if for some $M, P\{|X_i| < M\} = 1$ for all i, and (b) $\sum_{i=1}^{\infty} \sigma_i^2 = \infty$—then

$$P\left\{ \frac{\sum_{i=1}^{n}(X_i - \mu_i)}{\sqrt{\sum_{i=1}^{n} \sigma_i^2}} \leq a \right\} \rightarrow \Phi(a) \quad \text{as} \quad n \rightarrow \infty$$

Historical note

Pierre-Simon, Marquis de Laplace (1749–1827)

The central limit theorem was originally stated and proven by the French mathematician Pierre-Simon, Marquis de Laplace, who came to the theorem from his observations that errors of measurement (which can usually be regarded as being the sum of a large number of tiny forces) tend to be normally distributed. Laplace, who was also a famous astronomer (and indeed was called "the Newton of France"), was one of the great early contributors to both probability and statistics. Laplace was also a popularizer of the uses of probability in everyday life. He strongly believed in its importance, as is indicated by the following quotations taken from his published book *Analytical Theory of Probability*: "We see that the theory of probability is at bottom only common sense reduced to calculation; it makes us appreciate with exactitude what reasonable minds feel by a sort of instinct, often without being able to account for it.... It is remarkable that this science, which originated in the consideration of games of chance, should become the most important object of human knowledge.... The most important questions of life are, for the most part, really only problems of probability."

The application of the central limit theorem to show that measurement errors are approximately normally distributed is regarded as an important contribution to science. Indeed, in the seventeenth and eighteenth centuries, the central limit theorem was often called the *law of frequency of errors*. Listen to the words of Francis Galton (taken from his book *Natural Inheritance*, published in 1889): "I know of scarcely anything so apt to impress the imagination as the wonderful form of cosmic order expressed by the 'Law of Frequency of Error.' The Law would have been personified by the Greeks and deified, if they had known of it. It reigns with serenity and in complete self-effacement amidst the wildest confusion. The huger the mob and the greater the apparent anarchy, the more perfect is its sway. It is the supreme law of unreason."

8.4   The Strong Law of Large Numbers

The *strong law of large numbers* is probably the best-known result in probability theory. It states that the average of a sequence of independent random variables having a common distribution will, with probability 1, converge to the mean of that distribution.

Theorem 4.1

The strong law of large numbers

Let $X_1, X_2, \ldots$ be a sequence of independent and identically distributed random variables, each having a finite mean $\mu = E[X_i]$. Then, with probability 1,

$$\frac{X_1 + X_2 + \cdots + X_n}{n} \to \mu \qquad \text{as} \qquad n \to \infty^\dagger$$

As an application of the strong law of large numbers, suppose that a sequence of independent trials of some experiment is performed. Let E be a fixed event of the

---

†That is, the strong law of large numbers states that

$$P\{\lim_{n \to \infty} (X_1 + \cdots + X_n)/n = \mu\} = 1$$

experiment, and denote by $P(E)$ the probability that E occurs on any particular trial. Letting

$$X_i = \begin{cases} 1 & \text{if } E \text{ occurs on the } i\text{th trial} \\ 0 & \text{if } E \text{ does not occur on the } i\text{th trial} \end{cases}$$

we have, by the strong law of large numbers, that with probability 1,

$$\frac{X_1 + \cdots + X_n}{n} \to E[X] = P(E) \tag{4.1}$$

Since $X_1 + \cdots + X_n$ represents the number of times that the event E occurs in the first n trials, we may interpret Equation (4.1) as stating that with probability 1, the limiting proportion of time that the event E occurs is just $P(E)$.

Although the theorem can be proven without this assumption, our proof of the strong law of large numbers will assume that the random variables X_i have a finite fourth moment. That is, we will suppose that $E[X_i^4] = K < \infty$.

Proof of the Strong Law of Large Numbers: To begin, assume that μ, the mean of the X_i, is equal to 0. Let $S_n = \sum_{i=1}^{n} X_i$ and consider

$$E[S_n^4] = E[(X_1 + \cdots + X_n)(X_1 + \cdots + X_n) \\ \times (X_1 + \cdots + X_n)(X_1 + \cdots + X_n)]$$

Expanding the right side of the preceding equation results in terms of the form

$$X_i^4, \quad X_i^3 X_j, \quad X_i^2 X_j^2, \quad X_i^2 X_j X_k, \quad \text{and} \quad X_i X_j X_k X_l$$

where i, j, k, and l are all different. Because all the X_i have mean 0, it follows by independence that

$$E[X_i^3 X_j] = E[X_i^3] E[X_j] = 0$$
$$E[X_i^2 X_j X_k] = E[X_i^2] E[X_j] E[X_k] = 0$$
$$E[X_i X_j X_k X_l] = 0$$

Now, for a given pair i and j, there will be $\binom{4}{2} = 6$ terms in the expansion that will equal $X_i^2 X_j^2$. Hence, upon expanding the preceding product and taking expectations term by term, it follows that

$$E[S_n^4] = nE[X_i^4] + 6\binom{n}{2} E[X_i^2 X_j^2]$$
$$= nK + 3n(n-1)E[X_i^2]E[X_j^2]$$

where we have once again made use of the independence assumption. Now, since

$$0 \le \text{Var}(X_i^2) = E[X_i^4] - (E[X_i^2])^2$$

we have

$$(E[X_i^2])^2 \le E[X_i^4] = K$$

Therefore, from the preceding, we obtain

$$E[S_n^4] \le nK + 3n(n-1)K$$

which implies that

$$E\left[\frac{S_n^4}{n^4}\right] \le \frac{K}{n^3} + \frac{3K}{n^2}$$

Therefore,

$$E\left[\sum_{n=1}^{\infty}\frac{S_n^4}{n^4}\right] = \sum_{n=1}^{\infty}E\left[\frac{S_n^4}{n^4}\right] < \infty$$

But the preceding implies that with probability 1, $\sum_{n=1}^{\infty} S_n^4/n^4 < \infty$. (For if there is a positive probability that the sum is infinite, then its expected value is infinite.) But the convergence of a series implies that its nth term goes to 0; so we can conclude that with probability 1,

$$\lim_{n\to\infty}\frac{S_n^4}{n^4} = 0$$

But if $S_n^4/n^4 = (S_n/n)^4$ goes to 0, then so must S_n/n; hence, we have proven that with probability 1,

$$\frac{S_n}{n} \to 0 \qquad \text{as} \qquad n \to \infty$$

When μ, the mean of the X_i, is not equal to 0, we can apply the preceding argument to the random variables $X_i - \mu$ to obtain that with probability 1,

$$\lim_{n\to\infty}\sum_{i=1}^{n}\frac{(X_i - \mu)}{n} = 0$$

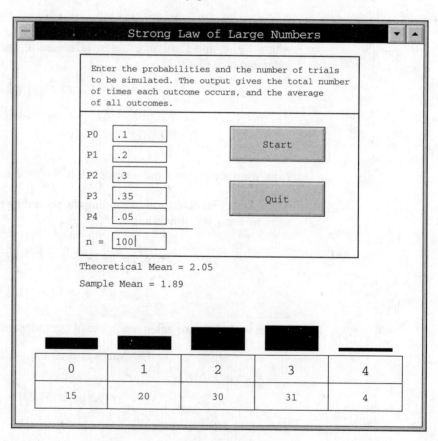

Figure 8.2(a)

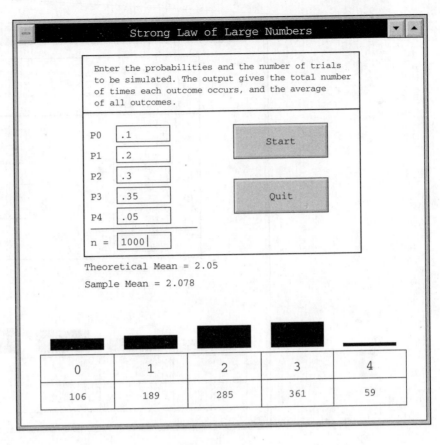

Figure 8.2(b)

or, equivalently,

$$\lim_{n \to \infty} \sum_{i=1}^{n} \frac{X_i}{n} = \mu$$

which proves the result. □

Figure 8.2 illustrates the strong law by giving the results of a simulation of n independent random variables having a specified probability mass function. The averages of the n variables are given when (a) $n = 100$, (b) $n = 1000$, and (c) $n = 10,000$.

Many students are initially confused about the difference between the weak and the strong laws of large numbers. The weak law of large numbers states that for any specified large value n^*, $(X_1 + \cdots + X_{n^*})/n^*$ is likely to be near μ. However, it does not say that $(X_1 + \cdots + X_n)/n$ is bound to stay near μ for all values of n larger than n^*. Thus, it leaves open the possibility that large values of $|(X_1 + \cdots + X_n)/n - \mu|$ can occur infinitely often (though at infrequent intervals). The strong law shows that this cannot occur. In particular, it implies that, with probability 1, for any positive value ε,

$$\left| \sum_{1}^{n} \frac{X_i}{n} - \mu \right|$$

will be greater than ε only a finite number of times.

The strong law of large numbers was originally proven, in the special case of Bernoulli random variables, by the French mathematician Borel. The general form of the strong law presented in Theorem 4.1 was proven by the Russian mathematician A. N. Kolmogorov.

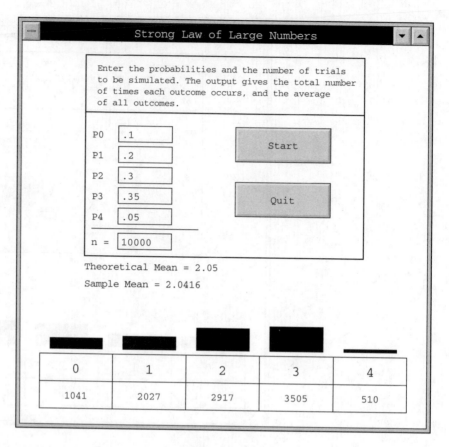

Figure 8.2(c)

8.5 Other Inequalities

We are sometimes confronted with situations in which we are interested in obtaining an upper bound for a probability of the form $P\{X - \mu \geq a\}$, where a is some positive value and when only the mean $\mu = E[X]$ and variance $\sigma^2 = \text{Var}(X)$ of the distribution of X are known. Of course, since $X - \mu \geq a > 0$ implies that $|X - \mu| \geq a$, it follows from Chebyshev's inequality that

$$P\{X - \mu \geq a\} \leq P\{|X - \mu| \geq a\} \leq \frac{\sigma^2}{a^2} \quad \text{when} \quad a > 0$$

However, as the following proposition shows, it turns out that we can do better.

Proposition 5.1

One-sided Chebyshev inequality

If X is a random variable with mean 0 and finite variance σ^2, then, for any $a > 0$,

$$P\{X \geq a\} \leq \frac{\sigma^2}{\sigma^2 + a^2}$$

Proof Let $b > 0$ and note that

$$X \geq a \quad \text{is equivalent to} \quad X + b \geq a + b$$

Hence,

$$P\{X \geq a\} = P\{X + b \geq a + b\}$$
$$\leq P\{(X + b)^2 \geq (a + b)^2\}$$

where the inequality is obtained by noting that since $a + b > 0, X + b \geq a + b$ implies that $(X + b)^2 \geq (a + b)^2$. Upon applying Markov's inequality, the preceding yields that

$$P\{X \geq a\} \leq \frac{E[(X + b)^2]}{(a + b)^2} = \frac{\sigma^2 + b^2}{(a + b)^2}$$

Letting $b = \sigma^2/a$ [which is easily seen to be the value of b that minimizes $(\sigma^2 + b^2)/(a + b)^2$] gives the desired result. □

Example 5a

If the number of items produced in a factory during a week is a random variable with mean 100 and variance 400, compute an upper bound on the probability that this week's production will be at least 120.

Solution It follows from the one-sided Chebyshev inequality that

$$P\{X \geq 120\} = P\{X - 100 \geq 20\} \leq \frac{400}{400 + (20)^2} = \frac{1}{2}$$

Hence, the probability that this week's production will be 120 or more is at most $\frac{1}{2}$.

If we attempted to obtain a bound by applying Markov's inequality, then we would have obtained

$$P\{X \geq 120\} \leq \frac{E(X)}{120} = \frac{5}{6}$$

which is a far weaker bound than the preceding one. ∎

Suppose now that X has mean μ and variance σ^2. Since both $X - \mu$ and $\mu - X$ have mean 0 and variance σ^2, it follows from the one-sided Chebyshev inequality that, for $a > 0$,

$$P\{X - \mu \geq a\} \leq \frac{\sigma^2}{\sigma^2 + a^2}$$

and

$$P\{\mu - X \geq a\} \leq \frac{\sigma^2}{\sigma^2 + a^2}$$

Thus, we have the following corollary.

Corollary 5.1

If $E[X] = \mu$ and $\text{Var}(X) = \sigma^2$, then, for $a > 0$,

$$P\{X \geq \mu + a\} \leq \frac{\sigma^2}{\sigma^2 + a^2}$$

$$P\{X \leq \mu - a\} \leq \frac{\sigma^2}{\sigma^2 + a^2}$$

Example 5b

A set of 200 people consisting of 100 men and 100 women is randomly divided into 100 pairs of 2 each. Give an upper bound to the probability that at most 30 of these pairs will consist of a man and a woman.

Solution Number the men arbitrarily from 1 to 100, and for $i = 1, 2, \ldots 100$, let

$$X_i = \begin{cases} 1 & \text{if man } i \text{ is paired with a woman} \\ 0 & \text{otherwise} \end{cases}$$

Then X, the number of man–woman pairs, can be expressed as

$$X = \sum_{i=1}^{100} X_i$$

Because man i is equally likely to be paired with any of the other 199 people, of which 100 are women, we have

$$E[X_i] = P\{X_i = 1\} = \frac{100}{199}$$

Similarly, for $i \neq j$,

$$E[X_i X_j] = P\{X_i = 1, X_j = 1\}$$

$$= P\{X_i = 1\}P\{X_j = 1|X_i = 1\} = \frac{100}{199}\frac{99}{197}$$

where $P\{X_j = 1|X_i = 1\} = 99/197$, since, given that man i is paired with a woman, man j is equally likely to be paired with any of the remaining 197 people, of which 99 are women. Hence, we obtain

$$E[X] = \sum_{i=1}^{100} E[X_i]$$

$$= (100)\frac{100}{199}$$

$$\approx 50.25$$

$$\text{Var}(X) = \sum_{i=1}^{100} \text{Var}(X_i) + 2\sum\sum_{i<j} \text{Cov}(X_i, X_j)$$

$$= 100\frac{100}{199}\frac{99}{199} + 2\binom{100}{2}\left[\frac{100}{199}\frac{99}{197} - \left(\frac{100}{199}\right)^2\right]$$

$$\approx 25.126$$

The Chebyshev inequality then yields

$$P\{X \leq 30\} \leq P\{|X - 50.25| \geq 20.25\} \leq \frac{25.126}{(20.25)^2} \approx .061$$

Thus, there are fewer than 6 chances in 100 that fewer than 30 men will be paired with women. However, we can improve on this bound by using the one-sided Chebyshev inequality, which yields

$$P\{X \leq 30\} = P\{X \leq 50.25 - 20.25\}$$

$$\leq \frac{25.126}{25.126 + (20.25)^2}$$

$$\approx .058 \qquad \blacksquare$$

When the moment generating function of the random variable X is known, we can obtain even more effective bounds on $P\{X \geq a\}$. Let

$$M(t) = E[e^{tX}]$$

be the moment generating function of the random variable X. Then, for $t > 0$,

$$P\{X \geq a\} = P\{e^{tX} \geq e^{ta}\}$$
$$\leq E[e^{tX}]e^{-ta} \quad \text{by Markov's inequality}$$

Similarly, for $t < 0$,

$$P\{X \leq a\} = P\{e^{tX} \geq e^{ta}\}$$
$$\leq E[e^{tX}]e^{-ta}$$

Thus, we have the following inequalities, known as *Chernoff bounds*.

Proposition 5.2

Chernoff bounds

$$P\{X \geq a\} \leq e^{-ta}M(t) \quad \text{for all} \quad t > 0$$
$$P\{X \leq a\} \leq e^{-ta}M(t) \quad \text{for all} \quad t < 0$$

Since the Chernoff bounds hold for all t in either the positive or negative quadrant, we obtain the best bound on $P\{X \geq a\}$ by using the t that minimizes $e^{-ta}M(t)$.

Example 5c

Chernoff bounds for the standard normal random variable

If Z is a standard normal random variable, then its moment generating function is $M(t) = e^{t^2/2}$, so the Chernoff bound on $P\{Z \geq a\}$ is given by

$$P\{Z \geq a\} \leq e^{-ta}e^{t^2/2} \quad \text{for all} \quad t > 0$$

Now the value of $t, t > 0$, that minimizes $e^{t^2/2-ta}$ is the value that minimizes $t^2/2 - ta$, which is $t = a$. Thus, for $a > 0$, we have

$$P\{Z \geq a\} \leq e^{-a^2/2}$$

Similarly, we can show that, for $a < 0$,

$$P\{Z \leq a\} \leq e^{-a^2/2}$$

∎

Example 5d

Chernoff bounds for the Poisson random variable

If X is a Poisson random variable with parameter λ, then its moment generating function is $M(t) = e^{\lambda(e^t-1)}$. Hence, the Chernoff bound on $P\{X \geq i\}$ is

$$P\{X \geq i\} \leq e^{\lambda(e^t-1)}e^{-it} \quad t > 0$$

Minimizing the right side of the preceding inequality is equivalent to minimizing $\lambda(e^t - 1) - it$, and calculus shows that the minimal value occurs when $e^t = i/\lambda$. Provided that $i/\lambda > 1$, this minimizing value of t will be positive. Therefore, assuming that $i > \lambda$ and letting $e^t = i/\lambda$ in the Chernoff bound yields

$$P\{X \geq i\} \leq e^{\lambda(i/\lambda-1)}\left(\frac{\lambda}{i}\right)^i$$

or, equivalently,

$$P\{X \geq i\} \leq \frac{e^{-\lambda}(e\lambda)^i}{i^i}$$

∎

Example 5e

Consider a gambler who is equally likely to either win or lose 1 unit on every play, independently of his past results. That is, if X_i is the gambler's winnings on the ith play, then the X_i are independent and

$$P\{X_i = 1\} = P\{X_i = -1\} = \frac{1}{2}$$

Let $S_n = \sum_{i=1}^{n} X_i$ denote the gambler's winnings after n plays. We will use the Chernoff bound on $P\{S_n \geq a\}$. To start, note that the moment generating function of X_i is

$$E[e^{tX}] = \frac{e^t + e^{-t}}{2}$$

Now, using the McLaurin expansions of e^t and e^{-t}, we see that

$$
\begin{aligned}
e^t + e^{-t} &= 1 + t + \frac{t^2}{2!} + \frac{t^3}{3!} + \cdots + \left(1 - t + \frac{t^2}{2!} - \frac{t^3}{3!} + \cdots\right) \\
&= 2\left\{1 + \frac{t^2}{2!} + \frac{t^4}{4!} + \cdots\right\} \\
&= 2\sum_{n=0}^{\infty} \frac{t^{2n}}{(2n)!} \\
&\leq 2\sum_{n=0}^{\infty} \frac{(t^2/2)^n}{n!} \quad \text{since } (2n)! \geq n!2^n \\
&= 2e^{t^2/2}
\end{aligned}
$$

Therefore,

$$E[e^{tX}] \geq e^{t^2/2}$$

Since the moment generating function of the sum of independent random variables is the product of their moment generating functions, we have

$$
\begin{aligned}
E[e^{tS_n}] &= (E[e^{tX}])^n \\
&\leq e^{nt^2/2}
\end{aligned}
$$

Using the preceding result along with the Chernoff bound gives

$$P\{S_n \geq a\} \leq e^{-ta}e^{nt^2/2} \quad t > 0$$

The value of t that minimizes the right side of the preceding is the value that minimizes $nt^2/2 - ta$, and this value is $t = a/n$. Supposing that $a > 0$ (so that the minimizing t is positive) and letting $t = a/n$ in the preceding inequality yields

$$P\{S_n \geq a\} \leq e^{-a^2/2n} \quad a > 0$$

This latter inequality yields, for example,

$$P\{S_{10} \geq 6\} \leq e^{-36/20} \approx .1653$$

whereas the exact probability is

$$P\{S_{10} \geq 6\} = P\{\text{gambler wins at least 8 of the first 10 games}\}$$

$$= \frac{\dbinom{10}{8} + \dbinom{10}{9} + \dbinom{10}{10}}{2^{10}} = \frac{56}{1024} \approx .0547 \qquad \blacksquare$$

The next inequality is one having to do with expectations rather than probabilities. Before stating it, we need the following definition.

> **Definition**
> A twice-differentiable real-valued function $f(x)$ is said to be *convex* if $f''(x) \geq 0$ for all x; similarly, it is said to be *concave* if $f''(x) \leq 0$.

Some examples of convex functions are $f(x) = x^2$, $f(x) = e^{ax}$, and $f(x) = -x^{1/n}$ for $x \geq 0$. If $f(x)$ is convex, then $g(x) = -f(x)$ is concave, and vice versa.

Proposition 5.3 **Jensen's inequality**

If $f(x)$ is a convex function, then

$$E[f(X)] \geq f(E[X])$$

provided that the expectations exist and are finite.

Proof Expanding $f(x)$ in a Taylor's series expansion about $\mu = E[X]$ yields

$$f(x) = f(\mu) + f'(\mu)(x - \mu) + \frac{f''(\xi)(x - \mu)^2}{2}$$

where ξ is some value between x and μ. Since $f''(\xi) \geq 0$, we obtain

$$f(x) \geq f(\mu) + f'(\mu)(x - \mu)$$

Hence,

$$f(X) \geq f(\mu) + f'(\mu)(X - \mu)$$

Taking expectations yields

$$E[f(X)] \geq f(\mu) + f'(\mu)E[X - \mu] = f(\mu)$$

and the inequality is established. $\qquad \square$

Example 5f

An investor is faced with the following choices: Either she can invest all of her money in a risky proposition that would lead to a random return X that has mean m, or she can put the money into a risk-free venture that will lead to a return of m with probability 1. Suppose that her decision will be made on the basis of maximizing the expected value of $u(R)$, where R is her return and u is her utility function. By Jensen's inequality, it follows that if u is a concave function, then $E[u(X)] \leq u(m)$, so the risk-free alternative is preferable, whereas if u is convex, then $E[u(X)] \geq u(m)$, so the risky investment alternative would be preferred. $\qquad \blacksquare$

8.6 Bounding the Error Probability When Approximating a Sum of Independent Bernoulli Random Variables by a Poisson Random Variable

In this section, we establish bounds on how closely a sum of independent Bernoulli random variables is approximated by a Poisson random variable with the same mean. Suppose that we want to approximate the sum of independent Bernoulli random variables with respective means $p_1, p_2, \ldots, p_n$. Starting with a sequence $Y_1, \ldots, Y_n$ of independent Poisson random variables, with Y_i having mean p_i, we will construct a sequence of independent Bernoulli random variables $X_1, \ldots, X_n$ with parameters $p_1, \ldots, p_n$ such that

$$P\{X_i \neq Y_i\} \leq p_i^2 \qquad \text{for each } i$$

Letting $X = \sum_{i=1}^{n} X_i$ and $Y = \sum_{i=1}^{n} Y_i$, we will use the preceding inequality to conclude that

$$P\{X \neq Y\} \leq \sum_{i=1}^{n} p_i^2$$

Finally, we will show that the preceding inequality implies that for any set of real numbers A,

$$|P\{X \in A\} - P\{Y \in A\}| \leq \sum_{i=1}^{n} p_i^2$$

Since X is the sum of independent Bernoulli random variables and Y is a Poisson random variable, the latter inequality will yield the desired bound.

To show how the task is accomplished, let $Y_i, i = 1, \ldots, n$ be independent Poisson random variables with respective means p_i. Now let $U_1, \ldots, U_n$ be independent random variables that are also independent of the Y_i's and are such that

$$U_i = \begin{cases} 0 & \text{with probability } (1 - p_i)e^{p_i} \\ 1 & \text{with probability } 1 - (1 - p_i)e^{p_i} \end{cases}$$

This definition implicitly makes use of the inequality

$$e^{-p} \geq 1 - p$$

in assuming that $(1 - p_i)e^{p_i} \leq 1$.

Next, define the random variables $X_i, i = 1, \ldots, n$, by

$$X_i = \begin{cases} 0 & \text{if } Y_i = U_i = 0 \\ 1 & \text{otherwise} \end{cases}$$

Note that

$$P\{X_i = 0\} = P\{Y_i = 0\}P\{U_i = 0\} = e^{-p_i}(1 - p_i)e^{p_i} = 1 - p_i$$
$$P\{X_i = 1\} = 1 - P\{X_i = 0\} = p_i$$

Now, if X_i is equal to 0, then so must Y_i equal 0 (by the definition of X_i). Therefore,

$$
\begin{aligned}
P\{X_i \neq Y_i\} &= P\{X_i = 1, Y_i \neq 1\} \\
&= P\{Y_i = 0, X_i = 1\} + P\{Y_i > 1\} \\
&= P\{Y_i = 0, U_i = 1\} + P\{Y_i > 1\} \\
&= e^{-p_i}[1 - (1 - p_i)e^{p_i}] + 1 - e^{-p_i} - p_i e^{-p_i} \\
&= p_i - p_i e^{-p_i} \\
&\leq p_i^2 \qquad \text{(since } 1 - e^{-p} \leq p)
\end{aligned}
$$

Now let $X = \sum_{i=1}^{n} X_i$ and $Y = \sum_{i=1}^{n} Y_i$, and note that X is the sum of independent Bernoulli random variables and Y is Poisson with the expected value $E[Y] = E[X] = \sum_{i=1}^{n} p_i$. Note also that the inequality $X \neq Y$ implies that $X_i \neq Y_i$ for some i, so

$$
\begin{aligned}
P\{X \neq Y\} &\leq P\{X_i \neq Y_i \text{ for some } i\} \\
&\leq \sum_{i=1}^{n} P\{X_i \neq Y_i\} \qquad \text{(Boole's inequality)} \\
&\leq \sum_{i=1}^{n} p_i^2
\end{aligned}
$$

For any event B, let I_B, the indicator variable for the event B, be defined by

$$
I_B = \begin{cases} 1 & \text{if } B \text{ occurs} \\ 0 & \text{otherwise} \end{cases}
$$

Note that for any set of real numbers A,

$$
I_{\{X \in A\}} - I_{\{Y \in A\}} \leq I_{\{X \neq Y\}}
$$

The preceding inequality follows from the fact that since an indicator variable is either 0 or 1, the left-hand side equals 1 only when $I_{\{X \in A\}} = 1$ and $I_{\{Y \in A\}} = 0$. But this would imply that $X \in A$ and $Y \notin A$, which means that $X \neq Y$, so the right side would also equal 1. Upon taking expectations of the preceding inequality, we obtain

$$
P\{X \in A\} - P\{Y \in A\} \leq P\{X \neq Y\}
$$

By reversing X and Y, we obtain, in the same manner,

$$
P\{Y \in A\} - P\{X \in A\} \leq P\{X \neq Y\}
$$

Thus, we can conclude that

$$
|P\{X \in A\} - P\{Y \in A\}| \leq P\{X \neq Y\}
$$

Therefore, we have proven that with $\lambda = \sum_{i=1}^{n} p_i$,

$$
\left| P\left\{ \sum_{i=1}^{n} X_i \in A \right\} - \sum_{i \in A} \frac{e^{-\lambda}\lambda^i}{i!} \right| \leq \sum_{i=1}^{n} p_i^2
$$

Remark When all the p_i are equal to p, X is a binomial random variable. Hence, the preceding inequality shows that, for any set of nonnegative integers A,

$$\left| \sum_{i \in A} \binom{n}{i} p^i (1-p)^{n-i} - \sum_{i \in A} \frac{e^{-np}(np)^i}{i!} \right| \le np^2 \qquad \blacksquare$$

Summary

Two useful probability bounds are provided by the *Markov* and *Chebyshev* inequalities. The Markov inequality is concerned with nonnegative random variables and says that for X of that type,

$$P\{X \ge a\} \le \frac{E[X]}{a}$$

for every positive value a. The Chebyshev inequality, which is a simple consequence of the Markov inequality, states that if X has mean μ and variance σ^2, then, for every positive k,

$$P\{|X - \mu| \ge k\sigma\} \le \frac{1}{k^2}$$

The two most important theoretical results in probability are the *central limit theorem* and the *strong law of large numbers*. Both are concerned with a sequence of independent and identically distributed random variables. The central limit theorem says that if the random variables have a finite mean μ and a finite variance σ^2, then the distribution of the sum of the first n of them is, for large n, approximately that of a normal random variable with mean $n\mu$ and variance $n\sigma^2$. That is, if $X_i, i \ge 1$, is the sequence, then the central limit theorem states that for every real number a,

$$\lim_{n \to \infty} P\left\{ \frac{X_1 + \cdots + X_n - n\mu}{\sigma \sqrt{n}} \le a \right\} = \frac{1}{\sqrt{2\pi}} \int_{-\infty}^{a} e^{-x^2/2}\, dx$$

The *strong law of large numbers* requires only that the random variables in the sequence have a finite mean μ. It states that with probability 1, the average of the first n of them will converge to μ as n goes to infinity. This implies that if A is any specified event of an experiment for which independent replications are performed, then the limiting proportion of experiments whose outcomes are in A will, with probability 1, equal $P(A)$. Therefore, if we accept the interpretation that "with probability 1" means "with certainty," we obtain the theoretical justification for the long-run relative frequency interpretation of probabilities.

Problems

8.1. Suppose that X is a random variable with mean and variance both equal to 10. Find the bound for $P\{X \le 20\}$

8.2. From past experience, a professor knows that the test score of a student taking her final examination is a random variable with mean 75.
(a) Give an upper bound for the probability that a student's test score will exceed 85.
(b) Suppose, in addition, that the professor knows that the variance of a student's test score is equal to 25. What can be said about the probability that a student will score between 65 and 85?
(c) How many students would have to take the examination to ensure with probability at least .9 that the class average would be within 5 of 75? Do not use the central limit theorem.

8.3. Use the central limit theorem to solve part (c) of Problem 8.2.

8.4. Let $X_1, \ldots, X_{30}$ be independent Bernoulli random variables with success probability $p = 0.6$.

(a) Use the Markov inequality to obtain a bound on

$$P\left\{ \sum_{i=1}^{30} X_i > 20 \right\}$$

(b) Use the central limit theorem to approximate

$$P\left\{ \sum_{i=1}^{30} X_i > 20 \right\}.$$

8.5. Fifty numbers are rounded off to the nearest integer and then summed. If the individual round-off errors are uniformly distributed over $(-.5, .5)$, approximate the probability that the resultant sum differs from the exact sum by more than 3.

8.6. A die is continually rolled until the total sum of all rolls exceeds 200. How many times (n) one need to roll the die so that probability of at least $n + 1$ rolls are 0.98.

8.7. A person has 100 light bulbs whose lifetimes are independent exponentials with mean 5 hours. If the bulbs are used one at a time, with a failed bulb being replaced immediately by a new one, approximate the probability that there is still a working bulb after 525 hours.

8.8. In Problem 8.7, suppose that it takes a random time, uniformly distributed over (0, .5), to replace a failed bulb. Approximate the probability that all bulbs have failed by time 550.

8.9. If X is a Chi square random variable with n degrees of freedom, approximately how large need n be so that

$$P\left\{\left|\frac{X}{2n} - \frac{1}{2}\right| > 0.01\right\} \leq 0.01?$$

8.10. Civil engineers believe that W, the amount of weight (in units of 1000 pounds) that a certain span of a bridge can withstand without structural damage resulting, is normally distributed with mean 400 and standard deviation 40. Suppose that the weight (again, in units of 1000 pounds) of a car is a random variable with mean 3 and standard deviation .3. Approximately how many cars would have to be on the bridge span for the probability of structural damage to exceed .1?

8.11. Many people believe that the daily change of price of a company's stock on the stock market is a random variable with mean 0 and variance σ^2. That is, if Y_n represents the price of the stock on the nth day, then

$$Y_n = Y_{n-1} + X_n \quad n \geq 1$$

where $X_1, X_2, \ldots$ are independent and identically distributed random variables with mean 0 and variance σ^2. Suppose that the stock's price today is 100. If $\sigma^2 = 1$, what can you say about the probability that the stock's price will exceed 105 after 10 days?

8.12. We have 100 components that we will put in use in a sequential fashion. That is, component 1 is initially put in use, and upon failure, it is replaced by component 2, which is itself replaced upon failure by component 3, and so on. If the lifetime of component i is exponentially distributed with mean $10 + i/10, i = 1, \ldots, 100$, estimate the probability that the total life of all components will exceed 1200. Now repeat when the life distribution of component i is uniformly distributed over $(0, 20 + i/5), i = 1, \ldots, 100$.

8.13. Student scores on exams given by a certain instructor have mean 74 and standard deviation 14. This instructor is about to give two exams, one to a class of size 25 and the other to a class of size 64.

(a) Approximate the probability that the average test score in the class of size 25 exceeds 80.

(b) Repeat part (a) for the class of size 64.

(c) Approximate the probability that the average test score in the larger class exceeds that of the other class by more than 2.2 points.

(d) Approximate the probability that the average test score in the smaller class exceeds that of the other class by more than 2.2 points.

8.14. A certain component a flight must be replaced immediately upon failure. If the mean lifetime of this type of component is 1000 hours and its standard deviation is 100 hours, how many of these components must be in stock so that the probability that the system is in continual operation for the next 10000 hours is at least .95?

8.15. An insurance company has 10,00 automobile policyholders. The expected yearly claim per policyholder is 10000 rupees, with a standard deviation of 1000 rupees. Approximate the probability that the total yearly claim exceeds 90 lakhs rupees.

8.16. A.J. has 20 jobs that she must do in sequence, with the times required to do each of these jobs being independent random variables with mean 50 minutes and standard deviation 10 minutes. M.J. has 20 jobs that he must do in sequence, with the times required to do each of these jobs being independent random variables with mean 52 minutes and standard deviation 15 minutes.

(a) Find the probability that A.J. finishes in less than 900 minutes.

(b) Find the probability that M.J. finishes in less than 900 minutes.

(c) Find the probability that A.J. finishes before M.J.

8.17. Redo Example 5b under the assumption that the number of man–woman pairs is (approximately) normally distributed. Does this seem like a reasonable supposition?

8.18. Repeat part (a) of Problem 8.2 when it is known that the variance of a student's test score is equal to 25.

8.19. A lake contains 4 distinct types of fish. Suppose that each fish caught is equally likely to be any one of these types. Let Y denote the number of fish that need be caught to obtain at least one of each type.

(a) Give an interval (a, b) such that $P\{a \leq Y \leq b\} \geq .90$.

(b) Using the one-sided Chebyshev inequality, how many fish need we plan on catching so as to be at least 90 percent certain of obtaining at least one of each type?

8.20. If X is a nonnegative random variable with mean 5 and variance 2, what can be said about

(a) $E[X^2]$

(b) $E[\sqrt{X}]$

(c) $E[\log X]$

(d) $E[X^3]$

8.21. Let X be a nonnegative random variable and define $h[x] = \dfrac{f[x]}{1-F[x]}$. Prove that

(a) $E(\log([X])) \leq -\log(E[X])$

(b) $E\left(\dfrac{X}{h[X]}\right) \leq E^2[X]$

8.22. Would the results of Example 5f change if the investor were allowed to divide her money and invest the fraction $\alpha, 0 < \alpha < 1$, in the risky proposition and invest the remainder in the risk-free venture? Her return for such a split investment would be $R = \alpha X + (1 - \alpha)m$.

8.23. Let X be a Poisson random variable with mean 20.

(a) Use the Markov inequality to obtain an upper bound on

$$p = P\{X \geq 26\}$$

(b) Use the one-sided Chebyshev inequality to obtain an upper bound on p.

(c) Use the Chernoff bound to obtain an upper bound on p.

(d) Approximate p by making use of the central limit theorem.

(e) Determine p by running an appropriate program.

8.24. If X is binomial random variable with parameter $n = 10000$ and $p = 0.01$. Then find $P\{X > 120\}$.

Theoretical Exercises

8.1. If X has variance σ^2, then σ, the positive square root of the variance, is called the *standard deviation*. If X has mean μ and standard deviation σ, show that

$$P\{|x - \mu| \leq k\sigma\} \geq 1 - \frac{1}{k^2}$$

8.2. If X has mean μ and standard deviation σ, the ratio $r \equiv |\mu|/\sigma$ is called the *measurement signal-to-noise ratio* of X. The idea is that X can be expressed as $X = \mu + (X - \mu)$, with μ representing the signal and $X - \mu$ the noise. If we define $|(X - \mu)/\mu| \equiv D$ as the relative deviation of X from its signal (or mean) μ, show that for $\alpha > 0$,

$$P\{D \leq \alpha\} \geq 1 - \frac{1}{r^2\alpha^2}$$

8.3. Compute the measurement signal-to-noise ratio—that is, $|\mu|/\sigma$, where $\mu = E[X]$ and $\sigma^2 = \text{Var}(X)$—of the following random variables:

(a) Poisson with mean λ;

(b) binomial with parameters n and p;

(c) geometric with mean $1/p$;

(d) uniform over (a, b);

(e) exponential with mean $1/\lambda$;

(f) normal with parameters μ, σ^2.

8.4. Let $Z_n, n \geq 1$, be a sequence of random variables and c a constant such that for each $\varepsilon > 0, P\{|Z_n - c| > \varepsilon\} \to 0$ as $n \to \infty$. Show that for any bounded continuous function g,

$$E[g(Z_n)] \to g(c) \quad \text{as} \quad n \to \infty$$

8.5. Let $f(x)$ be a continuous function defined for $0 \leq x \leq 1$. Consider the functions

$$B_n(x) = \sum_{k=0}^{n} f\left(\frac{k}{n}\right)\binom{n}{k} x^k(1 - x)^{n-k}$$

(called *Bernstein polynomials*) and prove that

$$\lim_{n \to \infty} B_n(x) = f(x)$$

Hint: Let $X_1, X_2, \ldots$ be independent Bernoulli random variables with mean x. Show that

$$B_n(x) = E\left[f\left(\frac{X_1 + \cdots + X_n}{n}\right)\right]$$

and then use Theoretical Exercise 8.4.

Since it can be shown that the convergence of $B_n(x)$ to $f(x)$ is uniform in x, the preceding reasoning provides a probabilistic proof of the famous Weierstrass theorem of analysis, which states that any continuous function on a closed interval can be approximated arbitrarily closely by a polynomial.

8.6. (a) Let X be a discrete random variable whose possible values are $1, 2, \ldots$. If $P\{X = k\}$ is nonincreasing in $k = 1, 2, \ldots$, prove that

$$P\{X = k\} \leq 2\frac{E[X]}{k^2}$$

(b) Let X be a nonnegative continuous random variable having a nonincreasing density function. Show that

$$f(x) \leq \frac{2E[X]}{x^2} \quad \text{for all} \quad x > 0$$

8.7. Suppose that one chose a number from the set $\{1, 2, 3, 4, 5\}$ and he continue the experiment 30 times. Let X_i be the number obtained on the i-th turn. Compute an approximation for

$$P\left\{\prod_{i=1}^{30} X_i \le a^{30}\right\}, \quad 1 < a < 5.$$

8.8. Let $X_1, X_2, ..., X_{100}$ be the Bernoulli random variable with success probability p. Denote $Y = \sum_{i=1}^{100} X_i^2$. Find $P(Y > 50)$ when $p = 0.5$ and $p = 0.6$.

8.9. Suppose a fair coin is tossed 1000 times. If the first 100 tosses all result in heads, what proportion of heads would you expect on the final 900 tosses? Comment on the statement "The strong law of large numbers swamps but does not compensate."

8.10. If X is a Poisson random variable with mean λ, show that for $i < \lambda$,

$$P\{X \le i\} \le \frac{e^{-\lambda}(e\lambda)^i}{i^i}$$

8.11. Let $X_1, X_2, ..., X_{10}$ be standard normal random variable Find an approximation to the probability that $\sum_{i=1}^{10} X_i$ is larger than $\sum_{i=1}^{100} X_i^2$.

8.12. The Chernoff bound on a standard normal random variable Z gives $P\{Z > a\} \le e^{-a^2/2}, a > 0$. Show, by considering the density of Z, that the right side of the inequality can be reduced by the factor 2. That is, show that

$$P\{Z > a\} \le \frac{1}{2}e^{-a^2/2} \quad a > 0$$

8.13. Show that if $E[X] < 0$ and $\theta \ne 0$ is such that $E[e^{\theta X}] = 1$, then $\theta > 0$.

8.14. Let $X_{(1)} = \min\{X_1, X_2, ..., X_n\}$, where X_i, $i = 1, 2, ..., n$ is distributed as $U(0,1)$. Find the asymptotic distribution of $nX_{(1)}$.

Self-Test Problems And Exercises

8.1. The number of automobiles sold weekly at a certain dealership is a random variable with expected value 16. Give an upper bound to the probability that

(a) next week's sales exceed 18;

(b) next week's sales exceed 25.

8.2. Suppose in Problem 8.14 that the variance of the number of automobiles sold weekly is 9.

(a) Give a lower bound to the probability that next week's sales are between 10 and 22, inclusively.

(b) Give an upper bound to the probability that next week's sales exceed 18.

8.3. If

$$E[X] = 100, \quad E[Y] = 1005, \quad \text{Var}(X) = 10,$$
$$\text{Var}(Y) = 22, \quad \text{Cov}(X, Y) = 7$$

give an upper bound to

(a) $P\{|X - Y| > 25\}$

(b) $PX > Y + 25$

(c) $PY > X + 25$

8.4. Suppose that the number of units produced daily at factory A is a random variable with mean 20 and standard deviation 3 and the number produced at factory B is a random variable with mean 18 and standard deviation 6. Assuming independence, derive an upper bound for the probability that more units are produced today at factory B than at factory A.

8.5. The amount of time that a certain type of component functions before failing is a random variable with probability density function

$$f(x) = 2x \quad 0 < x < 1$$

Once the component fails, it is immediately replaced by another one of the same type. If we let X_i denote the lifetime of the ith component to be put in use, then $S_n = \sum_{i=1}^{n} X_i$ represents the time of the nth failure. The long-term rate at which failures occur, call it r, is defined by

$$r = \lim_{n \to \infty} \frac{n}{S_n}$$

Assuming that the random variables X_i, $i \ge 1$, are independent, determine r.

8.6. In Self-Test Problem 8.5, how many components would one need to have on hand to be approximately 90 percent certain that the stock would last at least 35 days?

8.7. The servicing of a machine requires two separate steps, with the time needed for the first step being an exponential random variable with mean .2 hour and the time for the second step being an independent exponential random variable with mean .3 hour. If a repair person has 20 machines to service, approximate the probability that all the work can be completed in 8 hours.

8.8. On each bet, a gambler loses 1 with probability .7, loses 2 with probability .2, or wins 10 with probability .1. Approximate the probability that the gambler will be losing after his first 100 bets.

8.9. Determine t so that the probability that the repair person in Self-Test Problem 8.7 finishes the 20 jobs within time t is approximately equal to .95.

8.10. A tobacco company claims that the amount of nicotine in one of its cigarettes is a random variable with mean 2.2 mg and standard deviation .3 mg. However, the average nicotine content of 100 randomly chosen cigarettes was 3.1 mg. Approximate the probability that the average would have been as high as or higher than 3.1 if the company's claims were true.

8.11. Each of the batteries in a collection of 40 batteries is equally likely to be either a type A or a type B battery. Type A batteries last for an amount of time that has mean 50 and standard deviation 15; type B batteries last for an amount of time that has mean 30 and standard deviation 6.

(a) Approximate the probability that the total life of all 40 batteries exceeds 1700.

(b) Suppose it is known that 20 of the batteries are type A and 20 are type B. Now approximate the probability that the total life of all 40 batteries exceeds 1700.

8.12. Let X be Cauchy random variable with probability density function given by

$$f(x) = \frac{1}{\pi} \frac{1}{1 + (x - \theta)^2}, \quad -\infty < x, \theta < \infty.$$

Show that average value do not converges to θ for large n.

8.13. The strong law of large numbers states that with probability 1, the successive arithmetic averages of a sequence of independent and identically distributed random variables converge to their common mean μ. What do the successive geometric averages converge to? That is, what is

$$\lim_{n \to \infty} \left(\prod_{i=1}^{n} X_i \right)^{1/n}$$

8.14. In a bank suppose that it takes average 5 minutes with standard deviation 2 to serve a customer. If one staff has to serve 50 customer.

(a) Approximate the probability that it will take more than 240 minutes to serve all costumer.

(b) Approximate the probability that at least 30 customer will be served in the first 140 minutes

Chapter

9

ADDITIONAL TOPICS IN PROBABILITY

Contents

9.1 The Poisson Process

9.2 Markov Chains

9.3 Surprise, Uncertainty, and Entropy

9.4 Coding Theory and Entropy

9.1 The Poisson Process

Before we define a Poisson process, let us recall that a function f is said to be $o(h)$ if

$$\lim_{h \to 0} \frac{f(h)}{h} = 0.$$

That is, f is $o(h)$ if, for small values of h, $f(h)$ is small even in relation to h. Suppose now that "events" are occurring at random points at time, and let $N(t)$ denote the number of events that occur in the time interval $[0, t]$. The collection of random variables $\{N(t), t \geq 0\}$ is said to be a *Poisson process having rate* λ, $\lambda > 0$, if

(i) $N(0) = 0$.
(ii) The numbers of events that occur in disjoint time intervals are independent.
(iii) The distribution of the number of events that occur in a given interval depends only on the length of that interval and not on its location.
(iv) $P\{N(h) = 1\} = \lambda h + o(h)$.
(v) $P\{N(h) \geq 2\} = o(h)$.

Thus, condition (i) states that the process begins at time 0. Condition (ii), the *independent increment* assumption, states, for instance, that the number of events that occur by time t [that is, $N(t)$] is independent of the number of events that occur between t and $t + s$ [that is, $N(t + s) - N(t)$]. Condition (iii), the *stationary increment* assumption, states that the probability distribution of $N(t + s) - N(t)$ is the same for all values of t.

In Chapter 4, we presented an argument, based on the Poisson distribution being a limiting version of the binomial distribution, that the foregoing conditions imply that $N(t)$ has a Poisson distribution with mean λt. We will now obtain this result by a different method.

Lemma
1.1

For a Poisson process with rate λ,

$$P\{N(t) = 0\} = e^{-\lambda t}$$

Proof Let $P_0(t) = P\{N(t) = 0\}$. We derive a differential equation for $P_0(t)$ in the following manner:

$$\begin{aligned}
P_0(t + h) &= P\{N(t + h) = 0\} \\
&= P\{N(t) = 0, N(t + h) - N(t) = 0\} \\
&= P\{N(t) = 0\}P\{N(t + h) - N(t) = 0\} \\
&= P_0(t)[1 - \lambda h + o(h)]
\end{aligned}$$

where the final two equations follow from condition (ii) plus the fact that conditions (iv) and (v) imply that $P\{N(h) = 0\} = 1 - \lambda h + o(h)$. Hence,

$$\frac{P_0(t + h) - P_0(t)}{h} = -\lambda P_0(t) + \frac{o(h)}{h}$$

Now, letting $h \to 0$, we obtain

$$P_0'(t) = -\lambda P_0(t)$$

or, equivalently,

$$\frac{P_0'(t)}{P_0(t)} = -\lambda$$

which implies, by integration, that

$$\log P_0(t) = -\lambda t + c$$

or

$$P_0(t) = Ke^{-\lambda t}$$

Since $P_0(0) = P\{N(0) = 0\} = 1$, we arrive at

$$P_0(t) = e^{-\lambda t} \qquad \qquad \square$$

For a Poisson process, let T_1 denote the time the first event occurs. Further, for $n > 1$, let T_n denote the time elapsed between the $(n - 1)$ and the nth event. The sequence $\{T_n, n = 1, 2, \ldots\}$ is called the *sequence of interarrival times*. For instance, if $T_1 = 5$ and $T_2 = 10$, then the first event of the Poisson process would have occurred at time 5 and the second at time 15.

We shall now determine the distribution of the T_n. To do so, we first note that the event $\{T_1 > t\}$ takes place if and only if no events of the Poisson process occur in the interval $[0, t]$; thus,

$$P\{T_1 > t\} = P\{N(t) = 0\} = e^{-\lambda t}$$

Hence, T_1 has an exponential distribution with mean $1/\lambda$. Now,

$$P\{T_2 > t\} = E[P\{T_2 > t | T_1\}]$$

However,

$$\begin{aligned}
P\{T_2 > t | T_1 = s\} &= P\{0 \text{ events in } (s, s + t] | T_1 = s\} \\
&= P\{0 \text{ events in } (s, s + t]\} \\
&= e^{-\lambda t}
\end{aligned}$$

where the last two equations followed from the assumptions about independent and stationary increments. From the preceding, we conclude that T_2 is also an exponential random variable with mean $1/\lambda$ and, furthermore, that T_2 is independent of T_1. Repeating the same argument yields Proposition 1.1.

Proposition 1.1 $T_1, T_2, \ldots$ are independent exponential random variables, each with mean $1/\lambda$.

Another quantity of interest is S_n, the arrival time of the nth event, also called the *waiting time* until the nth event. It is easily seen that

$$S_n = \sum_{i=1}^{n} T_i \quad n \ge 1$$

hence, from Proposition 1.1 and the results of Section 5.6.1, it follows that S_n has a gamma distribution with parameters n and λ. That is, the probability density of S_n is given by

$$f_{S_n}(x) = \lambda e^{-\lambda x} \frac{(\lambda x)^{n-1}}{(n-1)!} \quad x \ge 0$$

We are now ready to prove that $N(t)$ is a Poisson random variable with mean λt.

Theorem 1.1 For a Poisson process with rate λ,

$$P\{N(t) = n\} = \frac{e^{-\lambda t}(\lambda t)^n}{n!}$$

Proof Note that the nth event of the Poisson process will occur before or at time t if and only if the number of events that occur by t is at least n. That is,

$$N(t) \ge n \Leftrightarrow S_n \le t$$

so

$$\begin{aligned}
P\{N(t) = n\} &= P\{N(t) \ge n\} - P\{N(t) \ge n+1\} \\
&= P\{S_n \le t\} - P\{S_{n+1} \le t\} \\
&= \int_0^t \lambda e^{-\lambda x} \frac{(\lambda x)^{n-1}}{(n-1)!} \, dx - \int_0^t \lambda e^{-\lambda x} \frac{(\lambda x)^n}{n!} \, dx
\end{aligned}$$

But the integration-by-parts formula $\int u \, dv = uv - \int v \, du$ with $u = e^{-\lambda x}$ and $dv = \lambda[(\lambda x)^{n-1}/(n-1)!] \, dx$ yields

$$\int_0^t \lambda e^{-\lambda x} \frac{(\lambda x)^{n-1}}{(n-1)!} \, dx = e^{-\lambda t} \frac{(\lambda t)^n}{n!} + \int_0^t \lambda e^{-\lambda x} \frac{(\lambda x)^n}{n!} \, dx$$

which completes the proof. $\qquad \square$

9.2 Markov Chains

Consider a sequence of random variables $X_0, X_1, \ldots$, and suppose that the set of possible values of these random variables is $\{0, 1, \ldots, M\}$. It will be helpful to interpret X_n as being the state of some system at time n, and, in accordance with this interpretation, we say that the system is in state i at time n if $X_n = i$. The sequence of random variables is said to form a *Markov chain* if, each time the system is in state i, there is some fixed probability—call it P_{ij}—that the system will next be in state j. That is, for all $i_0, \ldots, i_{n-1}, i, j$,

$$P\{X_{n+1} = j | X_n = i, X_{n-1} = i_{n-1}, \ldots, X_1 = i_1, X_0 = i_0\} = P_{ij}$$

The values $P_{ij}, 0 \leq i \leq M, 0 \leq j \leq N$, are called the *transition probabilities* of the Markov chain, and they satisfy

$$P_{ij} \geq 0 \qquad \sum_{j=0}^{M} P_{ij} = 1 \qquad i = 0, 1, \ldots, M$$

(Why?) It is convenient to arrange the transition probabilities P_{ij} in a square array as follows:

$$\begin{Vmatrix} P_{00} & P_{01} & \cdots & P_{0M} \\ P_{10} & P_{11} & \cdots & P_{1M} \\ \vdots & & & \\ P_{M0} & P_{M1} & \cdots & P_{MM} \end{Vmatrix}$$

Such an array is called a *matrix*.

Knowledge of the transition probability matrix and of the distribution of X_0 enables us, in theory, to compute all probabilities of interest. For instance, the joint probability mass function of $X_0, \ldots, X_n$ is given by

$$P\{X_n = i_n, X_{n-1} = i_{n-1}, \ldots, X_1 = i_1, X_0 = i_0\}$$
$$= P\{X_n = i_n | X_{n-1} = i_{n-1}, \ldots, X_0 = i_0\} P\{X_{n-1} = i_{n-1}, \ldots, X_0 = i_0\}$$
$$= P_{i_{n-1}, i_n} P\{X_{n-1} = i_{n-1}, \ldots, X_0 = i_0\}$$

and continual repetition of this argument demonstrates that the preceding is equal to

$$P_{i_{n-1}, i_n} P_{i_{n-2}, i_{n-1}} \cdots P_{i_1, i_2} P_{i_0, i_1} P\{X_0 = i_0\}$$

Example 2a

Suppose that whether it rains tomorrow depends on previous weather conditions only through whether it is raining today. Suppose further that if it is raining today, then it will rain tomorrow with probability α, and if it is not raining today, then it will rain tomorrow with probability β.

If we say that the system is in state 0 when it rains and state 1 when it does not, then the preceding system is a two-state Markov chain having transition probability matrix

$$\begin{Vmatrix} \alpha & 1 - \alpha \\ \beta & 1 - \beta \end{Vmatrix}$$

That is, $P_{00} = \alpha = 1 - P_{01}, P_{10} = \beta = 1 - P_{11}$. ∎

Example 2b

Consider a gambler who either wins 1 unit with probability p or loses 1 unit with probability $1 - p$ at each play of the game. If we suppose that the gambler will quit playing when his fortune hits either 0 or M, then the gambler's sequence of fortunes is a Markov chain having transition probabilities

$$P_{i,i+1} = p = 1 - P_{i,i-1} \quad i = 1, \ldots, M - 1$$
$$P_{00} = P_{MM} = 1$$

∎

Example 2c

The husband-and-wife physicists Paul and Tatyana Ehrenfest considered a conceptual model for the movement of molecules in which M molecules are distributed among 2 urns. At each time point, one of the molecules is chosen at random and is removed from its urn and placed in the other one. If we let X_n denote the number of molecules in the first urn immediately after the nth exchange, then $\{X_0, X_1, \ldots\}$ is a Markov chain with transition probabilities

$$P_{i,i+1} = \frac{M-i}{M} \quad 0 \leq i \leq M$$

$$P_{i,i-1} = \frac{i}{M} \quad 0 \leq i \leq M$$

$$P_{ij} = 0 \quad \text{if } j = i \text{ or } |j - i| > 1 \qquad \blacksquare$$

Thus, for a Markov chain, P_{ij} represents the probability that a system in state i will enter state j at the next transition. We can also define the two-stage transition probability $P_{ij}^{(2)}$ that a system presently in state i will be in state j after two additional transitions. That is,

$$P_{ij}^{(2)} = P\{X_{m+2} = j | X_m = i\}$$

The $P_{ij}^{(2)}$ can be computed from the P_{ij} as follows:

$$
\begin{aligned}
P_{ij}^{(2)} &= P\{X_2 = j | X_0 = i\} \\
&= \sum_{k=0}^{M} P\{X_2 = j, X_1 = k | X_0 = i\} \\
&= \sum_{k=0}^{M} P\{X_2 = j | X_1 = k, X_0 = i\} P\{X_1 = k | X_0 = i\} \\
&= \sum_{k=0}^{M} P_{kj} P_{ik}
\end{aligned}
$$

In general, we define the n-stage transition probabilities, denoted as $P_{ij}^{(n)}$, by

$$P_{ij}^{(n)} = P\{X_{n+m} = j | X_m = i\}$$

Proposition 2.1, known as the Chapman–Kolmogorov equations, shows how the $P_{ij}^{(n)}$ can be computed.

Proposition 2.1

The Chapman–Kolmogorov equations

$$P_{ij}^{(n)} = \sum_{k=0}^{M} P_{ik}^{(r)} P_{kj}^{(n-r)} \quad \text{for all } 0 < r < n$$

Proof

$$
\begin{aligned}
P_{ij}^{(n)} &= P\{X_n = j | X_0 = i\} \\
&= \sum_{k} P\{X_n = j, X_r = k | X_0 = i\} \\
&= \sum_{k} P\{X_n = j | X_r = k, X_0 = i\} P\{X_r = k | X_0 = i\} \\
&= \sum_{k} P_{kj}^{(n-r)} P_{ik}^{(r)} \qquad \square
\end{aligned}
$$

Example 2d

A random walk

An example of a Markov chain having a countably infinite state space is the *random walk*, which tracks a particle as it moves along a one-dimensional axis. Suppose that at each point in time, the particle will move either one step to the right or one step to the left with respective probabilities p and $1 - p$. That is, suppose the particle's path follows a Markov chain with transition probabilities

$$P_{i,i+1} = p = 1 - P_{i,i-1} \quad i = 0, \pm 1, \ldots$$

If the particle is at state i, then the probability that it will be at state j after n transitions is the probability that $(n - i + j)/2$ of these steps are to the right and $n - [(n - i + j)/2] = (n + i - j)/2$ are to the left. Since each step will be to the right, independently of the other steps, with probability p, it follows that the preceding is just the binomial probability

$$P_{ij}^n = \binom{n}{(n - i + j)/2} p^{(n-i+j)/2} (1 - p)^{(n+i-j)/2}$$

where $\binom{n}{x}$ is taken to equal 0 when x is not a nonnegative integer less than or equal to n. The preceding formula can be rewritten as

$$P_{i,i+2k}^{2n} = \binom{2n}{n + k} p^{n+k} (1 - p)^{n-k} \quad k = 0, \pm 1, \ldots, \pm n$$

$$P_{i,i+2k+1}^{2n+1} = \binom{2n + 1}{n + k + 1} p^{n+k+1} (1 - p)^{n-k}$$

$$k = 0, \pm 1, \ldots, \pm n, -(n + 1) \qquad \blacksquare$$

Although the $P_{ij}^{(n)}$ denote conditional probabilities, we can use them to derive expressions for unconditional probabilities by conditioning on the initial state. For instance,

$$P\{X_n = j\} = \sum_i P\{X_n = j | X_0 = i\} P\{X_0 = i\}$$

$$= \sum_i P_{ij}^{(n)} P\{X_0 = i\}$$

For a large number of Markov chains, it turns out that $P_{ij}^{(n)}$ converges, as $n \to \infty$, to a value π_j that depends only on j. That is, for large values of n, the probability of being in state j after n transitions is approximately equal to π_j, no matter what the initial state was. It can be shown that a sufficient condition for a Markov chain to possess this property is that for some $n > 0$,

$$P_{ij}^{(n)} > 0 \quad \text{for all } i, j = 0, 1, \ldots, M \tag{2.1}$$

Markov chains that satisfy Equation (2.1) are said to be *ergodic*. Since Proposition 2.1 yields

$$P_{ij}^{(n+1)} = \sum_{k=0}^{M} P_{ik}^{(n)} P_{kj}$$

it follows, by letting $n \to \infty$, that for ergodic chains,

$$\pi_j = \sum_{k=0}^{M} \pi_k P_{kj} \tag{2.2}$$

Furthermore, since $1 = \sum\limits_{j=0}^{M} P_{ij}^{(n)}$, we also obtain, by letting $n \to \infty$,

$$\sum_{j=0}^{M} \pi_j = 1 \qquad (2.3)$$

In fact, it can be shown that the $\pi_j, 0 \leq j \leq M$, are the unique nonnegative solutions of Equations (2.2) and (2.3). All this is summed up in Theorem 2.1, which we state without proof.

Theorem 2.1

For an ergodic Markov chain,

$$\pi_j = \lim_{n \to \infty} P_{ij}^{(n)}$$

exists, and the $\pi_j, 0 \leq j \leq M$, are the unique nonnegative solutions of

$$\pi_j = \sum_{k=0}^{M} \pi_k P_{kj}$$

$$\sum_{j=0}^{M} \pi_j = 1$$

Example 2e

Consider Example 2a, in which we assume that if it rains today, then it will rain tomorrow with probability α, and if it does not rain today, then it will rain tomorrow with probability β. From Theorem 2.1, it follows that the limiting probabilities π_0 and π_1 of rain and of no rain, respectively, are given by

$$\pi_0 = \alpha \pi_0 + \beta \pi_1$$
$$\pi_1 = (1 - \alpha)\pi_0 + (1 - \beta)\pi_1$$
$$\pi_0 + \pi_1 = 1$$

which yields

$$\pi_0 = \frac{\beta}{1 + \beta - \alpha} \qquad \pi_1 = \frac{1 - \alpha}{1 + \beta - \alpha}$$

For instance, if $\alpha = .6$ and $\beta = .3$, then the limiting probability of rain on the nth day is $\pi_0 = \frac{3}{7}$. ∎

The quantity π_j is also equal to the long-run proportion of time that the Markov chain is in state $j, j = 0, \ldots, M$. To see intuitively why this might be so, let P_j denote the long-run proportion of time the chain is in state j. (It can be proven using the strong law of large numbers that for an ergodic chain, such long-run proportions exist and are constants.) Now, since the proportion of time the chain is in state k is P_k, and since, when in state k, the chain goes to state j with probability P_{kj}, it follows that the proportion of time the Markov chain is entering state j from state k is equal to $P_k P_{kj}$. Summing over all k shows that P_j, the proportion of time the Markov chain is entering state j, satisfies

$$P_j = \sum_k P_k P_{kj}$$

Since clearly it is also true that

$$\sum_j P_j = 1$$

it thus follows, since by Theorem 2.1 the $\pi_j, j = 0, \ldots, M$ are the unique solution of the preceding, that $P_j = \pi_j, j = 0, \ldots, M$. The long-run proportion interpretation of π_j is generally valid even when the chain is not ergodic.

Example 2f

Suppose in Example 2c that we are interested in the proportion of time that there are j molecules in urn 1, $j = 0, \ldots, M$. By Theorem 2.1, these quantities will be the unique solution of

$$\pi_0 = \pi_1 \times \frac{1}{M}$$

$$\pi_j = \pi_{j-1} \times \frac{M - j + 1}{M} + \pi_{j+1} \times \frac{j + 1}{M} \quad j = 1, \ldots, M$$

$$\pi_M = \pi_{M-1} \times \frac{1}{M}$$

$$\sum_{j=0}^{M} \pi_j = 1$$

However, as it is easily checked that

$$\pi_j = \binom{M}{j} \left(\frac{1}{2} \right)^M \quad j = 0, \ldots, M$$

satisfy the preceding equations, it follows that these are the long-run proportions of time that the Markov chain is in each of the states. (See Problem 9.11 for an explanation of how one might have guessed at the foregoing solution.) ∎

9.3 Surprise, Uncertainty, and Entropy

Consider an event E that can occur when an experiment is performed. How surprised would we be to hear that E does, in fact, occur? It seems reasonable to suppose that the amount of surprise engendered by the information that E has occurred should depend on the probability of E. For instance, if the experiment consists of rolling a pair of dice, then we would not be too surprised to hear that E has occurred when E represents the event that the sum of the dice is even (and thus has probability $\frac{1}{2}$), whereas we would certainly be more surprised to hear that E has occurred when E is the event that the sum of the dice is 12 (and thus has probability $\frac{1}{36}$).

In this section, we attempt to quantify the concept of surprise. To begin, let us agree to suppose that the surprise one feels upon learning that an event E has occurred depends only on the probability of E, and let us denote by $S(p)$ the surprise evoked by the occurrence of an event having probability p. We determine the functional form of $S(p)$ by first agreeing on a set of reasonable conditions that $S(p)$ should satisfy and then proving that these axioms require that $S(p)$ have a specified form. We assume throughout that $S(p)$ is defined for all $0 < p \leq 1$ but is not defined for events having $p = 0$.

Our first condition is just a statement of the intuitive fact that there is no surprise in hearing that an event that is sure to occur has indeed occurred.

Axiom 1

$$S(1) = 0$$

Our second condition states that the more unlikely an event is to occur, the greater is the surprise evoked by its occurrence.

Axiom 2

$S(p)$ is a strictly decreasing function of p; that is, if $p < q$, then $S(p) > S(q)$.

The third condition is a mathematical statement of the fact that we would intuitively expect a small change in p to correspond to a small change in $S(p)$.

Axiom 3

$S(p)$ is a continuous function of p.

To motivate the final condition, consider two independent events E and F having respective probabilities $P(E) = p$ and $P(F) = q$. Since $P(EF) = pq$, the surprise evoked by the information that both E and F have occurred is $S(pq)$. Now, suppose that we are told first that E has occurred and then, afterward, that F has also occurred. Since $S(p)$ is the surprise evoked by the occurrence of E, it follows that $S(pq) - S(p)$ represents the additional surprise evoked when we are informed that F has also occurred. However, because F is independent of E, the knowledge that E occurred does not change the probability of F; hence, the additional surprise should just be $S(q)$. This reasoning suggests the final condition.

Axiom 4

$$S(pq) = S(p) + S(q) \qquad 0 < p \le 1, \quad 0 < q \le 1$$

We are now ready for Theorem 3.1, which yields the structure of $S(p)$.

Theorem 3.1

If $S(\cdot)$ satisfies Axioms 1 through 4, then

$$S(p) = -C \log_2 p$$

where C is an arbitrary positive integer.

Proof It follows from Axiom 4 that

$$S(p^2) = S(p) + S(p) = 2S(p)$$

and by induction that

$$S(p^m) = mS(p) \tag{3.1}$$

Also, since, for any integral n, $S(p) = S(p^{1/n} \cdots p^{1/n}) = n\, S(p^{1/n})$, it follows that

$$S(p^{1/n}) = \frac{1}{n} S(p) \tag{3.2}$$

Thus, from Equations (3.1) and (3.2), we obtain

$$S(p^{m/n}) = mS(p^{1/n})$$
$$= \frac{m}{n} S(p)$$

which is equivalent to

$$S(p^x) = xS(p) \tag{3.3}$$

whenever x is a positive rational number. But by the continuity of S (Axiom 3), it follows that Equation (3.3) is valid for all nonnegative x. (Reason this out.)

Now, for any $p, 0 < p \le 1$, let $x = -\log_2 p$. Then $p = \left(\frac{1}{2}\right)^x$, and from Equation (3.3),

$$S(p) = S\left(\left(\frac{1}{2}\right)^x\right) = xS\left(\frac{1}{2}\right) = -C \log_2 p$$

where $C = S\left(\frac{1}{2}\right) > S(1) = 0$ by Axioms 2 and 1. $\qquad \square$

It is usual to let C equal 1, in which case the surprise is said to be expressed in units of *bits* (short for *binary digits*).

Next, consider a random variable X that must take on one of the values $x_1, \ldots, x_n$ with respective probabilities $p_1, \ldots, p_n$. Since $-\log p_i$ represents the surprise evoked if X takes on the value x_i,[†] it follows that the expected amount of surprise we shall receive upon learning the value of X is given by

$$H(X) = -\sum_{i=1}^{n} p_i \log p_i$$

The quantity $H(X)$ is known in information theory as the *entropy* of the random variable X. (In case one of the $p_i = 0$, we take $0 \log 0$ to equal 0.) It can be shown (and we leave it as an exercise) that $H(X)$ is maximized when all of the p_i are equal. (Is this intuitive?)

Since $H(X)$ represents the average amount of surprise one receives upon learning the value of X, it can also be interpreted as representing the amount of *uncertainty* that exists as to the value of X. In fact, in information theory, $H(X)$ is interpreted as the average amount of *information* received when the value of X is observed. Thus, the average surprise evoked by X, the uncertainty of X, or the average amount of information yielded by X all represent the same concept viewed from three slightly different points of view.

Now consider two random variables X and Y that take on the respective values $x_1, \ldots, x_n$ and $y_1, \ldots, y_m$ with joint mass function

$$p(x_i, y_j) = P\{X = x_i, Y = y_j\}$$

It follows that the uncertainty as to the value of the random vector (X, Y), denoted by $H(X, Y)$, is given by

$$H(X, Y) = -\sum_i \sum_j p(x_i, y_j) \log p(x_i, y_j)$$

Suppose now that Y is observed to equal y_j. In this situation, the amount of uncertainty remaining in X is given by

$$H_{Y=y_j}(X) = -\sum_i p(x_i|y_j) \log p(x_i|y_j)$$

where

$$p(x_i|y_j) = P\{X = x_i|Y = y_j\}$$

Hence, the average amount of uncertainty that will remain in X after Y is observed is given by

$$H_Y(X) = \sum_j H_{Y=y_j}(X) p_Y(y_j)$$

where

$$p_Y(y_j) = P\{Y = y_j\}$$

Proposition 3.1 relates $H(X, Y)$ to $H(Y)$ and $H_Y(X)$. It states that the uncertainty as to the value of X and Y is equal to the uncertainty of Y plus the average uncertainty remaining in X when Y is to be observed.

[†]For the remainder of this chapter, we write $\log x$ for $\log_2 x$. Also, we use $\ln x$ for $\log_e x$.

Proposition
3.1
$$H(X, Y) = H(Y) + H_Y(X)$$

Proof Using the identity $p(x_i, y_j) = p_Y(y_j)p(x_i|y_j)$ yields

$$H(X, Y) = -\sum_i \sum_j p(x_i, y_j) \log p(x_i, y_j)$$

$$= -\sum_i \sum_j p_Y(y_j)p(x_i|y_j)[\log p_Y(y_j) + \log p(x_i|y_j)]$$

$$= -\sum_j p_Y(y_j) \log p_Y(y_j) \sum_i p(x_i|y_j)$$

$$- \sum_j p_Y(y_j) \sum_i p(x_i|y_j) \log p(x_i|y_j)$$

$$= H(Y) + H_Y(X) \qquad \square$$

It is a fundamental result in information theory that the amount of uncertainty in a random variable X will, on the average, decrease when a second random variable Y is observed. Before proving this statement, we need the following lemma, whose proof is left as an exercise.

Lemma
3.1
$$\ln x \leq x - 1 \quad x > 0$$

with equality only at $x = 1$.

Theorem
3.2
$$H_Y(X) \leq H(X)$$

with equality if and only if X and Y are independent.

Proof

$$H_Y(X) - H(X) = -\sum_i \sum_j p(x_i|y_j) \log[p(x_i|y_j)]p(y_j)$$

$$+ \sum_i \sum_j p(x_i, y_j) \log p(x_i)$$

$$= \sum_i \sum_j p(x_i, y_j) \log \left[\frac{p(x_i)}{p(x_i|y_j)}\right]$$

$$\leq \log e \sum_i \sum_j p(x_i, y_j) \left[\frac{p(x_i)}{p(x_i|y_j)} - 1\right] \quad \text{by Lemma 3.1}$$

$$= \log e \left[\sum_i \sum_j p(x_i)p(y_j) - \sum_i \sum_j p(x_i, y_j)\right]$$

$$= \log e[1 - 1]$$

$$= 0 \qquad \square$$

9.4 Coding Theory and Entropy

Suppose that the value of a discrete random vector X is to be observed at location A and then transmitted to location B via a communication network that consists of two signals, 0 and 1. In order to do this, it is first necessary to encode each possible value of X in terms of a sequence of 0's and 1's. To avoid any ambiguity, it is usually required that no encoded sequence can be obtained from a shorter encoded sequence by adding more terms to the shorter.

For instance, if X can take on four possible values x_1, x_2, x_3, and x_4, then one possible coding would be

$$
\begin{array}{c}
x_1 \leftrightarrow 00 \\
x_2 \leftrightarrow 01 \\
x_3 \leftrightarrow 10 \\
x_4 \leftrightarrow 11
\end{array}
\qquad (4.1)
$$

That is, if $X = x_1$, then the message 00 is sent to location B, whereas if $X = x_2$, then 01 is sent to B, and so on. A second possible coding is

$$
\begin{array}{c}
x_1 \leftrightarrow 0 \\
x_2 \leftrightarrow 10 \\
x_3 \leftrightarrow 110 \\
x_4 \leftrightarrow 111
\end{array}
\qquad (4.2)
$$

However, a coding such as

$$
\begin{array}{c}
x_1 \leftrightarrow 0 \\
x_2 \leftrightarrow 1 \\
x_3 \leftrightarrow 00 \\
x_4 \leftrightarrow 01
\end{array}
$$

is not allowed because the coded sequences for x_3 and x_4 are both extensions of the one for x_1.

One of the objectives in devising a code is to minimize the expected number of bits (that is, binary digits) that need to be sent from location A to location B. For example, if

$$
\begin{aligned}
P\{X = x_1\} &= \frac{1}{2} \\
P\{X = x_2\} &= \frac{1}{4} \\
P\{X = x_3\} &= \frac{1}{8} \\
P\{X = x_4\} &= \frac{1}{8}
\end{aligned}
$$

then the code given by Equation (4.2) would expect to send $\frac{1}{2}(1) + \frac{1}{4}(2) + \frac{1}{8}(3) + \frac{1}{8}(3) = 1.75$ bits, whereas the code given by Equation (4.1) would expect to send 2 bits. Hence, for the preceding set of probabilities, the encoding in Equation (4.2) is more efficient than that in Equation (4.1).

The preceding discussion raises the following question: For a given random vector X, what is the maximum efficiency achievable by an encoding scheme? The answer is that for any coding, the average number of bits that will be sent is at least as large as the entropy of X. To prove this result, known in information theory as the *noiseless coding theorem*, we shall need Lemma 4.1.

Lemma 4.1

Let X take on the possible values $x_1, \ldots, x_N$. Then, in order to be able to encode the values of X in binary sequences (none of which is an extension of another) of respective lengths $n_1, \ldots, n_N$, it is necessary and sufficient that

$$\sum_{i=1}^{N} \left(\frac{1}{2}\right)^{n_i} \le 1$$

Proof For a fixed set of N positive integers $n_1, \ldots, n_N$, let w_j denote the number of the n_i that are equal to $j, j = 1, \ldots$. For there to be a coding that assigns n_i bits to the value $x_i, i = 1, \ldots, N$, it is clearly necessary that $w_1 \le 2$. Furthermore, because no binary sequence is allowed to be an extension of any other, we must have $w_2 \le 2^2 - 2w_1$. (This follows because 2^2 is the number of binary sequences of length 2, whereas $2w_1$ is the number of sequences that are extensions of the w_1 binary sequence of length 1.) In general, the same reasoning shows that we must have

$$w_n \le 2^n - w_1 2^{n-1} - w_2 2^{n-2} - \cdots - w_{n-1} 2 \qquad (4.3)$$

for $n = 1, \ldots$. In fact, a little thought should convince the reader that these conditions are not only necessary, but also sufficient for a code to exist that assigns n_i bits to $x_i, i = 1, \ldots, N$.

Rewriting inequality (4.3) as

$$w_n + w_{n-1} 2 + w_{n-2} 2^2 + \cdots + w_1 2^{n-1} \le 2^n \quad n = 1, \ldots$$

and dividing by 2^n yields the necessary and sufficient conditions, namely,

$$\sum_{j=1}^{n} w_j \left(\frac{1}{2}\right)^j \le 1 \quad \text{for all } n \qquad (4.4)$$

However, because $\sum_{j=1}^{n} w_j \left(\frac{1}{2}\right)^j$ is increasing in n, it follows that Equation (4.4) will be true if and only if

$$\sum_{j=1}^{\infty} w_j \left(\frac{1}{2}\right)^j \le 1$$

The result is now established, since, by the definition of w_j as the number of n_i that equal j, it follows that

$$\sum_{j=1}^{\infty} w_j \left(\frac{1}{2}\right)^j = \sum_{i=1}^{N} \left(\frac{1}{2}\right)^{n_i}$$

□

We are now ready to prove Theorem 4.1.

Theorem 4.1

The noiseless coding theorem

Let X take on the values $x_1, \ldots, x_N$ with respective probabilities $p(x_1), \ldots, p(x_N)$. Then, for any coding of X that assigns n_i bits to x_i,

$$\sum_{i=1}^{N} n_i p(x_i) \ge H(X) = -\sum_{i=1}^{N} p(x_i) \log p(x_i)$$

Proof Let $P_i = p(x_i), q_i = 2^{-n_i} / \sum_{j=1}^{N} 2^{-n_j}$, $i = 1, \ldots, N$. Then

$$-\sum_{i=1}^{N} P_i \log \left(\frac{P_i}{q_i} \right) = -\log e \sum_{i=1}^{N} P_i \ln \left(\frac{P_i}{q_i} \right)$$

$$= \log e \sum_{i=1}^{N} P_i \ln \left(\frac{q_i}{P_i} \right)$$

$$\leq \log e \sum_{i=1}^{N} P_i \left(\frac{q_i}{P_i} - 1 \right) \quad \text{by Lemma 3.1}$$

$$= 0 \quad \text{since} \quad \sum_{i=1}^{N} P_i = \sum_{i=1}^{N} q_i = 1$$

Hence,

$$-\sum_{i=1}^{N} P_i \log P_i \leq -\sum_{i=1}^{N} P_i \log q_i$$

$$= \sum_{i=1}^{N} n_i P_i + \log \left(\sum_{j=1}^{N} 2^{-n_j} \right)$$

$$\leq \sum_{i=1}^{N} n_i P_i \quad \text{by Lemma 4.1}$$

□

Example 4a

Consider a random variable X with probability mass function

$$p(x_1) = \frac{1}{2} \quad p(x_2) = \frac{1}{4} \quad p(x_3) = p(x_4) = \frac{1}{8}$$

Since

$$H(X) = -\left[\frac{1}{2} \log \frac{1}{2} + \frac{1}{4} \log \frac{1}{4} + \frac{1}{4} \log \frac{1}{8} \right]$$

$$= \frac{1}{2} + \frac{2}{4} + \frac{3}{4}$$

$$= 1.75$$

it follows from Theorem 4.1 that there is no more efficient coding scheme than

$$x_1 \leftrightarrow 0$$
$$x_2 \leftrightarrow 10$$
$$x_3 \leftrightarrow 110$$
$$x_4 \leftrightarrow 111$$

■

For most random vectors, there does not exist a coding for which the average number of bits sent attains the lower bound $H(X)$. However, it is always possible to devise a code such that the average number of bits is within 1 of $H(X)$. To prove this, define n_i to be the integer satisfying

$$-\log p(x_i) \leq n_i < -\log p(x_i) + 1$$

Now,

$$\sum_{i=1}^{N} 2^{-n_i} \le \sum_{i=1}^{N} 2^{\log p(x_i)} = \sum_{i=1}^{N} p(x_i) = 1$$

so, by Lemma 4.1, we can associate sequences of bits having lengths n_i with the $x_i, i = 1, \ldots, N$. The average length of such a sequence,

$$L = \sum_{i=1}^{N} n_i \, p(x_i)$$

satisfies

$$-\sum_{i=1}^{N} p(x_i) \log p(x_i) \le L < -\sum_{i=1}^{N} p(x_i) \log p(x_i) + 1$$

or

$$H(X) \le L < H(X) + 1$$

Example 4b

Suppose that 10 independent tosses of a coin having probability p of coming up heads are made at location A and the result is to be transmitted to location B. The outcome of this experiment is a random vector $X = (X_1, \ldots, X_{10})$, where X_i is 1 or 0 according to whether or not the outcome of the ith toss is heads. By the results of this section, it follows that L, the average number of bits transmitted by any code, satisfies

$$H(X) \le L$$

with

$$L < H(X) + 1$$

for at least one code. Now, since the X_i are independent, it follows from Proposition 3.1 and Theorem 3.2 that

$$H(X) = H(X_1, \ldots, X_{10}) = \sum_{i=1}^{10} H(X_i)$$
$$= -10[p \log p + (1 - p) \log(1 - p)]$$

If $p = \frac{1}{2}$, then $H(X) = 10$, and it follows that we can do no better than just encoding X by its actual value. For example, if the first 5 tosses come up heads and the last 5 tails, then the message 1111100000 is transmitted to location B.

However, if $p \neq \frac{1}{2}$, we can often do better by using a different coding scheme. For instance, if $p = \frac{1}{4}$, then

$$H(X) = -10\left(\frac{1}{4} \log \frac{1}{4} + \frac{3}{4} \log \frac{3}{4}\right) = 8.11$$

Thus, there is an encoding for which the average length of the encoded message is no greater than 9.11.

One simple coding that is more efficient in this case than the identity code is to break up $(X_1, \ldots, X_{10})$ into 5 pairs of 2 random variables each and then, for $i = 1, 3, 5, 7, 9$, code each of the pairs as follows:

$$X_i = 0, X_{i+1} = 0 \leftrightarrow 0$$
$$X_i = 0, X_{i+1} = 1 \leftrightarrow 10$$
$$X_i = 1, X_{i+1} = 0 \leftrightarrow 110$$
$$X_i = 1, X_{i+1} = 1 \leftrightarrow 111$$

The total message transmitted is the successive encodings of the preceding pairs.

For instance, if the outcome $TTTHHTTTTH$ is observed, then the message 010110010 is sent. The average number of bits needed to transmit the message with this code is

$$5\left[1\left(\frac{3}{4}\right)^2 + 2\left(\frac{1}{4}\right)\left(\frac{3}{4}\right) + 3\left(\frac{1}{4}\right)\left(\frac{3}{4}\right) + 3\left(\frac{1}{4}\right)^2\right] = \frac{135}{16}$$
$$\approx 8.44 \qquad \blacksquare$$

Up to this point, we have assumed that the message sent at location A is received without error at location B. However, there are always certain errors that can occur because of random disturbances along the communications channel. Such random disturbances might lead, for example, to the message 00101101, sent at A, being received at B in the form 01101101.

Let us suppose that a bit transmitted at location A will be correctly received at location B with probability p, independently from bit to bit. Such a communications system is called a *binary symmetric channel*. Suppose further that $p = .8$ and we want to transmit a message consisting of a large number of bits from A to B. Thus, direct transmission of the message will result in an error probability of .20 for each bit, which is quite high. One way to reduce this probability of bit error would be to transmit each bit 3 times and then decode by majority rule. That is, we could use the following scheme:

Encode	Decode		Encode	Decode	
$0 \to 000$	$\left.\begin{matrix}000\\001\\010\\100\end{matrix}\right\}$	$\to 0$	$1 \to 111$	$\left.\begin{matrix}111\\110\\101\\011\end{matrix}\right\}$	$\to 1$

Note that if no more than one error occurs in transmission, then the bit will be correctly decoded. Hence, the probability of bit error is reduced to

$$(.2)^3 + 3(.2)^2(.8) = .104$$

a considerable improvement. In fact, it is clear that we can make the probability of bit error as small as we want by repeating the bit many times and then decoding by majority rule. For instance, the scheme

Encode	Decode
$0 \to$ string of 17 0's	By majority rule
$1 \to$ string of 17 1's	

will reduce the probability of bit error to below .01.

Table 9.1 Repetition of Bits Encoding Scheme.	
Probability of error (per bit)	Rate (bits transmitted per signal)
.20	1
.10	$.33 \left(= \frac{1}{3}\right)$
.01	$.06 \left(= \frac{1}{17}\right)$

The problem with this type of encoding scheme is that although it decreases the probability of bit error, it does so at the cost of also decreasing the effective rate of bits sent per signal. (See Table 9.1.)

In fact, at this point it may appear inevitable to the reader that decreasing the probability of bit error to 0 *always* results in also decreasing the effective rate at which bits are transmitted per signal to 0. However, a remarkable result of information theory known as the *noisy coding theorem* and due to Claude Shannon demonstrates that this is not the case. We now state this result as Theorem 4.2.

Theorem 4.2

The noisy coding theorem

There is a number C such that for any value R that is less than C, and for any $\varepsilon > 0$, there exists a coding–decoding scheme that transmits at an average rate of R bits sent per signal and with an error (per bit) probability of less than ε. The largest such value of C—call it $C^{*\dagger}$—is called the channel capacity, and for the binary symmetric channel,

$$C^* = 1 + p \log p + (1 - p) \log(1 - p)$$

Summary

The *Poisson process* having rate λ is a collection of random variables $\{N(t), t \geq 0\}$ that relate to an underlying process of randomly occurring events. For instance, $N(t)$ represents the number of events that occur between times 0 and t. The defining features of the Poisson process are as follows:

(i) The number of events that occur in disjoint time intervals are independent.

(ii) The distribution of the number of events that occur in an interval depends only on the length of the interval.

(iii) Events occur one at a time.

(iv) Events occur at rate λ.

It can be shown that $N(t)$ is a Poisson random variable with mean λt. In addition, if $T_i, i \geq 1$, are the times between the successive events, then they are independent exponential random variables with rate λ.

A sequence of random variables $X_n, n \geq 0$, each of which takes on one of the values $0, \ldots, M$, is said to be a *Markov chain* with transition probabilities $P_{i,j}$ if, for all $n, i_0, \ldots, i_n, i, j$,

$$P\{X_{n+1} = j | X_n = i, X_{n-1} = i_{n-1}, \ldots, X_0 = i_0\} = P_{i,j}$$

If we interpret X_n as the state of some process at time n, then a Markov chain is a sequence of successive states of a process that has the property that whenever it enters state i, then, independently of all past states, the next state is j with probability $P_{i,j}$, for all states i and j. For many Markov chains, the probability of being in state j at time n converges to a limiting value that does not depend on the initial state. If we let $\pi_j, j = 0, \ldots, M$, denote these limiting probabilities, then they are the unique solution of the equations

$$\pi_j = \sum_{i=0}^{M} \pi_i P_{i,j} \quad j = 0, \ldots, M$$

$$\sum_{j=1}^{M} \pi_j = 1$$

Moreover, π_j is equal to the long-run proportion of time that the chain is in state j.

---

†For an entropy interpretation of C^*, see Theoretical Exercise 9.18.

Let X be a random variable that takes on one of n possible values according to the set of probabilities $\{p_1,\ldots,p_n\}$. The quantity

$$H(X) = -\sum_{i=1}^{n} p_i \log_2(p_i)$$

is called the *entropy* of X. It can be interpreted as representing either the average amount of uncertainty that exists regarding the value of X or the average information received when X is observed. Entropy has important implications for binary codings of X.

Problems and Theoretical Exercises

9.1. Customers arrive at a bank at a Poisson rate λ. Suppose that two customers arrived during the first hour. What is the probability that

(a) both arrived during the first 20 minutes?

(b) at least one arrived during the first 20 minutes?

9.2. A bus arrives at bus station according to a Poisson process with rate $\lambda = 10$ per minute. A person waits at the bus station for five minutes. If no bus arrive during that ve minutes, he hails a cab. What is the probability that the person has to hail a cab?

9.3. A telephone exchange receive incoming calls according to a Poisson process with rate $\lambda = 2$ per minute. The log book showed that one call arrived during 9.30 to 9.32. What is the probability that the call arrived after 9.31?

9.4. Suppose that 3 white and 3 black balls are distributed in two urns in such a way that each urn contains 3 balls. We say that the system is in state i if the first urn contains i white balls, $i = 0,1,2,3$. At each stage, 1 ball is drawn from each urn and the ball drawn from the first urn is placed in the second, and conversely with the ball from the second urn. Let X_n denote the state of the system after the nth stage, and compute the transition probabilities of the Markov chain $\{X_n, n \geq 0\}$.

9.5. Consider Example 2a. If there is a 50–50 chance of rain today, compute the probability that it will rain 3 days from now if $\alpha = .7$ and $\beta = .3$.

9.6. Compute the limiting probabilities for the model of Problem 9.4.

9.7. A transition probability matrix is said to be doubly stochastic if

$$\sum_{i=0}^{M} P_{ij} = 1$$

for all states $j = 0,1,\ldots,M$. Show that such a Markov chain is ergodic, then $\prod_j = 1/(M+1), j = 0,1,\ldots,M$.

9.8. The price of gold in a day depends only upon whether the price increased or decreased yesterday. If the price increased yesterday, then the probability that it will increase today is 0.6. If the decreased yesterday, then the probability that it will increase today is 0.5.

(a) Express this problem as Markov chain.

(b) Gold price increased on May, 10, 2018, what is the probability that price increases on May, 10, 2018

9.9. A game consists of randomly choosing a coin from a set of two coins, and tossing them repeatedly. If the one of the coin is unbiaed and the other has heads on both sides. Find the proportion of times that the unbiased coin shows head?

9.10. A certain person goes for a run each morning. When he leaves his house for his run, he is equally likely to go out either the front or the back door, and similarly, when he returns, he is equally likely to go to either the front or the back door. The runner owns 5 pairs of running shoes, which he takes off after the run at whichever door he happens to be. If there are no shoes at the door from which he leaves to go running, he runs barefooted. We are interested in determining the proportion of time that he runs barefooted.

(a) Set this problem up as a Markov chain. Give the states and the transition probabilities.

(b) Determine the proportion of days that he runs barefooted.

9.11. This problem refers to Example 2f.

(a) Verify that the proposed value of π_j satisfies the necessary equations.

(b) For any given molecule, what do you think is the (limiting) probability that it is in urn 1?

(c) Do you think that the events that molecule $j, j \geq 1$, is in urn 1 at a very large time would be (in the limit) independent?

(d) Explain why the limiting probabilities are as given.

9.12. When a pair of fair dice is rolled, determine the entropy that the both the dice shows the same number.

9.13. Prove that if X can take on any of n possible values with respective probabilities $P_1, \ldots, P_n$, then $H(X)$ is maximized when $P_i = 1/n, i = 1, \ldots, n$. What is $H(X)$ equal to in this case?

9.14. Two fair dice are rolled. Let X denotes the event that both the dice show six and Y be the event that the one of the dice show an even number. Find (a) $H(Y)$ (b) $H_Y(X)$ and (c) $H(X, Y)$.

9.15. A coin having probability $p = \frac{2}{3}$ of coming up heads is flipped 6 times. Compute the entropy of the outcome of this experiment.

9.16. A random variable can take on any of n possible values $x_1, \ldots, x_n$ with respective probabilities $p(x_i), i = 1, \ldots, n$. We shall attempt to determine the value of X by asking a series of questions, each of which can be answered "yes" or "no." For instance, we may ask "Is $X = x_1$?" or

"Is X equal to either x_1 or x_2 or x_3?" and so on. What can you say about the average number of such questions that you will need to ask to determine the value of X?

9.17. Show that for any discrete random variable X and function f,

$$H(f(X)) \leq H(X)$$

9.18. In transmitting a bit from location A to location B, if we let X denote the value of the bit sent at location A and Y denote the value received at location B, then $H(X) - H_Y(X)$ is called the *rate of transmission of information from A to B*. The maximal rate of transmission, as a function of $P\{X = 1\} = 1 - P\{X = 0\}$, is called the *channel capacity*. Show that for a binary symmetric channel with $P\{Y = 1 | X = 1\} = P\{Y = 0 | X = 0\} = p$, the channel capacity is attained by the rate of transmission of information when $P\{X = 1\} = \frac{1}{2}$ and its value is $1 + p \log p + (1 - p) \log(1 - p)$.

Self-Test Problems and Exercises

9.1. Events occur according to a Poisson process with rate $\lambda = 3$ per hour.

(a) What is the probability that no events occur between times 8 and 10 in the morning?
(b) What is the expected value of the number of events that occur between times 8 and 10 in the morning?
(c) What is the expected time of occurrence of the fifth event after 2 P.M.?

9.2. A police officer is assigned to catch speeding vehicles at a traffic intersection. The number of speeding vehicle follow a Poisson Process with rate $\lambda = 3$ per hour. The police officer spots the speeding car at a probability $p = 0.8$. Find the probability that the number of speeding cars spot by the police officer within 2 hour is 4.

9.3. Four out of every five trucks on the road are followed by a car, while one out of every six cars is followed

by a truck. What proportion of vehicles on the road are trucks?

9.4. A certain town's weather is classified each day as being rainy, sunny, or overcast, but dry. If it is rainy one day, then it is equally likely to be either sunny or overcast the following day. If it is not rainy, then there is one chance in three that the weather will persist in whatever state it is in for another day, and if it does change, then it is equally likely to become either of the other two states. In the long run, what proportion of days are sunny? What proportion are rainy?

9.5. Let X be a random variable that takes on 5 possible values with respective probabilities .35, .2, .2, .2, and .05. Also, let Y be a random variable that takes on 5 possible values with respective probabilities .05, .35, .1, .15, and .35.

(a) Show that $H(X) > H(Y)$.
(b) Using the result of Problem 9.13, give an intuitive explanation for the preceding inequality.

References

Sections 9.1 and 9.2

[1] KEMENY, J., L. SNELL, and A. KNAPP. *Denumerable Markov Chains*. New York: D. Van Nostrand Company, 1966.

[2] PARZEN, E. *Stochastic Processes*. San Francisco: Holden-Day, Inc., 1962.

[3] ROSS, S. M. *Introduction to Probability Models*, 10th ed. San Diego: Academic Press, Inc., 2010.

[4] ROSS, S. M. *Stochastic Processes*, 2d ed. New York: John Wiley & Sons, Inc., 1996.

Sections 9.3 and 9.4

[5] ABRAMSON, N. *Information Theory and Coding.* New York: McGraw-Hill Book Company, 1963.

[6] McELIECE, R. *Theory of Information and Coding.* Reading, MA: Addison-Wesley Publishing Co., Inc., 1977.

[7] PETERSON, W., and E. WELDON. *Error Correcting Codes*, 2d ed. Cambridge, MA: The MIT Press, 1972.

Chapter

10

SIMULATION

Contents

10.1 Introduction
10.2 General Techniques for Simulating
Continuous Random Variables

10.3 Simulating from Discrete Distributions
10.4 Variance Reduction Techniques

10.1 Introduction

How can we determine the probability of our winning a game of solitaire? (By solitaire, we mean any one of the standard solitaire games played with an ordinary deck of 52 playing cards and with some fixed playing strategy.) One possible approach is to start with the reasonable hypothesis that all (52)! possible arrangements of the deck of cards are equally likely to occur and then attempt to determine how many of these lead to a win. Unfortunately, there does not appear to be any systematic method for determining the number of arrangements that lead to a win, and as (52)! is a rather large number and the only way to determine whether a particular arrangement leads to a win seems to be by playing the game out, it can be seen that this approach will not work.

In fact, it might appear that the determination of the probability of winning at solitaire is mathematically intractable. However, all is not lost, for probability falls not only within the realm of mathematics, but also within the realm of applied science; and, as in all applied sciences, experimentation is a valuable technique. For our solitaire example, experimentation takes the form of playing a large number of such games or, better yet, programming a computer to do so. After playing, say, n games, if we let

$$X_i = \begin{cases} 1 & \text{if the } i\text{th game results in a win} \\ 0 & \text{otherwise} \end{cases}$$

then $X_i, i = 1, \ldots, n$ will be independent Bernoulli random variables for which

$$E[X_i] = P\{\text{win at solitaire}\}$$

Hence, by the strong law of large numbers, we know that

$$\sum_{i=1}^{n} \frac{X_i}{n} = \frac{\text{number of games won}}{\text{number of games played}}$$

will, with probability 1, converge to $P\{\text{win at solitaire}\}$. That is, by playing a large number of games, we can use the proportion of games won as an estimate of the probability of winning. This method of empirically determining probabilities by means of experimentation is known as *simulation*.

In order to use a computer to initiate a simulation study, we must be able to generate the value of a uniform $(0, 1)$ random variable; such variates are called *random numbers*. To generate them, most computers have a built-in subroutine, called a *random-number generator*, whose output is a sequence of *pseudorandom numbers*—a sequence of numbers that is, for all practical purposes, indistinguishable from a sample from the uniform $(0, 1)$ distribution. Most random-number generators start with an initial value X_0, called the *seed*, and then recursively compute values by specifying positive integers a, c, and m, and then letting

$$X_{n+1} = (aX_n + c) \text{ modulo } m \quad n \geq 0 \tag{1.1}$$

where the foregoing means that $aX_n + c$ is divided by m and the remainder is taken as the value of X_{n+1}. Thus, each X_n is either $0, 1, \ldots, m - 1$, and the quantity X_n/m is taken as an approximation to a uniform $(0, 1)$ random variable. It can be shown that subject to suitable choices for a, c, and m, Equation (1.1) gives rise to a sequence of numbers that look as if they were generated from independent uniform $(0, 1)$ random variables.

As our starting point in simulation, we shall suppose that we can simulate from the uniform $(0, 1)$ distribution, and we shall use the term *random numbers* to mean independent random variables from this distribution.

In the solitaire example, we would need to program a computer to play out the game starting with a given ordering of the cards. However, since the initial ordering is supposed to be equally likely to be any of the $(52)!$ possible permutations, it is also necessary to be able to generate a random permutation. Using only random numbers, the following algorithm shows how this can be accomplished. The algorithm begins by randomly choosing one of the elements and then putting it in position n; it then randomly chooses among the remaining elements and puts the choice in position $n - 1$, and so on. The algorithm efficiently makes a random choice among the remaining elements by keeping these elements in an ordered list and then randomly choosing a position on that list.

Example
1a

Generating a random permutation

Suppose we are interested in generating a permutation of the integers $1, 2, \ldots, n$ such that all $n!$ possible orderings are equally likely. Then, starting with any initial permutation, we will accomplish this after $n - 1$ steps, where we interchange the positions of two of the numbers of the permutation at each step. Throughout, we will keep track of the permutation by letting $X(i), i = 1, \ldots, n$ denote the number currently in position i. The algorithm operates as follows:

1. Consider any arbitrary permutation, and let $X(i)$ denote the element in position $i, i = 1 \ldots, n$. [For instance, we could take $X(i) = i, i = 1, \ldots, n$.]
2. Generate a random variable N_n that is equally likely to equal any of the values $1, 2, \ldots, n$.
3. Interchange the values of $X(N_n)$ and $X(n)$. The value of $X(n)$ will now remain fixed. [For instance, suppose that $n = 4$ and initially $X(i) = i, i = 1, 2, 3, 4$. If $N_4 = 3$, then the new permutation is $X(1) = 1, X(2) = 2, X(3) = 4, X(4) = 3$, and element 3 will remain in position 4 throughout.]
4. Generate a random variable N_{n-1} that is equally likely to be either $1, 2, \ldots, n - 1$.

5. Interchange the values of $X(N_{n-1})$ and $X(n-1)$. [If $N_3 = 1$, then the new permutation is $X(1) = 4, X(2) = 2, X(3) = 1, X(4) = 3$.]
6. Generate N_{n-2}, which is equally likely to be either $1, 2, \ldots, n-2$.
7. Interchange the values of $X(N_{n-2})$ and $X(n-2)$. [If $N_2 = 1$, then the new permutation is $X(1) = 2, X(2) = 4, X(3) = 1, X(4) = 3$, and this is the final permutation.]
8. Generate N_{n-3}, and so on. The algorithm continues until N_2 is generated, and after the next interchange the resulting permutation is the final one.

To implement this algorithm, it is necessary to be able to generate a random variable that is equally likely to be any of the values $1, 2, \ldots, k$. To accomplish this, let U denote a random number—that is, U is uniformly distributed on $(0, 1)$—and note that kU is uniform on $(0, k)$. Hence,

$$P\{i - 1 < kU < i\} = \frac{1}{k} \quad i = 1, \ldots, k$$

so if we take $N_k = [kU] + 1$, where $[x]$ is the integer part of x (that is, the largest integer less than or equal to x), then N_k will have the desired distribution.

The algorithm can now be succinctly written as follows:

Step 1. Let $X(1), \ldots, X(n)$ be any permutation of $1, 2, \ldots, n$. [For instance, we can set $X(i) = i, i = 1, \ldots, n$.]
Step 2. Let $I = n$.
Step 3. Generate a random number U and set $N = [IU] + 1$.
Step 4. Interchange the values of $X(N)$ and $X(I)$.
Step 5. Reduce the value of I by 1, and if $I > 1$, go to step 3.
Step 6. $X(1), \ldots, X(n)$ is the desired random generated permutation.

The foregoing algorithm for generating a random permutation is extremely useful. For instance, suppose that a statistician is developing an experiment to compare the effects of m different treatments on a set of n subjects. He decides to split the subjects into m different groups of respective sizes $n_1, n_2, \ldots, n_m$, where $\sum_{i=1}^{m} n_i = n$, with the members of the ith group to receive treatment i. To eliminate any bias in the assignment of subjects to treatments (for instance, it would cloud the meaning of the experimental results if it turned out that all the "best" subjects had been put in the same group), it is imperative that the assignment of a subject to a given group be done "at random." How is this to be accomplished?[†]

A simple and efficient procedure is to arbitrarily number the subjects 1 through n and then generate a random permutation $X(1), \ldots, X(n)$ of $1, 2, \ldots, n$. Now assign subjects $X(1), X(2), \ldots, X(n_1)$ to be in group 1; $X(n_1 + 1), \ldots, X(n_1 + n_2)$ to be in group 2; and, in general, group j is to consist of subjects numbered $X(n_1 + n_2 + \cdots + n_{j-1} + k), k = 1, \ldots, n_j$. ■

10.2 General Techniques for Simulating Continuous Random Variables

In this section, we present two general methods for using random numbers to simulate continuous random variables.

[†]Another technique for randomly dividing the subjects when $m = 2$ was presented in Example 2g of Chapter 6. The preceding procedure is faster, but requires more space than the one of Example 2g.

10.2.1 The Inverse Transformation Method

A general method for simulating a random variable having a continuous distribution—called the *inverse transformation method*—is based on the following proposition.

Proposition 2.1 Let U be a uniform $(0, 1)$ random variable. For any continuous distribution function F, if we define the random variable Y by

$$Y = F^{-1}(U)$$

then the random variable Y has distribution function F. [$F^{-1}(x)$ is defined to equal that value y for which $F(y) = x$.]

Proof

$$F_Y(a) = P\{Y \leq a\}$$
$$= P\{F^{-1}(U) \leq a\} \tag{2.1}$$

Now, since $F(x)$ is a monotone function, it follows that $F^{-1}(U) \leq a$ if and only if $U \leq F(a)$. Hence, from Equation (2.1), we have

$$F_Y(a) = P\{U \leq F(a)\}$$
$$= F(a) \qquad \square$$

It follows from Proposition 2.1 that we can simulate a random variable X having a continuous distribution function F by generating a random number U and then setting $X = F^{-1}(U)$.

Example 2a

Simulating an exponential random variable

If $F(x) = 1 - e^{-x}$, then $F^{-1}(u)$ is that value of x such that

$$1 - e^{-x} = u$$

or

$$x = -\log(1 - u)$$

Hence, if U is a uniform $(0, 1)$ variable, then

$$F^{-1}(U) = -\log(1 - U)$$

is exponentially distributed with mean 1. Since $1 - U$ is also uniformly distributed on $(0, 1)$, it follows that $-\log U$ is exponential with mean 1. Since cX is exponential with mean c when X is exponential with mean 1, it follows that $-c \log U$ is exponential with mean c. ∎

The results of Example 2a can also be utilized to stimulate a gamma random variable.

Example 2b

Simulating a gamma (n, λ) random variable

To simulate from a gamma distribution with parameters (n, λ) when n is an integer, we use the fact that the sum of n independent exponential random variables, each having rate λ, has this distribution. Hence, if $U_1, \ldots, U_n$ are independent uniform $(0, 1)$ random variables, then

$$X = -\sum_{i=1}^{n} \frac{1}{\lambda} \log U_i = -\frac{1}{\lambda} \log \left(\prod_{i=1}^{n} U_i \right)$$

has the desired distribution. ∎

10.2.2 The Rejection Method

Suppose that we have a method for simulating a random variable having density function $g(x)$. We can use this method as the basis for simulating from the continuous distribution having density $f(x)$ by simulating Y from g and then accepting the simulated value with a probability proportional to $f(Y)/g(Y)$.

Specifically, let c be a constant such that

$$\frac{f(y)}{g(y)} \le c \quad \text{for all } y$$

We then have the following technique for simulating a random variable having density f.

Rejection Method

Step 1. Simulate Y having density g and simulate a random number U.
Step 2. If $U \le f(Y)/cg(Y)$, set $X = Y$. Otherwise return to step 1.

The rejection method is expressed pictorially in Figure 10.1. We now prove that it works.

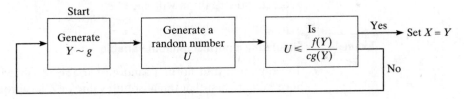

Figure 10.1 Rejection method for simulating a random variable X having density function f.

Proposition 2.2 The random variable X generated by the rejection method has density function f.

Proof Let X be the value obtained and let N denote the number of necessary iterations. Then

$$P\{X \le x\} = P\{Y_N \le x\}$$
$$= P\left\{ Y \le x | U \le \frac{f(Y)}{cg(Y)} \right\}$$
$$= \frac{P\left\{ Y \le x, U \le \frac{f(Y)}{cg(Y)} \right\}}{K}$$

where $K = P\{U \le f(Y)/cg(Y)\}$. Now, by independence, the joint density function of Y and U is

$$f(y, u) = g(y) \quad 0 < u < 1$$

so, using the foregoing, we have

$$P\{X \le x\} = \frac{1}{K} \iint\limits_{\substack{y \le x \\ 0 \le u \le f(y)/cg(y)}} g(y)\, du\, dy$$

$$= \frac{1}{K} \int_{-\infty}^{x} \int_{0}^{f(y)/cg(y)} du\, g(y)\, dy$$

$$= \frac{1}{cK} \int_{-\infty}^{x} f(y)\, dy \tag{2.2}$$

Letting X approach ∞ and using the fact that f is a density gives

$$1 = \frac{1}{cK} \int_{-\infty}^{\infty} f(y)\, dy = \frac{1}{cK}$$

Hence, from Equation (2.2), we obtain

$$P\{X \le x\} = \int_{-\infty}^{x} f(y)\, dy$$

which completes the proof. $\qquad\qquad\square$

Remarks   (a) Note that the way in which we "accept the value Y with probability $f(Y)/cg(Y)$" is by generating a random number U and then accepting Y if $U \le f(Y)/cg(Y)$.

(b) Since each iteration will independently result in an accepted value with probability $P\{U \le f(Y)/cg(Y)\} = K = 1/c$, it follows that the number of iterations has a geometric distribution with mean c. $\qquad\qquad\blacksquare$

Example 2c

Simulating a normal random variable

To simulate a unit normal random variable Z (that is, one with mean 0 and variance 1), note first that the absolute value of Z has probability density function

$$f(x) = \frac{2}{\sqrt{2\pi}} e^{-x^2/2} \quad 0 < x < \infty \tag{2.3}$$

We will start by simulating from the preceding density function by using the rejection method, with g being the exponential density function with mean 1—that is,

$$g(x) = e^{-x} \quad 0 < x < \infty$$

Now, note that

$$\frac{f(x)}{g(x)} = \sqrt{\frac{2}{\pi}} \exp\left\{ \frac{-(x^2 - 2x)}{2} \right\}$$

$$= \sqrt{\frac{2}{\pi}} \exp\left\{ \frac{-(x^2 - 2x + 1)}{2} + \frac{1}{2} \right\}$$

$$= \sqrt{\frac{2e}{\pi}} \exp\left\{ \frac{-(x - 1)^2}{2} \right\} \tag{2.4}$$

$$\le \sqrt{\frac{2e}{\pi}}$$

Hence, we can take $c = \sqrt{2e/\pi}$; so, from Equation (2.4),

$$\frac{f(x)}{cg(x)} = \exp\left\{\frac{-(x-1)^2}{2}\right\}$$

Therefore, using the rejection method, we can simulate the absolute value of a unit normal random variable as follows:

(a) Generate independent random variables Y and U, Y being exponential with rate 1 and U being uniform on $(0, 1)$.

(b) If $U \le \exp\{-(Y-1)^2/2\}$, set $X = Y$. Otherwise, return to (a).

Once we have simulated a random variable X having Equation (2.3) as its density function, we can then generate a unit normal random variable Z by letting Z be equally likely to be either X or $-X$.

In step (b), the value Y is accepted if $U \le \exp\{-(Y-1)^2/2\}$, which is equivalent to $-\log U \ge (Y-1)^2/2$. However, in Example 2a, it was shown that $-\log U$ is exponential with rate 1, so steps (a) and (b) are equivalent to

(a$'$) Generate independent exponentials Y_1 and Y_2, each with rate 1.

(b$'$) If $Y_2 \ge (Y_1 - 1)^2/2$, set $X = Y_1$. Otherwise, return to (a$'$).

Suppose now that the foregoing results in Y_1 being accepted—so we know that Y_2 is larger than $(Y_1 - 1)^2/2$. By how much does the one exceed the other? To answer this question, recall that Y_2 is exponential with rate 1; hence, given that it exceeds some value, the amount by which Y_2 exceeds $(Y_1 - 1)^2/2$ [that is, its "additional life" beyond the time $(Y_1 - 1)^2/2$] is (by the memoryless property) also exponentially distributed with rate 1. That is, when we accept step (b$'$), not only do we obtain X (the absolute value of a unit normal), but, by computing $Y_2 - (Y_1 - 1)^2/2$, we also can generate an exponential random variable (that is independent of X) having rate 1.

Summing up, then, we have the following algorithm that generates an exponential with rate 1 and an independent unit normal random variable:

Step 1. Generate Y_1, an exponential random variable with rate 1.
Step 2. Generate Y_2, an exponential random variable with rate 1.
Step 3. If $Y_2 - (Y_1 - 1)^2/2 > 0$, set $Y = Y_2 - (Y_1 - 1)^2/2$ and go to step 4. Otherwise, go to step 1.
Step 4. Generate a random number U, and set

$$Z = \begin{cases} Y_1 & \text{if } U \le \frac{1}{2} \\ -Y_1 & \text{if } U > \frac{1}{2} \end{cases}$$

The random variables Z and Y generated by the foregoing algorithm are independent, with Z being normal with mean 0 and variance 1 and Y being exponential with rate 1. (If we want the normal random variable to have mean μ and variance σ^2, we just take $\mu + \sigma Z$.)

Remarks (a) Since $c = \sqrt{2e/\pi} \approx 1.32$, the algorithm requires a geometrically distributed number of iterations of step 2 with mean 1.32.

(b) If we want to generate a sequence of unit normal random variables, then we can use the exponential random variable Y obtained in step 3 as the initial exponential needed in step 1 for the next normal to be generated. Hence, on the average, we can simulate a unit normal by generating 1.64($= 2 \times 1.32 - 1$) exponentials and computing 1.32 squares. ∎

Example 2d

Simulating normal random variables: the polar method

It was shown in Example 7b of Chapter 6 that if X and Y are independent unit normal random variables, then their polar coordinates $R = \sqrt{X^2 + Y^2}$, $\Theta = \tan^{-1}(Y/X)$ are independent, with R^2 being exponentially distributed with mean 2 and Θ being uniformly distributed on $(0, 2\pi)$. Hence, if U_1 and U_2 are random numbers, then, using the result of Example 2a, we can set

$$R = (-2 \log U_1)^{1/2}$$
$$\Theta = 2\pi U_2$$

from which it follows that

$$X = R \cos \Theta = (-2 \log U_1)^{1/2} \cos(2\pi U_2)$$
$$Y = R \sin \Theta = (-2 \log U_1)^{1/2} \sin(2\pi U_2) \qquad (2.5)$$

are independent unit normals. ■

The preceding approach to generating unit normal random variables is called the *Box–Muller approach*. Its efficiency suffers somewhat from its need to compute the sine and cosine values. There is, however, a way to get around this potentially time-consuming difficulty. To begin, note that if U is uniform on $(0, 1)$, then $2U$ is uniform on $(0, 2)$, so $2U - 1$ is uniform on $(-1, 1)$. Thus, if we generate random numbers U_1 and U_2 and set

$$V_1 = 2U_1 - 1$$
$$V_2 = 2U_2 - 1$$

then (V_1, V_2) is uniformly distributed in the square of area 4 centered at $(0, 0)$. (See Figure 10.2.)

Suppose now that we continually generate such pairs (V_1, V_2) until we obtain one that is contained in the disk of radius 1 centered at $(0, 0)$—that is, until $V_1^2 + V_2^2 \leq 1$. It then follows that such a pair (V_1, V_2) is uniformly distributed in the disk.

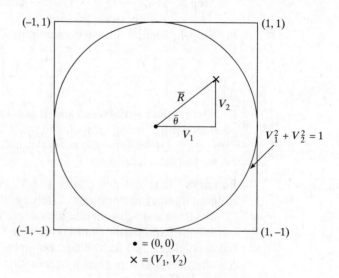

$\bullet = (0, 0)$
$\times = (V_1, V_2)$

Figure 10.2

Now, let $\overline{R}, \overline{\Theta}$ denote the polar coordinates of this pair. Then it is easy to verify that $\overline{R}$ and $\overline{\Theta}$ are independent, with $\overline{R}^2$ being uniformly distributed on $(0, 1)$ and $\overline{\Theta}$ being uniformly distributed on $(0, 2\pi)$. (See Problem 10.13.)
Since

$$\sin\overline{\Theta} = \frac{V_2}{\overline{R}} = \frac{V_2}{\sqrt{V_1^2 + V_2^2}}$$

$$\cos\overline{\Theta} = \frac{V_1}{\overline{R}} = \frac{V_1}{\sqrt{V_1^2 + V_2^2}}$$

it follows from Equation (2.5) that we can generate independent unit normals X and Y by generating another random number U and setting

$$X = (-2\log U)^{1/2} V_1/\overline{R}$$
$$Y = (-2\log U)^{1/2} V_2/\overline{R}$$

In fact, because (conditional on $V_1^2 + V_2^2 \leq 1$) $\overline{R}^2$ is uniform on $(0, 1)$ and is independent of $\overline{\theta}$, we can use it instead of generating a new random number U, thus showing that

$$X = (-2\log \overline{R}^2)^{1/2}\frac{V_1}{\overline{R}} = \sqrt{\frac{-2\log S}{S}}V_1$$

$$Y = (-2\log \overline{R}^2)^{1/2}\frac{V_2}{\overline{R}} = \sqrt{\frac{-2\log S}{S}}V_2$$

are independent unit normals, where

$$S = \overline{R}^2 = V_1^2 + V_2^2$$

Summing up, we have the following approach to generating a pair of independent unit normals:

Step 1. Generate random numbers U_1 and U_2.
Step 2. Set $V_1 = 2U_1 - 1, V_2 = 2U_2 - 1, S = V_1^2 + V_2^2$.
Step 3. If $S > 1$, return to step 1.
Step 4. Return the independent unit normals

$$X = \sqrt{\frac{-2\log S}{S}}V_1, Y = \sqrt{\frac{-2\log S}{S}}V_2$$

The preceding algorithm is called the *polar method*. Since the probability that a random point in the square will fall within the circle is equal to $\pi/4$ (the area of the circle divided by the area of the square), it follows that, on average, the polar method will require $4/\pi \approx 1.273$ iterations of step 1. Hence, it will, on average, require 2.546 random numbers, 1 logarithm, 1 square root, 1 division, and 4.546 multiplications to generate 2 independent unit normals.

Example 2e

Simulating a chi-squared random variable

The chi-squared distribution with n degrees of freedom is the distribution of $\chi_n^2 = Z_1^2 + \cdots + Z_n^2$, where $Z_i, i = 1, \ldots, n$ are independent unit normals. Now, it was shown in Section 6.3 of Chapter 6 that $Z_1^2 + Z_2^2$ has an exponential distribution with rate $\frac{1}{2}$. Hence, when n is even (say, $n = 2k$), χ_{2k}^2 has a gamma distribution with parameters $\left(k, \frac{1}{2}\right)$. Thus, $-2\log(\prod_{i=1}^{k} U_i)$ has a chi-squared distribution with $2k$ degrees of freedom. Accordingly, we can simulate a chi-squared random variable with $2k + 1$ degrees of freedom by first simulating a unit normal random variable Z and then adding Z^2 to the foregoing. That is,

$$\chi^2_{2k+1} = Z^2 - 2\log\left(\prod_{i=1}^{k} U_i\right)$$

where $Z, U_1, \ldots, U_n$ are independent, Z is a unit normal, and $U_1, \ldots, U_n$ are uniform $(0, 1)$ random variables.

10.3 Simulating from Discrete Distributions

All of the general methods for simulating random variables from continuous distributions have analogs in the discrete case. For instance, if we want to simulate a random variable Z having probability mass function

$$P\{X = x_j\} = P_j, \quad j = 0, 1, \ldots, \quad \sum_j P_j = 1$$

we can use the following discrete time analog of the inverse transform technique:

To simulate X for which $P\{X = x_j\} = P_j$, let U be uniformly distributed over $(0, 1)$ and set

$$X = \begin{cases} x_1 & \text{if } U \le P_1 \\ x_2 & \text{if } P_1 < U \le P_1 + P_2 \\ \vdots \\ x_j & \text{if } \sum_{1}^{j-1} P_i < U \le \sum_{i}^{j} P_i \\ \vdots \end{cases}$$

Since

$$P\{X = x_j\} = P\left\{\sum_{1}^{j-1} P_i < U \le \sum_{1}^{j} P_i\right\} = P_j$$

it follows that X has the desired distribution.

Example 3a

The geometric distribution

Suppose that independent trials, each of which results in a "success" with probability $p, 0 < p < 1$, are continually performed until a success occurs. Letting X denote the necessary number of trials; then

$$P\{X = i\} = (1 - p)^{i-1} p \quad i \ge 1$$

which is seen by noting that $X = i$ if the first $i - 1$ trials are all failures and the ith trial is a success. The random variable X is said to be a *geometric random variable with parameter p*. Since

$$\sum_{i=1}^{j-1} P\{X = i\} = 1 - P\{X > j - 1\}$$

$$= 1 - P\{\text{first } j - 1 \text{ are all failures}\}$$

$$= 1 - (1 - p)^{j-1} \quad j \geq 1$$

we can simulate such a random variable by generating a random number U and then setting X equal to that value j for which

$$1 - (1 - p)^{j-1} < U \leq 1 - (1 - p)^{j}$$

or, equivalently, for which

$$(1 - p)^{j} \leq 1 - U < (1 - p)^{j-1}$$

Since $1 - U$ has the same distribution as U, we can define X by

$$X = \min\{j : (1 - p)^{j} \leq U\}$$

$$= \min\{j : j \log(1 - p) \leq \log U\}$$

$$= \min\left\{j : j \geq \frac{\log U}{\log(1 - p)}\right\}$$

where the inequality has changed sign because $\log(1-p)$ is negative [since $\log(1-p) > \log 1 = 0$]. Using the notation $[x]$ for the integer part of x (that is, $[x]$ is the largest integer less than or equal to x), we can write

$$X = 1 + \left[\frac{\log U}{\log(1 - p)}\right] \qquad \blacksquare$$

As in the continuous case, special simulating techniques have been developed for the more common discrete distributions. We now present two of these.

Example 3b

Simulating a binomial random variable

A binomial (n, p) random variable can easily be simulated by recalling that it can be expressed as the sum of n independent Bernoulli random variables. That is, if $U_1, \ldots, U_n$ are independent uniform $(0, 1)$ variables, then letting

$$X_i = \begin{cases} 1 & \text{if } U_i < p \\ 0 & \text{otherwise} \end{cases}$$

it follows that $X \equiv \sum_{i=1}^{n} X_i$ is a binomial random variable with parameters n and p.

Example 3c

Simulating a Poisson random variable

To simulate a Poisson random variable with mean λ, generate independent uniform $(0, 1)$ random variables $U_1, U_2, \ldots$ stopping at

$$N = \min\left\{n : \prod_{i=1}^{n} U_i < e^{-\lambda}\right\}$$

The random variable $X \equiv N - 1$ has the desired distribution. That is, if we continue generating random numbers until their product falls below $e^{-\lambda}$, then the number required, minus 1, is Poisson with mean λ.

That $X \equiv N - 1$ is indeed a Poisson random variable having mean λ can perhaps be most easily seen by noting that

$$X + 1 = \min \left\{ n: \prod_{i=1}^{n} U_i < e^{-\lambda} \right\}$$

is equivalent to

$$X = \max \left\{ n: \prod_{i=1}^{n} U_i \geq e^{-\lambda} \right\} \quad \text{where} \quad \prod_{i=1}^{0} U_i \equiv 1$$

or, taking logarithms, to

$$X = \max \left\{ n: \sum_{i=1}^{n} \log U_i \geq -\lambda \right\}$$

or

$$X = \max \left\{ n: \sum_{i=1}^{n} -\log U_i \leq \lambda \right\}$$

However, $-\log U_i$ is exponential with rate 1, so X can be thought of as being the maximum number of exponentials having rate 1 that can be summed and still be less than λ. But by recalling that the times between successive events of a Poisson process having rate 1 are independent exponentials with rate 1, it follows that X is equal to the number of events by time λ of a Poisson process having rate 1; thus, X has a Poisson distribution with mean λ. ∎

10.4 Variance Reduction Techniques

Let $X_1, \ldots, X_n$ have a given joint distribution, and suppose that we are interested in computing

$$\theta \equiv E[g(X_1, \ldots, X_n)]$$

where g is some specified function. It sometimes turns out that it is extremely difficult to analytically compute θ, and when such is the case, we can attempt to use simulation to estimate θ. This is done as follows: Generate $X_1^{(1)}, \ldots, X_n^{(1)}$ having the same joint distribution as $X_1, \ldots, X_n$ and set

$$Y_1 = g(X_1^{(1)}, \ldots, X_n^{(1)})$$

Now let $X_1^{(2)}, \ldots, X_n^{(2)}$ simulate a second set of random variables (independent of the first set) having the distribution of $X_1, \ldots, X_n$ and set

$$Y_2 = g(X_1^{(2)}, \ldots, X_n^{(2)})$$

Continue this until you have generated k (some predetermined number) sets and so have also computed $Y_1, Y_2, \ldots, Y_k$. Now, $Y_1, \ldots, Y_k$ are independent and identically distributed random variables, each having the same distribution as $g(X_1, \ldots, X_n)$. Thus, if we let $\overline{Y}$ denote the average of these k random variables—that is, if

$$\overline{Y} = \sum_{i=1}^{k} \frac{Y_i}{k}$$

then

$$E[\overline{Y}] = \theta$$
$$E[(\overline{Y} - \theta)^2] = \text{Var}(\overline{Y})$$

Hence, we can use $\overline{Y}$ as an estimate of θ. Since the expected square of the difference between $\overline{Y}$ and θ is equal to the variance of $\overline{Y}$, we would like this quantity to be as small as possible. [In the preceding situation, $\text{Var}(\overline{Y}) = \text{Var}(Y_i)/k$, which is usually not known in advance, but must be estimated from the generated values $Y_1, \ldots, Y_n$.] We now present three general techniques for reducing the variance of our estimator.

10.4.1   Use of Antithetic Variables

In the foregoing situation, suppose that we have generated Y_1 and Y_2, which are identically distributed random variables having mean θ. Now,

$$\text{Var}\left(\frac{Y_1 + Y_2}{2}\right) = \frac{1}{4}[\text{Var}(Y_1) + \text{Var}(Y_2) + 2\text{Cov}(Y_1, Y_2)]$$
$$= \frac{\text{Var}(Y_1)}{2} + \frac{\text{Cov}(Y_1, Y_2)}{2}$$

Hence, it would be advantageous (in the sense that the variance would be reduced) if Y_1 and Y_2 were negatively correlated rather than being independent. To see how we could arrange this, let us suppose that the random variables $X_1, \ldots, X_n$ are independent and, in addition, that each is simulated via the inverse transform technique. That is, X_i is simulated from $F_i^{-1}(U_i)$, where U_i is a random number and F_i is the distribution of X_i. Thus, Y_1 can be expressed as

$$Y_1 = g(F_1^{-1}(U_1), \ldots, F_n^{-1}(U_n))$$

Now, since $1 - U$ is also uniform over $(0, 1)$ whenever U is a random number (and is negatively correlated with U), it follows that Y_2 defined by

$$Y_2 = g(F_1^{-1}(1 - U_1), \ldots, F_n^{-1}(1 - U_n))$$

will have the same distribution as Y_1. Hence, if Y_1 and Y_2 were negatively correlated, then generating Y_2 by this means would lead to a smaller variance than if it were generated by a new set of random numbers. (In addition, there is a computational savings because, rather than having to generate n additional random numbers, we need only subtract each of the previous n numbers from 1.) Although we cannot, in general, be certain that Y_1 and Y_2 will be negatively correlated, this often turns out to be the case, and indeed it can be proven that it will be so whenever g is a monotonic function.

10.4.2 Variance Reduction by Conditioning

Let us start by recalling the conditional variance formula (see Section 7.5.4)

$$\text{Var}(Y) = E[\text{Var}(Y|Z)] + \text{Var}(E[Y|Z])$$

Now, suppose that we are interested in estimating $E[g(X_1, \ldots, X_n)]$ by simulating $\mathbf{X} = (X_1, \ldots, X_n)$ and then computing $Y = g(\mathbf{X})$. If, for some random variable Z we can compute $E[Y|Z]$, then, since $\text{Var}(Y|Z) \geq 0$, it follows from the preceding conditional variance formula that

$$\text{Var}(E[Y|Z]) \leq \text{Var}(Y)$$

Thus, since $E[E[Y|Z]] = E[Y]$, it follows that $E[Y|Z]$ is a better estimator of $E[Y]$ than is Y.

Example 4a

Estimation of π

Let U_1 and U_2 be random numbers and set $V_i = 2U_i - 1, i = 1, 2$. As noted in Example 2d, (V_1, V_2) will be uniformly distributed in the square of area 4 centered at $(0, 0)$. The probability that this point will fall within the inscribed circle of radius 1 centered at $(0, 0)$ (see Figure 10.2) is equal to $\pi/4$ (the ratio of the area of the circle to that of the square). Hence, upon simulating a large number n of such pairs and setting

$$I_j = \begin{cases} 1 & \text{if the } j\text{th pair falls within the circle} \\ 0 & \text{otherwise} \end{cases}$$

it follows that $I_j, j = 1, \ldots, n$, will be independent and identically distributed random variables having $E[I_j] = \pi/4$. Thus, by the strong law of large numbers,

$$\frac{I_1 + \cdots + I_n}{n} \to \frac{\pi}{4} \quad \text{as } n \to \infty$$

Therefore, by simulating a large number of pairs (V_1, V_2) and multiplying the proportion of them that fall within the circle by 4, we can accurately approximate π.

The preceding estimator can, however, be improved upon by using conditional expectation. If we let I be the indicator variable for the pair (V_1, V_2), then, rather than using the observed value of I, it is better to condition on V_1 and so utilize

$$\begin{aligned} E[I|V_1] &= P\{V_1^2 + V_2^2 \leq 1 | V_1\} \\ &= P\{V_2^2 \leq 1 - V_1^2 | V_1\} \end{aligned}$$

Now,

$$\begin{aligned} P\{V_2^2 \leq 1 - V_1^2 | V_1 = v\} &= P\{V_2^2 \leq 1 - v^2\} \\ &= P\{-\sqrt{1 - v^2} \leq V_2 \leq \sqrt{1 - v^2}\} \\ &= \sqrt{1 - v^2} \end{aligned}$$

so

$$E[I|V_1] = \sqrt{1 - V_1^2}$$

Thus, an improvement on using the average value of I to estimate $\pi/4$ is to use the average value of $\sqrt{1 - V_1^2}$. Indeed, since

$$E\left[\sqrt{1 - V_1^2}\right] = \int_{-1}^{1} \frac{1}{2}\sqrt{1 - v^2}dv = \int_{0}^{1} \sqrt{1 - u^2}du = E\left[\sqrt{1 - U^2}\right]$$

where U is uniform over $(0, 1)$, we can generate n random numbers U and use the average value of $\sqrt{1 - U^2}$ as our estimate of $\pi/4$. (Problem 10.14 shows that this estimator has the same variance as the average of the n values, $\sqrt{1 - V^2}$.)

The preceding estimator of π can be improved even further by noting that the function $g(u) = \sqrt{1 - u^2}, 0 \le u \le 1$, is a monotonically decreasing function of u, and so the method of antithetic variables will reduce the variance of the estimator of $E[\sqrt{1 - U^2}]$. That is, rather than generating n random numbers and using the average value of $\sqrt{1 - U^2}$ as an estimator of $\pi/4$, we would obtain an improved estimator by generating only $n/2$ random numbers U and then using one-half the average of $\sqrt{1 - U^2} + \sqrt{1 - (1 - U)^2}$ as the estimator of $\pi/4$.

The following table gives the estimates of π resulting from simulations, using $n = 10,000$, based on the three estimators.

Method	Estimate of π
Proportion of the random points that fall in the circle	3.1612
Average value of $\sqrt{1 - U^2}$	3.128448
Average value of $\sqrt{1 - U^2} + \sqrt{1 - (1 - U)^2}$	3.139578

A further simulation using the final approach and $n = 64,000$ yielded the estimate 3.143288. ∎

10.4.3 Control Variates

Again, suppose that we want to use simulation to estimate $E[g(\mathbf{X})]$, where $\mathbf{X} = (X_1, \ldots, X_n)$. But suppose now that for some function f, the expected value of $f(\mathbf{X})$ is known—say, it is $E[f(\mathbf{X})] = \mu$. Then, for any constant a, we can also use

$$W = g(\mathbf{X}) + a[f(\mathbf{X}) - \mu]$$

as an estimator of $E[g(\mathbf{X})]$. Now,

$$\text{Var}(W) = \text{Var}[g(\mathbf{X})] + a^2\text{Var}[f(\mathbf{X})] + 2a\,\text{Cov}[g(\mathbf{X}), f(\mathbf{X})] \tag{4.1}$$

Simple calculus shows that the foregoing is minimized when

$$a = \frac{-\text{Cov}[f(\mathbf{X}), g(\mathbf{X})]}{\text{Var}[f(\mathbf{X})]} \tag{4.2}$$

and for this value of a,

$$\text{Var}(W) = \text{Var}[g(\mathbf{X})] - \frac{\text{Cov}[f(\mathbf{X}), g(\mathbf{X})]^2}{\text{Var}[f(\mathbf{X})]} \tag{4.3}$$

Unfortunately, neither $\text{Var}[f(\mathbf{X})]$ nor $\text{Cov}[f(\mathbf{X})], g(\mathbf{X})]$ is usually known, so we cannot in general obtain the foregoing reduction in variance. One approach in practice is to use the simulated data to estimate these quantities. This approach usually yields almost all of the theoretically possible reduction in variance.

Summary

Let F be a continuous distribution function and U a uniform $(0, 1)$ random variable. Then the random variable $F^{-1}(U)$ has distribution function F, where $F^{-1}(u)$ is that value x such that $F(x) = u$. Applying this result, we can use the values of uniform $(0, 1)$ random variables, called *random numbers*, to generate the values of other random variables. This technique is called the *inverse transform* method.

Another technique for generating random variables is based on the *rejection* method. Suppose that we have an efficient procedure for generating a random variable from the density function g and that we desire to generate a random variable having density function f. The rejection method for accomplishing this starts by determining a constant c such that

$$\max \frac{f(x)}{g(x)} \le c$$

It then proceeds as follows:

1. Generate Y having density g.
2. Generate a random number U.

3. If $U \le f(Y)/cg(Y)$, set $X = Y$ and stop.
4. Return to step 1.

The number of passes through step 1 is a geometric random variable with mean c.

Standard normal random variables can be efficiently simulated by the rejection method (with g being exponential with mean 1) or by the technique known as the *polar algorithm*.

To estimate a quantity θ, one often generates the values of a partial sequence of random variables whose expected value is θ. The efficiency of this approach is increased when these random variables have a small variance. Three techniques that can often be used to specify random variables with mean θ and relatively small variances are

1. the use of antithetic variables,
2. the use of conditional expectations, and
3. the use of control variates.

Problems

10.1. The following algorithm will generate a random permutation of the elements $1, 2, \ldots, n$. It is somewhat faster than the one presented in Example 1a but is such that no position is fixed until the algorithm ends. In this algorithm, $P(i)$ can be interpreted as the element in position i.

Step 1. Set $k = 1$.
Step 2. Set $P(1) = 1$.
Step 3. If $k = n$, stop. Otherwise, let $k = k + 1$.
Step 4. Generate a random number U and let

$$P(k) = P([kU] + 1)$$
$$P([kU] + 1) = k$$

Go to step 3.
(a) Explain in words what the algorithm is doing.
(b) Show that at iteration k—that is, when the value of $P(k)$ is initially set—$P(1), P(2), \ldots, P(k)$ is a random permutation of $1, 2, \ldots, k$.
Hint: Use induction and argue that

$$P_k\{i_1, i_2, \ldots, i_{j-1}, k, i_j, \ldots, i_{k-2}, i\}$$
$$= P_{k-1}\{i_1, i_2, \ldots, i_{j-1}, i, i_j, \ldots, i_{k-2}\}\frac{1}{k}$$
$$= \frac{1}{k!} \text{ by the induction hypothesis}$$

10.2. Develop a technique for simulating a random variable having density function

$$f(x) = \begin{cases} \dfrac{1}{2} e^x, & -\infty < x < 0 \\ \dfrac{1}{2} e^{-x}, & 0 < x < \infty \end{cases}$$

10.3. Give a technique for simulating a random variable having the probability density function

$$f(x) = \begin{cases} x, & 0 \le x < 1 \\ (2 - x), & 1 \le x \le 2 \\ 0, & \text{otherwise} \end{cases}$$

10.4. Present a method for simulating a random variable having distribution function

$$F(x) = \begin{cases} 0, & x < 1 \\ \dfrac{x}{2}, & 1 \le x < 2 \\ 1, & x \ge 2 \end{cases}$$

10.5. Use the inverse transformation method to present an approach for generating a random variable from the Weibull distribution

$$F(t) = 1 - e^{-at^\beta} \quad t \geq 0$$

10.6. Give a method for simulating a random variable having failure rate function

(a) $\lambda(t) = c$;

(b) $\lambda(t) = ct$;

(c) $\lambda(t) = ct^2$;

(d) $\lambda(t) = ct^3$.

10.7. Let F be the distribution function

$$F(x) = x^n \quad 0 < x < 1$$

(a) Give a method for simulating a random variable having distribution F that uses only a single random number.

(b) Let $U_1, \ldots, U_n$ be independent random numbers. Show that

$$P\{\max(U_1, \ldots, U_n) \leq x\} = x^n$$

(c) Use part (b) to give a second method of simulating a random variable having distribution F.

10.8. Suppose it is relatively easy to simulate from F_i for each $i = 1, \ldots, n$. How can we simulate from

(a) $F(x) = \prod_{i=1}^{n} F_i(x)$?

(b) $F(x) = 1 - \prod_{i=1}^{n} [1 - F_i(x)]$?

10.9. Suppose we have a method for simulating random variables from the distributions F_1 and F_2. Explain how to simulate from the distribution

$$F(x) = pF_1(x) + (1 - p)F_2(x) \quad 0 < p < 1$$

Give a method for simulating from

$$F(x) = \begin{cases} \frac{1}{3}(1 - e^{-3x}) + \frac{2}{3}x & 0 < x \leq 1 \\ \frac{1}{3}(1 - e^{-3x}) + \frac{2}{3} & x > 1 \end{cases}$$

10.10. Find an algorithm for simulating discrete Weibull with distribution function $F(x) = 1 - q^{(x+1)^\beta}$, $x = 0, 1, \ldots$, and $0 < q$, $\beta < 1$.

10.11. Use rejection method to determine an algorithm for simulating a random variable having density function

$$f(x) = 6x(1 - x), 0 < x < 1$$

Hint: Take $g(x) = 1, 0 < x, 1$.

10.12. Explain how you could use random numbers to approximate $\int_0^\infty k(x)\, dx$ provided the integral exist, where $k(x)$ is an arbitrary function.

Hint: If X is exponential random variable with mean 1, what is $E[k(X)e^x]$

10.13. Let (X, Y) be uniformly distributed in the circle of radius 1 centered at the origin. Its joint density is thus

$$f(x, y) = \frac{1}{\pi} \quad 0 \leq x^2 + y^2 \leq 1$$

Let $R = (X^2 + Y^2)^{1/2}$ and $\theta = \tan^{-1}(Y/X)$ denote the polar coordinates of (X, Y). Show that R and θ are independent, with R^2 being uniform on $(0, 1)$ and θ being uniform on $(0, 2\pi)$.

10.14. In Example 4a, we showed that

$$E[(1 - V^2)^{1/2}] = E[(1 - U^2)^{1/2}] = \frac{\pi}{4}$$

when V is uniform $(-1, 1)$ and U is uniform $(0, 1)$. Now show that

$$\text{Var}[(1 - V^2)^{1/2}] = \text{Var}[(1 - U^2)^{1/2}]$$

and find their common value.

10.15. (a) Verify that the minimum of (4.1) occurs when a is as given by (4.2).

(b) Verify that the minimum of (4.1) is given by (4.3).

10.16. Let X be a random variable on $(0, 1)$ whose density is $f(x)$. Show that we can estimate $\int_0^1 g(x)\, dx$ by simulating X and then taking $g(X)/f(X)$ as our estimate. This method, called *importance sampling*, tries to choose f similar in shape to g, so that $g(X)/f(X)$ has a small variance.

Self-Test Problems and Exercises

10.1. Let X be a discrete random variable with probability mass function $f(x) = P(X = x)$ and V is a uniformly distributed random variable on $(0, 1)$ and independent of X. Define a quantity

$$F(x, v) = P(X < x) + Vf(x)$$

Prove that $F(x, v)$ is distributed as uniform random variable on $(0, 1)$.

10.2. Give an approach for simulating a random variable having probability density function

$$f(x) = 30(x^2 - 2x^3 + x^4) \quad 0 < x < 1$$

10.3. Give an efficient algorithm to simulate the value of a random variable X represents

(a) The number of heads when an unbiased coin tosses two times.

(b) The face appeared when an unbiased die is rolled once.

10.4. Denote $F(x)$ as the distribution function of a discrete random variable. Using the result stated in Problem 10.1 fnd $E(F(X))$. Verify the result when X is a geometric random random variable specified by

$$f(x) = p(1-p)^x, 0 < p < 1, x = 0, 1, \ldots,.$$

10.5. Let X and Y be independent exponential random variables with mean 1.

(a) Explain how we could use simulation to estimate $E[e^{XY}]$.

(b) Show how to improve the estimation approach in part (a) by using a control variate.

Reference

[1] Ross, S. M. *Simulation*. 5th ed. San Diego: Academic Press, Inc., 2012.

ANSWERS TO SELECTED PROBLEMS

Chapter 1

1. (a) $6^4 = 12096$; (b) $\binom{6}{4} = 15$ **2.** 1296 **4.** 24; 4
5. 60 minutes **6.** 2401 **7.** 720; 72; 144; 72 **8.** (a) 120 (b) 60 (c) 30240 **9.** 27,720 **10.** 40,320; 10,080; 1152; 2880; 384 **11.** 720; 72; 144 **12.** 24,300,000; 17,100,720 **13.** 190 **14.** 2^{16} **16.** 7350 **17.** 604,800 **18.** 92378 **19.** 896; 1000; 910 **20.** 36; 26 **21.** 35 **22.** 18 **23.** 48 **24.** $16x^{16} + 4x^{12}y + 6x^8y^2 + 4x^4y^3 + y^4$ **25.** (a) 56 (b) 52 **27.** 1260 **28.** 65,536; 2520 **29.** 21 ways **30.** 8!, $4 \times 6!$ **31.** 165; 35 **32.** 1287; 14,112 **33.** 220; 572

Chapter 2

4. (a) 1/4 (b) 1/4 (c) 2/5 **7.** $6^{10} - 3^{10}$ **8.** 14/15 **9.** 74 **10.** .4; .1 **11.** 70; 2 **12.** .5; .32; 149/198 **13.** 20,000; 12,000; 11,00; 68,000; 10,000 **14.** 1.057 **15.** .0020; .4226; .0475; .0211; .00024 **17.** 9.10947×10^{-6} **18.** $\dfrac{6283420}{20358520}$
19. $2^{10}(10!)^2 / 20!$ **20.** .9052 **22.** $(n+1)/2^n$ **23.** 1/12 **24.** 1/2 and 1/2 **25.** .4 **26.** .492929 **27.** 8/9 **28.** .0888; .2477; .1243; .2099 **30.** 1/18; 1/6; 1/2 **31.** 2/9; 1/9 **33.** 70/323 **34.** 1001; 120; 495 **35.** (a) 0.0274 (b) 0.06923 (c) 0.9 (d) 0.28296 **36.** 55/221 **37.** .0833; .5 **38.** 4 **39.** 2/8 **40.** $P(1) = 3/27, P(2) = 18/27, P(3) = 6/27$ **41.** .5177 **44.** .3; .2; .1 **46.** 5 **47.** 1/6 **48.** .01697 **49.** .4329
50. $\dfrac{\binom{N-3}{r-1}}{\binom{N-1}{r-1}}$ **52.** 3/8 **53.** 12/35 **54.** 1/6 **55.** 4/7

Chapter 3

1. 1/3 **2.** 0.8 **3.** (a) 1/3 (b) yes **5.** 6/91 **6.** 1/2 **7.** 2/3 **8.** 1/51 **9.** 7/11 **10.** .22 **11.** 1/17; 1/33 **12.** .504; .3629 **14.** 2197/20825 **15.** 38/47 **16.** (a) $1 - 12^3/13^3$, (b) 3/13 **17.** 0.148 **18.** .331; .383; .286; .4862 **19.** (a) 0.90476; (b) 0.94117 **20.** 16/17 **21.** .496; 3/14; 9/62 **22.** 5/9; 1/6; 5/54 **23.** 0.66, 0.47 **24.** 2/3 **26.** (a) 2/3, (b) yes no **27.** (a) 4/7 (b) 3/7 **28.** 3/128; 29/1536 **29.** 1/6 **30.** 1/3 **33.** 1/10 **34.** 0.1 **35.** .62, 10/19 **36.** (a) 2/3, b)1/2 no **37.** 1/3; 1/5; 1 **38.** 12/37 **39.** 46/185 **40.** 3/13; 5/13; 5/52; 15/52 **41.** 43/459 **42.** 1.03 percent; .3046 **43.** 6/17 **44.** 0.432 **45.** 1/11 **48.** (a) 4/27, (b) 95/601 **50.** .175; 38/165; 17/33 **51.** (a) 13/36, (b) 9/13, (c) 89/156 **52.** .11; 16/89; 12/27; 3/5; 9/25 **55.** 25 **57.** (a) 0.25, (b) 0.75764 **60.** 2/3; 1/3; 3/4
61. 1/6; 3/20 **65.** (a) 15/36 **68.** $(1/4)^n \sum_{i=0}^{n} \binom{2n}{i}$ **69.** 9; 9; 18; 110; 4; 4; 8; 120 all over 128 **70.** 1/9; 1/18 **71.** 38/64; 13/64 **73.** 1/16; 1/32; 5/16; 1/4; 31/32 **74.** 2/3 **75.** 3/4, 7/12 **78.** $2p^3(1-p) + 2p(1-p)^3$; $p^2/(1-2p+2p^2)$ **79.** 23/24 **81.** .9530 **83.** .5; .6; .8 **84.** 1/2 and 2/3 **85.** C is correct **87.** 9/16 **90.** 97/142; 15/26; 33/102

Chapter 4

1. $p(4) = 6/91; p(2) = 8/91; p(1) = 32/91; p(0) = 1/91; p(-1) = 16/91; p(-2) = 28/91$ **2.** (a) $P(X=0) = 6/36, P(X=1) = 10/36, P(X=2) = 8/36, P(X=3) = 6/36, P(X=4) = 4/36, P(X=5) = 2/36$; **4.** (a) $P(X=0) = 1/32, P(X=1) = 5/32, P(X=2) = 10/32, P(X=3) = 10/32, P(X=4) = 5/32, P(X=5) = 1/32$; **5.** $n - 2i; i = 0, ..., n$ **6.** $p(3) = p(-3) = 1/8; p(1) = p(-1) = 3/8$ **12.** $p(4) = 1/16; p(3) = 1/8; p(2) = 1/16; p(0) = 1/2; p(-i) = p(i); p(0) = 1$ **13.** 450, 104.4 **14.** $p(0) = 1/2; p(1) = 1/6; p(2) = 1/12; p(3) = 1/20; p(4) = 1/5$

17. $f(x) = \begin{cases} 1/12, & x=1 \\ 1/4, & x=2 \\ 1/6, & x=3 \\ 1/2, & x=4 \end{cases}$ 18. $F(x) = \begin{cases} & 0 < x, \\ & 0 <= x < 1, \\ & 1 <= x < 2, \\ & 2 <= x < 3, \\ & x >= 3 \end{cases}$

$F(x) = \begin{cases} 1/8, & x=0 \\ 3/8, & x=1 \\ 3/8, & x=2 \\ 1/8, & x=3 \\ 1, & \text{otherwise} \end{cases}$ **19.** 1/2; 1/10; 1/5; 1/10; 1/10 **20.** (a) $P(X=0) = 42/90, P(X=1) = 42/90, P(X=2) = 6/90$ (b) $E(X) = 54/90$ (c) $E(Y) = -54/90$ **21.** Same Expectations, $E(X) = E(Y) = 1$ **24.** $p = 11/18$; maximum $= 23/72$ **25.** (a) 0.2824 (b) 0.3724 (c) 1.2 **26.** 11/2; 17/5 **27.** Not Fair, $E(X) = -1/3$ **28.** -19/6 **31.** p^* **32.** $11 - 10(.9)^{10}$ **33.** 2 Cakes, Expected Max Profit $= 40$ **35.** -.067; 1.089 **37.** 82.2; 84.5 **38.** $E(X) = 10, \text{Var}(X) = 25$ **39.** 3/8 **40.** 0.61722 **41.** 0.1296 **42.** 0.0463 **43.** 0.200658 **45.** 3 **50.** 1/10; 1/10 **51.** 0.35041 **53.** $1 - e^{-.6}$; $1 - e^{-219.18}$ **56.** 253 **57.** .5768; .6070 **59.** (a) 0.95021 (b) 0.39207 **60.** 0.3235 **61.** $1 - 0.0083ne^{-0.0083n} - e^{-0.0083n}$ **63.** (a) 0.71653 (b) 0.0398 **64.** 0.18474 **65.** .3935; .2293; .3935 **66.** $2/(2n-1)$; $2/(2n-2)$; e^{-1} **67.** $2/n$; $(2n-3)/(n-1)^2$; e^{-2} **68.** e^{-10e-5} **70.** $p + (1-p)e^{-\lambda t}$ **71.** (a) 0.001 (b) 0.09 (c) 9 **73.** 9 **74.** 32/243; 4864/6561; 160/729; 160/729 **75.** 0.1285 **78.** 0.1479 **79.** (a) 0.779 b) 0.9999 **81.** 3/10; 5/6; 75/138 **82.** .3439 **83.** $E(X) = 14,000 \text{ Var}(X) = 16,000$

Chapter 5

1. $c = 12/7$, $F(x) = \begin{cases} 0, & x \le 0 \\ \frac{12}{7}x^2(1-x), & 0 < x < 1 \\ 1, & x \ge 1 \end{cases}$ 2. $3.5e^{-5/2}$
3. no; no **4.** (a) 1/16; (b) 7/16; (c)1 **5.** $1 - (.01)^{1/5}$ **6.** $4, 0, \infty$ **7.** $u = 2\ v = 3$ **8.** 2 **10.** 2/3; 2/3 **11.** 2/5 **13.** (a) 0.3 (b) 0.6 **15.** .7977; .6827; .3695; .9522; .1587 **16.** $(.9938)^{10}$ **17.** .315; .136 **18.** 22.66 **19.** $a = 96.08, b = 103.92$ **20.** 665 **21.** 15.8655 **22.** .974 **23.** .9253; .1767 **26.** 0.0729 **27.** 0.31561 **28.** 0.5596 **29.** .9993 **32.** (a) $1 - e^{-0.5}$; (b) 0.2 $e^{-0.5}$ **33.** 1.05 **34.** $e^{-1}; 1/3$ **36.** (a) $1 - e^{-1}$; (b) $e^{-1} - e^{-2}$; (c) e^{-1} **38.** 3/5 **40.** Weibull (2, 1)

Chapter 6

1. (a)

	$X = 0$	$X = 1$	$X = 2$
$Y = 0$	10/66	15/66	3/66
$Y = 1$	20/66	12/66	0
$Y = 2$	6/66	0	0

(b)

	$X = 0$	$X = 1$	$X = 2$
$Y = 0$	6/66	12/66	3/66
$Y = 1$	20/66	10/66	0
$Y = 2$	15/66	0	0

(c)

	$X = 0$	$X = 1$
$Y = 0$	6/66	15/66
$Y = 1$	30/66	15/66

2. (a) 14/39; 10/39; 10/39;
5/39 (b) 84; 70; 70; 70; 40; 40; 40; 15 all divided by 429
3. 15/26; 5/26; 5/26; 1/26   **4.** (a) 64/169; 40/169; 40/169;
25/169; 64/169 **7.** $p(i,j) = p^2(1-p)^{i+j}$ **8.** $c=1/8$; $E[X]=0$
9. (a) Yes (b) $(5/6)(x + 1/3)$ (c) $(5/6)(1/2 + y^2)$ (d) 3/7 (e) 3/5
(f) 3/5 **10.** $1/2$; $1-e^{-a}$ **11.** 7/48 **12.** $39.3e^{-5}$ **13.** 0.75 **15.** $\pi/4$
16. $n(1/2)^{n-1}$ **17.** 1/3 **18.** 7/9 **19.** $-\log(y), 0 < y < 1$;
$1, 0 < x < 1$; $1/2$; $1/4$ **20.** (a) Yes. (b) $f_X(x) = xe^{-x}$ and
$f_Y(y) = e^{-y}$ (c) $5/e^2$. **21.** (a) 2/3 (b) 2/3 (c) 4/3. **22.** (a) 1/210
(b) $f_X(x) = (4x + 5)/84$, $2 < x < 6$, $f_Y(y) = (2y + 6)/105$,
$0 < y < 5$ (c) 29/70 **23.** (a) No (b) 0 (c) 0 (d) 1/3 (e) 1/3
25. $e^{-1}/i!$ **27.** 3/4. **28.** $\frac{1}{2}e^{-t}$; $1-3e^{-2}$ **29.** (a) 1/2 (b) 3/8
30. (a) 0.0808 (b) 0.003398 **31.** .0829; .3766 **32.** 5/16; .0228
33. e^{-2}; $1-3e^{-2}$ **34.** 48/103 **35.** 5/13; 8/13 **36.** 1/6; 5/6;
1/4; 3/4 **38.**

Y/X	1	2	3	4	5	6
0	6/36	5/36	4/36	3/36	2/36	1/36
1	0	1/36	2/36	3/36	4/36	5/36

*	1	2	3	4	5	6
$P(X/Y)$	6/21	5/21	4/21	3/21	2/21	1/21

39. $P(X = x, Y = y) = (1/6)x$
$yp^y(1-p)^{x-y}$, not independent. **41.** $(y + 1)^2$
$xe^{-x(y+1)}$; xe^{-xy}; e^{-x} **42.** $1/2 + 3y/(4x) - y^3/(4x^3)$
44. 1/4 and 2 **46.** 1/4 **47.** $(1-\ln2)/2$ **48.** $1 - e^{-5\lambda a}$; $(1-e^{-\lambda a})^5$
52. r/π **53.** r **55.** 1/3 **56.** (a) $u/(v + 1)^2$ **59.** (a) 0.74971
(b) 1.3699

Chapter 7

1. 52.5/12   **2.** 324; 198.8   **3.** 1/2; 1/4; 0   **4.** (a) 4/9
(b) 8/21 (c) 2/7   **5.** 3/2   **6.** 35   **7.** (a) 7.6282 (b) 5.3333
(c) 5.3333   **8.** $(1 - (1 - p)^N)/p$ **10.** (a) 1/4 (b) 0
11. $2(n-1)p(1-p)$ **12.** (a) $\dfrac{nm}{(n+m)(n+m-1)}[2 + nm$
$(n-1) + nm(m-1) + n(m-1)^2]$ (b) $\dfrac{nm}{(n+m-2)(n+m-1)}$
$[nm(n-1) + nm(m-1) + n(m-1)^2]$ **13.** 1 **14.** $m/(1-p)$
15. 1/2 **18.** 4 **21.** .9301; 87.5755 **22.** 14.7 **23.** 147/110
26. (a) 1 (b) 1 **29.** $\frac{437}{35}$; 12; 4; $\frac{123}{35}$ **30.** $-2\sigma^2$ **31.** 9
32. 2 **33.** (a) 2 (b) 16 **34.** (a) 16/15 (b) 1916/1575 **35.** 21.2;
18.929; 49.214 **36.** $-n/4$ **37.** 0 **38.** 0 **41.** $E[X] =$
6 $\text{Var}[X] = 1.959$ **42.** (a) $E[X] = 10/19$ $\text{Var}[X] = 2.639$
(b) (a) $E[X] = 1/19$ $\text{Var}[X] = 0.5279$ **45.** (a) $\rho = -1/2$
(b) $\rho = 0$ **47.** $1/(n-1)$ **48.** (a) 2 (b) 3/2 (c) 11/2
49. 150/16 **50.** 2/5 **51.** $\dfrac{y^2}{2(e^y - 1)}$ **52.** 3/2 **53.** 12 **54.** 8
56. $N(1 - e^{-10/N})$ **57.** 12.5 **58.** (a) 3 (b) 1/2 **63.** $-96/145$
64. (a) $E[X] = \mu_1 p + \mu_2(1 - p)$ (b) $\text{Var}[X] = \sigma_1^2 p + \sigma_2^2$
$(1-p) + \mu_2^2(1-p) - [\mu_1 p + \mu_2(1-p)]^2$ where $p = m/(m+n)$
65. $E[X] = 3.2$ $\text{Var}[X] = 3.36$ **66.** 218 **67.** $x[1 + (2p-1)^2]^n$
69. 1/2; 1/16; 2/81 **70.** 1/2, 1/3 **72.** $1/i$; $[i(i+1)]^{-1}$; ∞
73. μ; $1 + \sigma^2$; yes; σ^2 **75.** (a) 0.5054 (b) 0.7076 (c) 0.3333
76. $(1/36) \displaystyle\sum_{x=1}^{5} \sum_{y=1}^{5} e^{t_1 x + t_2 y}$ **77.** $M_{X,Y}(t,s) = 1/(1-t)(1-s)$
(b) $M_X(t) = 1/(1-t)$, $M_Y(t) = 1/(1-s)$ **79.** .176; .141

Chapter 8

1. e^{-5} **2.** 15/17; $\geq 3/4$; ≥ 10 **3.** ≥ 3 **4.** $\leq 4/3$; .8428
5. .1416 **6.** .9431 **7.** .3085 **8.** .6932 **9.** $n = 258 \times 129$
10. 117 **11.** $\geq$.057 **13.** .0162; .0003; .2514; .2514
14. $n \geq 23$ **16.** .013; .018; .691 **18.** $\leq$.2 **23.** .769; .357;
.4267; .1093; .112184 **24.** answer is (a)

Chapter 9

1. 1/9; 5/9 **2.** e^{-50} **3.** 1/2 **8.** b) 0.56 **9.** 0.5 **10.** (b)1/6
12. $(5/6)\log(5/6) - (1/6)\log(6)$ **14.** a) $-\log(2)$ (b) $(17/66)$
$\log(17/18) - (1/36)\log(18)$ (c) $(17/66)\log(17/18) - (1/36)$
$\log(18) - \log(2)$ **15.** 5.5098

SOLUTIONS TO SELF-TEST PROBLEMS AND EXERCISES

Chapter 1

1.1. (a) There are 4! different orderings of the letters C, D, E, F. For each of these orderings, we can obtain an ordering with A and B next to each other by inserting A and B, either in the order A, B or in the order B, A, in any of 5 places, namely, either before the first letter of the permutation of C, D, E, F, or between the first and second, and so on. Hence, there are $2 \cdot 5 \cdot 4! = 240$ arrangements. Another way of solving this problem is to imagine that B is glued to the back of A. Then there are 5! orderings in which A is immediately before B. Since there are also 5! orderings in which B is immediately before A, we again obtain a total of $2 \cdot 5! = 240$ different arrangements.

(b) There are $6! = 720$ possible arrangements, and since there are as many with A before B as with B before A, there are 360 arrangements.

(c) Of the 720 possible arrangements, there are as many that have A before B before C as have any of the 3! possible orderings of A, B, and C. Hence, there are $720/6 = 120$ possible orderings.

(d) Of the 360 arrangements that have A before B, half will have C before D and half D before C. Hence, there are 180 arrangements having A before B and C before D.

(e) Gluing B to the back of A and D to the back of C yields $4! = 24$ different orderings in which B immediately follows A and D immediately follows C. Since the order of A and B and of C and D can be reversed, there are $4 \cdot 24 = 96$ different arrangements.

(f) There are 5! orderings in which E is last. Hence, there are $6! - 5! = 600$ orderings in which E is not last.

1.2. Shirts can be arranged in 5! ways. Trousers could be placed in any of the six places between shirts.

Therefore no. of ways trousers ca be arranged $= \binom{6}{4} \times 4!$
$= 360$

So total possible arrangements are $360 \times 5! = 43200$

1.3. (a) 9!

(b) $2 * 8!$

(c) $2 * 5!$

1.4. Total possible breakfast combinations $= \binom{10}{3} = 120$

Breakfast combinations possible with maximum 1 milk shake $= \binom{7}{3} + 3 \times \binom{7}{2} = 98$

1.5. 4^2 ways , 12 ways

1.6. There are $\binom{7}{3} = 35$ choices of the three places for the letters. For each choice, there are $(26)^3 (10)^4$ different license

plates. Hence, altogether there are $35 \cdot (26)^3 \cdot (10)^4$ different plates.

1.7. Any choice of r of the n items is equivalent to a choice of $n - r$, namely, those items not selected.

1.8. (a) $10 \cdot 9 \cdot 9 \cdots 9 = 10 \cdot 9^{n-1}$

(b) $\binom{n}{i} 9^{n-i}$, since there are $\binom{n}{i}$ choices of the i places to put the zeroes and then each of the other $n - i$ positions can be any of the digits $1, \ldots, 9$.

1.9. (a) $\binom{3n}{3}$

(b) $3 \binom{n}{3}$

(c) $\binom{3}{1}\binom{2}{1}\binom{n}{2}\binom{n}{1} = 3n^2(n-1)$

(d) n^3

(e) $\binom{3n}{3} = 3\binom{n}{3} + 3n^2(n-1) + n^3$

1.10. Total numbers possible $= 14 \times 10^6$

1.11. (a) We can regard this as a seven-stage experiment. First choose the 6 married couples that have a representative in the group, and then select one of the members of each of these couples. By the generalized basic principle of counting, there are $\binom{10}{6}2^6$ different choices.

(b) First select the 6 married couples that have a representative in the group, and then select the 3 of those couples that are to contribute a man. Hence, there are $\binom{10}{6}\binom{6}{3} = \frac{10!}{4!3!3!}$ different choices. Another way to solve this is to first select 3 men and then select 3 women not related to the selected men. This shows that there are $\binom{10}{3}\binom{7}{3} = \frac{10!}{3!3!4!}$ different choices.

1.12. Total samples possible $= \binom{6}{2} \times \binom{7}{2} \times \binom{8}{2} \times \binom{15}{1} = 132300$

1.13. (number of solutions of $x_1 + \cdots + x_5 = 4$) (number of solutions of $x_1 + \cdots + x_5 = 5$) (number of solutions of $x_1 + \cdots + x_5 = 6$) $= \binom{8}{4}\binom{9}{4}\binom{10}{4}$.

435

1.14. Since there are $\binom{j-1}{n-1}$ positive vectors whose sum is j, there must be $\sum_{j=n}^{k} \binom{j-1}{n-1}$ such vectors. But $\binom{j-1}{n-1}$ is the number of subsets of size n from the set of numbers $\{1, \ldots, k\}$ in which j is the largest element in the subset. Consequently, $\sum_{j=n}^{k} \binom{j-1}{n-1}$ is just the total number of subsets of size n from a set of size k, showing that the preceding answer is equal to $\binom{k}{n}$.

1.15. Let us first determine the number of different results in which k people pass. Because there are $\binom{n}{k}$ different groups of size k and $k!$ possible orderings of their scores, it follows that there are $\binom{n}{k} k!$ possible results in which k people pass.

Consequently, there are $\sum_{k=0}^{n} \binom{n}{k} k!$ possible results.

1.16. The number of subsets of size 4 is $\binom{20}{4} = 4845$. Because the number of these that contain none of the first five elements is $\binom{15}{4} = 1365$, the number that contain at least one is 3480. Another way to solve this problem is to note that there are $\binom{5}{i}\binom{15}{4-i}$ that contain exactly i of the first five elements and sum this for $i = 1, 2, 3, 4$.

1.17. Multiplying both sides by 2, we must show that

$$n(n-1) = k(k-1) + 2k(n-k) + (n-k)(n-k-1)$$

This follows because the right side is equal to

$$k^2(1 - 2 + 1) + k(-1 + 2n - n - n + 1) + n(n-1)$$

For a combinatorial argument, consider a group of n items and a subgroup of k of the n items. Then $\binom{k}{2}$ is the number of subsets of size 2 that contain 2 items from the subgroup of size k, $k(n-k)$ is the number that contain 1 item from the subgroup, and $\binom{n-k}{2}$ is the number that contain 0 items from the subgroup. Adding these terms gives the total number of subgroups of size 2, namely, $\binom{n}{2}$.

1.18. There are 3 choices that can be made from families consisting of a single parent and 1 child; there are $3 \cdot 1 \cdot 2 = 6$ choices that can be made from families consisting of a single parent and 2 children; there are $5 \cdot 2 \cdot 1 = 10$ choices that can be made from families consisting of 2 parents and a single child; there are $7 \cdot 2 \cdot 2 = 28$ choices that can be made from families consisting of 2 parents and 2 children; there are $6 \cdot 2 \cdot 3 = 36$ choices that can be made from families consisting of 2 parents and 3 children. Hence, there are 83 possible choices.

1.19. First choose the 3 positions for the digits, and then put in the letters and digits. Thus, there are $\binom{8}{3} \cdot 26 \cdot 25 \cdot 24 \cdot 23 \cdot 22 \cdot 10 \cdot 9 \cdot 8$ different plates. If the digits must be consecutive, then there are 6 possible positions for the digits, showing that there are now $6 \cdot 26 \cdot 25 \cdot 24 \cdot 23 \cdot 22 \cdot 10 \cdot 9 \cdot 8$ different plates.

1.20. There are r^n different n letter sequences that can be formed using the first r letters of the alphabet. For given nonnegative integers $x_1, \ldots, x_r$ such that $\sum_{i=1}^{n} x_i = r$, the number of the different sequences that use letter i exactly x_i times for each $i = 1, \ldots, n$, is the number of permutations of n values, of which x_i are equal to i for each $i = 1, \ldots, r$; which is equal to $\frac{n!}{x_1! \cdots x_r!}$. As each n letter sequence is of exactly one of the preceding types, the result follows.

Chapter 2

2.1. (a) $2 \cdot 3 \cdot 4 = 24$

(b) $2 \cdot 3 = 6$

(c) $3 \cdot 4 = 12$

(d) $AB = \{(c, \text{pasta}, i), (c, \text{rice}, i), (c, \text{potatoes}, i)\}$

(e) 8

(f) $ABC = \{(c, \text{rice}, i)\}$

2.2 $P(V) = 0.30, P(P) = 0.35\ P(S) = 0.28,$
$P(VS) = 0.19, P(VP) = 0.18, P(SP) = 0.22, P(VSP) = 0.15$

(a) Reqd. Probability $= 1 - P(V \cup P \cup S) = 0.51$
(b) Reqd. Probability $= 0.44$

2.3. By symmetry, the 14th card is equally likely to be any of the 52 cards; thus, the probability is 4/52. A more formal argument is to count the number of the 52! outcomes for which the 14th card is an ace. This yields

$$p = \frac{4 \cdot 51 \cdot 50 \cdots 2 \cdot 1}{(52)!} = \frac{4}{52}$$

Letting A be the event that the first ace occurs on the 14th card, we have

$$P(A) = \frac{48 \cdot 47 \cdots 36 \cdot 4}{52 \cdot 51 \cdots 40 \cdot 39} = .0312$$

2.4. Let D denote the event that the minimum temperature is 70 degrees. Then

$$P(A \cup B) = P(A) + P(B) - P(AB) = .7 - P(AB)$$
$$P(C \cup D) = P(C) + P(D) - P(CD) = .2 + P(D) - P(DC)$$

Since $A \cup B = C \cup D$ and $AB = CD$, subtracting one of the preceding equations from the other yields

$$0 = .5 - P(D)$$

or $P(D) = .5$.

2.5 (a) Reqd. Probability $= 0.05989$
(b) Reqd. Probability $= 0.00001846$

2.6. Let R be the event that both balls are red, and let B be the event that both are black. Then

$$P(R \cup B) = P(R) + P(B) = \frac{3 \cdot 4}{6 \cdot 10} + \frac{3 \cdot 6}{6 \cdot 10} = 1/2$$

2.7. (a) $\dfrac{1}{\binom{40}{8}} = 1.3 \times 10^{-8}$

(b) $\dfrac{\binom{8}{7}\binom{32}{1}}{\binom{40}{8}} = 3.3 \times 10^{-6}$

(c) $\dfrac{\binom{8}{6}\binom{32}{2}}{\binom{40}{8}} + 1.3 \times 10^{-8} + 3.3 \times 10^{-6} = 1.8 \times 10^{-4}$

2.8. (a) $\dfrac{3 \cdot 4 \cdot 4 \cdot 3}{\binom{14}{4}} = .1439$

(b) $\dfrac{\binom{4}{2}\binom{4}{2}}{\binom{14}{4}} = .0360$

(c) $\dfrac{\binom{8}{4}}{\binom{14}{4}} = .0699$

2.9. Let $S = \bigcup\limits_{i=1}^{n} A_i$, and consider the experiment of randomly choosing an element of S. Then $P(A) = N(A)/N(S)$, and the results follow from Propositions 4.3 and 4.4.

2.10. Since there are $5! = 120$ outcomes in which the position of horse number 1 is specified, it follows that $N(A) = 360$. Similarly, $N(B) = 120$, and $N(AB) = 2 \cdot 4! = 48$. Hence, from Self-Test Problem 2.9, we obtain $N(A \cup B) = 432$.

2.11 Reqd. Probability $= (1 - P(\text{same rank}))/2 = (1 - (3/51))/2 = 8/17$

2.12. There are $(10)!/2^5$ different divisions of the 10 players into a first roommate pair, a second roommate pair, and so on. Hence, there are $(10)!/(5!2^5)$ divisions into 5 roommate pairs. There are $\binom{6}{2}\binom{4}{2}$ ways of choosing the frontcourt and backcourt players to be in the mixed roommate pairs and then 2 ways of pairing them up. As there is then 1 way to pair up the remaining two backcourt players and $4!/(2!2^2) = 3$ ways of making two roommate pairs from the remaining four frontcourt players, the desired probability is

$$P\{2 \text{ mixed pairs}\} = \frac{\binom{6}{2}\binom{4}{2}(2)(3)}{(10)!/(5!2^5)} = .5714$$

2.13 Let A_i indicate that the ith letter is placed in the ith position.

Required Probability $= 1 - P(A_1 \cup A_2 \cup ... \cup A_5)$

But $P(A_1 \cup A_2 \cup ... \cup A_5) =$

$\sum P(A_i) - \sum P(A_i A_j) ... + P(A_1 ... A_5)$

Required Probability $= 1 - (1/2!) + (1/3!) - (1/4!) + (1/5!)$
$= 0.3666$

2.14. Let $B_1 = A_1, B_i = A_i \left(\bigcup\limits_{j=1}^{i-1} A_j \right)^c, i > 1$. Then

$$P\left(\bigcup\limits_{i=1}^{\infty} A_i \right) = P\left(\bigcup\limits_{i=1}^{\infty} B_i \right)$$

$$= \sum\limits_{i=1}^{\infty} P(B_i)$$

$$\leq \sum\limits_{i=1}^{\infty} P(A_i)$$

where the final equality uses the fact that the B_i are mutually exclusive. The inequality then follows, since $B_i \subset A_i$.

2.15.

$$P\left(\bigcap\limits_{i=1}^{\infty} A_i \right) = 1 - P\left(\left(\bigcap\limits_{i=1}^{\infty} A_i \right)^c \right)$$

$$= 1 - P\left(\bigcup\limits_{i=1}^{\infty} A_i^c \right)$$

$$\geq 1 - \sum\limits_{i=1}^{\infty} P(A_i^c)$$

$$= 1$$

2.16. The number of partitions for which $\{1\}$ is a subset is equal to the number of partitions of the remaining $n - 1$ elements into $k - 1$ nonempty subsets, namely, $T_{k-1}(n - 1)$. Because there are $T_k(n - 1)$ partitions of $\{2, ..., n - 1\}$ into k nonempty subsets and then a choice of k of them in which to place element 1, it follows that there are $kT_k(n - 1)$ partitions for which $\{1\}$ is not a subset. Hence, the result follows.

2.17 (a) Total ways $= 4096$, favourable ways $= 1521$
Probability $= 0.37133$
(b) Total ways $= 560$, favourable ways $= 234$
Probability $= 0.417857$

2.18. (a) $\frac{8\cdot7\cdot6\cdot5\cdot4}{17\cdot16\cdot15\cdot14\cdot13} = \frac{2}{221}$

(b) Because there are 9 nonblue balls, the probability is $\frac{9\cdot8\cdot7\cdot6\cdot5}{17\cdot16\cdot15\cdot14\cdot13} = \frac{9}{442}$.

(c) Because there are 3! possible orderings of the different colors and all possibilities for the final 3 balls are equally likely, the probability is $\frac{3!\cdot4\cdot8\cdot5}{17\cdot16\cdot15} = \frac{4}{17}$.

(d) The probability that the red balls are in a specified 4 spots is $\frac{4\cdot3\cdot2\cdot1}{17\cdot16\cdot15\cdot14}$. Because there are 14 possible locations of the red balls where they are all together, the probability is $\frac{14\cdot4\cdot3\cdot2\cdot1}{17\cdot16\cdot15\cdot14} = \frac{1}{170}$.

2.19. (a) The probability that the 10 cards consist of 4 spades, 3 hearts, 2 diamonds, and 1 club is $\dfrac{\binom{13}{4}\binom{13}{3}\binom{13}{2}\binom{13}{1}}{\binom{52}{10}}$.

Because there are 4! possible choices of the suits to have 4, 3, 2, and 1 cards, respectively, it follows that the probability is $\dfrac{24\binom{13}{4}\binom{13}{3}\binom{13}{2}\binom{13}{1}}{\binom{52}{10}}$.

(b) Because there are $\binom{4}{2} = 6$ choices of the two suits that are to have 3 cards and then 2 choices for the suit to have 4 cards, the probability is $\dfrac{12\binom{13}{3}\binom{13}{3}\binom{13}{4}}{\binom{52}{10}}$.

2.20 The Required probability is nothing but the probability that last drawn card is a spade = P(first drawn card is spade) = 13/26 =1/2
Adding of the other 26 cards doesn't change the required probability.

Chapter 3

3.1. (a) $P(\text{no aces}) = \binom{35}{13} / \binom{39}{13}$

(b) $1 - P(\text{no aces}) - \dfrac{4\binom{35}{12}}{\binom{39}{13}}$

(c) $P(i \text{ aces}) = \dfrac{\binom{3}{i}\binom{36}{13-i}}{\binom{39}{13}}$

3.2. Let L_i denote the event that the life of the battery is greater than $10,000 \times i$ miles.
(a) $P(L_2|L_1) = P(L_1L_2)/P(L_1) = P(L_2)/P(L_1) = 1/2$
(b) $P(L_3|L_1) = P(L_1L_3)/P(L_1) = P(L_3)/P(L_1) = 1/8$

3.3. Let A be the event that first written code was 0 and B be the event that it was 1. Let X denote the event that the last observed output was code zero. Therefore required probability is $P(A/X)$ which can be obtained using Bayes theorem.
$$P(X|A) = (2/3)^3 + 3(2/3)(1/3)^2 = 14/27$$
$$P(X|B) = (1/3)^3 + 3(1/3)(2/3)^2 = 14/27$$
Therefore $P(A/X) = 14/27$

3.4. Prob that child is sick = P(mother is a carrier) × P(father is a carrier) × P(child has genetic type containing the recesive gene from both parents say aa) = (2/3)(2/21)(1/4) = 1.58

3.5. $P(A) = P(B)$, So, $2P(A) > 1$ or $P(A) > 1/2$

3.6. Let B_i denote the event that ball i is black, and let $R_i = B_i^c$. Then

$$P(B_1|R_2) = \frac{P(R_2|B_1)P(B_1)}{P(R_2|B_1)P(B_1) + P(R_2|R_1)P(R_1)}$$
$$= \frac{[r/[(b+r+c)][b/(b+r)]}{[r/(b+r+c)][b/(b+r)] + [(r+c)/(b+r+c)][r/(b+r)]}$$
$$= \frac{b}{b+r+c}$$

3.7. Let B denote the event that both cards are aces.

(a) $P\{B|\text{yes to ace of spades}\} = \dfrac{P\{B, \text{yes to ace of spades}\}}{P\{\text{yes to ace of spades}\}}$
$$= \frac{\binom{1}{1}\binom{3}{1}}{\binom{52}{2}} \bigg/ \frac{\binom{1}{1}\binom{51}{1}}{\binom{52}{2}}$$
$$= 3/51$$

(b) Since the second card is equally likely to be any of the remaining 51, of which 3 are aces, we see that the answer in this situation is also 3/51.

(c) Because we can always interchange which card is considered first and which is considered second, the result should be the same as in part (b). A more formal argument is as follows:

$$P\{B|\text{second is ace}\} = \frac{P\{B, \text{second is ace}\}}{P\{\text{second is ace}\}}$$
$$= \frac{P(B)}{P(B) + P\{\text{first is not ace, second is ace}\}}$$
$$= \frac{(4/52)(3/51)}{(4/52)(3/51) + (48/52)(4/51)}$$
$$= 3/51$$

(d) $P\{B|\text{at least one}\} = \dfrac{P(B)}{P\{\text{at least one}\}}$
$$= \frac{(4/52)(3/51)}{1 - (48/52)(47/51)}$$
$$= 1/33$$

3.8. $\frac{P(H|E)}{P(G|E)} = \frac{P(HE)}{P(GE)} = \frac{P(H)P(E|H)}{P(G)P(E|G)}$

Hypothesis H is 1.5 times as likely.

3.9. Required Prob. = Prob. that all three tell the truth + Prob. that A tells the truth and B and C lies = 5/9

3.10. The probabilities are obtained using bayes theorem as
(a) 20/41
(b) 9/41
(c)12/41

3.11. Let W be the event that the battery works, and let C and D denote the events that the battery is a type C and that it is a type D battery, respectively.

(a) $P(W) = P(W|C)P(C) + P(W|D)P(D) = .7(8/14) + .4(6/14) = 4/7$

(b) $P(C|W^c) = \frac{P(CW^c)}{P(W^c)} = \frac{P(W^c|C)P(C)}{3/7} = \frac{.3(8/14)}{3/7} = .4$

3.12. Let L_i be the event that Maria likes book $i, i = 1,2$. Then

$$P(L_2|L_1^c) = \frac{P(L_1^c L_2)}{P(L_1^c)} = \frac{P(L_1^c L_2)}{.4}$$

Using that L_2 is the union of the mutually exclusive events $L_1 L_2$ and $L_1^c L_2$, we see that

$$.5 = P(L_2) = P(L_1 L_2) + P(L_1^c L_2) = .4 + P(L_1^c L_2)$$

Thus,

$$P\left(L_2|L_1^c\right) = \frac{.1}{.4} = .25$$

3.13. (a) This is the probability that the last ball removed is blue. Because each of the 30 balls is equally likely to be the last one removed, the probability is 1/3.
(b) This is the probability that the last red or blue ball to be removed is a blue ball. Because it is equally likely to be any of the 30 red or blue balls, the probability that it is blue is 1/3.
(c) Let B_1, R_2, G_3 denote, respectively, the events that the first color removed is blue, the second is red, and the third is green. Then

$$P(B_1 R_2 G_3) = P(G_3)P(R_2|G_3)P(B_1|R_2 G_3) = \frac{8}{38} \frac{20}{30} = \frac{8}{57}$$

where $P(G_3)$ is just the probability that the very last ball is green and $P(R_2|G_3)$ is computed by noting that given that the last ball is green, each of the 20 red and 10 blue balls is equally likely to be the last of that group to be removed,

so the probability that it is one of the red balls is 20/30. (Of course, $P(B_1|R_2 G_3) = 1$.)
(d) $P(B_1) = P(B_1 G_2 R_3) + P(B_1 R_2 G_3) = \frac{20}{38} \frac{8}{18} + \frac{8}{57} = \frac{64}{171}$

3.14. (a) Probability = $(1/2)(2/3) + (1/2)(1/3) = 1/2$
(b) Required Probability = 3/5
(c) Using Bayes theorem Conditional Prob =

$$\frac{(2/3)^n}{(1/3)^n + (2/3)^n} = \frac{2^n}{1+2^n}$$

3.15. Since the black rat has a brown sibling, we can conclude that both of its parents have one black and one brown gene.
(a) $P(2 \text{ black}|\text{at least one}) = \frac{P(2)}{P(\text{at least one})} = \frac{1/4}{3/4} = \frac{1}{3}$
(b) Let F be the event that all 5 offspring are black, let B_2 be the event that the black rat has 2 black genes, and let B_1 be the event that it has 1 black and 1 brown gene. Then

$$P(B_2|F) = \frac{P(F|B_2)P(B_2)}{P(F|B_2)P(B_2) + P(F|B_1)P(B_1)}$$
$$= \frac{(1)(1/3)}{(1)(1/3) + (1/2)^5(2/3)} = \frac{16}{17}$$

3.16. (a) $P(A) = 3/13\, P(B) = 1/4\, P(A \cap B) = 3/52$
$P(A|B) = 3/13 = P(A)$.
(b) $P(A) = 11/51\, P(B) = 12/51\, P(A \cap B) = 2/51$
$P(A|B) = 2/12 \neq P(A)$.
(c) $P(A) = 612/2652\, P(B) = 663/2652\, P(A \cap B) = 153/2652$
$P(A|B) = 153/663 = P(A)$.

3.17. Let A be the event that component 1 is working, and let F be the event that the system functions.
(a) $P(A|F) = \frac{P(AF)}{P(F)} = \frac{P(A)}{P(F)} = \frac{1/2}{1-(1/2)^2} = \frac{2}{3}$
where $P(F)$ was computed by noting that it is equal to 1 minus the probability that components 1 and 2 are both failed.
(b) $P(A|F) = \frac{P(AF)}{P(F)} = \frac{P(F|A)P(A)}{P(F)} = \frac{(3/4)(1/2)}{(1/2)^3+3(1/2)^3} = \frac{3}{4}$
where $P(F)$ was computed by noting that it is equal to the probability that all 3 components work plus the three probabilities relating to exactly 2 of the components working.

3.18. Required probability is 0.75151

3.19. Condition on the outcome of the initial tosses:

$$P(A \text{ odd}) = P_1(1 - P_2)(1 - P_3) + (1 - P_1)P_2 P_3$$
$$+ P_1 P_2 P_3 P(A \text{ odd})$$
$$+ (1 - P_1)(1 - P_2)(1 - P_3)P(A \text{ odd})$$

so,

$$P(A \text{ odd}) = \frac{P_1(1 - P_2)(1 - P_3) + (1 - P_1)P_2P_3}{P_1 + P_2 + P_3 - P_1P_2 - P_1P_3 - P_2P_3}$$

3.20. Let A and B be the events that the first trial is larger and that the second is larger, respectively. Also, let E be the event that the results of the trials are equal. Then

$$1 = P(A) + P(B) + P(E)$$

But, by symmetry, $P(A) = P(B)$: thus,

$$P(B) = \frac{1 - P(E)}{2} = \frac{1 - \sum_{i=1}^{n} p_i^2}{2}$$

Another way of solving the problem is to note that

$$P(B) = \sum_i \sum_{j>i} P\{\text{first trial results in } i, \text{ second trial results in } j\}$$

$$= \sum_i \sum_{j>i} p_i p_j$$

To see that the two expressions derived for $P(B)$ are equal, observe that

$$1 = \sum_{i=1}^{n} p_i \sum_{j=1}^{n} p_j$$

$$= \sum_i \sum_j p_i p_j$$

$$= \sum_i p_i^2 + \sum_i \sum_{j \neq i} p_i p_j$$

$$= \sum_i p_i^2 + 2 \sum_i \sum_{j>i} p_i p_j$$

3.21. Let $E = \{A \text{ gets more heads than } B\}$; then

$$P(E) = P(E|A \text{ leads after both flip } n)P(A \text{ leads after both flip } n)$$
$$\quad + P(E| \text{ even after both flip } n)P(\text{even after both flip } n)$$
$$\quad + P(E|B \text{ leads after both flip } n)P(B \text{ leads after both flip } n)$$

$$= P(A \text{ leads}) + \frac{1}{2}P(\text{even})$$

Now, by symmetry,

$$P(A \text{ leads}) = P(B \text{ leads})$$
$$= \frac{1 - P(\text{even})}{2}$$

Hence,

$$P(E) = \frac{1}{2}$$

3.22. (a) Not true: In rolling 2 dice, let $E = \{\text{sum is } 7\}$, $F = \{\text{1st die does not land on } 4\}$, and $G = \{\text{2nd die does not land on } 3\}$. Then

$$P(E|F \cup G) = \frac{P\{7, \text{not } (4,3)\}}{P\{\text{not } (4,3)\}} = \frac{5/36}{35/36} = 5/35 \neq P(E)$$

(b)
$$P(E(F \cup G)) = P(EF \cup EG)$$
$$= P(EF) + P(EG) \quad \text{since } EFG = \emptyset$$
$$= P(E)[P(F) + P(G)]$$
$$= P(E)P(F \cup G) \quad \text{since } FG = \emptyset$$

(c)
$$P(G|EF) = \frac{P(EFG)}{P(EF)}$$
$$= \frac{P(E)P(FG)}{P(EF)} \quad \text{since } E \text{ is independent of } FG$$
$$= \frac{P(E)P(F)P(G)}{P(E)P(F)} \quad \text{by independence}$$
$$= P(G).$$

3.23. (a) necessarily false; if they were mutually exclusive, then we would have

$$0 = P(AB) \neq P(A)P(B)$$

(b) necessarily false; if they were independent, then we would have

$$P(AB) = P(A)P(B) > 0$$

(c) necessarily false; if they were mutually exclusive, then we would have

$$P(A \cup B) = P(A) + P(B) = 1.2$$

(d) possibly true

3.24. Order is $a > c > b$.

3.25. Let $D_i, i = 1, 2$, denote the event that radio i is defective. Also, let A and B be the events that the radios were produced at factory A and at factory B, respectively. Then

$$P(D_2|D_1) = \frac{P(D_1 D_2)}{P(D_1)}$$
$$= \frac{P(D_1 D_2|A)P(A) + P(D_1 D_2|B)P(B)}{P(D_1|A)P(A) + P(D_1|B)P(B)}$$
$$= \frac{(.05)^2(1/2) + (.01)^2(1/2)}{(.05)(1/2) + (.01)(1/2)}$$
$$= 13/300$$

3.26. We are given that $P(AB) = P(B)$ and must show that this implies that $P(B^c A^c) = P(A^c)$. One way is as follows:

$$P(B^c A^c) = P((A \cup B)^c)$$
$$= 1 - P(A \cup B)$$
$$= 1 - P(A) - P(B) + P(AB)$$
$$= 1 - P(A)$$
$$= P(A^c)$$

3.27. The result is true for $n = 0$. With A_i denoting the event that there are i red balls in the urn after stage n, assume that

$$P(A_i) = \frac{1}{n+1}, \qquad i = 1, \ldots, n+1$$

Now let $B_j, j = 1, \ldots, n+2$, denote the event that there are j red balls in the urn after stage $n+1$. Then

$$P(B_j) = \sum_{i=1}^{n+1} P(B_j|A_i)P(A_i)$$

$$= \frac{1}{n+1} \sum_{i=1}^{n+1} P(B_j|A_i)$$

$$= \frac{1}{n+1}[P(B_j|A_{j-1}) + P(B_j|A_j)]$$

Because there are $n+2$ balls in the urn after stage n, it follows that $P(B_j|A_{j-1})$ is the probability that a red ball is chosen when $j-1$ of the $n+2$ balls in the urn are red and $P(B_j|A_j)$ is the probability that a red ball is not chosen when j of the $n+2$ balls in the urn are red. Consequently,

$$P(B_j|A_{j-1}) = \frac{j-1}{n+2}, \qquad P(B_j|A_j) = \frac{n+2-j}{n+2}$$

Substituting these results into the equation for $P(B_j)$ gives

$$P(B_j) = \frac{1}{n+1}\left[\frac{j-1}{n+2} + \frac{n+2-j}{n+2}\right] = \frac{1}{n+2}$$

This completes the induction proof.

3.28. Let the teams play all $2n+1$ games. Therefore, team 1 will win the match iff team 1 will win at least n of the first $2n$ games.
Therefore, required probability

$$= (1/2)^n \sum_{k=n}^{2n} \binom{2n}{k} = (1/2) + (1/2)^{2n+1}\binom{2n}{k}$$

3.29. (a) For any permutation $i_1, \ldots, i_n$ of $1, 2, \ldots, n$, the probability that the successive types collected is $i_1, \ldots, i_n$ is $p_{i_1} \cdots p_{i_n} = \prod_{i=1}^{n} p_i$. Consequently, the desired probability is $n! \prod_{i=1}^{n} p_i$.
(b) For $i_1, \ldots, i_k$ all distinct,

$$P(E_{i_1} \cdots E_{i_k}) = \left(\frac{n-k}{n}\right)^n$$

which follows because there are no coupons of types $i_1, \ldots, i_k$ when each of the n independent selections is one of the other $n-k$ types. It now follows by the inclusion–exclusion identity that

$$P(\cup_{i=1}^{n} E_i) = \sum_{k=1}^{n} (-1)^{k+1}\binom{n}{k}\left(\frac{n-k}{n}\right)^n$$

Because $1 - P(\cup_{i=1}^{n} E_i)$ is the probability that one of each type is obtained, by part (a) it is equal to $\frac{n!}{n^n}$. Substituting this into the preceding equation gives

$$1 - \frac{n!}{n^n} = \sum_{k=1}^{n}(-1)^{k+1}\binom{n}{k}\left(\frac{n-k}{n}\right)^n$$

or

$$n! = n^n - \sum_{k=1}^{n}(-1)^{k+1}\binom{n}{k}(n-k)^n$$

or

$$n! = \sum_{k=0}^{n}(-1)^{k}\binom{n}{k}(n-k)^n$$

3.30. $P(E|E \cup F) = P(E|F(E \cup F))P(F|E \cup F)$
$$+ P(E|F^c(E \cup F))P(F^c|E \cup F)$$

Using

$$F(E \cup F) = F \quad \text{and} \quad F^c(E \cup F) = F^c E$$

gives

$$P(E|E \cup F) = P(E|F)P(F|E \cup F) + P(E|EF^c)P(F^c|E \cup F)$$
$$= P(E|F)P(F|E \cup F) + P(F^c|E \cup F)$$
$$\geq P(E|F)P(F|E \cup F) + P(E|F)P(F^c|E \cup F)$$
$$= P(E|F)$$

3.31. $P(A \cup B) = P(A \cup B|A)P(A) + P(A \cup B|A^c)P(A^c)$
$$= 1(.6) + .1(.4) = .64$$

Chapter 4

4.1. Since the probabilities sum to 1, we must have $4P\{X = 3\} + .5 = 1$, implying that $P\{X = 0\} = .375, P\{X = 3\} = .125$. Hence, $E[X] = 1(.3) + 2(.2) + 3(.125) = 1.075$.

4.2. The relationship implies that $p_i = c^i p_0, i = 1, 2$, where $p_i = P\{X = i\}$. Because these probabilities sum to 1, it follows that

$$p_0(1 + c + c^2) = 1 \Rightarrow p_0 = \frac{1}{1 + c + c^2}$$

Hence,

$$E[X] = p_1 + 2p_2 = \frac{c + 2c^2}{1 + c + c^2}$$

4.3. $P(X = x) = (5/6)^{x-2}(1/6) \; x = 2, 3, 4, 5 \ldots$
$$E(X) = \sum_{x=2}^{\infty} x(1/6)(5/6)^{x-2} = 7$$

4.4. The probability that a randomly chosen family will have i children is n_i/m. Thus,

$$E[X] = \sum_{i=1}^{r} in_i/m$$

Also, since there are in_i children in families having i children, it follows that the probability that a randomly chosen child is from a family with i children is $in_i / \sum_{i=1}^{r} in_i$. Therefore,

$$E[Y] = \frac{\sum_{i=1}^{r} i^2 n_i}{\sum_{i=1}^{r} in_i}$$

Thus, we must show that

$$\frac{\sum_{i=1}^{r} i^2 n_i}{\sum_{i=1}^{r} in_i} \geq \frac{\sum_{i=1}^{r} in_i}{\sum_{i=1}^{r} n_i}$$

or, equivalently, that

$$\sum_{j=1}^{r} n_j \sum_{i=1}^{r} i^2 n_i \geq \sum_{i=1}^{r} in_i \sum_{j=1}^{r} jn_j$$

or, equivalently, that

$$\sum_{i=1}^{r} \sum_{j=1}^{r} i^2 n_i n_j \geq \sum_{i=1}^{r} \sum_{j=1}^{r} ijn_i n_j$$

But, for a fixed pair i, j, the coefficient of $n_i n_j$ in the left-side summation of the preceding inequality is $i^2 + j^2$, whereas its coefficient in the right-hand summation is $2ij$. Hence, it suffices to show that

$$i^2 + j^2 \geq 2ij$$

which follows because $(i - j)^2 \geq 0$.

4.5. Let $p = P\{X = 1\}$. Then $E[X] = p$ and $\text{Var}(X) = p(1 - p)$, so

$$p = 3p(1 - p)$$

implying that $p = 2/3$. Hence, $P\{X = 0\} = 1/3$.

4.6. If you wager x on a bet that wins the amount wagered with probability p and loses that amount with probability $1 - p$, then your expected winnings are

$$xp - x(1 - p) = (2p - 1)x$$

which is positive (and increasing in x) if and only if $p > 1/2$. Thus, if $p \leq 1/2$, one maximizes one's expected return by wagering 0, and if $p > 1/2$, one maximizes one's expected

return by wagering the maximal possible bet. Therefore, if the information is that the .6 coin was chosen, then you should bet 10; if the information is that the .3 coin was chosen, then you should bet 0. Hence, your expected payoff is

$$\frac{1}{2}(1.2 - 1)10 + \frac{1}{2}0 - C = 1 - C$$

Since your expected payoff is 0 without the information (because in this case the probability of winning is $\frac{1}{2}(.6) + \frac{1}{2}(.3) < 1/2$), it follows that if the information costs less than 1, then it pays to purchase it.

4.7. (a) If you turn over the red paper and observe the value x, then your expected return if you switch to the blue paper is

$$2x(1/2) + x/2(1/2) = 5x/4 > x$$

Thus, it would always be better to switch.

(b) Suppose the philanthropist writes the amount x on the red paper. Then the amount on the blue paper is either $2x$ or $x/2$. Note that if $x/2 \geq y$, then the amount on the blue paper will be at least y and will thus be accepted. Hence, in this case, the reward is equally likely to be either $2x$ or $x/2$, so

$$E[R_y(x)] = 5x/4, \quad \text{if } x/2 \geq y$$

If $x/2 < y \leq 2x$, then the blue paper will be accepted if its value is $2x$ and rejected if it is $x/2$. Therefore,

$$E[R_y(x)] = 2x(1/2) + x(1/2) = 3x/2, \quad \text{if } x/2 < y \leq 2x$$

Finally, if $2x < y$, then the blue paper will be rejected. Hence, in this case, the reward is x, so

$$R_y(x) = x, \quad \text{if } 2x < y$$

That is, we have shown that when the amount x is written on the red paper, the expected return under the y-policy is

$$E[R_y(x)] = \begin{cases} x & \text{if } x < y/2 \\ 3x/2 & \text{if } y/2 \leq x < 2y \\ 5x/4 & \text{if } x \geq 2y \end{cases}$$

4.8. Suppose that n independent trials, each of which results in a success with probability p, are performed. Then the number of successes will be less than or equal to i if and only if the number of failures is greater than or equal to $n - i$. But since each trial is a failure with probability $1 - p$, it follows that the number of failures is a binomial random variable with parameters n and $1 - p$. Hence,

$$P\{\text{Bin}(n, p) \leq i\} = P\{\text{Bin}(n, 1 - p) \geq n - i\}$$
$$= 1 - P\{\text{Bin}(n, 1 - p) \leq n - i - 1\}$$

The final equality follows from the fact that the probability that the number of failures is greater than or equal to $n - i$ is 1 minus the probability that it is less than $n - i$.

4.9. $np = 4$, $npq = 3$ $\Rightarrow$ $p = 1/4$ and $n = 16$
Therefore $P(X \le 2) = 0.6776$

4.10. Let X_i, $i = 1, \ldots, m$, denote the number on the ith ball drawn. Then

$$P\{X \le k\} = P\{X_1 \le k, X_2 \le k, \ldots, X_m \le k\}$$
$$= P\{X_1 \le k\}P\{X_2 \le k\} \cdots P\{X_m \le k\}$$
$$= \left(\frac{k}{n}\right)^m$$

Therefore,

$$P\{X = k\} = P\{X \le k\} - P\{X \le k - 1\} = \left(\frac{k}{n}\right)^m - \left(\frac{k-1}{n}\right)^m$$

4.11. (a) Given that A wins the first game, it will win the series if, from then on, it wins 2 games before team B wins 3 games. Thus,

$$P\{A \text{ wins}|A \text{ wins first}\} = \sum_{i=2}^{4} \binom{4}{i} p^i (1-p)^{4-i}$$

(b)
$$P\{A \text{ wins first}|A \text{ wins}\} = \frac{P\{A \text{ wins}|A \text{ wins first}\}P\{A \text{ wins first}\}}{P\{A \text{ wins}\}}$$

$$= \frac{\sum_{i=2}^{4} \binom{4}{i} p^{i+1}(1-p)^{4-i}}{\sum_{i=3}^{5} \binom{5}{i} p^i (1-p)^{5-i}}$$

4.12. To obtain the solution, condition on whether the team wins this weekend:

$$.5 \sum_{i=3}^{4} \binom{4}{i} (.4)^i(.6)^{4-i} + .5 \sum_{i=3}^{4} \binom{4}{i} (.7)^i(.3)^{4-i}$$

4.13. Let

$$X_i = \begin{cases} 1, & \text{if the } i \text{ th ball is blue} \\ 0, & \text{otherwise} \end{cases}$$

$\sum_{i=1}^{n} X_i$ is the total number of blue balls in the sample.

$$X_i \sim B(1, P/P + Q) \quad \text{and} \quad \sum_{i=1}^{n} X_i \sim B(n, P/P + Q)$$

Hence

$$E\left(\sum_{i=3}^{n} X_i\right) = nP/(P + Q)$$

4.14. $6P(X = 3) = P(X = 2)$

$$6\frac{\lambda^3 e^{-\lambda}}{3!} = \frac{\lambda^2 e^{-\lambda}}{2!}$$

$$\lambda = 1/2$$

4.15.
$$E[Y] = \sum_{i=1}^{\infty} iP\{X = i\}/P\{X > 0\}$$
$$= E[X]/P\{X > 0\}$$
$$= \frac{\lambda}{1 - e^{-\lambda}}$$

4.16. (a) $1/n$

(b) Let D be the event that girl i and girl j choose different boys. Then

$$P(G_iG_j) = P(G_iG_j|D)P(D) + P(G_iG_j|D^c)P(D^c)$$
$$= (1/n)^2(1 - 1/n)$$
$$= \frac{n-1}{n^3}$$

Therefore,

$$P(G_i|G_j) = \frac{n-1}{n^2}$$

(c), (d) Because, when n is large, $P(G_i|G_j)$ is small and nearly equal to $P(G_i)$, it follows from the Poisson paradigm that the number of couples is approximately Poisson distributed with mean $\sum_{i=1}^{n} P(G_i) = 1$. Hence, $P_0 \approx e^{-1}$ and $P_k \approx e^{-1}/k!$

(e) To determine the probability that a given set of k girls all are coupled, condition on whether or not D occurs, where D is the event that they all choose different boys. This gives

$$P(G_{i_1} \cdots G_{i_k}) = P(G_{i_1} \cdots G_{i_k}|D)P(D)$$
$$+ P(G_{i_1} \cdots G_{i_k}|D^c)P(D^c)$$
$$= P(G_{i_1} \cdots G_{i_k}|D)P(D)$$
$$= (1/n)^k \frac{n(n-1) \cdots (n-k+1)}{n^k}$$
$$= \frac{n!}{(n-k)!n^{2k}}$$

Therefore,

$$\sum_{i_1 < \ldots < i_k} P(G_{i_1} \cdots G_{i_k}) = \binom{n}{k} P(G_{i_1} \cdots G_{i_k})$$
$$= \frac{n!n!}{(n-k)!(n-k)!k!n^{2k}}$$

and the inclusion–exclusion identity yields

$$1 - P_0 = P(\cup_{i=1}^{n} G_i) = \sum_{k=1}^{n} (-1)^{k+1} \frac{n!n!}{(n-k)!(n-k)!k!n^{2k}}$$

4.17. (a) Because woman i is equally likely to be paired with any of the remaining $2n - 1$ people, $P(W_i) = \frac{1}{2n-1}$

(b) Because, conditional on W_j, woman i is equally likely to be paired with any of $2n - 3$ people, $P(W_i|W_j) = \frac{1}{2n-3}$

(c) When n is large, the number of wives paired with their husbands will approximately be Poisson with mean

$\sum_{i=1}^{n} P(W_i) = \frac{n}{2n-1} \approx 1/2$. Therefore, the probability that there is no such pairing is approximately $e^{-1/2}$.

(d) It reduces to the match problem.

4.18. $X \sim geo\,(1/12)$

$$P(X \leq n) > 0.90$$

$$(11/12)^n < 0.1$$

Taking logarithm and solving, we get $n > 26.466$. Therefore required $n = 27$.

4.19. (a) $f(k = 0) = \dfrac{\dbinom{10}{0}\dbinom{90}{10}}{\dbinom{100}{10}}$

$f(k = 0) = 0.33047$

(b) $1 - f(k = 0) = 0.66953$

4.20. Let $q = 1 - p$. Then

$$E[1/X] = \sum_{i=1}^{\infty} \frac{1}{i} q^{i-1} p$$

$$= \frac{p}{q} \sum_{i=1}^{\infty} q^i / i$$

$$= \frac{p}{q} \sum_{i=1}^{\infty} \int_0^q x^{i-1}\, dx$$

$$= \frac{p}{q} \int_0^q \sum_{i=1}^{\infty} x^{i-1}\, dx$$

$$= \frac{p}{q} \int_0^q \frac{1}{1-x}\, dx$$

$$= \frac{p}{q} \int_p^1 \frac{1}{y}\, dy$$

$$= -\frac{p}{q} \log(p)$$

4.21. Since $\frac{X-b}{a-b}$ will equal 1 with probability p or 0 with probability $1 - p$, it follows that it is a Bernoulli random variable with parameter p. Because the variance of such a Bernoulli random variable is $p(1 - p)$, we have

$$p(1 - p) = \text{Var}\left(\frac{X - b}{a - b}\right) = \frac{1}{(a - b)^2}\text{Var}(X - b)$$

$$= \frac{1}{(a - b)^2}\text{Var}(X)$$

Hence,

$$\text{Var}(X) = (a - b)^2 p(1 - p)$$

4.22. (a) Let X be the number of games played and $Y = X - 10$ taking values $0, 1, 2...$

Therefore $E(Y) = \dfrac{p(1-(1-p)^{10}}{(1-p)^2}$

and $E(X) = E(Y + 10) = 10 + \dfrac{p(1-(1-p)^{10}}{(1-p)^2}$

(b) Let Z denote the number of winnings in the match and W the number of wins in the first 10 games, where $W \sim binom(10, p)$ therefore

$$E(Z) = E(W) + 1*(1 - P(W = 0)) = 10p + (1 - (1 - p)^{10})$$

(c) Let $L1$ denote number of losses in first 10 games and $L2$ the number of losses after the 10 games. $L1 \sim binom(10, 1-p)$ and $L2 \sim geo(p)$. If L is the total number of losses,

$$E(L) = E(L1) + (1 - (1-p)^{10})E(L2)$$

$$= 10(1-p) + (1 - (1-p)^{10}) \times \frac{1-p}{p}$$

4.23. P[Selecting a black ball in any draw] $= N/(M + N)$
P[Selecting a White ball in any draw] $= M/(M + N)$

(a) $N/(M + N)$
(b) $MN/(M + N)(M + N - 1)$
(c) $2MN/(M + N)(M + N - 1)$

4.24. Because each ball independently goes into urn i with the same probability p_i, it follows that X_i is a binomial random variable with parameters $n = 10$, $p = p_i$.

First note that $X_i + X_j$ is the number of balls that go into either urn i or urn j. Then, because each of the 10 balls independently goes into one of these urns with probability $p_i + p_j$, it follows that $X_i + X_j$ is a binomial random variable with parameters 10 and $p_i + p_j$.

By the same logic, $X_1 + X_2 + X_3$ is a binomial random variable with parameters 10 and $p_1 + p_2 + p_3$. Therefore,

$$P\{X_1 + X_2 + X_3 = 7\} = \binom{10}{7}(p_1 + p_2 + p_3)^7 (p_4 + p_5)^3$$

4.25. Let X_i equal 1 if person i has a match, and let it equal 0 otherwise. Then

$$X = \sum_{i=1}^{n} X_i$$

is the number of matches. Taking expectations gives

$$E[X] = E\left[\sum_{i=1}^{n} X_i\right] = \sum_{i=1}^{n} E[X_i] = \sum_{i=1}^{n} P\{X_i = 1\} = \sum_{i=1}^{n} 1/n = 1$$

where the final equality follows because person i is equally likely to end up with any of the n hats.

To compute $\text{Var}(X)$, we use Equation (9.1), which states that

$$E[X^2] = \sum_{i=1}^{n} E[X_i] + \sum_{i=1}^{n}\sum_{j \neq i} E[X_i X_j]$$

Now, for $i \neq j$,

$$E[X_i X_j] = P\{X_i = 1, X_j = 1\} = P\{X_i = 1\}P\{X_j = 1 | X_i = 1\}$$

$$= \frac{1}{n}\frac{1}{n-1}$$

Hence,

$$E[X^2] = 1 + \sum_{i=1}^{n}\sum_{j \neq i} \frac{1}{n(n-1)}$$

$$= 1 + n(n-1)\frac{1}{n(n-1)} = 2$$

which yields

$$\text{Var}(X) = 2 - 1^2 = 1$$

4.26. With $q = 1 - p$, we have, on the one hand,

$$P(E) = \sum_{i=1}^{\infty} P\{X = 2i\}$$

$$= \sum_{i=1}^{\infty} pq^{2i-1}$$

$$= pq\sum_{i=1}^{\infty}(q^2)^{i-1}$$

$$= pq\frac{1}{1 - q^2}$$

$$= \frac{pq}{(1-q)(1+q)} = \frac{q}{1+q}$$

On the other hand,

$$P(E) = P(E|X = 1)p + P(E|X > 1)q = qP(E|X > 1)$$

However, given that the first trial is not a success, the number of trials needed for a success is 1 plus the geometrically distributed number of additional trials required. Therefore,

$$P(E|X > 1) = P(X + 1 \text{ is even}) = P(E^c) = 1 - P(E)$$

which yields $P(E) = q/(1 + q)$.

4.27. The probability that either team wins 3 of the first 4 games is $2\binom{4}{3}(1/2)^4 = 1/2$. Because the team with only 1 win would then have to win the following 3 games, the desired probability is 1/16.

4.28. (a) The negative binomial represents the number of balls withdrawn in a similar experiment but with the excep-

tion that the withdrawn ball would be replaced before the next drawing.
(b) Using the hint, we note that $X = r$ if the first $r - 1$ balls withdrawn contain exactly $k - 1$ white balls and the next withdrawn ball is white. Hence,

$$P(X = r) = \frac{\binom{n}{k-1}\binom{m}{r-k}}{\binom{n+m}{r-1}}\frac{n-k+1}{n+m-r+1},$$

$$k \leq r \leq m + k$$

Chapter 5

5.1. Let X be the number of minutes played.
(a) $P\{X > 15\} = 1 - P\{X \leq 15\} = 1 - 5(.025) = .875$
(b) $P\{20 < X < 35\} = 10(.05) + 5(.025) = .625$
(c) $P\{X < 30\} = 10(.025) + 10(.05) = .75$
(d) $P\{X > 36\} = 4(.025) = .1$

5.2. (a) $1 = \int_0^1 cx^n dx = c/(n + 1) \Rightarrow c = n + 1$

(b) $P\{X > x\} = (n + 1)\int_x^1 x^n dx = x^{n+1}\Big|_x^1 = 1 - x^{n+1}$

5.3. Integrating the pdf and equating to 1 gives $c = 2/\pi$. Expected points $= 10P(X$ lies within 0 and $1/\sqrt{3}) + 5P$ (X lies within $1/\sqrt{3}$ and 1) $+ 2P(X$ lies within 1 and $\sqrt{3}$) $= 10\pi/4 + 5(\pi/3 - \pi/4) + 2(3\pi/4 - \pi/3) = 15\pi/4$

5.4. (a) No. of minutes in a day $= 1440$, Prob that the first birth is within the 10 minutes interval till midnight $= 10/1440 = 1/144$.
(b) No. of minutes in 365 days $= 525600$, Prob that the first birth occur during the last 10 minute interval of the final day midnight $= 10/525600 = 1/52560$.

5.5. For $i = 1, \ldots, n$,

$$P\{X = i\} = P\{\text{Int}(nU) = i - 1\}$$

$$= P\{i - 1 \leq nU < i\}$$

$$= P\left\{\frac{i-1}{n} \leq U < \frac{i}{n}\right\}$$

$$= 1/n$$

5.6. If you bid $x, 70 \leq x \leq 140$, then you will either win the bid and make a profit of $x - 100$ with probability $(140 - x)/70$ or lose the bid and make a profit of 0 otherwise. Therefore, your expected profit if you bid x is

$$\frac{1}{70}(x - 100)(140 - x) = \frac{1}{70}(240x - x^2 - 14000)$$

Differentiating and setting the preceding equal to 0 gives

$$240 - 2x = 0$$

Therefore, you should bid $120,000. Your expected profit will be 40/7 thousand dollars.

5.7. (a) $P\{U > .1\} = 9/10$

(b) $P\{U > .2|U > .1\} = P\{U > .2\}/P\{U > .1\} = 8/9$

(c) $P\{U > .3|U > .2, U > .1\} = P\{U > .3\}/P\{U > .2\} = 7/8$

(d) $P\{U > .3\} = 7/10$

The answer to part (d) could also have been obtained by multiplying the probabilities in parts (a), (b), and (c).

5.8. (a) $P(Z < -1) = 0.1587$

(b) $P(-0.5 < Z < 1.25) = 0.5858$

(c) $P(Z > 1) = 0.1587$

5.9. $P(Z > (365 - 300)/60) = P(Z > 1.0833) = 0.1393$

5.10. (a) 0.187

(b) 0.2185

(c) Reqd. Probability $= P(X \geq 800 \cap X \geq 600)/P(X \geq 600)$
$= 0.187/0.9088 = 0.20576$.

5.11. Let X be next year's rainfall and let $Z = (X - 40.2)/8.4$.

(a) $P\{X > 44\} = P\{Z > 3.8/8.4\} \approx P\{Z > .4524\} \approx .3255$

(b) $\begin{pmatrix} 7 \\ 3 \end{pmatrix} (.3255)^3 (.6745)^4$

5.12. Let M_i and W_i denote, respectively, the numbers of men and women in the samples that earn, in units of $1,000, at least i per year. Also, let Z be a standard normal random variable.

(a)

$P\{W_{25} \geq 70\}$

$= P\{W_{25} \geq 69.5\}$

$= P\left\{ \dfrac{W_{25} - 200(.34)}{\sqrt{200(.34)(.66)}} \geq \dfrac{69.5 - 200(.34)}{\sqrt{200(.34)(.66)}} \right\}$

$\approx P\{Z \geq .2239\}$

$\approx .4114$

(b)

$P\{M_{25} \leq 120\}$

$= P\{M_{25} \leq 120.5\}$

$= P\left\{ \dfrac{M_{25} - (200)(.587)}{\sqrt{(200)(.587)(.413)}} \leq \dfrac{120.5 - (200)(.587)}{\sqrt{(200)(.587)(.413)}} \right\}$

$\approx P\{Z \leq .4452\}$

$\approx .6719$

(c)

$P\{M_{20} \geq 150\}$

$= P\{M_{20} \geq 149.5\}$

$= P\left\{ \dfrac{M_{20} - (200)(.745)}{\sqrt{(200)(.745)(.255)}} \geq \dfrac{149.5 - (200)(.745)}{\sqrt{(200)(.745)(.255)}} \right\}$

$\approx P\{Z \geq .0811\}$

$\approx .4677$

$P\{W_{20} \geq 100\}$

$= P\{W_{20} \geq 99.5\}$

$= P\left\{ \dfrac{W_{20} - (200)(.534)}{\sqrt{(200)(.534)(.466)}} \geq \dfrac{99.5 - (200)(.534)}{\sqrt{(200)(.534)(.466)}} \right\}$

$\approx P\{Z \geq -1.0348\}$

$\approx .8496$

Hence,

$$P\{M_{20} \geq 150\}P\{W_{20} \geq 100\} \approx .3974$$

5.13. Due to memoryless property of exponential distribution, the time for second hand usage also follows exponential with mean 30 months.

Therefore the required probability $= e^{-12/30} = e^{-0.4} = 0.6703$.

5.14. (a) $e^{-2^2} = e^{-4}$

(b) $F(3) - F(1) = e^{-1} - e^{-9}$

(c) $\lambda(t) = 2te^{-t^2}/e^{-t^2} = 2t$

(d) Let Z be a standard normal random variable. Use the identity $E[X] = \int_0^\infty P\{X > x\} dx$ to obtain

$$E[X] = \int_0^\infty e^{-x^2} dx$$
$$= 2^{-1/2} \int_0^\infty e^{-y^2/2} dy$$
$$= 2^{-1/2} \sqrt{2\pi} P\{Z > 0\}$$
$$= \sqrt{\pi}/2$$

(e) Use the result of Theoretical Exercise 5.5 to obtain

$$E[X^2] = \int_0^\infty 2xe^{-x^2} dx = -e^{-x^2} \Big|_0^\infty = 1$$

Hence, $\text{Var}(X) = 1 - \pi/4$.

5.15. (a) $P\{X > 6\} = \exp\{-\int_0^6 \lambda(t)dt\} = e^{-3.45}$

(b) $P\{X < 8|X > 6\} = 1 - P\{X > 8|X > 6\}$
$= 1 - P\{X > 8\}/P\{X > 6\}$
$= 1 - e^{-5.65}/e^{-3.45}$
$\approx .8892$

5.16. For $x \geq 0$,

$$F_{1/X}(x) = P\{1/X \leq x\}$$
$$= P\{X \leq 0\} + P\{X \geq 1/x\}$$
$$= 1/2 + 1 - F_X(1/x)$$

Differentiation yields

$$f_{1/X}(x) = x^{-2} f_X(1/x)$$
$$= \frac{1}{x^2 \pi (1 + (1/x)^2)}$$
$$= f_X(x)$$

The proof when $x < 0$ is similar.

5.17. If X denotes the number of the first n bets that you win, then the amount that you will be winning after n bets is

$$35X - (n - X) = 36X - n$$

Thus, we want to determine

$$a = P\{36X - n > 0\} = P\{X > n/36\}$$

when X is a binomial random variable with parameters n and $p = 1/38$.
(a) When $n = 34$,

$$a = P\{X \geq 1\}$$
$$= P\{X > .5\} \qquad \text{(the continuity correction)}$$
$$= P\left\{ \frac{X - 34/38}{\sqrt{34(1/38)(37/38)}} > \frac{.5 - 34/38}{\sqrt{34(1/38)(37/38)}} \right\}$$
$$= P\left\{ \frac{X - 34/38}{\sqrt{34(1/38)(37/38)}} > -.4229 \right\}$$
$$\approx \Phi(.4229)$$
$$\approx .6638$$

(Because you will be ahead after 34 bets if you win at least 1 bet, the exact probability in this case is $1 - (37/38)^{34} = .5961$.)
(b) When $n = 1000$,

$$a = P\{X > 27.5\}$$
$$= P\left\{ \frac{X - 1000/38}{\sqrt{1000(1/38)(37/38)}} > \frac{27.5 - 1000/38}{\sqrt{1000(1/38)(37/38)}} \right\}$$
$$\approx 1 - \Phi(.2339)$$
$$\approx .4075$$

The exact probability—namely, the probability that a binomial $n = 1000$, $p = 1/38$ random variable is greater than 27—is .3961.
(c) When $n = 100,000$,

$$a = P\{X > 2777.5\}$$
$$= P\left\{ \frac{X - 100000/38}{\sqrt{100000(1/38)(37/38)}} > \frac{2777.5 - 100000/38}{\sqrt{100000(1/38)(37/38)}} \right\}$$
$$\approx 1 - \Phi(2.883)$$
$$\approx .0020$$

The exact probability in this case is .0021.

5.18. If X denotes the lifetime of the battery, then the desired probability, $P\{X > s + t | X > t\}$, can be determined as follows:

$$P\{X > s + t | X > t\} = \frac{P\{X > s + t, X > t\}}{P\{X > t\}}$$
$$= \frac{P\{X > s + t\}}{P\{X > t\}}$$
$$= \frac{\begin{array}{l} P\{X > s+t | \text{battery is type 1}\}p_1 \\ + P\{X > s+t | \text{battery is type 2}\}p_2 \end{array}}{\begin{array}{l} P\{X > t | \text{battery is type 1}\}p_1 \\ + P\{X > t | \text{battery is type 2}\}p_2 \end{array}}$$
$$= \frac{e^{-\lambda_1(s+t)}p_1 + e^{-\lambda_2(s+t)}p_2}{e^{-\lambda_1 t}p_1 + e^{-\lambda_2 t}p_2}$$

Another approach is to directly condition on the type of battery and then use the lack-of-memory property of exponential random variables. That is, we could do the following:

$$P\{X > s + t | X > t\}$$
$$= P\{X > s + t | X > t, \text{type 1}\}P\{\text{type 1} | X > t\}$$
$$\quad + P\{X > s + t | X > t, \text{type 2}\}P\{\text{type 2} | X > t\}$$
$$= e^{-\lambda_1 s} P\{\text{type 1} | X > t\} + e^{-\lambda_2 s} P\{\text{type 2} | X > t\}$$

Now for $i = 1, 2$, use

$$P\{\text{type } i | X > t\} = \frac{P\{\text{type } i, X > t\}}{P\{X > t\}}$$
$$= \frac{P\{X > t | \text{type } i\}p_i}{P\{X > t | \text{type 1}\}p_1 + P\{X > t | \text{type 2}\}p_2}$$
$$= \frac{e^{-\lambda_i t}p_i}{e^{-\lambda_1 t}p_1 + e^{-\lambda_2 t}p_2}$$

5.19. Let X_i be an exponential random variable with mean i, $i = 1, 2$.
(a) The value c should be such that $P\{X_1 > c\} = .05$. Therefore,

$$e^{-c} = .05 = 1/20$$

or $c = \log(20) = 2.996$.
(b) $P\{X_2 > c\} = e^{-c/2} = \frac{1}{\sqrt{20}} = .2236$

5.20. (a)

$$E[(Z - c)^+] = \frac{1}{\sqrt{2\pi}} \int_{-\infty}^{\infty} (x - c)^+ e^{-x^2/2} \, dx$$
$$= \frac{1}{\sqrt{2\pi}} \int_{c}^{\infty} (x - c) e^{-x^2/2} \, dx$$
$$= \frac{1}{\sqrt{2\pi}} \int_{c}^{\infty} x e^{-x^2/2} \, dx - \frac{1}{\sqrt{2\pi}} \int_{c}^{\infty} c \, e^{-x^2/2} \, dx$$
$$= -\frac{1}{\sqrt{2\pi}} e^{-x^2/2} \Big|_{c}^{\infty} - c(1 - \Phi(c))$$
$$= \frac{1}{\sqrt{2\pi}} e^{-c^2/2} - c(1 - \Phi(c))$$

(b) Using the fact that X has the same distribution as $\mu + \sigma Z$, where Z is a standard normal random variable, yields

$$E[(X - c)^+] = E[(\mu + \sigma Z - c)^+]$$

$$= E\left[\left(\sigma\left(Z - \frac{c - \mu}{\sigma}\right)\right)^+\right]$$

$$= E\left[\sigma\left(Z - \frac{c - \mu}{\sigma}\right)^+\right]$$

$$= \sigma E\left[\left(Z - \frac{c - \mu}{\sigma}\right)^+\right]$$

$$= \sigma\left[\frac{1}{\sqrt{2\pi}}e^{-a^2/2} - a(1 - \Phi(a))\right]$$

where $a = \frac{c-\mu}{\sigma}$.

5.21. Only (b) is true.

5.22. (a) If $b > 0$, then for $0 < x < b$,

$$P(bU < x) = P\{U < x/b\} = x/b.$$

Hence,

$$f_{bU}(x) = 1/b, 0 < x < b$$

The argument when $b < 0$ is similar.

(b) For $a < x < 1 + a$,

$$P\{a + U < x\} = P\{U < x - a\} = x - a$$

Differentiation yields

$$f_{a+U}(x) = 1, a < x < 1 + a$$

(c) $a + (b - a)U$

(d) For $0 < x < 1/2$,

$$P\left\{\min(U, 1 - U) < x\right\} = P\left(\{U < x\} \cup \{U > 1 - x\}\right)$$
$$= P\{U < x\} + P\{U > 1 - x\} = 2x$$

Differentiating gives

$$f_{\min(U, 1-U)}(x) = 2, \quad 0 < x < 1/2$$

(e) Using that $\max(U, 1 - U) = 1 - \min(U, 1 - U)$, the result follows from (a), (b), and (d). A direct argument is that, for $1/2 < x < 1$,

$$P\left\{\max(U, 1 - U) < x\right\} = 1 - P\left\{\max(U, 1 - U) > x\right\}$$
$$= 1 - P\left(\{U > x\} \cup \{U < 1 - x\}\right)$$
$$= 1 - (1 - x) - (1 - x) = 2x - 1$$

Hence,

$$f_{\max(U, 1-U)}(x) = 2, \quad 1/2 < x < 1$$

Chapter 6

6.1. (a) $k = 21$

(b) 0.31874

(c) 0.09791

(d) 0.48523

6.2. (a) $-1/4$

(b) 1/4

6.3. The joint density of X and Y is given by $f(x,y) = kxy$, if $0 < 2y < x < 1$ and 0, elsewhere.

(a) $k = 32$

(b) $f_X(x) = 4x^3$, if $0 < x < 1$

(c) $f_Y(y) = 16y - 64y^3$, if $0 < y < 1/2$

(d) $E[X] = 4/5$

(e) $E[Y] = 4/15$.

6.4. The multinomial random variables $X_i, i = 1, \ldots, r$, represent the numbers of each of the types of outcomes $1, \ldots, r$ that occur in n independent trials when each trial results in one of the outcomes $1, \ldots, r$ with respective probabilities $p_1, \ldots, p_r$. Now, say that a trial results in a category 1 outcome if that trial resulted in any of the outcome types $1, \ldots, r_1$; say that a trial results in a category 2 outcome if that trial resulted in any of the outcome types $r_1 + 1, \ldots, r_1 + r_2$; and so on. With these definitions, $Y_1, \ldots, Y_k$ represent the numbers of category 1 outcomes, category 2 outcomes, up to category k outcomes when n independent trials that each result in one of the categories $1, \ldots, k$ with respective probabilities $\sum_{j=r_{i-1}+1}^{r_{i-1}+r_i} p_j$, $i = 1, \ldots, k$, are performed. But by definition, such a vector has a multinomial distribution.

6.5. (a) Letting $p_j = P\{XYZ = j\}$, we have

$$p_1 = 1/8, \quad p_2 = 3/8, \quad p_4 = 3/8, \quad p_8 = 1/8$$

(b) Letting $p_j = P\{XY + XZ + YZ = j\}$, we have

$$p_3 = 1/8, \quad p_5 = 3/8, \quad p_8 = 3/8, \quad p_{12} = 1/8$$

(c) Letting $p_j = P\{X^2 + YZ = j\}$, we have

$$p_2 = 1/8, \quad p_3 = 1/4, \quad p_5 = 1/4, \quad p_6 = 1/4, \quad p_8 = 1/8$$

6.6. (a) $c = -72$

(b) $f_X(x) = 12x^2(1 - x)$

$$f_Y(y) = -6y(y - 1)$$

6.7. (a) Yes, the joint density function factors.

(b) $f_X(x) = x \int_0^2 y\,dy = 2x, \quad 0 < x < 1$

(c) $f_Y(y) = y \int_0^1 x\,dx = y/2, \quad 0 < y < 2$

(d)

$$P\{X < x, Y < y\} = P\{X < x\}P\{Y < y\}$$
$$= \min(1, x^2)\min(1, y^2/4), \quad x > 0, y > 0$$

(e) $E[Y] = \int_0^2 y^2/2 \, dy = 4/3$

(f) $P\{X + Y < 1\} = \int_0^1 x \int_0^{1-x} y \, dy \, dx$

$$= \frac{1}{2} \int_0^1 x(1 - x)^2 \, dx = 1/24$$

6.8. Let T_i denote the time at which a shock type i, of $i = 1, 2, 3$, occurs. For $s > 0, t > 0$,

$$P\{X_1 > s, X_2 > t\} = P\{T_1 > s, T_2 > t, T_3 > \max(s, t)\}$$
$$= P\{T_1 > s\}P\{T_2 > t\}P\{T_3 > \max(s, t)\}$$
$$= \exp\{-\lambda_1 s\}\exp\{-\lambda_2 t\}\exp\{-\lambda_3 \max(s, t)\}$$
$$= \exp\{-(\lambda_1 s + \lambda_2 t + \lambda_3 \max(s, t))\}$$

6.9. (a) No, advertisements on pages having many ads are less likely to be chosen than are ones on pages with few ads.

(b) $\frac{1}{m}\frac{n(i)}{n}$

(c) $\dfrac{\sum\limits_{i=1}^{m} n(i)}{nm} = \bar{n}/n$, where $\bar{n} = \sum\limits_{i=1}^{m} n(i)/m$

(d) $(1 - \bar{n}/n)^{k-1}\dfrac{1}{m}\dfrac{n(i)}{n}\dfrac{1}{n(i)} = (1 - \bar{n}/n)^{k-1}/(nm)$

(e) $\sum\limits_{k=1}^{\infty} \dfrac{1}{nm}(1 - \bar{n}/n)^{k-1} = \dfrac{1}{\bar{n}m}$.

(f) The number of iterations is geometric with mean $n\sqrt{n}$

6.10. (a) $P\{X = i\} = 1/m, \quad i = 1, \ldots, m.$

(b) Step 2. Generate a uniform $(0, 1)$ random variable U. If $U < n(X)/n$, go to step 3. Otherwise return to step 1.

Step 3. Generate a uniform $(0, 1)$ random variable U, and select the element on page X in position $[n(X)U] + 1$.

6.11. Yes, they are independent. This can be easily seen by considering the equivalent question of whether X_N is independent of N. But this is indeed so, since knowing when the first random variable greater than c occurs does not affect the probability distribution of its value, which is the uniform distribution on $(c, 1)$.

6.12. Let p_i denote the probability of obtaining i points on a single throw of the dart. Then

$$p_{30} = \pi/36$$
$$p_{20} = 4\pi/36 - p_{30} = \pi/12$$
$$p_{10} = 9\pi/36 - p_{20} - p_{30} = 5\pi/36$$
$$p_0 = 1 - p_{10} - p_{20} - p_{30} = 1 - \pi/4$$

(a) $\pi/12$

(b) $\pi/9$

(c) $1 - \pi/4$

(d) $\pi(30/36 + 20/12 + 50/36) = 35\pi/9$

(e) $(\pi/4)^2$

(f) $2(\pi/36)(1 - \pi/4) + 2(\pi/12)(5\pi/36)$

6.13. Let Z be a standard normal random variable.

(a)

$$P\left\{\sum_{i=1}^{4} X_i > 0\right\} = P\left\{\frac{\sum\limits_{i=1}^{4} X_i - 6}{\sqrt{24}} > \frac{-6}{\sqrt{24}}\right\}$$
$$\approx P\{Z > -1.2247\} \approx .8897$$

(b)

$$P\left\{\sum_{i=1}^{4} X_i > 0 \,\bigg|\, \sum_{i=1}^{2} X_i = -5\right\} = P\{X_3 + X_4 > 5\}$$
$$= P\left\{\frac{X_3 + X_4 - 3}{\sqrt{12}} > 2/\sqrt{12}\right\}$$
$$\approx P\{Z > .5774\} \approx .2818$$

(c)

$$P\left\{\sum_{i=1}^{4} X_i > 0 \,\big|\, X_1 = 5\right\} = P\{X_2 + X_3 + X_4 > -5\}$$
$$= P\left\{\frac{X_2 + X_3 + X_4 - 4.5}{\sqrt{18}} > -9.5/\sqrt{18}\right\}$$
$$\approx P\{Z > -2.239\} \approx .9874$$

6.14. $f_{X(i), X(j)}(u, v) =$

$$\frac{n!}{(i-1)!(j-1-i)!(n-j)!}[F_X(u)]^{i-1}[F_X(v) - $$
$$F_X(u)]^{j-1-i}[1 - F_X(v)]^{n-kj} f_X(u)f_X(v)$$

Plugging in $j = 4, i = 3$ and $n = 4$, we get for the uniform distribution, $f_R(x) = 12x^2(1 - x)$

6.15. Z has a uniform$(-1, 1)$ distribution.

6.16. Let U be a uniform random variable on $(7, 11)$. If you bid $x, 7 \le x \le 10$, you will be the high bidder with probability

$$(P\{U < x\})^3 = \left(P\left\{\frac{U - 7}{4} < \frac{x - 7}{4}\right\}\right)^3 = \left(\frac{x - 7}{4}\right)^3$$

Hence, your expected gain—call it $E[G(x)]$—if you bid x is

$$E[G(x)] = \frac{1}{64}(x - 7)^3(10 - x)$$

Calculus shows this is maximized when $x = 37/4$.

6.17. Let $i_1, i_2, \ldots, i_n$, be a permutation of $1, 2, \ldots, n$. Then

$$P\{X_1 = i_1, X_2 = i_2, \ldots, X_n = i_n\}$$
$$= P\{X_1 = i_1\}P\{X_2 = i_2\} \cdots P\{X_n = i_n\}$$
$$= p_{i_1}p_{i_2} \cdots p_{i_n}$$
$$= p_1 p_2 \cdots p_n$$

Therefore, the desired probability is $n! \, p_1 p_2 \cdots p_n$, which reduces to $\frac{n!}{n^n}$ when all $p_i = 1/n$.

6.18. (a) Because $\sum_{i=1}^{n} X_i = \sum_{i=1}^{n} Y_i$, it follows that $N = 2M$.

(b) Consider the $n - k$ coordinates whose Y-values are equal to 0, and call them the red coordinates. Because the k coordinates whose X-values are equal to 1 are equally likely to be any of the $\binom{n}{k}$ sets of k coordinates, it follows that the number of red coordinates among these k coordinates has the same distribution as the number of red balls chosen when one randomly chooses k of a set of n balls of which $n - k$ are red. Therefore, M is a hypergeometric random variable.

(c) $E[N] = E[2M] = 2E[M] = \frac{2k(n-k)}{n}$

(d) Using the formula for the variance of a hypergeometric given in Example 8j of Chapter 4, we obtain

$$\mathrm{Var}(N) = 4\,\mathrm{Var}(M) = 4\frac{n-k}{n-1}k(1 - k/n)(k/n)$$

6.19. (a) First note that $S_n - S_k = \sum_{i=k+1}^{n} Z_i$ is a normal random variable with mean 0 and variance $n - k$ that is independent of S_k. Consequently, given that $S_k = y$, S_n is a normal random variable with mean y and variance $n - k$.

(b) Because the conditional density function of S_k given that $S_n = x$ is a density function whose argument is y, anything that does not depend on y can be regarded as a constant. (For instance, x is regarded as a fixed constant.) In the following, the quantities $C_i, i = 1, 2, 3, 4$ are all constants that do not depend on y:

$$f_{S_k|S_n}(y|x) = \frac{f_{S_k,S_n}(y,x)}{f_{S_n}(x)}$$

$$= C_1 f_{S_n|S_k}(x|y) f_{S_k}(y) \quad \left(\text{where } C_1 = \frac{1}{f_{S_n}(x)}\right)$$

$$= C_1 \frac{1}{\sqrt{2\pi}\sqrt{n-k}} e^{-(x-y)^2/2(n-k)} \frac{1}{\sqrt{2\pi}\sqrt{k}} e^{-y^2/2k}$$

$$= C_2 \exp\left\{-\frac{(x-y)^2}{2(n-k)} - \frac{y^2}{2k}\right\}$$

$$= C_3 \exp\left\{\frac{2xy}{2(n-k)} - \frac{y^2}{2(n-k)} - \frac{y^2}{2k}\right\}$$

$$= C_3 \exp\left\{-\frac{n}{2k(n-k)}\left(y^2 - 2\frac{k}{n}xy\right)\right\}$$

$$= C_3 \exp\left\{-\frac{n}{2k(n-k)}\left[\left(y - \frac{k}{n}x\right)^2 - \left(\frac{k}{n}x\right)^2\right]\right\}$$

$$= C_4 \exp\left\{-\frac{n}{2k(n-k)}\left(y - \frac{k}{n}x\right)^2\right\}$$

But we recognize the preceding as the density function of a normal random variable with mean $\frac{k}{n}x$ and variance $\frac{k(n-k)}{n}$.

6.20. (a)

$$P\{X_6 > X_1|X_1 = \max(X_1, \ldots, X_5)\}$$
$$= \frac{P\{X_6 > X_1, X_1 = \max(X_1, \ldots, X_5)\}}{P\{X_1 = \max(X_1, \ldots, X_5)\}}$$
$$= \frac{P\{X_6 = \max(X_1, \ldots, X_6), X_1 = \max(X_1, \ldots, X_5)\}}{1/5}$$
$$= 5\frac{1}{6}\frac{1}{5} = \frac{1}{6}$$

Thus, the probability that X_6 is the largest value is independent of which is the largest of the other five values. (Of course, this would not be true if the X_i had different distributions.)

(b) One way to solve this problem is to condition on whether $X_6 > X_1$. Now,

$$P\{X_6 > X_2|X_1 = \max(X_1, \ldots, X_5), X_6 > X_1\} = 1$$

Also, by symmetry,

$$P\{X_6 > X_2|X_1 = \max(X_1, \ldots, X_5), X_6 < X_1\} = \frac{1}{2}$$

From part (a),

$$P\{X_6 > X_1|X_1 = \max(X_1, \ldots, X_5)\} = \frac{1}{6}$$

Thus, conditioning on whether $X_6 > X_1$ yields the result

$$P\{X_6 > X_2|X_1 = \max(X_1, \ldots, X_5)\} = \frac{1}{6} + \frac{1}{2}\frac{5}{6} = \frac{7}{12}$$

6.21. $P\{X > s, Y > t\}$
$$= 1 - P\left(\{X \le s\} \cup \{Y \le t\}\right)$$
$$= 1 - P\{X \le s\} - P\{Y \le t\} + P\{X \le s, Y \le t\}$$

Chapter 7

7.1. (a) $d = \sum_{i=1}^{m} 1/n(i)$

(b) $P\{X = i\} = P\{[mU] = i - 1\} = P\{i - 1 \le mU < i\} = 1/m, \quad i = 1, \ldots, m$

(c) $E\left[\frac{m}{n(X)}\right] = \sum_{i=1}^{m} \frac{m}{n(i)} P\{X = i\} = \sum_{i=1}^{m} \frac{m}{n(i)}\frac{1}{m} = d$

7.2. Let $X = X_1 + \cdots + X_n$, where X_i indicates the event that the ith white ball is followed by a white ball. Let $Y = Y_1 + \cdots + Y_n$, where Y_j indicates the event that the jth black ball is followed by a black ball. By the linearity of expectation we have

$$E(X) = \sum_1^{n+m-1} E(X_i) = (n+m-1)E(X_1)$$

and $E(Y) = \sum_1^{n+m-1} E(Y_i) = (n+m-1)E(Y_1)$

To find $E(X_1)$, we find $\Pr(X_1 = 1)$.

$$\Pr(X_1 = 1) = \frac{n}{m+n} \frac{n-1}{m+n-1}.$$

Therefore $E(X) = \dfrac{n(n-1)}{m+n-1}.$

Similarly $E(Y) = \dfrac{m(m-1)}{m+n-1}.$

Required expectation $= E(X) + E(Y) = \dfrac{n(n-1)+m(m-1)}{m+n-1}$

7.3. Arbitrarily number the couples, and then let I_j equal 1 if married couple number $j, j = 1, \ldots, 10$, is seated at the same table. Then, if X represents the number of married couples that are seated at the same table, we have

$$X = \sum_{j=1}^{10} I_j$$

so

$$E[X] = \sum_{j=1}^{10} E[I_j]$$

(a) To compute $E[I_j]$ in this case, consider wife number j. Since each of the $\binom{19}{3}$ groups of size 3 not including her is equally likely to be the remaining members of her table, it follows that the probability that her husband is at her table is

$$\frac{\binom{1}{1}\binom{18}{2}}{\binom{19}{3}} = \frac{3}{19}$$

Hence, $E[I_j] = 3/19$ and so

$$E[X] = 30/19$$

(b) In this case, since the 2 men at the table of wife j are equally likely to be any of the 10 men, it follows that the probability that one of them is her husband is 2/10, so

$$E[I_j] = 2/10 \quad \text{and} \quad E[X] = 2$$

7.4. Let T be the number of rolls needed for appearance of all the 6 sides, and let t_i be the time umber of rolls needed for appearance of the i-th side after i - 1 sides have appeared. Observe that the probability of appearance of a new face is $p_i = (6 - (i-1))/6$. Therefore, t_i has geometric distribution with expectation $(1/p_i)$. By the linearity of expectations we have:

$$E(T) = E(t_1) + E(T_2) + \ldots E(t_6)$$
$$= 6[(1/1) + (1/2) + \ldots (1/6)] = 14.7$$

Expected number of times six appears $= 14.7/6 = 2.45$. For the second case, we use the poisson approximation formula given to obtain,

$$\int_0^\infty \left(1 - (1 - e^{-t/6} - (t/6)e^{-t/6})^6\right)dt \approx 24.134.$$

Expected number of times six appears $= 24.134/6 = 4.022$.

7.5. Let I_j equal 1 if we win 1 when the jth red card to show is turned over, and let I_j equal 0 otherwise. (For instance, I_1 will equal 1 if the first card turned over is red.) Hence, if X is our total winnings, then

$$E[X] = E\left[\sum_{j=1}^n I_j\right] = \sum_{j=1}^n E[I_j]$$

Now, I_j will equal 1 if j red cards appear before j black cards. By symmetry, the probability of this event is equal to 1/2; therefore, $E[I_j] = 1/2$ and $E[X] = n/2$.

7.6. To see that $N \leq n - 1 + I$, note that if all events occur, then both sides of the preceding inequality are equal to n, whereas if they do not all occur, then the inequality reduces to $N \leq n - 1$, which is clearly true in this case. Taking expectations yields

$$E[N] \leq n - 1 + E[I]$$

However, if we let I_i equal 1 if A_i occurs and 0 otherwise, then

$$E[N] = E\left[\sum_{i=1}^n I_i\right] = \sum_{i=1}^n E[I_i] = \sum_{i=1}^n P(A_i)$$

Since $E[I] = P(A_1 \cdots A_n)$, the result follows.

7.7. Note that $|X_1 - X_2| = X_{(2)} - X_1 - X_2$. Hence

$E|X_1 - X_2| = E(X_{(2)}) - 2E(X_1)$. Clearly

$G = E(X_{(2)}) - 2E(X_1)$.

Again $|X_1 - X_2| = X_1 + X_2 - X_{(1)}$ so that

$$G = 2E(X_1) - E(X_{(1)}).$$

Hence from the above two expressions for G we obtain

$$G = \frac{E(X_{(2)}) - E(X_{(1)})}{2}.$$

$$P\{X \geq j\} = \frac{\dbinom{n-j+1}{k}}{\dbinom{n}{k}} = \frac{\dbinom{n-k}{j-1}}{\dbinom{n}{j-1}}$$

which shows that X has the same distribution as the random variable of Example 3e (with the notational change that the total number of balls is now n and the number of special balls is k).

7.8. Let X denote the number of families that depart after the Sanchez family leaves. Arbitrarily number all the $N-1$ non-Sanchez families, and let I_r, $1 \leq r \leq N-1$, equal 1 if family r departs after the Sanchez family does. Then

$$X = \sum_{r=1}^{N-1} I_r$$

Taking expectations gives

$$E[X] = \sum_{r=1}^{N-1} P\{\text{family } r \text{ departs after the Sanchez family}\}$$

Now consider any non-Sanchez family that checked in k pieces of luggage. Because each of the $k+j$ pieces of luggage checked in either by this family or by the Sanchez family is equally likely to be the last of these $k+j$ to appear, the probability that this family departs after the Sanchez family is $\frac{k}{k+j}$. Because the number of non-Sanchez families who checked in k pieces of luggage is n_k when $k \neq j$, or $n_j - 1$ when $k = j$, we obtain

$$E[X] = \sum_k \frac{k n_k}{k+j} - \frac{1}{2}$$

7.9. Let the neighborhood of any point on the rim be the arc starting at that point and extending for a length 1. Consider a uniformly chosen point on the rim of the circle—that is, the probability that this point lies on a specified arc of length x is $\frac{x}{2\pi}$—and let X denote the number of points that lie in its neighborhood. With I_j defined to equal 1 if item number j is in the neighborhood of the random point and to equal 0 otherwise, we have

$$X = \sum_{j=1}^{19} I_j$$

Taking expectations gives

$$E[X] = \sum_{j=1}^{19} P\{\text{item } j \text{ lies in the neighborhood of the random point}\}$$

But because item j will lie in its neighborhood if the random point is located on the arc of length 1 going from item j in the counterclockwise direction, it follows that

$$P\{\text{item } j \text{ lies in the neighborhood of the random point}\} = \frac{1}{2\pi}$$

Hence,

$$E[X] = \frac{19}{2\pi} > 3$$

Because $E[X] > 3$, at least one of the possible values of X must exceed 3, proving the result.

7.10. If $g(x) = x^{1/2}$, then

$$g'(x) = \frac{1}{2}x^{-1/2}, \quad g''(x) = -\frac{1}{4}x^{-3/2}$$

so the Taylor series expansion of $\sqrt{x}$ about λ gives

$$\sqrt{X} \approx \sqrt{\lambda} + \frac{1}{2}\lambda^{-1/2}(X-\lambda) - \frac{1}{8}\lambda^{-3/2}(X-\lambda)^2$$

Taking expectations yields

$$E[\sqrt{X}] \approx \sqrt{\lambda} + \frac{1}{2}\lambda^{-1/2}E[X-\lambda] - \frac{1}{8}\lambda^{-3/2}E[(X-\lambda)^2]$$

$$= \sqrt{\lambda} - \frac{1}{8}\lambda^{-3/2}\lambda$$

$$= \sqrt{\lambda} - \frac{1}{8}\lambda^{-1/2}$$

Hence,

$$\text{Var}(\sqrt{X}) = E[X] - (E[\sqrt{X}])^2$$

$$\approx \lambda - \left(\sqrt{\lambda} - \frac{1}{8}\lambda^{-1/2}\right)^2$$

$$= 1/4 - \frac{1}{64\lambda}$$

$$\approx 1/4$$

7.11. Number the tables so that tables 1, 2, and 3 are the ones with four seats and tables 4, 5, 6, and 7 are the ones with two seats. Also, number the women, and let $X_{i,j}$ equal 1 if woman i is seated with her husband at table j. Note that

$$E[X_{i,j}] = \frac{\dbinom{2}{2}\dbinom{18}{2}}{\dbinom{20}{4}} = \frac{3}{95}, \quad j = 1, 2, 3$$

and

$$E[X_{i,j}] = \frac{1}{\dbinom{20}{2}} = \frac{1}{190}, \quad j = 4, 5, 6, 7$$

Now, X denotes the number of married couples that are seated at the same table, we have

$$E[X] = E\left[\sum_{i=1}^{10}\sum_{j=1}^{7}X_{i,j}\right]$$

$$= \sum_{i=1}^{10}\sum_{j=1}^{3}E[X_{i,j}] + \sum_{i=1}^{10}\sum_{j=4}^{7}E[X_{i,j}]$$

7.12. Let X_i equal 1 if individual i does not recruit anyone, and let X_i equal 0 otherwise. Then

$$E[X_i] = P\{i \text{ does not recruit any of } i+1, i+2, \ldots, n\}$$

$$= \frac{i-1}{i}\frac{i}{i+1}\cdots\frac{n-2}{n-1}$$

$$= \frac{i-1}{n-1}$$

Hence,

$$E\left[\sum_{i=1}^{n}X_i\right] = \sum_{i=1}^{n}\frac{i-1}{n-1} = \frac{n}{2}$$

From the preceding, we also obtain

$$\text{Var}(X_i) = \frac{i-1}{n-1}\left(1 - \frac{i-1}{n-1}\right) = \frac{(i-1)(n-i)}{(n-1)^2}$$

Now, for $i < j$,

$$E[X_iX_j] = \frac{i-1}{i}\cdots\frac{j-2}{j-1}\frac{j-2}{j}\frac{j-1}{j+1}\cdots\frac{n-3}{n-1}$$

$$= \frac{(i-1)(j-2)}{(n-2)(n-1)}$$

Thus,

$$\text{Cov}(X_i, X_j) = \frac{(i-1)(j-2)}{(n-2)(n-1)} - \frac{i-1}{n-1}\frac{j-1}{n-1}$$

$$= \frac{(i-1)(j-n)}{(n-2)(n-1)^2}$$

Therefore,

$$\text{Var}\left(\sum_{i=1}^{n}X_i\right) = \sum_{i=1}^{n}\text{Var}(X_i) + 2\sum_{i=1}^{n-1}\sum_{j=i+1}^{n}\text{Cov}(X_i, X_j)$$

$$= \sum_{i=1}^{n}\frac{(i-1)(n-i)}{(n-1)^2} + 2\sum_{i=1}^{n-1}\sum_{j=i+1}^{n}\frac{(i-1)(j-n)}{(n-2)(n-1)^2}$$

$$= \frac{1}{(n-1)^2}\sum_{i=1}^{n}(i-1)(n-i)$$

$$- \frac{1}{(n-2)(n-1)^2}\sum_{i=1}^{n-1}(i-1)(n-i)(n-i-1)$$

7.13. Let X_i equal 1 if the ith triple consists of one of each type of player. Then

$$E[X_i] = \frac{\binom{2}{1}\binom{3}{1}\binom{4}{1}}{\binom{9}{3}} = \frac{2}{7}$$

Hence, for part (a), we obtain

$$E\left[\sum_{i=1}^{3}X_i\right] = 6/7$$

It follows from the preceding that

$$\text{Var}(X_i) = (2/7)(1 - 2/7) = 10/49$$

Also, for $i \neq j$,

$$E[X_iX_j] = P\{X_i = 1, X_j = 1\}$$

$$= P\{X_i = 1\}P\{X_j = 1 | X_i = 1\}$$

$$= \frac{\binom{2}{1}\binom{3}{1}\binom{4}{1}\binom{1}{1}\binom{2}{1}\binom{3}{1}}{\binom{9}{3}\binom{6}{3}}$$

$$= 6/70$$

Hence, for part (b), we obtain

$$\text{Var}\left(\sum_{i=1}^{3}X_i\right) = \sum_{i=1}^{3}\text{Var}(X_i) + 2\sum\sum_{j>1}\text{Cov}(X_i, X_j)$$

$$= 30/49 + 2\binom{3}{2}\left(\frac{6}{70} - \frac{4}{49}\right)$$

$$= \frac{312}{490}$$

7.14. Let $X_i, i = 1, \ldots, 13$, equal 1 if the ith card is an ace and let X_i be 0 otherwise. Let Y_j equal 1 if the jth card is a spade and let $Y_j = 0$ otherwise. Now,

$$\text{Cov}(X, Y) = \text{Cov}\left(\sum_{i=1}^{13}X_i, \sum_{j=1}^{13}Y_j\right)$$

$$= \sum_{i=1}^{13}\sum_{j=1}^{13}\text{Cov}(X_i, Y_j)$$

However, X_i is clearly independent of Y_j because knowing the suit of a particular card gives no information about whether it is an ace and thus cannot affect the probability that another specified card is an ace. More formally, let $A_{i,s}, A_{i,h}, A_{i,d}, A_{i,c}$ be the events, respectively, that card i is a spade, a heart, a diamond, and a club. Then

$$P\{Y_j = 1\} = \frac{1}{4}(P\{Y_j = 1|A_{i,s}\} + P\{Y_j = 1|A_{i,h}\}$$
$$+ P\{Y_j = 1|A_{i,d}\} + P\{Y_j = 1|A_{i,c}\})$$

But, by symmetry, we have

$$P\{Y_j = 1|A_{i,s}\} = P\{Y_j = 1|A_{i,h}\} = P\{Y_j = 1|A_{i,d}\}$$
$$= P\{Y_j = 1|A_{i,c}\}$$

Therefore,

$$P\{Y_j = 1\} = P\{Y_j = 1|A_{i,s}\}$$

As the preceding implies that

$$P\{Y_j = 1\} = P\{Y_j = 1|A_{i,s}^c\}$$

we see that Y_j and X_i are independent. Hence, $\text{Cov}(X_i, Y_j) = 0$, and thus $\text{Cov}(X, Y) = 0$.

The random variables X and Y, although uncorrelated, are not independent. This follows, for instance, from the fact that

$$P\{Y = 13|X = 4\} = 0 \neq P\{Y = 13\}$$

7.15. (a) Your expected gain without any information is 0.
(b) You should predict heads if $p > 1/2$ and tails otherwise.
(c) Conditioning on V, the value of the coin, gives

$$E[\text{Gain}] = \int_0^1 E[\text{Gain}|V = p]\,dp$$
$$= \int_0^{1/2} [1(1-p)-1(p)]\,dp + \int_{1/2}^1 [1(p)-1(1-p)]\,dp$$
$$= 1/2$$

7.16. Given that the name chosen appears in $n(X)$ different positions on the list, since each of these positions is equally likely to be the one chosen, it follows that

$$E[I|n(X)] = P\{I = 1|n(X)\} = 1/n(X)$$

Hence,

$$E[I] = E[1/n(X)]$$

Thus, $E[mI] = E[m/n(X)] = d$.

7.17. Letting X_i equal 1 if a collision occurs when the ith item is placed, and letting it equal 0 otherwise, we can express the total number of collisions X as

$$X = \sum_{i=1}^m X_i$$

Therefore,

$$E[X] = \sum_{i=1}^m E[X_i]$$

To determine $E[X_i]$, condition on the cell in which it is placed.

$$E[X_i] = \sum_j E[X_i| \text{ placed in cell } j]p_j$$
$$= \sum_j P\{i \text{ causes collision}|\text{placed in cell } j\}p_j$$
$$= \sum_j [1 - (1 - p_j)^{i-1}]p_j$$
$$= 1 - \sum_j (1 - p_j)^{i-1}p_j$$

The next to last equality used the fact that, conditional on item i being placed in cell j, item i will cause a collision if any of the preceding $i - 1$ items were put in cell j. Thus,

$$E[X] = m - \sum_{i=1}^m \sum_{j=1}^n (1 - p_j)^{i-1}p_j$$

Interchanging the order of the summations gives

$$E[X] = m - n + \sum_{j=1}^n (1 - p_j)^m$$

Looking at the result shows that we could have derived it more easily by taking expectations of both sides of the identity

$$\text{number of nonempty cells} = m - X$$

The expected number of nonempty cells is then found by defining an indicator variable for each cell, equal to 1 if that cell is nonempty and to 0 otherwise, and then taking the expectation of the sum of these indicator variables.

7.18. Let L denote the length of the initial run. Conditioning on the first value gives

$$E[L] = E[L|\text{first value is one}]\frac{n}{n + m}$$
$$+ E[L|\text{first value is zero}]\frac{m}{n + m}$$

Now, if the first value is one, then the length of the run will be the position of the first zero when considering the remaining $n + m - 1$ values, of which $n - 1$ are ones and m are zeroes. (For instance, if the initial value of the remaining $n + m - 1$ is zero, then $L = 1$.) As a similar result is true given that the first value is a zero, we obtain from the preceding, upon using the result from Example 3e, that

$$E[L] = \frac{n + m}{m + 1}\frac{n}{n + m} + \frac{n + m}{n + 1}\frac{m}{n + m}$$
$$= \frac{n}{m + 1} + \frac{m}{n + 1}$$

7.19. Let X be the number of flips needed for both boxes to become empty, and let Y denote the number of heads in the first $n + m$ flips. Then

$$E[X] = \sum_{i=0}^{n+m} E[X|Y=i]P\{Y=i\}$$

$$= \sum_{i=0}^{n+m} E[X|Y=i] \binom{n+m}{i} p^i (1-p)^{n+m-i}$$

Now, if the number of heads in the first $n+m$ flips is i, $i \le n$, then the number of additional flips is the number of flips needed to obtain an additional $n-i$ heads. Similarly, if the number of heads in the first $n+m$ flips is $i, i > n$, then, because there would have been a total of $n+m-i < m$ tails, the number of additional flips is the number needed to obtain an additional $i-n$ heads. Since the number of flips needed for j outcomes of a particular type is a negative binomial random variable whose mean is j divided by the probability of that outcome, we obtain

$$E[X] = \sum_{i=0}^{n} \frac{n-i}{p} \binom{n+m}{i} p^i (1-p)^{n+m-i}$$

$$+ \sum_{i=n+1}^{n+m} \frac{i-n}{1-p} \binom{n+m}{i} p^i (1-p)^{n+m-i}$$

7.20. (a) $E(X^n) = \int_0^\infty x^n f(x)dx.$

$$= \int_0^\infty (n\int_0^x y^{n-1}dy) f(x)dx.$$

$$= n\int_0^\infty (\int_x^\infty f(x)dx)y^{n-1}dy$$

$$= n\int_0^\infty x^{n-1}\bar{F}(x)dx.$$

(b) Consider a uniform random variable distributed on $(-1, 1)$. Clearly $E(X) = 0$. Consider

$$\int_{-1}^1 \bar{F}(x)dx = \int_{-1}^1 \frac{1-x}{2}dx = \int_{-1}^1 \frac{1}{2}dx = 1,$$

which is not equal to $E(X)$.

7.21. Consider a random permutation $I_1, \ldots, I_n$ that is equally likely to be any of the $n!$ permutations. Then

$$E[a_{I_j}a_{I_{j+1}}] = \sum_k E[a_{I_j}a_{I_{j+1}}|I_j=k]P\{I_j=k\}$$

$$= \frac{1}{n}\sum_k a_k E[a_{I_{j+1}}|I_j=k]$$

$$= \frac{1}{n}\sum_k a_k \sum_i a_i P\{I_{j+1}=i|I_j=k\}$$

$$= \frac{1}{n(n-1)}\sum_k a_k \sum_{i \ne k} a_i$$

$$= \frac{1}{n(n-1)}\sum_k a_k(-a_k)$$

$$< 0$$

where the final equality followed from the assumption that $\sum_{i=1}^n a_i = 0$. Since the preceding shows that

$$E\left[\sum_{j=1}^{n-1} a_{I_j}a_{I_{j+1}}\right] < 0$$

it follows that there must be some permutation $i_1, \ldots, i_n$ for which

$$\sum_{j=1}^{n-1} a_{i_j}a_{i_{j+1}} < 0$$

7.22. (a) $E[X] = \lambda_1 + \lambda_2, \quad E[Y] = \lambda_2 + \lambda_3$

(b) $\text{Cov}(X, Y) = \text{Cov}(X_1 + X_2, X_2 + X_3)$

$$= \text{Cov}(X_1, X_2 + X_3) + \text{Cov}(X_2, X_2 + X_3)$$

$$= \text{Cov}(X_2, X_2)$$

$$= \text{Var}(X_2)$$

$$= \lambda_2$$

(c) Conditioning on X_2 gives

$$P\{X=i, Y=j\}$$

$$= \sum_k P\{X=i, Y=j|X_2=k\}P\{X_2=k\}$$

$$= \sum_k P\{X_1=i-k, X_3=j-k|X_2=k\}e^{-\lambda_2}\lambda_2^k/k!$$

$$= \sum_k P\{X_1=i-k, X_3=j-k\}e^{-\lambda_2}\lambda_2^k/k!$$

$$= \sum_k P\{X_1=i-k\}P\{X_3=j-k\}e^{-\lambda_2}\lambda_2^k/k!$$

$$= \sum_{k=0}^{\min(i,j)} e^{-\lambda_1}\frac{\lambda_1^{i-k}}{(i-k)!}e^{-\lambda_3}\frac{\lambda_3^{j-k}}{(j-k)!}e^{-\lambda_2}\frac{\lambda_2^k}{k!}$$

7.23. $\text{Corr}\left(\sum_i X_i, \sum_j Y_j\right) = \frac{\text{Cov}(\sum_i X_i, \sum_j Y_j)}{\sqrt{\text{Var}(\sum_i X_i)\text{Var}(\sum_j Y_j)}}$

$$= \frac{\sum_i \sum_j \text{Cov}(X_i, Y_j)}{\sqrt{n\sigma_x^2 n\sigma_y^2}}$$

$$= \frac{\sum_i \text{Cov}(X_i, Y_i) + \sum_i \sum_{j \ne i} \text{Cov}(X_i, Y_j)}{n\sigma_x\sigma_y}$$

$$= \frac{n\rho\sigma_x\sigma_y}{n\sigma_x\sigma_y}$$

$$= \rho$$

where the next to last equality used the fact that $\text{Cov}(X_i, Y_i) = \rho\sigma_x\sigma_y$

7.24. (a) $E[X|$ the King of spades is chosen]

$$= \frac{\binom{48}{3}}{\binom{51}{3}} + 2\frac{\binom{3}{1}\binom{48}{2}}{\binom{51}{3}} + 3\frac{\binom{3}{2}\binom{48}{1}}{\binom{51}{3}} + 4\frac{\binom{3}{3}}{\binom{51}{3}} = \quad 1.17647$$

(b) Prob of selecting atleast 1 King is 0.28126, Using Conditional estimation definition, $E[X|$ atleast one King is chosen]

$$= 1 + \left[2\frac{\binom{4}{2}\binom{48}{2}}{\binom{52}{4}} + 3\frac{\binom{4}{3}\binom{48}{1}}{\binom{52}{4}} + 4\frac{\binom{4}{4}}{\binom{52}{4}} \right] \div 0.28126 = 1.1853$$

(c) Prob of selecting atleast 2 Kings is 0.02571, Using Conditional estimation definition, $E[X|$ atleast one King is chosen] $= 2 + + \left[3\frac{\binom{4}{3}\binom{48}{1}}{\binom{52}{4}} + 4\frac{\binom{4}{4}}{\binom{52}{4}} \right] \div 0.02571 = 2.02772$

7.25. (a) $E[I|X = x] = P\{Z < X|X = x\} = P\{Z < x|X = x\}$
$= P\{Z < x\} = \Phi(x)$
(b) It follows from part (a) that $E[I|X] = \Phi(X)$. Therefore,

$$E[I] = E[E[I|X]] = E[\Phi(X)]$$

The result now follows because $E[I] = P\{I = 1\} = P\{Z < X\}$.
(c) Since $X - Z$ is normal with mean μ and variance 2, we have

$$P\{X > Z\} = P\{X - Z > 0\}$$
$$= P\left\{ \frac{X - Z - \mu}{\sqrt{2}} > \frac{-\mu}{\sqrt{2}} \right\}$$
$$= 1 - \Phi\left(\frac{-\mu}{\sqrt{2}} \right)$$
$$= \Phi\left(\frac{\mu}{\sqrt{2}} \right)$$

7.26. Let N be the number of heads in the first $n + m - 1$ flips. Let $M = \max(X, Y)$ be the number of flips needed to amass at least n heads and at least m tails. Conditioning on N gives

$$E[M] = \sum_i E[M|N = i]P\{N = i\}$$
$$= \sum_{i=0}^{n-1} E[M|N = i]P\{N = i\} + \sum_{i=n}^{n+m-1} E[M|N = i]P\{N = i\}$$

Now, suppose we are given that there are a total of i heads in the first $n + m - 1$ trials. If $i < n$, then we have already obtained at least m tails, so the additional number of flips needed is equal to the number needed for an additional $n - i$ heads; similarly, if $i \geq n$, then we have already obtained at least n heads, so the additional number of flips needed is equal to the number needed for an additional $m - (n + m - 1 - i)$ tails. Consequently, we have

$$E[M] = \sum_{i=0}^{n-1} \left(n + m - 1 + \frac{n-i}{p} \right) P\{N = i\}$$
$$+ \sum_{i=n}^{n+m-1} \left(n + m - 1 + \frac{i+1-n}{1-p} \right) P\{N = i\}$$
$$= n + m - 1 + \sum_{i=0}^{n-1} \frac{n-i}{p} \binom{n+m-1}{i} p^i (1-p)^{n+m-1-i}$$
$$+ \sum_{i=n}^{n+m-1} \frac{i+1-n}{1-p} \binom{n+m-1}{i} p^i (1-p)^{n+m-1-i}$$

The expected number of flips to obtain either n heads or m tails, $E[\min(X, Y)]$, is now given by

$$E[\min(X, Y)] = E[X + Y - M] = \frac{n}{p} + \frac{m}{1-p} - E[M]$$

7.27. This is just the expected time to collect $n - 1$ of the n types of coupons in Example 2i. By the results of that example the solution is

$$1 + \frac{n}{n-1} + \frac{n}{n-2} + \ldots + \frac{n}{2}$$

7.28. Let $p_k = P(X = k)$. Consider

$$E(X) = \sum_{k=0}^{\infty} kP(X = k)$$
$$= p_1 + 2p_2 + 3p_3 = P(X \geq 1) + P(X \geq 2) + \ldots$$
$$= \sum_{k=1}^{\infty} P(X \geq k).$$

7.29. The third central moment of X_1 is equal to $p(1-p)(1-2p)$. Using the identity $n.\text{Cov}(\bar{X}, S^2) = E((X - \mu)^3)$, we obtain $\text{Cov}(\bar{X}, S^2) = p(1-p)(1-2p)/2$, which is zero when $p = 0.5$. Consider

$$P(S^2 = 0 | \bar{X} = 1) = 1 \neq \frac{1}{2} = P(S^2 = 0).$$

Hence $\bar{X}$ and S^2 are not independent.

7.30. Using the result stated in Q 28 above we have

$$E(X) = \sum_{k=1}^{\infty} P(X \geq k) = \sum_{k=1}^{n} P(X \geq k)$$

$$= \sum_{k=1}^{n} (1 - p)^{k-1}$$

$$= \frac{1 - (1 - p)^n}{p}.$$

7.31. Consider independent standard normal random variables $Z_1,...,Z_5$ and define

$$W = Z_1^2 + Z_2^2 + Z_3^2 + Z_4^2, \quad X = WZ_5 \text{ and } Y = W^{-1}$$

Then $E[XY] = E[Z_5] = 0$, $E[W] = 4$, $E[Y] = 1/2$ and

$$\mathrm{Cov}(X,Y) = 0.$$

But ρ can not be defined as $E(Y^2)$ is not finite.

7.32. Take expectations, using that the expected value of a sum is the sum of the expectations, and then differentiate.

Chapter 8

8.1. Let X denote the number of sales made next week, and note that X is integral. From Markov's inequality, we obtain the following:

(a) $P\{X > 18\} = P\{X \geq 19\} \leq \dfrac{E[X]}{19} = 16/19$

(b) $P\{X > 25\} = P\{X \geq 26\} \leq \dfrac{E[X]}{26} = 16/26$

8.2. (a) $P\{10 \leq X \leq 22\} = P\{|X - 16| \leq 6\}$

$$= P\{|X - \mu| \leq 6\}$$

$$= 1 - P\{|X - \mu| > 6\}$$

$$\geq 1 - 9/36 = 3/4$$

(b) $P\{X \geq 19\} = P\{X - 16 \geq 3\} \leq \dfrac{9}{9 + 9} = 1/2$

In part (a), we used Chebyshev's inequality; in part (b), we used its one-sided version. (See Proposition 5.1.)

8.3. We use Chebyshevs inequality in part (a) and the one-sided version in parts (b) and (c). Consider

$$\mathrm{Var}(X - Y) = \mathrm{Var}(X) + \mathrm{Var}(Y) - 2\mathrm{Cov}(X,Y)$$

$$= 10 + 22 - 7 = 25$$

(a) $P\{|X - Y| > 25\} \leq 25/525 = 1/25$

(b) $P\{X - Y > 25\} \leq 25/(25 + 525) = 1/26$

(c) $P\{Y - X > 25\} \leq 25/(25 + 525) = 1/26$

8.4. If X is the number produced at factory A and Y the number produced at factory B, then

$$E[Y - X] = -2, \quad \mathrm{Var}(Y - X) = 36 + 9 = 45$$
$$P\{Y - X > 0\} = P\{Y - X \geq 1\}$$
$$= P\{Y - X + 2 \geq 3\} \leq \frac{45}{45 + 9} = 45/54$$

8.5. Note first that

$$E[X_i] = \int_0^1 2x^2\, dx = 2/3$$

Now use the strong law of large numbers to obtain

$$r = \lim_{n \to \infty} \frac{n}{S_n}$$

$$= \lim_{n \to \infty} \frac{1}{S_n/n}$$

$$= \frac{1}{\lim_{n \to \infty} S_n/n}$$

$$= 1/(2/3) = 3/2$$

8.6. Because $E[X_i] = 2/3$ and

$$E[X_i^2] = \int_0^1 2x^3\, dx = 1/2$$

we have $\mathrm{Var}(X_i) = 1/2 - (2/3)^2 = 1/18$. Thus, if there are n components on hand, then

$$P\{S_n \geq 35\} = P\{S_n \geq 34.5\} \quad \text{(the continuity correction)}$$

$$= P\left\{ \frac{S_n - 2n/3}{\sqrt{n/18}} \geq \frac{34.5 - 2n/3}{\sqrt{n/18}} \right\}$$

$$\approx P\left\{ Z \geq \frac{34.5 - 2n/3}{\sqrt{n/18}} \right\}$$

where Z is a standard normal random variable. Since

$$P\{Z > -1.284\} = P\{Z < 1.284\} \approx .90$$

we see that n should be chosen so that

$$(34.5 - 2n/3) \approx -1.284\sqrt{n/18}$$

A numerical computation gives the result $n = 55$.

8.7. If X is the time required to service a machine, then

$$E[X] = .2 + .3 = .5$$

Also, since the variance of an exponential random variable is equal to the square of its mean, we have

$$\mathrm{Var}(X) = (.2)^2 + (.3)^2 = .13$$

Therefore, with X_i being the time required to service job $i, i = 1, \ldots, 20$, and Z being a standard normal random variable, it follows that

$$P\{X_1 + \cdots + X_{20} < 8\} = P\left\{\frac{X_1 + \cdots + X_{20} - 10}{\sqrt{2.6}} < \frac{8 - 10}{\sqrt{2.6}}\right\}$$
$$\approx P\{Z < -1.24035\}$$
$$\approx .1074$$

8.8. Note first that if X is the gambler's winnings on a single bet, then

$$E[X] = -.7 - .4 + 1 = -.1, E[X^2] = .7 + .8 + 10 = 11.5$$
$$\rightarrow \text{Var}(X) = 11.49$$

Therefore, with Z having a standard normal distribution,

$$P\{X_1 + \cdots + X_{100} \le -.5\} = P\left\{\frac{X_1 + \cdots + X_{100} + 10}{\sqrt{11.49}} \le \frac{-.5 + 10}{\sqrt{11.49}}\right\}$$
$$\approx P\{Z \le .2803\}$$
$$\approx .6104$$

8.9. Using the notation of Problem 8.7, we have

$$P\{X_1 + \cdots + X_{20} < t\} = P\left\{\frac{X_1 + \cdots + X_{20} - 10}{\sqrt{2.6}} < \frac{t - 10}{\sqrt{2.6}}\right\}$$
$$\approx P\left\{Z < \frac{t - 10}{\sqrt{2.6}}\right\}$$

Now, $P\{Z < 1.645\} \approx .95$, so t should be such that

$$\frac{t - 10}{\sqrt{2.6}} \approx 1.645$$

which yields $t \approx 12.65$.

8.10. If the claim were true, then, by the central limit theorem, the average nicotine content (call it X) would approximately have a normal distribution with mean 2.2 and standard deviation .03. Thus, the probability that it would be as high as 3.1 is

$$P\{X > 3.1\} = P\left\{\frac{X - 2.2}{.03} > \frac{3.1 - 2.2}{.03}\right\}$$
$$\approx P\{Z > 30\}$$
$$\approx 0$$

where Z is a standard normal random variable.

8.11. (a) If we arbitrarily number the batteries and let X_i denote the life of battery $i, i = 1, \ldots, 40$, then the X_i are independent and identically distributed random variables. To compute the mean and variance of the life of, say, battery 1, we condition on its type. Letting I equal 1 if battery 1 is type A and letting it equal 0 if it is type B, we have

$$E[X_1 | I = 1] = 50, \qquad E[X_1 | I = 0] = 30$$

yielding

$$E[X_1] = 50P\{I = 1\} + 30P\{I = 0\} = 50(1/2) + 30(1/2) = 40$$

In addition, using the fact that $E[W^2] = (E[W])^2 + \text{Var}(W)$, we have

$$E[X_1^2 | I = 1] = (50)^2 + (15)^2 = 2725,$$
$$E[X_1^2 | I = 0] = (30)^2 + 6^2 = 936$$

yielding

$$E[X_1^2] = (2725)(1/2) + (936)(1/2) = 1830.5$$

Thus, $X_1, \ldots, X_{40}$ are independent and identically distributed random variables having mean 40 and variance $1830.5 - 1600 = 230.5$. Hence, with $S = \sum_{i=1}^{40} X_i$, we have

$$E[S] = 40(40) = 1600, \qquad \text{Var}(S) = 40(230.5) = 9220$$

and the central limit theorem yields

$$P\{S > 1700\} = P\left\{\frac{S - 1600}{\sqrt{9220}} > \frac{1700 - 1600}{\sqrt{9220}}\right\}$$
$$\approx P\{Z > 1.041\}$$
$$= 1 - \Phi(1.041) = .149$$

(b) For this part, let S_A be the total life of all the type A batteries and let S_B be the total life of all the type B batteries. Then, by the central limit theorem, S_A has approximately a normal distribution with mean $20(50) = 1000$ and variance $20(225) = 4500$, and S_B has approximately a normal distribution with mean $20(30) = 600$ and variance $20(36) = 720$. Because the sum of independent normal random variables is also a normal random variable, it follows that $S_A + S_B$ is approximately normal with mean 1600 and variance 5220. Consequently, with $S = S_A + S_B$,

$$P\{S > 1700\} = P\left\{\frac{S - 1600}{\sqrt{5220}} > \frac{1700 - 1600}{\sqrt{5220}}\right\}$$
$$\approx P\{Z > 1.384\}$$
$$= 1 - \Phi(1.384) = .083$$

8.12. Note that $\bar{X} = \frac{1}{n}\sum_{i=1}^{n} X_i$ is distributed as that of X. Hence using Chebyshev's inequality we have

$$P\{|x - \theta| \ge \varepsilon\} = P\{|x - \theta| \ge \varepsilon\} \le \frac{\text{Var}(X)}{k^2},$$

which is independent of n.

8.13. Take logarithms and then apply the strong law of large numbers to obtain

$$\log\left[\left(\prod_{i=1}^{n} X_i\right)^{1/n}\right] = \frac{1}{n}\sum_{i=1}^{n}\log(X_i)\to E[\log(X_i)]$$

Therefore,

$$\left(\prod_{i=1}^{n} X_i\right)^{1/n} \to e^{E[\log(X_i)]}$$

4. Let X_i be the time taken to serve a customer. Also let $= \sum_{i=1}^{n} X_i$. Let Z be the standard normal random variable.

(a) Consider

$$P(S_{50} > 240) = P\left(\frac{S_{50} - 250}{\sqrt{50\times2}} > \frac{240 - 250}{\sqrt{50\times2}}\right)$$

$$= P\left(Z > \frac{-10}{\sqrt{50\times2}}\right) = P(Z > -1) = 0.841$$

(b) Consider

$$P(S_{30} \le 140) = P\left(\frac{S_{30} - 150}{\sqrt{30\times2}} \le \frac{140 - 150}{\sqrt{30\times2}}\right)$$

$$= P\left(Z \le \frac{-10}{\sqrt{30\times2}}\right) = P\left(Z \le -\sqrt{5/2}\right) = 0.057$$

Chapter 9

9.1. From axiom (iii), it follows that the number of events that occur between times 8 and 10 has the same distribution as the number of events that occur by time 2 and thus is a Poisson random variable with mean 6. Hence, we obtain the following solutions for parts (a) and (b):

(a) $P\{N(10) - N(8) = 0\} = e^{-6}$

(b) $E[N(10) - N(8)] = 6$

(c) It follows from axioms (ii) and (iii) that from any point of time onward, the process of events occurring is a Poisson process with rate λ. Hence, the expected time of the fifth event after 2 P.M. is $2 + E[S_5] = 2 + 5/3$. That is, the expected time of this event is 3:40 P.M.

9.2. Let A_r denotes the event that $(n + r)$ the speeding cars passed the intersection by time t and exactly n out of the $(n + r)$ occurrences are spotted by the policeman. Hence

$$\left(\begin{matrix}P(A_r) = n + r \\ np^n(1-p)^r\end{matrix}\right)$$

Required probability $=$

$$P(A) = \sum_{r=0}^{\infty} P(A_r)P(n + r \text{ events occur in time } t)$$

$$= \sum_{r=0}^{\infty}\binom{n+r}{r}p^n(1-p)^r e^{-\lambda}\frac{\lambda^{r+n}}{(r+n)!} = \frac{\lambda p^n e^{-\lambda p}}{n!}$$

Hence the answer is

$$\frac{4.8^4 e^{4.8}}{4!}$$

$$= 0.182029$$

9.3. Fix a point on the road and let X_n equal 0 if the nth vehicle to pass is a car and let it equal 1 if it is a truck, $n \ge 1$. We now suppose that the sequence $X_n, n \ge 1$, is a Markov chain with transition probabilities

$$P_{0,0} = 5/6, \quad P_{0,1} = 1/6, \quad P_{1,0} = 4/5, \quad P_{1,1} = 1/5$$

Then the long-run proportion of times is the solution of

$$\pi_0 = \pi_0(5/6) + \pi_1(4/5)$$
$$\pi_1 = \pi_0(1/6) + \pi_1(1/5)$$
$$\pi_0 + \pi_1 = 1$$

Solving the preceding equations gives

$$\pi_0 = 24/29 \qquad \pi_1 = 5/29$$

Thus, $2400/29 \approx 83$ percent of the vehicles on the road are cars.

9.4. The successive weather classifications constitute a Markov chain. If the states are 0 for rainy, 1 for sunny, and 2 for overcast, then the transition probability matrix is as follows:

$$\mathbf{P} = \begin{matrix} 0 & 1/2 & 1/2 \\ 1/3 & 1/3 & 1/3 \\ 1/3 & 1/3 & 1/3 \end{matrix}$$

The long-run proportions satisfy

$$\pi_0 = \pi_1(1/3) + \pi_2(1/3)$$
$$\pi_1 = \pi_0(1/2) + \pi_1(1/3) + \pi_2(1/3)$$
$$\pi_2 = \pi_0(1/2) + \pi_1(1/3) + \pi_2(1/3)$$
$$1 = \pi_0 + \pi_1 + \pi_2$$

The solution of the preceding system of equations is

$$\pi_0 = 1/4, \quad \pi_1 = 3/8, \quad \pi_2 = 3/8$$

Hence, three-eighths of the days are sunny and one-fourth are rainy.

9.5. (a) A direct computation yields

$$H(X)/H(Y) \approx 1.06$$

(b) Both random variables take on two of their values with the same probabilities .35 and .05. The difference is that if they do not take on either of those values, then X, but not Y, is equally likely to take on any of its three remaining possible values. Hence, from Theoretical Exercise 9.13, we would expect the result of part (a).

Chapter 10

10.1. (a) $1 = C \int_0^1 e^x dx \Rightarrow C = 1/(e - 1)$

(b) $F(x) = C \int_0^x e^y dy = \frac{e^x - 1}{e - 1}, \quad 0 \le x \le 1$

Hence, if we let $X = F^{-1}(U)$, then

$$U = \frac{e^X - 1}{e - 1}$$

or

$$X = \log(U(e - 1) + 1)$$

Thus, we can simulate the random variable X by generating a random number U and then setting $X = \log(U(e - 1) + 1)$.

10.2. Use the acceptance–rejection method with $g(x) = 1, 0 < x < 1$. Calculus shows that the maximum value of $f(x)/g(x)$ occurs at a value of $x, 0 < x < 1$, such that

$$2x - 6x^2 + 4x^3 = 0$$

or, equivalently, when

$$4x^2 - 6x + 2 = (4x - 2)(x - 1) = 0$$

The maximum thus occurs when $x = 1/2$, and it follows that

$$C = \max f(x)/g(x) = 30(1/4 - 2/8 + 1/16) = 15/8$$

Hence, the algorithm is as follows:

Step 1. Generate a random number U_1.
Step 2. Generate a random number U_2.
Step 3. If $U_2 \le 16(U_1^2 - 2U_1^3 + U_1^4)$, set $X = U_1$; else return to Step 1.

10.3. (a) The probability mass function is given by $p_0 = 0.25$, $p_1 = 0.25$ and $p_2 = 0.25$

Hence algorithm is given by

Step 1. Generate a random number U.
Step 2. If $U \le 0.25$, set $X = 0$ and stop.
Step 3. If $0.25 < U \le 0.75$, set $X = 1$ and stop.
Step 4. If $U \ge 0.75$, set $X = 2$ and stop.

(b) The probability mass function is given by $p_i = 1/$ $i = 1, 2, \ldots, n$. Once can easily obtain the algorithm as in (a

10.4. Write

$$F(x) = P(X \le x) = P(X < x) + Vf(x) + (1 - V)f(x$$
$$= F(x, v) + (1 - V)f(x).$$

Hence

$$E(F(X)) = E(F(x, v)) + E((1 - V))E(f(X))$$

$$= \frac{1}{2} + \frac{1}{2}E(f(X))$$

$$= \frac{1}{2} + \frac{1}{2}\frac{p}{1+q} = \frac{1}{1+q}$$

For geometric random variable we know $F(x) = 1 - q^x$
Hence

$$E(F(X)) = 1 - E(q^{x+1}) = 1 - \frac{q}{1+q} = \frac{1}{1+q}$$

10.5. (a) Generate $2n$ independent exponential rando variables with mean $1, X_i, Y_i, i = 1, \ldots, n$, and then use th estimator $\sum_{i=1}^{n} e^{X_i Y_i}/n$.

(b) We can use XY as a control variate to obtain an estimato of the type

$$\sum_{i=1}^{n} (e^{X_i Y_i} + cX_i Y_i)/n$$

Another possibility would be to use $XY + X^2Y^2/2$ as th control variate and so obtain an estimator of the type

$$\sum_{i=1}^{n} (e^{X_i Y_i} + c[X_i Y_i + X_i^2 Y_i^2/2 - 1/2])/n$$

The motivation behind the preceding formula is based on th fact that the first three terms of the MacLaurin series expan sion of e^{xy} are $1 + xy + (x^2y^2)/2$.

INDEX

A

absolutely continuous random variables, *see* continuous random variables

Analytic Theory of Probability (Laplace), 378

antithetic variables, 427

Archimedes, 197

Ars Conjectandi, 135, 370

associative law for events, 24

axioms of probability, 25–27

axioms of surprise, 402

B

ballot problem, 107

Banach match problem, 150

basic principle of counting, 2
   generalized, 2

Bayes's formula, 69–75

Bernoulli, Jacques, 135

Bernoulli, James, 86, 127, 135, 370

Bernoulli, Nicholas, 135, 370

Bernoulli random variable, 127

Bernoulli trials, 107

Bernstein polynomials, 392

Bertrand's paradox, 186

best prize problem, 326–327

beta distribution, 207, 216, 264

binary symmetric channel, 410

binomial coefficients, 7

binomial random variable, 127–128, 132, 173, 249
   normal approximation, 193–196
   approximation to hypergeometric, 153–154
   computing its mass function, 134
   moments of, 131–132, 299
   simulation of, 425
   sums of independent, 247, 339
   with randomly chosen success probability, 327–328

binomial theorem, 7–8

birthday problem, 37, 139–140, 171

bivariate exponential distribution, 278

bivariate normal distribution, 253–254, 319–320

Bonferroni's inequality, 53, 363

Boole's inequality, 55, 283

Borel, 381

Box-Muller simulation technique, 422

branching process, 362

bridge, 36, 58

Buffon's needle problem, 231–232, 275

C

Cantor distribution, 360

Cauchy distribution, 206

Cauchy-Schwarz inequality, 360

center of gravity, 121

central limit theorem, 187, 370–371, 377

channel capacity, 411, 413

Chapman-Kolmogorov equations, 399

Chebychev's inequality, 368
   one-sided, 382
   and weak law of large numbers, 370

Chernoff bound, 385

chi-squared distribution, 204, 242–243
   density function, 243
   relation to gamma distribution, 242–243
   simulation of, 423–424

coding theory, 405
   and entropy, 407

combinations, 5–9

combinatorial analysis, 1

combinatorial identities, 7, 17–19, 116

commutative law for events, 24

complement of an event, 23

complete graph, 88

computing probabilities by conditioning, 62–69, 325

concave function, 287

conditional covariance formula, 360

conditional distribution,
   continuous case, 250–252
   discrete case, 248–250

conditional expectation, 313–314
   computing expectations by conditioning, 315
   use in prediction, 330
   use in simulation, 428

conditional independence, 94

conditional probability, 56–57, 106
   as a long run relative frequency, 61–62
   as a probability function, 89–90
   satisfying axioms of probability, 89–90

conditional probability density function, 250–251

conditional probability distribution function, 248

conditional probability mass function, 248

conditional variance, 328–329

conditional variance formula, 351

continuity correction, 195

continuity property of probability, 42–44

continuous random variable, 176

control variate, 429

convex function, 387

convolution, 239

correlation, 310–311

correlation coefficient, 305–313

coupon collecting problems, 114–116, 286, 297, 301–304

covariance, 305

craps, 50, 317–319

cumulative distribution function, 116
   properties of, 159–160

D

de Mere, Chevalier, 81

DeMoivre, A., 193, 196–197, 372

DeMoivre-Laplace limit theorem, 193–194

DeMorgan's laws, 25

dependent events, 75

dependent random variables, 229

discrete random variables, 116–117

discrete uniform random variable, 116

distribution function, *see* cumulative distribution function,

distribution of a function of a random variable, 208–209

distributive law for events, 24

DNA match, 73

dominant genes, 102

double exponential distribution, *see* Laplace distribution

doubly stochastic matrix, 412

E

Ehrenfest urn model, 398–399

entropy, 404

ergodic Markov chain, 400–401

Erlang distribution, 204

evaluating evidence, 70

event, 22
   decreasing sequence of, 42
   increasing sequence of, 42
   independent, 75
   mutually exclusive, 23

exchangeable random variables, 267

expectation, 119, 215, 280, 349–350
   as a center of gravity, 121
   of a beta random variable, 208
   of a binomial random variable, 131–132, 284
   of a continuous random variable, 179–180
   of an exponential random variable, 198
   of a function of a random variable, 121–122, 181

expectation (*Continued*)
    of a gamma random variable, 205
    of a geometric random variable, 148
    of a hypergeometric random
        variable, 153–154, 285
    of a negative binomial random
        variable, 150–151, 284
    of a nonnegative random variable,
        170
    of a normal random variable, 189
    of number of matches, 285–286
    of number of runs, 287
    of a Poisson random variable, 137
    of sums of a random number of
        random variables, 317, 341–343
    of sums of random variables,
        155–157, 281
    of the number of successes,
        157–158, 298
    of uniform random variables, 185
    table of, 339–340
expected value, *see* expectation
exponential random variable, 197,
    215–216, 265–266
    rate of, 202
    relation to half life, 237
    simulation of, 418
    sums of, 242

F

failure rate function, *see* hazard rate
    function
Fermat, P., 81, 86
Fermat's combinatorial identity, 18
first moment, *see* mean
frequency interpretation of
    probability, 26, 119

G

Galton, F., 378
gambler's ruin problem, 84–87
    multiple player, 83–84
game theory, 165
gamma distribution, 203–204, 216,
    242, 264
    relation to chi-squared
        distribution, 204, 242–243
    relation to exponential
        distribution, 242
    relation to Poisson process, 204
    simulation of, 418–419
gamma function, 203–204, 216
    relation to beta function, 208
Gauss, J.F.K., 196–197
Gaussian distribution, *see* normal
    distribution
genetics, 102, 104
geometric random variable, 147, 172

simulation of, 424–425
geometrical probability, 186

H

Hamilton path, 293–294
hazard rate function, 201–202
Huygens, C., 86
hypergeometric random variable, 151
    relation to binomial, 153–154
    moments of, 299–300

I

importance sampling, 431
inclusion-exclusion, 30–31, 291
    bounds, 31–32
independent events, 75–79, 107
    conditional, 94
independent increments, 395
independent random variables, 228,
    233–234, 238–239
indicator random variables, 120
information, 404–405
interarrival times, 396
integer solutions of equations, 12–14
intersection of events, 22–23
inverse transform method, 418
    discrete, 424

J

Jensen's inequality, 387
joint cumulative probability
    distribution function, 220, 227
joint moment generating function, 343
joint probability density function,
    223–224, 227
    of functions of random variables,
        260, 264–265
joint probability mass function, 221
jointly continuous random variables,
    223, 227

K

k-of-n system, 103
keno, 169
Khintchine, 387
knockout tournament, 11
Kolmogorov, A., 381

L

Laplace, P., 193, 372, 378
Laplace distribution, 201–202
Laplace's rule of succession, 95, 109
law of frequency of errors,
law of total probability, 69
laws of large numbers, 367
Legendre theorem, 216
Liapounoff, 372
limit of events, 42

linear prediction, 333
lognormal distribution, 210, 245

M

marginal distribution, 221
Markov chain, 397
Markov's inequality, 367
matching problem, 39–40, 53, 60,
    93–94, 138, 301
maximum likelihood estimates, 170
maximums-minimums identity, 295–296
mean of a random variable, 125
measurable events, 28
median of a random variable, 215, 359
memoryless random variable, 199–200
Mendel, G., 129
midrange, 276
minimax theorem, 165
mode of a random variable, 215
moment generating function, 334–335
    of a binomial random variable, 336
    of a chi-squard random variable,
        341–342
    of an exponential random variable,
        337
    of a normal random variable,
        337–338
    of a Poisson random variable, 336
    of a sum of independent random
        variables, 338
    of a sum of a random number of
        random variables, 342
    tables for, 339–340
moments of a random variable, 125
    of the number of events that occur,
        298
multinomial coefficients, 9–10
multinomial distribution, 228,
    249–250, 312–313
multinomial theorem, 10
multiplication rule of probability, 59–60
multivariate normal distribution,
    345–346
mutually exclusive events, 23

N

negative binomial random variables,
    149
    relation to binomial, 172
    relation to geometric, 149
negative hypergeometric random
    variable, 175, 302–303
Newton, I., 197
noiseless coding theorem, 407
noisy coding theorem, 411
normal random variables, 187
    approximation to binomial, 193–195
    characterization of, 232–233

joint distribution of sample mean
  and sample variance, 348–349
moments of, 363
simulation, 263
simulation by polar method, 422–423
simulation by rejection method,
  419–420
sums of independent, 243–244, 341
null event, 23
null set, 23

O

odds of an event, 68
order statistics, 256

P

Parallel system, 78
Pareto, 155
partition, 52–53
Pascal, B., 81
Pascal random variable, *see* negative
  binomial random variable
Pearson, K., 197
permutations, 3–5
personal view of probability, 46
Poisson, S., 136
Poisson paradigm, 138–141
Poisson process, 144–145, 395
Poisson random variable, 135–136,
  170–171, 229–230, 249
    as an approximation to binomial,
      136, 388
    as an approximation to the number
      of events that occur, 138–141
    bounds on its probabilities, 385, 393
    computing its probabilities, 146
    simulation of, 425–426
    sums of independent, 246–247, 341
poker, 35–36
polar algorithm, 422–423
Polya's urn model, 268
posterior probability, 96
prior probability, 96
probabilistic method, 89, 293
probability of an event, 26
    as a continuous set function, 42–44
    as a limiting proportion, 25–26
    as a measure of belief, 46–47
probability density function, 176
    of a function of a random variable,
      209
    relation to cumulative distribution
      function, 177, 179
probability mass function, 116–117
    relation to cumulative distribution
      function, 118
problem of the points, 81–82, 150

Q

quick sort algorithm, 289–291

R

random number, 416
    pseudo, 416
random permutation, 416–417, 430
random sample, 259
random subset, 172, 234–236, 417
random variables, 112
random walk, 288–289, 399–400
range of a random sample, 259
Rayleigh density function, 203, 262
record value, 360
reduced sample space, 58
rejection method of simulation, 419–420
relative frequency definition of
  probability, 25–26
Riemann zeta function, 155
round robin tournament, 108–109
runs, 41–42, 53, 92–93
    longest, 140–144

S

sample mean, 283
sample median, 258
sample space, 21–22
sample variance, 307
sampling from a finite population, 196
sampling with replacement, 50
sequential updating of information,
  96–97
serve and rally games, 82–83
Shannon, C., 411
signal to noise ratio, 392
simulation, 415
St. Petersburg paradox, 165
standard deviation, 127, 392
    inequality, 366
standard normal distribution function,
  189–191, 215
    bounds, 385
    table of, 190
standard normal random variable,
  189, 215
    moments of, 362
stationary increments, 395
Stieltjes integral, 349–350
Stirling's approximation, 134
stochastically larger, 359
strong law of large numbers, 378–381
subjective probability, *see* personal
  probability
subset, 23
superset, 23
surprise, 402

T

t distribution, 252–253
transition probabilities of a Markov
  chain, 398
trials, 77
triangular distribution, 240
twin problem, 67

U

uncertainty, 404
uncorrelated random variables, 311–312
uniform random variables, 184
    sums of independent, 240–241
union of events, 22–23
    probability formula for, 28–30
unit normal random variable, *see*
  standard normal random variable
utility, 124–125

V

value at risk, 193
variance, 125–126, 215
    as a moment of inertia, 126
    of a beta random variable, 208
    of a binomial random variable, 132,
      308
    of an exponential random variable,
      198
    of a gamma random variable, 205
    of a geometric random variable,
      148–149, 321–322
    of a hypergeometric random
      variable, 153–154
    of a negative binomial random
      variable, 150–151
    of a normal random variable, 189
    of a Poisson random variable, 138
    of a sum of a random number of
      random variables, 317, 330
    of sums of random variables,
      306–307
    of a uniform random variable, 185
    of the number of successes, 158
    tables for, 339–340
Venn diagrams, 23–24
von Neumann, 165

W

weak law of large numbers, 369–370
Weibull distribution, 205, 216
    relation to exponential, 216
Weierstrass theorem, 392

Y

Yule-Simons distribution, 170–171

Z

zeta distribution, 155
Zipf distribution, *see* zeta distribution

COMMON DISCRETE DISTRIBUTIONS

- **Bernoulli**(p) X indicates whether a trial that results in a success with probability p is a success or not.

$$P\{X = 1\} = p$$
$$P\{X = 0\} = 1 - p$$

$E[X] = p, \quad \text{Var}(X) = p(1 - p).$

- **Binomial**(n, p) X represents the number of successes in n independent trials when each trial is a success with probability p.

$$P\{X = i\} = \binom{n}{i} p^i (1 - p)^{n-i}, \quad i = 0, 1, \ldots, n$$

$E[X] = np, \quad \text{Var}(X) = np(1 - p).$
Note. Binomial($1, p$) = Bernoulli(p).

- **Geometric**(p) X is the number of trials needed to obtain a success when each trial is independently a success with probability p.

$$P(X = i) = p(1 - p)^{i-1}, \quad i = 1, 2, \ldots,$$

$E[X] = \frac{1}{p}, \quad \text{Var}(X) = \frac{1-p}{p^2}.$

- **Negative Binomial**(r, p) X is the number of trials needed to obtain a total of r successes when each trial is independently a success with probability p.

$$P(X = i) = \binom{i - 1}{r - 1} p^r (1 - p)^{i-r}, \quad i = r, r + 1, r + 2, \ldots$$

$E[X] = \frac{r}{p}, \quad \text{Var}(X) = r\frac{1-p}{p^2}.$
Notes.
1. Negative Binomial($1, p$) = Geometric(p).
2. Sum of r independent Geometric(p) random variables is Negative Binomial(r, p)

- **Poisson**(λ) X is used to model the number of events that occur when these events are either independent or weakly dependent and each has a small probability of occurrence.

$$P\{X = i\} = e^{-\lambda} \lambda^i / i!, \quad i = 0, 1, 2, \ldots$$

$E[X] = \lambda, \quad \text{Var}(X) = \lambda.$
Notes.
1. A Poisson random variable X with parameter $\lambda = np$ provides a good approximation to a Binomial(n, p) random variable when n is large and p is small.
2. If events are occurring one at a time in a random manner for which (a) the number of events that occur in disjoint time intervals is independent and (b) the probability of an event occurring in any small time interval is approximately λ times the length of the interval, then the number of events in an interval of length t will be a Poisson(λt) random variable.

- **Hypergeometric** X is the number of white balls in a random sample of n balls chosen without replacement from an urn of N balls of which m are white.

$$P\{X = i\} = \frac{\binom{m}{i}\binom{N-m}{n-i}}{\binom{N}{n}}, \quad i = 0, 1, 2, \ldots$$

The preceding uses the convention that $\binom{r}{j} = 0$ if either $j < 0$ or $j > r$.

With $p = m/N$, $E[X] = np$, $\quad \mathrm{Var}(X) = \frac{N-n}{N-1} np(1-p)$

Note. If each ball were replaced before the next selection, then X would be a Binomial(n, p) random variable.

- **Negative Hypergeometric** X is the number of balls that need be removed from an urn that contains $n + m$ balls, of which n are white, until a total of r white balls has been removed, where $r \leq n$.

$$P\{X = k\} = \frac{\binom{n}{r-1}\binom{m}{k-r}}{\binom{n+m}{k-1}} \frac{n - r + 1}{n + m - k + 1}, \quad k \geq r$$

$$E[X] = r\frac{n+m+1}{n+1}, \quad \mathrm{Var}(X) = \frac{mr(n+1-r)(n+m+1)}{(n+1)^2(n+2)}$$

COMMON CONTINUOUS DISTRIBUTIONS

- **Uniform** (a, b) X is equally likely to be near each value in the interval (a, b). Its density function is

$$f(x) = \frac{1}{b - a}, \quad a < x < b$$

$E[X] = \frac{a+b}{2}, \quad \text{Var}(X) = \frac{(b-a)^2}{12}.$

- **Normal** (μ, σ^2) X is a random fluctuation arising from many causes. Its density function is

$$f(x) = \frac{1}{\sqrt{2\pi}\,\sigma} e^{-(x-\mu)^2/2\sigma^2}, \quad -\infty < x < \infty$$

$E[X] = \mu, \quad \text{Var}(X) = \sigma^2$

When $\mu = 0, \sigma = 1$, X is called a standard normal.

Notes.

1. If X is Normal(μ, σ^2), then $Z = \frac{X - \mu}{\sigma}$ is standard normal.
2. Sum of independent normal random variables is also normal.
3. An important result is the *central limit theorem*, which states that the distribution of the sum of the first n of a sequence of independent and identically distributed random variables becomes normal as n goes to infinity, for any distribution of these random variables that has a finite mean and variance.

- **Exponential** (λ) X is the waiting time until an event occurs when events are always occurring at a random rate $\lambda > 0$. Its density is

$$f(x) = \lambda e^{-\lambda x}, \quad x > 0$$

$E[X] = \frac{1}{\lambda}, \quad \text{Var}(X) = \frac{1}{\lambda^2}, \quad P(X > x) = e^{-\lambda x}, x > 0.$

Note. X is memoryless, in that the remaining life of an item whose life distribution is Exponential(λ) is also Exponential(λ), no matter what the current age of the item is.

- **Gamma** (α, λ) When $\alpha = n$, X is the waiting time until n events occur when events are always occurring at a random rate $\lambda > 0$. Its density is

$$f(t) = \frac{\lambda e^{-\lambda t}(\lambda t)^{\alpha-1}}{\Gamma(\alpha)}, \quad t > 0$$

where $\Gamma(\alpha) = \int_0^\infty e^{-x} x^{\alpha-1} dx$ is called the gamma function.

$E[X] = \frac{\alpha}{\lambda}, \quad \text{Var}(X) = \frac{\alpha}{\lambda^2}.$

Notes.

1. Gamma$(1, \lambda)$ is exponential(λ).
2. If the random variables are independent, then the sum of a Gamma(α_1, λ) and a Gamma(α_2, λ) is a Gamma$(\alpha_1 + \alpha_2, \lambda)$.
3. The sum of n independent and identically distributed exponentials with parameter λ is a Gamma(n, λ) random variable.

- **Beta** (a, b) X is the distribution of a random variable taking on values in the interval $(0, 1)$. Its density is

$$f(x) = \frac{1}{B(a,b)} x^{a-1}(1 - x)^{b-1}, \quad 0 < x < 1$$

where $B(a, b) = \int_0^1 x^{a-1}(1 - x)^{b-1} dx$ is called the beta function.

$E[X] = \frac{a}{a+b} \quad \text{Var}(X) = \frac{ab}{(a+b)^2(a+b+1)}$

Notes.

1. Beta$(1, 1)$ and Uniform$(0, 1)$ are identical.

2. The jth smallest of n independent uniform $(0, 1)$ random variables is a Beta$(j, n - j + 1)$ random variable.

- **Chi-Squared**(n) X is the sum of the squares of n independent standard normal random variables. Its density is

$$f(x) = \frac{e^{-x/2} x^{\frac{n}{2}-1}}{2^{n/2} \Gamma(n/2)}, \quad x > 0$$

Notes.

1. The Chi-Squared(n) distribution is the same as the Gamma$(n/2, 1/2)$ distribution.

2. The sample variance of n independent and identically distributed Normal(μ, σ^2) random variables multiplied by $\frac{n-1}{\sigma^2}$ is a Chi-Squared$(n - 1)$ random variable, and it is independent of the sample mean.

- **Cauchy** X is the tangent of a uniformly distributed random angle between $-\pi/2$ and $\pi/2$. Its density is

$$f(x) = \frac{1}{\pi(1 + x^2)}, \quad -\infty < x < \infty$$

$E[X] = 0 \quad \text{Var}(X) = \infty.$